ADVANCES IN LIPID RESEARCH

Volume 16

Advances in Lipid Research

Volume 16

Edited by

Rodolfo Paoletti

Institute of Pharmacology
Milan, Italy

David Kritchevsky

The Wistar Institute
Philadelphia, Pennsylvania

  1978

ACADEMIC PRESS
New York   San Francisco   London
A Subsidiary of Harcourt Brace Jovanovich, Publishers

ACADEMIC PRESS, INC.
111 Fifth Avenue, New York, New York 10003

United Kingdom Edition published by
ACADEMIC PRESS, INC. (LONDON) LTD.
24/28 Oval Road, London NW1 7DX

LIBRARY OF CONGRESS CATALOG CARD NUMBER: 63–22330

ISBN 0–12–024916–2

PRINTED IN THE UNITED STATES OF AMERICA

CONTENTS

Metabolism of Molecular Species
of Diacylglycerophospholipids

D. J. Holub and A. Kuksis

Fatty Acids and Immunity

Christopher J. Meade and Jürgen Mertin

Marginal Vitamin C Deficiency, Lipid Metabolism, and Atherogenesis

Emil Ginter

Arterial Enzymes of Cholesteryl Ester Metabolism

David Kritchevsky and H. V. Kothari

Phospholipase D

Michael Heller

Screening for Inhibitors of Prostaglandin and Thromboxane Biosynthesis

Ryszard J. Gryglewski

Atherosclerosis, Hypothyroidism, and Thyroid Hormone Therapy

Paul Starr

LIST OF CONTRIBUTORS

Numbers in parentheses indicate the pages on which the authors' contributions begin.

EMIL GINTER, *Institute for Human Nutrition Research, Bratislava, Czechoslovakia* (167)

RYSZARD J. GRYGLEWSKI, *Department of Pharmacology, Copernicus Academy of Medicine in Cracow, Cracow 16, Poland* (327)

MICHAEL HELLER, *Department of Biochemistry, The Hebrew University, Hadassah Medical School, Jerusalem, Israel* (267)

B. J. HOLUB,[1] *Department of Biochemistry and Banting and Best Department of Medical Research, University of Toronto, Ontario, Canada M5G 1L6* (1)

H. V. KOTHARI,[2] *The Wistar Institute of Anatomy, University of Pennsylvania, Philadelphia, Pennsylvania 19104* (221)

DAVID KRITCHEVSKY, *The Wistar Institute of Anatomy, University of Pennsylvania, Philadelphia, Pennsylvania 19104* (221)

A. KUKSIS, *Department of Biochemistry and Banting and Best Department of Medical Research, University of Toronto, Toronto, Ontario, Canada M5G 1L6* (1)

CHRISTOPHER J. MEADE, *Transplantation Biology Section, Clinical Research Centre, Harrow, Middlesex, England* (127)

JÜRGEN MERTIN, *Transplantation Biology Section, Clinical Research Centre, Harrow, Middlesex, England* (127)

PAUL STARR, *R.I.A. Laboratories, Inc., South Pasadena, California 91106* (345)

---

[1] Present address: Department of Nutrition, University of Guelph, Guelph, Ontario, Canada N1G 2W1.

[2] Present address: CIBA–Geigy Corporation, Ardsley, New York 10502.

PREFACE

This volume is devoted to a heterogeneous collection of subjects all of which are important to the chemistry or physiology of lipids. The first article contains a discussion of the metabolism of distinct molecular species of phospholipids. The individual members of this class of lipids are shown to possess strikingly different chemical and biological properties. The second article is devoted to a relatively new but potentially important area of lipid metabolism, namely, fatty acids and immunity. In the third article the author considers the influence of vitamin C on cholesterol metabolism, gallstone formation, and atherosclerosis. The possible relationship of latent vitamin C deficiency to lipid disorders is discussed.

The greatest chemical change in aging or atherosclerotic aortas is the large increase in esterified cholesterol. In article four the arterial enzymes of cholesteryl ester metabolism are described and discussed. The discussion covers synthesis and hydrolysis of cholesteryl esters under a variety of conditions. The fifth article is a thorough discussion of phospholipase D, the enzyme that cleaves the base from phospholipids. The occurrence, characteristics, and factors affecting reaction of this enzyme are among the subjects covered. Article six is a brief discussion of certain aspects of prostaglandin metabolism. The last article is a review of the effects of thyroid hormone on atherosclerosis. Its author is one of the pioneers of work with D-thyroxine.

RODOLFO PAOLETTI
DAVID KRITCHEVSKY

Metabolism of Molecular Species
of Diacylglycerophospholipids

B. J. HOLUB [1] AND A. KUKSIS

*Department of Biochemistry and Banting and Best Department of
Medical Research, University of Toronto
Toronto, Ontario, Canada*

I. Introduction

Detailed analyses of the structure of individual types of glycerophospholipids from natural sources have revealed that they are comprised of

[1] Present address: Department of Nutrition, University of Guelph, Guelph, Ontario, Canada.

populations of well-defined molecular species which occur in characteristic proportions in different tissues, cell types, and subcellular particles. Metabolic studies have shown that different molecular species of lipids are formed and catabolized at different rates and that these differences are due to the existence of complex enzyme systems which govern the fatty acid composition of the acylglycerols in a given tissue under physiological conditions.

It is well documented that different molecular species of diacylglycerophospholipids exhibit striking differences in their physicochemical properties. Since glycerophospholipids are major components of cellular membranes, membrane structure and function are determined by the physicochemical parameters associated with the complement of phospholipid molecules present. Furthermore, the characteristic metabolic transformations which these lipids undergo are known to be tightly coupled to lipoprotein turnover and function.

The following review summarizes the more recent developments in studies on the metabolism of molecular species of diacylglycerophospholipids along with evidence for their biochemical and physiological individuality. Reference to neutral acylglycerols is made only when these molecules bear direct relationship to acylphosphoglycerol structure or metabolism. The selection of material has been restricted to studies within the animal species. It is hoped that the knowledge summarized herein will help in the further study and better understanding of the role of phospholipids in cell biology and biochemistry.

Extensive reviews on the determination of the structure of the molecular species of diacylglycerophospholipids (Renkonen, 1967) and of diacylglycerols and diacylglycerophospholipids (Kuksis, 1972) are already available as are thoughtful discussions of the enzymes involved in the metabolism of glycerophospholipids (Hill and Lands, 1970; Van Den Bosch et al., 1972) and acylglycerols (Hubscher, 1970). The structure and metabolism of the glyceryl ethers have also been reviewed thoroughly elsewhere (Snyder, 1969, 1972) and will not be specifically considered herein.

II. Chemical Individuality of Molecular Species of Natural Diacylglycerophospholipids

Since the isolation of pure lipid classes, it has been recognized that most natural glycerophospholipids (Smedley-MacLean, 1932) and triacylglycerols (Hilditch, 1940) contain more than one kind of fatty acid per molecule and thus consist of mixtures of homologous molecular species.

Although synthetic work clearly demonstrated that pure molecular species of acylglycerols (Fischer and Baer, 1941) and diacylglycerophospholipids (Baer, 1963; van Deenen and de Haas, 1964) possessed distinctly different chemical and physical properties, little attention was attached to these findings since individual molecular species of natural glycerolipids were difficult to isolate and their metabolism impossible to study. Advances in analytical methodology have permitted more recent workers to overcome these difficulties and have provided evidence of the natural occurrence of a spectacular series of molecular species of diacylglycerophospholipids (Renkonen, 1967; Kuksis, 1972), which play a decisive role in the structure and function of such biological systems as lipoproteins and cell membranes (Van Den Bosch *et al.,* 1972). The main analytical and physicochemical evidence for the chemical individuality of the molecular species of glycerophospholipids is briefly documented in the following discussion.

A. NONRANDOM STRUCTURE

The preferential association of the saturated fatty acids with the *sn*-1 position and the unsaturated acids with the *sn*-2 position of diacylglycerophospholipids from most mammalian tissues is well established on the basis of hydrolyses with phospholipase A_2 (Tattrie, 1959; Hanahan *et al.,* 1960; de Haas *et al.,* 1962). The introduction of stereospecific analyses (Brockerhoff, 1965, 1975) has led to the demonstration of distinctly different fatty acid populations for the three positions of most natural triacylglycerol molecules. Furthermore, the development of chromatographic techniques which are capable of an effective separation of neutral glyceryl esters on the basis of molecular weight (Kuksis, 1965) and unsaturation (Padley, 1966) has allowed the determination of the molecular association of the fatty acids in acylglycerols. Detailed chromatographic analyses of the molecular association of the fatty acids is also possible for the diacylglycerophospholipids following degradation to diacylglycerols (Renkonen, 1965; Kuksis, 1965; Akino and Shimojo, 1970), phosphatidic acids (Luthra and Sheltawy, 1972a,b), chemical modification of the ethanolamine (Collins 1964; Renkonen, 1967; Sundler and Akesson, 1973; Yeung *et al.,* 1977) and serine (Collins, 1964; Yeung *et al.,* 1977) moieties, or by direct separation of the original choline (Arvidson, 1965), ethanolamine (Arvidson, 1967), inositol (Holub and Kuksis, 1971a) and serine (Salem *et al.,* 1976) phosphatides. These studies have indicated that characteristic association of fatty acids occurs in natural glycerophospholipids, which gives rise to specific molecular species. As a result, the simplified earlier notions of various random distributions of fatty acids in natural glyceryl esters have been largely dispelled.

1. Composition of Fatty Acids

The work of Hilditch (1940) and that of Futter and Shorland (1957) has shown that triacylglycerols and diacylglycerophospholipids from the same tissue exhibit appreciable differences in their fatty acid composition, while Klenk and Bohm (1951) and Hawke (1959) have demonstrated marked differences in the fatty acid composition of individual diacylglycerophospholipids isolated from the same tissue. Table I compares the total fatty acids of triacylglycerols and the choline, ethanolamine, inositol, and serine phosphatides of rat liver as determined by modern methods of analysis. Several consistent differences are found in the fatty acid proportions of these lipids. The triacylglycerols contain much smaller proportions of 18:0 and 20:4 and higher proportions of 18:1 and 18:2 acids than do the glycerophospholipids. The serine and inositol phosphatides contain relatively little 16:0, while the triacylglycerols and the choline and ethanolamine phosphatides are rich in this acid. The composition of the free fatty acid (Muto and Gibson, 1970), phosphatidic acid (Possmayer et al., 1969), and 1,2-diacyl-sn-glycerol (Akesson, 1969)

Table I
FATTY ACID COMPOSITION OF RAT LIVER GLYCEROLIPIDS

Fatty acids	Glycerolipids [d] (mole %)				
	TG [a]	PC [a]	PE [a]	PI [b]	PS [c]
16:0	31.1	32.6	23.8	7.1	4.1
16:1	4.4	1.3	—	tr	—
18:0	2.1	19.1	30.2	40.1	47.0
18:1 (n − 9)	33.4	7.1	5.8	3.1	2.6
18:2 (n − 6)	22.9	12.8	6.8	3.3	1.9
18:3 (n − 3)	1.6	—	—	tr	—
20:3 (n − 9)	—	—	—	3.2	0.7
20:4 (n − 6)	1.4	23.1	23.8	39.1	24.7
20:5 (n − 3)	—	—	—	0.2	2.0
22:5 (n − 3)	0.8	—	—	1.0	1.0
22:6 (n − 3)	2.7	3.9	9.7	2.2	15.9

[a] Akesson (1969).
[b] Holub and Kuksis (1971a).
[c] Yeung and Kuksis (1976).
[d] Abbreviations: TG, triacylglycerols; PC, phosphatidylcholines; PE, phosphatidylethanolamines; PI, phosphatidylinositols; PS, phosphatidylserines.

fractions also differ from those of the triacylglycerols and diacylglycerophospholipids of rat liver. Comparable differences in the fatty acid composition of the glycerolipids have been shown for various tissues of other animals, although they have not been investigated in as great detail (Kuksis, 1972; White, 1973; Kuksis, 1977). In addition, the ethanolamine phosphatides and to a lesser extent other glycerophospholipids contain, along with the common diacyl esters, alkyl ether and alkenyl ether analogues (Snyder, 1969) which are largely absent from the neutral acylglycerols. Recently, the fatty acid composition of CDP-diacylglycerol from bovine liver and brain has been shown to bear a close similarity to that of phosphatidylinositol from these tissues (Thompson and MacDonald, 1975; Thompson and MacDonald, 1976).

Striking differences, as well as similarities, are evident when comparisons are made among the fatty acids of the acylglycerols and acylglycerophospholipids from different fractions of a given tissue or a population of cells. Table II presents the fatty acid composition of the major diacylglycerophospholipids of the plasma membranes, microsomes, mitochondria, and the Golgi apparatus of rat liver (Keenan and Morré, 1970; Colbeau *et al.,* 1971). Apparently, highly specific compositions of fatty acids are maintained for these membrane fractions despite considerable rearrangement of acyl groups (Hill and Lands, 1970) and exchange of intact phospholipids (Dawson, 1973) known to take place between subcellular membranes. An examination of the fatty acid composition of the glycerophospholipids of the outer and inner membranes of mitochondria and of microsomes of the guinea pig liver has revealed a somewhat lesser specificity, although certain significant differences are present (Parkes and Thompson, 1970). This may indicate that the different membrane proteins preferentially accommodate specific molecular species of glycerophospholipids.

Only limited studies have thus far been made on the individual glycerophospholipids present in membrane subunits and individual lipoproteins. Table III gives the total fatty acid composition of the glycerophospholipids of purified ATPase and the parent sarcoplasmic reticulum of rabbit skeletal muscle (Marai and Kuksis, 1973a). Except for phosphatidylserine and diphosphatidylglycerol there was close similarity in the fatty acid and aldehyde composition among the corresponding phospholipid classes of the enzyme and the total membrane. This is probably due to the fact that the ATPase accounts for over 30% of the total lipid of the sarcoplasmic reticulum (MacLennan *et al.,* 1971). It is less likely, but not impossible, that this similarity in the lipid compositions results from a scrambling of the membrane lipids during the isolation of the enzyme in the presence of deoxycholate since lipoproteins are known to maintain characteristic lipid profiles despite relatively free exchange of lipids with

Table II
Fatty Acid Composition of Glycerophospholipids of Rat Liver Plasma Membrane, Microsomes, Golgi Apparatus, and Mitochondria

Fatty acids	PC [c] (wt %)				PE [c] (wt %)				PI [c] (wt %)				PS [c] (wt %)			DPG [c] (wt %)
	PM [a]	ER [a]	GA [b]	MT [a]	PM [a]	ER [a]	GA [b]	MT [a]	PM [a]	ER [a]	GA [b]	MT [a]	PM [b]	ER [b]	GA [b]	MT [a]
14:0	—	0.8	0.9	0.4	—	—	0.7	0.3	—	2.5	3.9	—	1.5	9.0	7.1	0.2
16:0	32.8	24.5	34.7	27.0	30.6	22.6	33.5	26.6	30.7	19.3	36.3	26.3	38.7	11.1	29.6	7.0
16:1	2.9	3.3	—	3.9	1.2	2.3	0.4	3.2	8.4	1.8	—	5.8	—	1.0	11.8	7.6
18:0	34.9	21.0	22.5	21.6	31.3	23.4	31.8	27.3	36.6	45.0	19.9	38.4	46.1	4.7	8.2	3.6
18:1	10.2	12.3	8.7	13.0	10.1	9.8	5.1	12.0	13.2	7.2	21.9	14.0	8.4	21.8	40.3	19.9
18:2	8.1	17.7	18.1	12.4	6.5	10.3	10.0	5.4	2.9	3.2	1.6	4.2	1.0	52.3	2.9	58.8
20:3	1.1	1.2	—	1.3	0.9	—	—	—	—	—	—	—	—	—	—	1.2
20:4	8.4	15.8	14.5	17.7	16.5	23.1	18.3	22.0	8.0	21.4	10.2	7.6	4.2	—	—	1.8
22:6	1.6	2.9	—	2.9	2.9	7.2	—	3.2	—	—	—	3.2	—	—	—	—

[a] Colbeau et al. (1971).

[b] Keenan and Morré (1970).

[c] PM, plasma membrane; ER, endoplasmic reticulum or microsomes; GA, Golgi apparatus; MT, mitochondria; DPG, diphosphatidylglycerols; other abbreviations as explained in text.

Table III

Fatty Acid Composition of Glycerophospholipids of ATPase and Sarcoplasmic Reticulum of Rabbit Skeletal Muscle [a]

Fatty acids	PC (mole %)		PE (mole %)		PS (mole %)		PI (mole %)		DPG (mole %)	
	SR [b]	ATPase	SR	ATPase	SR	ATPase	SR	ATPase	SR	ATPase
14:0	0.2	0.1	—	—	tr	tr	tr	tr	4.5	0.7
16:0A	6.3	5.4	21.0	21.4	—	—	—	—	5.6	2.9
16:0	34.0	33.9	4.6	2.7	8.2	5.5	3.2	2.6	7.1	2.7
16:1	0.8	0.8	1.4	1.0	2.4	11	0.5	0.3	2.6	2.3
18:0A	tr	tr	7.0	6.9	—	—	—	—	—	—
18:0	3.7	3.5	7.7	7.6	21.3	30.7	45.2	43.8	8.7	4.2
18:1A	—	—	6.1	6.4	—	—	—	—	—	—
18:1	16.8	18.6	13.6	12.9	9.6	10.0	6.4	5.0	14.3	14.3
18:2	24.7	25.5	6.0	7.0	7.5	1.0	2.5	2.7	41.9	62.1
20:1	0.6	0.5	0.7	0.9	3.0	0.9	1.1	0.4	0.4	1.0
20:2	0.4	0.2	tr	tr	tr	tr	—	—	0.4	2.6
20:3	1.3	1.3	0.3	0.7	3.2	2.3	7.9	8.6	1.3	1.6
20:4	7.5	7.3	16.0	15.8	9.5	10.0	30.3	31.2	4.9	2.4
20:5	0.4	0.4	0.6	0.6	0.2	tr	tr	tr	—	—
22:2	0.2	0.2	0.4	0.5	5.4	4.4	0.6	0.6	tr	1.1
22:3	1.2	1.2	4.9	5.6	8.0	7.9	0.8	2.0	1.3	1.5
22:4	0.6	0.8	2.5	2.9	12.1	5.5	0.4	0.7	3.5	tr
22:5	1.6	1.3	5.6	5.2	6.2	5.8	1.0	1.8	1.0	tr
22:6	0.3	0.3	1.7	1.7	3.2	4.8	tr	0.2	2.5	tr

[a] Recalculated from Marai and Kuksis (1973a).

[b] SR, sarcoplasmic reticulum; ATPase, adenosine triphosphatase; other abbreviations as in Tables I and II.

the medium (Scanu, 1972). The alkyl and alkenyl ether chains are found among the hydrophobic substituents of the glycerol molecule in acylglycerols and glycerophospholipids in other tissues also (Gray and MacFarlane, 1961). Apparently both saturated and unsaturated homologues occur and exhibit extremely high preference for certain phosphatide classes, tissues, and animal species (Snyder, 1969).

2. *Positional Distribution of Fatty Acids*

Further evidence for a nonrandom distribution of fatty acids in natural glycerolipids arises from examination of the positional placement of the fatty acids in these molecules. The stereochemical relationships between natural triacylglycerols and diacylglycerophospholipids were established by Baer and Fischer (1939) and are reflected in the stereospecific numbering system (Anonymous, 1967). On the basis of this reference system, phospholipase A$_2$ specifically releases the fatty acids from the 2 position of the *sn*-3-phosphatides (van Deenen and de Haas, 1963), while pancreatic lipase attacks the *sn*-1 and *sn*-3 positions of the neutral acylglycerols (Mattson and Beck, 1956; Savary and Desnuelle, 1956). Both of these enzymes have been employed extensively in the analysis of the positional distribution of fatty acids in natural glycerolipids (Kuksis, 1972) and in stereospecific analyses (Brockerhoff, 1975).

Table IV provides some examples of the distribution of fatty acids between the two positions of the more common glycerophospholipids, 1,2-diacyl-*sn*-glycerols and the 1,2-diacyl-*sn*-glycerol moieties of triacylglycerols isolated from rat liver. It is obvious that in both diacylglycerophospholipids and triacylglycerols the *sn*-1 and 2 positions are occupied predominantly by saturated and unsaturated fatty acids, respectively. The latter distributions are consistent with those found in their potential metabolic precursors, phosphatidic acids and free 1,2-diacyl-*sn*-glycerols, although the fatty acid compositions themselves are not congruent with any simple precursor–product relationship. This specific positional placement of fatty acids is maintained in phosphatidylinositol from bovine brain (Holub *et al.*, 1970) as found also for its potential precursor in this tissue, CDP-diacylglycerol (Thompson and MacDonald, 1976). The mono- and diphosphates of brain phosphatidylinositol also show similar positional distributions of saturated and unsaturated fatty acids (Thompson, 1969), as does phosphatidylserine (Wood and Harlow, 1969b). These selective patterns appear to hold for the glycerophospholipids isolated from most total lipid extracts prepared from animal sources. Some exceptions have been noted, however, for triacylglycerols. Thus, analyses of the fatty acid distribution in the glycerolipids of pig kidney and adipose tissue have

Table IV

Positional Distribution of Fatty Acids in *sn*-1 and 2 Positions of Endogenous Phosphatidic Acids, 1,2-Diacyl-*sn*-Glycerols, Diacylglycerophospholipids, and Triacylglycerols of Rat Liver

Fatty acids	PA [a,e] (mole %)		DG [b,e] (mole %)		PC [c,e] (mole %)		PE [c,e] (mole %)		PI [d,e] (mole %)		TG [b,e] (mole %)	
	Pos. 1	Pos. 2	Pos. 1	Pos. 2	Pos. 1	Pos. 2	Pos. 1	Pos. 2	Pos. 1	Pos. 2	Pos. 1	Pos. 2
16:0	51.2	8.2	59.2	14.3	23.3	5.6	25.2	11.2	6.0	4.3	71.9	5.9
18:0	32.7	2.7	18.6	2.4	64.9	3.8	65.3	8.2	92.9	5.2	4.9	0.9
18:1	7.4	29.7	12.0	37.1	7.4	13.3	8.1	8.4	0.7	4.2	13.6	45.3
18:2	4.5	35.3	4.8	29.1	1.3	22.5	—	10.1	—	3.6	5.2	41.8
20:4	2.1	20.3	0.9	9.4	0.2	39.4	—	45.9	—	70.7	—	0.9
22:6	—	—	—	1.8	—	7.0	—	13.2	—	2.1	—	0.5

[a] Possmayer *et al.* (1969).
[b] Akesson (1969).
[c] Wood and Harlow (1969a).
[d] Wood and Harlow (1969b).
[e] Pos., position in glycerol moiety; PA, phosphatidic acids; DG, 1,2-diacyl-*sn*-glycerols; other abbreviations as given in text.

revealed mainly saturated fatty acids in the 2 position of the triacylglycerols and unsaturated fatty acids in the 2 position of the diacylglycerophospholipids (Hagen, 1971; Grigor et al., 1971).

Extracts of specialized subcellular structures or lipoproteins have been
shown to deviate markedly from these general patterns of animal tissues.
The phosphatidylcholines of the intestinal mucosa (Arvidson and Nilsson,
1972) and the diphosphatidylglycerols (Courtade et al., 1967) of several
animal tissues have been found to contain large amounts of unsaturated
fatty acids in both positions. Conversely, lung surfactant is greatly enriched
in dipalmitoylphosphatidylcholine (Goerke, 1974). Although the positional
data, therefore, are not indicative of any absolute specificity involved in
creating these patterns, as will be shown later (see Section IV), they
indicate the degree of selectivity that must be anticipated in various enzymic
transformations responsible for their formation.

The presence of alkyl and alkenyl ether chains in the 1 position of the
glycerol moiety introduces a highly limiting influence upon the composition
and positional placement of the fatty acids in the acylglycerol and acylglyc-
erophospholipid molecules (Snyder, 1969, 1972). This is especially prominent in the phosphatidylethanolamines of certain animal tissues where the
plasmalogen content may rise above 75% (Gray and MacFarlane, 1961).
In triacylglycerols, only the alkyl ether chains would appear to occur, and
only the sn-1-isomer of the two possible primary substitution products has
been found (Snyder, 1969).

3. *Molecular Association of Fatty Acids*

The characteristic composition and positional distribution of fatty
acids found in natural glycerolipids give rise to specific molecular species.
The relative frequency of occurrence of the individual species in the phosphatides can be estimated from a knowledge of the positional distribution of the fatty acids (Tattrie et al., 1968) or may be measured exactly
following their separation by application of TLC (Renkonen, 1965;
Arvidson, 1967), TLC and GLC (Renkonen, 1967; Kuksis and Marai,
1967), or GLC/MS (Hasegawa and Suzuki, 1975; Myher et al., 1978)
techniques. Table V gives the experimental and random association of
fatty acids in selected phosphatidylcholines from a variety of rat tissues
(Kuksis et al., 1968). In most instances, the pairing is far from random.
As expected from the positional distribution, saturated and unsaturated
acids are paired in the individual phosphatide molecules. Some phosphatides
pair nearly exclusively, palmitic and linoleic, and stearic and arachidonic
acids (Renkonen, 1965). In other instances, one of the tetraunsaturated
acid homologues may be paired with palmitic, the other with stearic acid

(Holub and Kuksis, 1969). Identical fatty acid molecules in both acyl positions of the glycerophospholipid molecule occur only rarely in animal tissues and usually make up only a small proportion of the total phosphatide. In the mammalian lung, however, the dipalmitoyl species of phosphatidylcholine represents the bulk of the phospholipid and serves an obvious physiological function (Clements *et al.*, 1961; Goerke, 1974).

In the alkyl and alkenyl ether derivatives of glycerophospholipids, the alcohol chains take the place of the saturated fatty acids, as revealed by the determination of the molecular association (Renkonen, 1968). Table VI compares the distribution of the alkenyl acyl and the diacyl species of phosphatidylethanolamines of rabbit and human skeletal muscle (Marai and Kuksis, 1973b) and dog and pig kidney (Yeung and Kuksis, 1974). The alkyl acyl, alkenyl acyl, and diacyl species of the phosphatidylcholines of bovine brain have also been examined in a similar manner (Renkonen, 1966). There appears to be a tendency for the 1-alkenyl 2-acyl phosphatides to be more unsaturated than the corresponding diacyl species. Differences are also seen in the chain lengths or carbon number distributions of the three types of the choline phosphatides examined.

4. Differences among Diacylglycerols and Diacylglycerophospholipids

According to generally accepted metabolic schemes (Kennedy, 1961), the biosynthesis of natural acylglycerols and diacylglycerophospholipids involves phosphatidic acid and free 1,2-diacyl-*sn*-glycerols as obligatory intermediates. Thus, as pointed out by Hawke (1959), the metabolic pathways proposed by Kennedy and Weiss (1956) in their simplest form would give rise to individual glycerophospholipid and triacylglycerol classes of very similar fatty acid composition when these lipids are isolated from the same tissue. Detailed analyses of the molecular species of 1,2-diacyl-*sn*-glycerols and diacylglycerophospholipids, however, have confirmed the discrepancies claimed earlier in their fatty acid composition. Further distinct differences exist also in the positional distribution of the acids between the various end products and the presumed phosphatidic acid and 1,2-diacyl-*sn*-glycerol intermediates. Table VII compares the compositions of the major molecular species of the rat liver triacylglycerols and diacylglycerophospholipids to those found in their potential phosphatidic acid and 1,2-diacyl-*sn*-glycerol precursors. In general, the composition of the molecular species of the endogenous phosphatidic acids is seen to be similar to that of the 1,2-diacyl-*sn*-glycerols which is in agreement with reports that phosphatidate phosphohydrolase shows little or no specificity towards different unsaturated phosphatidic acids in rat liver both *in vitro* (Hill *et al.*, 1968a) and *in vivo* (Akesson *et al.*, 1970a). Thus, 55–60% of the mo-

Table V

MOLECULAR ASSOCIATION OF FATTY ACIDS IN SELECTED PHOSPHATIDYLCHOLINES [a,b]

Fatty acids		Lung (mole %)		Liver (mole %)		Intestine (mole %)		Red blood cells (mole %)	
Pos. 1	Pos. 2	Exper.[c]	Random	Exper.[c]	Random	Exper.[c]	Random	Exper.[c]	Random
14:0	16:0	8	11	1	1	12	1	2	1
16:0	16:0	90	59	80	34	54	43	81	57
18:0	16:0	2 {46}	25	19 {1}	48	20 {2}	45	17 {25}	35 {32}
18:0	18:0		3 {42}		17 {19}		11 {17}		
18:0	14:0					14			
14:0	18:1	20	4	11	9	14	15	4	5
16:0	16:1	22	28	71 {9}	46	59 {11}	52	69 {21}	69 {16}
16:0	18:1	52 {32}	50	5	7	5	7	4	2
18:0	16:1	6	6	13	33	22	26 {12}	21	21
18:0	18:1		11 {26}						
16:0	18:2	40	44	56	53	56	60	62	64
18:0	18:2	35 {16}	9	32 {28}	39	36 {44}	31	28 {20}	20
18:i	18:1	25	10	7	6	5	6	4	9
16:1	18:1		11 {17}	4	2 {14}	3	3 {23}	1	1 {18}
16:1	18:2		6	13	13	13	20	tr	5
18:1	18:2		70 {3}	47 {3}	69 {4}	72 {8}	66 {9}	37 {2}	70 {5}
20:1	18:2			6		15	9		
16:0	20:3		6	16	10		3	21	15
18:0	20:3		2	18	8		1	15	15

Fatty acids								
14:0 20:4	10 ⎫	6 ⎫	46 ⎫	52 ⎫	52 ⎫	51 ⎫	3 ⎫	tr ⎫
16:0 20:4	30 ⎬6	70 ⎬9	51 ⎬41	37 ⎬19	32 ⎬27	37 ⎬19	32 ⎬17	62 ⎬12
18:0 20:4	60 ⎭	15	2		8	1	44	19
18:1 20:3			1	11	7	11	5	2
18:2 18:2		6					16	15
16:0 20:5		24 ⎫	19 ⎫	35 ⎫	16 ⎫	18 ⎫	20 ⎫	
18:0 20:5		5 ⎬	8 ⎬7	17 ⎬5	8 ⎬5	11 ⎬3	6 ⎬6	
16:1 20:4	36 ⎫		11	10	16	26		
18:1 20:4	64 ⎬3		51	31	59	24		
16:0 22:5		51 ⎫	5	7		21		
18:0 22:5		19 ⎬	5					
14:0 22:6		44 ⎫	28 ⎫	21 ⎫	10 ⎫	3 ⎫	tr ⎫	
16:0 22:6		51 ⎬11	20 ⎬12	50 ⎬3	5 ⎬8	33 ⎬12	40 ⎬7	
18:0 22:6		5	5	29	3	19	13	
18:1 20:5	tr				82	3	5	
18:2 20:4	100 ⎭1		47			25	35	

[a] Estimated best fit only, not absolute identities or proportions.

[b] Abbreviated from Kuksis *et al.* (1968).

[c] Exper., experimental.

Table VI

Molecular Species of Ethanolamine Phosphatides of Rat and Human Skeletal Muscle and Dog and Pig Kidney

Chemical species [d]	Skeletal muscle [a] (mole %) Rat	Human	Kidney [b] (mole %) Dog	Pig
Saturates				
16:0A 16:0			0.2	
17:0A 16:0			0.2	
18:0A 16:0			0.1	
Monoenes				
16:0 16:1			0.3	
16:0 18:1	2.6	3.4	6.8	2.9
18:0 18:1			1.1	2.1
16:0A 18:1	1.1	2.3	1.7	3.0
18:0A 18:1	0.6	0.6	0.4	0.1
17:0bA 18:1			0.6	0.4
Dienes				
18:1 18:1	2.2	3.4	0.6	3.0
16:0 18:2	6.2	6.8	6.1	1.5
17:0 18:2			0.2	
18:0 18:2	2.4	3.4	2.2	3.5
18:1A 18:1			0.2	
16:0A 18:2	1.1	4.5	1.0	2.2
17:0bA 18:2			0.4	0.3
17:0A 18:2			0.2	
18:0A 18:2	0.4	2.3	1.2	0.2

Chemical species	Skeletal muscle (mole %) Rat	Human	Kidney (mole %) Dog	Pig
Tetraenes				
16:0 20:4	5.5	10.2	15.4	4.5
17:0 20:4			0.3	0.5
18:0 20:4	6.6	13.6	14.6	15.5
16:0A 20:4	8.8	14.8	16.4	35.1
17:0bA 20:4			3.9	1.5
17:0A 20:4			1.3	
18:0A 20:4	2.8	6.8	9.3	3.9
14:0A 20:4				1.1
15:0A 20:4				1.1
16:0A 22:4 [c]	tr	2.3		1.6
18:0A 22:4 [c]	tr	1.1		0.2
18:1 22:3	1.1	1.1		
Pentaenes				
16:1 20:4	2.1	1.1	0.1	0.2
18:1 20:4	2.2	2.3	6.3	7.9
16:0A 22:5				
17:1A 20:4			0.1	
18:1A 20:4			6.3	0.5
16:0 22:5	1.1	1.1		0.2
18:0 22:5				0.3
18:0A 22:5	2.8	1.7		

Trienes

18:0A 22:3 [c]	2.8		4.0
18:1 18:2		2.4	4.1
16:0 20:3			0.2
18:0 20:3			0.4
16:0A 20:3			1.0
16:0A 22:3 [c]	1.7		2.8

Hexaenes

18:2 20:4	7.2	1.1	0.5
16:0 22:6	17.7	4.5	0.2
18:0 22:6	9.9	2.3	0.2
16:0A 22:6	11.0	2.3	
18:0A 22:6			

[a] Marai and Kuksis (1973b).
[b] Yeung and Kuksis (1974).
[c] Includes the corresponding acyl derivative of each unsaturation class.
[d] b, branched chain; A, alkenyl.

Table VII

Molecular Classes of Endogenous Phosphatidic Acid,
1,2-Diacyl-sn-Glycerols, Diacylglycerophospholipids, and
1,2-Diacyl-sn-Glycerol Moieties in Triaclyglycerols of Rat Liver

Chemical classes [e]	Glycerolipids (mole %)					
	PA [a]	Free DG [b]	PC [c]	PE [c]	PI [c]	Bound DG [b,d]
SS	3.4	6.9	1.0	tr	tr	3.6
SM	31.8	24.8	9.0	1.3	0.5	36.5
MM	6.4	10.2	3.1	0.3	0.3	10.4
SD	19.2	19.7	24.7	12.7	4.2	28.5
MD	5.3	10.6	2.0	1.5	0.2	9.7
DD	4.7	10.3	0.4	0.5	0.8	2.6
STri	29.2	10.4	1.0	1.2	3.9	6.0
STet			40.6	50.3	82.2	
> STet		7.1	18.0	32.3	7.9	

[a] Akesson et al. (1970a).

[b] Akesson (1969).

[c] Holub and Kuksis (1971c).

[d] 1,2-Diacyl-sn-glycerol moieties in triacylglycerols.

[e] S, saturated; M, monounsaturated; D, diunsaturated; Tri, triunsaturated; and Tet, tetraunsaturated acyl groups.

lecular species in both phosphatidic acid and the 1,2-diacyl-sn-glycerols are monoenes and dienes. However, the free 1,2-diacyl-sn-glycerols were found to contain considerably fewer molecules made up of stearic and arachidonic acid (tetraenes) than the diacylglycerophospholipids of rat liver. From detailed analyses of the various molecular species associated with the different phosphatidic acid and 1,2-diacyl-sn-glycerol subclasses, it has been shown that 83–98% of the monoenoic and dienoic species were of the palmitoyl type whereas the tetraenoic species were largely of the stearoyl type (Akesson, 1969; Akesson et al., 1970a).

Table VIII gives the mass distribution of the individual molecular species of the three major rat liver glycerophospholipids, as reported by Holub and Kuksis (1971c). While the monoenoic and dienoic species of all three phosphatides are similar in their structure and approach to some extent the composition of the intermediate phosphatidic acids and 1,2-diacyl-sn-glycerols, the tetraenes and higher polyenes are markedly different and greatly exceed the relative mass proportions of the potential precursor pools. Since phosphatidylinositol is formed from phosphatidate directly (Paulus and Kennedy, 1960), an especially close relationship would be expected between the phosphatidate precursors and the inositol phosphatide

Table VIII
Comparison of the Molecular Species of Phosphatidylcholines, Phosphatidylethanolamines, and Phosphatidylinositols in Rat Liver [a]

Chemical classes	Fatty acids		mole %		
	1-	2-	PC	PE	PI
Saturates	16:0	14:0	0.01	—	—
	16:0	16:0	0.80	tr	tr
	18:0	16:0	0.19	tr	tr
	18:0	18:0	—	tr	tr
	18:0	14:0	—	—	—
Monoenes	16:0	16:1	0.99	0.05	0.05
	16:0	18:1	6.39	0.89	0.20
	16:0	20:1	—	0.03	—
	18:0	16:1	0.45	0.08	0.05
	18:0	18:1	1.17	0.21	0.20
Dienes	16:0	18:2	15.68	7.16	1.75
	16:0	20:2	—	0.13	—
	18:0	18:2	8.96	5.34	2.20
	18:0	20:2	—	0.13	0.25
	18:1	18:1	1.96	0.13	0.25
	16:1	18:1	1.12	0.13	0.05
Triene I	16:1	18:2	0.40	0.03	—
	16:1	20:2	—	0.03	—
	18:1	18:2	1.42	1.23	0.17
	18:1	20:2	—	0.06	—
	20:1	18:2	0.18	0.07	—
	20:1	20:2	—	0.03	—
Triene II	16:0	18:3	—	0.02	—
	16:0	20:3	0.47	0.27	0.43
	18:0	18:3	—	0.04	—
	18:0	20:3	0.53	0.89	3.48
Tetraenes	16:0	20:4	18.86	14.22	4.14
	18:0	20:4	20.91	35.03	77.00
	18:1	20:3	0.82	1.01	0.09
	18:2	18:2	0.41	0.51	0.83
	18:1	22:3	—	—	0.96
Pentaenes	16:0	20:5	1.68	0.07	—
	18:0	20:5	0.35	0.07	—
	16:1	20:4	—	0.13	—
	18:1	20:4	3.57	4.05	0.95
	18:1	22:4	—	0.07	—
	20:1	20:4	—	0.13	—
	18:2	22:3	—	0.07	—
	16:0	22:5	1.33	1.11	0.08
	18:0	22:5	—	0.85	0.24

(*continued*)

Table VIII (*Continued*)

Chemical classes	Fatty acids		mole %		
	1-	2-	PC	PE	PI
Hexaenes	16:0	22:6	4.84	12.37	0.71
	16:1	20:5	—	0.52	—
	18:0	22:6	5.61	8.76	3.24
	18:1	20:5	—	2.31	0.40
	18:1	22:5	—	1.03	1.98
	18:2	20:4	0.55	0.52	0.24
	20:2	20:4	—	0.26	—

[a] Recalculated from Holub and Kuksis (1971c). Estimated best fit only, not absolute identities or proportions.

end products. However, in sharp contrast to the composition of the phosphatidic acids, there are only minor amounts of the monoenoic and dienoic and large amounts of the tetraenoic species in the phosphatidylinositol. A closer relationship exists between the relative abundance of molecular species in phosphatidylinositol and CDP-diacylglycerol from bovine brain, where 1-stearoyl 2-arachidonoyl molecules represent 60% and 35%, respectively, of these two glycerolipids (Holub *et al.,* 1970; Thompson and MacDonald, 1976). The composition of the molecular species of phosphatidylinositol phosphate and diphosphate in bovine brain is similar to that of phosphatidylinositol (Holub *et al.,* 1970).

Wood and Harlow (1969a) have shown a lack of agreement between the carbon number distribution of the triacylglycerols determined experimentally and that calculated from the composition of the 1,2-diacyl-*sn*-glycerols derived from either the choline or ethanolamine phosphatides plus the values of fatty acids at the *sn*-3 position of the triacylglycerols. Likewise, studies by Christie and Moore (1970) employing stereospecific analyses of the triacylglycerols isolated from egg yolk lipids, and the data of Kuksis and Marai (1967) and Holub and Kuksis (1969) for egg yolk choline and ethanolamine phosphatides, demonstrated that no simple biosynthetic relationship was apparent among their structures in agreement with the work for rat liver glycerolipids already referred to. There were, however, certain similarities in the arrangement of the fatty acids in 1,2-diacyl-*sn*-glycerol moieties of the triacylglycerols and phosphatidylcholines. Subsequently, Gornall and Kuksis (1971) and Husbands (1970) have confirmed the findings of Christie and Moore (1970). Thus, in egg yolk and rat liver, for which complete accounts of positional distribution and molecular association of fatty acids exist, it has been impossible to demonstrate a simple biosynthetic relationship between the major glycerolipid classes. Furthermore, it has been shown by Hagen (1971) that the triacylglycerols from pig kidney are esterified predominantly with saturated acids in the 2 position while the phosphatides have predominantly unsaturated fatty acids in this position. Such an inversion of the normal structure of triacylglycerols and diacylglycerophospholipids was assumed to indicate that the synthesis of structural polar lipids involved other steps than the reaction of free 1,2-diacyl-*sn*-glycerols with CDP-ethanolamine or CDP-choline.

Finally, additional discord into the harmonious proposals for unified origin of glycerolipids via phosphatidic acid and 1,2-diacyl-*sn*-glycerol intermediates is introduced by the finding of large proportions of alkyl and alkenyl substituents in both triacylglycerols and diacylglycerophospholipids of certain tissues without a concomitant isolation of the corresponding phosphatidic acids and 1,2-diacyl-*sn*-glycerols (Snyder, 1972).

On the basis of the discrepancies originally demonstrated in the fatty acid composition, Hawke (1959) suggested that if the mechanisms for synthesis of glycerophospholipids proposed by Smith *et al.* (1957) occurred *in vivo,* the enzymes responsible for the reaction between different cytidine diphosphate derivatives and the 1,2-diacyl-*sn*-glycerols must exhibit different specificities for different molecular species. Such a suggestion was also offered later by Weiss *et al.* (1960) to explain differences in fatty acid composition of triacylglycerols and the choline and ethanolamine phosphatides isolated from the same source. As pointed out in Section IV,B, the cytidine diphosphate nitrogenous base phosphotransferases have failed to show the degree of specificity required for obtaining and maintaining the characteristic diacylglycerol composition of the glycerophospholipids. Wood and Harlow (1969a) have suggested that the discrepancy may be due to a diacylglycerol selectivity in the biosynthesis of triacylglycerols, because these compounds contain only small percentages of C_{20} and C_{22} polyunsaturated fatty acids, thereby leaving nonrandom diacylglycerol species for the synthesis of other lipid classes. It is possible, however, that the diacylglycerols and phosphatidic acids isolated from tissues are not fully representative of the intermediates involved in the biosynthesis of either the triacylglycerols or diacylglycerophospholipids because of compartmentation even within subcellular fractions. Thus, the 1,2-diacyl-*sn*-glycerols may have been also formed somewhat independently of the phosphatidic acid pathway such as, e.g., the monoacylglycerol pathway (Johnston *et al.,* 1970), or by a partial reversal of the enzymic steps catalyzed by the nitrogenous base phosphotransferases (Bjornstad and Bremer, 1966). Likewise, part of the phosphatidic acid might have been derived by a diacylglycerol kinase (Lapetina and Hawthorne, 1971; Luthra and Sheltawy, 1976) or by a reversal of the reactions involved in phosphatidylinositol biosynthesis (Jungalwala *et al.,* 1971; Geison *et al.,* 1976). There is good evidence (see Section IV) to indicate that the monoenoic and dienoic diacylglycerophospholipids are derived mainly by *de novo* synthesis, while the tetraenes are also formed to a considerable extent by retailoring reactions involving deacylation–reacylation cycles (Hill and Lands, 1968; Van Golde *et al.,* 1969). The overall structural features of the tissue diacylglycerophospholipids and triacylglycerols are therefore extremely complex, if not necessarily unique, and not subject to a simple interrelationship based on known mass compositions of the presumed precursors and products.

B.   PHYSICOCHEMICAL DIFFERENCES

The various molecular species of acylglycerols and acylglycerophospholipids exhibit significant differences in their physicochemical properties within each lipid class. These differences are due to variations in the chain length and unsaturation of the component fatty acids. The molecular association of the fatty acids in the acylglycerols and acylglycerophospholipids determines the packing density of these lipid esters and the shape and degree of cavitation of their aggregates in an aqueous environment. A knowledge of the physicochemical parameters of molecular species of acylglycerolipids should therefore help in understanding the structure and function of biological membranes, which contain glycerolipids as major components. Numerous publications have appeared dealing with the molecular shape and cross-sectional area characteristics (Shah, 1970; Pethica, 1969) as well as the solid-state behavior and thermotropic phase transitions of various glycerophospholipids (Chapman and Leslie, 1970; Chapman, 1973, 1975). Reviews have also appeared which deal with the physicochemical interactions of glycerophospholipids with cholesterol, protein, metal ions, and specific metabolites since such phenomena bear direct relevance to the role of lipids in maintaining the integrity and functionality of biological membranes (Bangham, 1972; Gitler, 1972; Finean, 1973; Papahadjopoulos, 1973; Chapman, 1975). Unfortunately, most of these investigations have been conducted with ill-defined mixtures of molecular species from natural sources (e.g., egg yolk, rat liver, bovine brain), or individual synthetic molecules which bear little resemblance to the major molecular species of glycerolipids in natural membranes (see Section II,A). In the following discussion, only those studies have been reviewed which have dealt with molecular species of known structure.

1.   *Molecular Shape and Cross-Sectional Area*

The different molecular species of acylglycerols and acylglycerophospholipids within each lipid class derive their shape largely from the fatty acid components. The normal chain acids may be represented to possess

straight paraffin chains with a characteristic bond angle of 111° (Nicolaides and Laves, 1958). As a result of kinking, these chains may undergo
shortening and packing into kink-blocks, which may make up a significant
proportion of the total fatty ester mass at liquid crystalline conditions
(Trauble and Haynes, 1971). A single double bond in the trans configuration causes only a minor deviation of the axis of the fatty acyl chain from
a straight line (Nicolaides and Laves, 1958), while a cis configuration, as
in erucic (Craven, 1959) and oleic (Abrahamson and Ryderstedt-Nahringbauer, 1962) acid, produces about 45° bending of the chain. In linoleic
acid, the overall chain bending may be estimated to be nearly 90°. In
the polyethylenic structures containing three to six double bonds (generally all cis), the fatty acid molecule assumes almost circular shape with
the methyl end of the molecule approaching the carboxyl end (Bottino
et al., 1967). The hydrocarbon chains of the fatty acids may become dis-
torted also on account of the presence of methyl, hydroxy, and keto
groups as well as cyclic structures (Salem, 1962). The exact nature of
the distortion of the unsaturated chains depends on the location of the
double bonds in the major unsaturated fatty acids occurring naturally
(Schneider *et al.,* 1949).

Langmuir (1917) showed that the long-chain fatty acids form films in
which the molecules occupy the same area (about 20 Å^2/ molecule) in spite
of varying chain length. Subsequent work has revealed significant differences between saturated acids of different chain lengths and between
saturated and unsaturated fatty acids. Thus, the limiting area of oleic acid
is 22 Å^2 while that of stearic acid is 18.5 Å^2. Palmitic and myristic acids
have been shown to possess limiting areas of 19.5 and 23.5 Å^2 (Dervichian
and Joly, 1939). Other investigators have found the limiting areas of the
di- and polyunsaturated fatty acids to be nearly double those of the saturated and mono-unsaturated long-chain fatty acids (Schneider *et al.,* 1949).
Appropriate increases in the cross-sectional areas have also been recorded
for branched-chain fatty acids (O'Brien, 1967) and for fatty acids containing cyclic structures (Stoffel and Michaelis, 1976). Obviously, the
fatty acids are aligned with their hydrocarbon chains in parallel, but a
tight packing is possible only with completely extended normal chains.

The limiting cross-sectional areas of the common diacylglycerols and
diacylglycerophospholipids in hydrophobic media also have been shown
to vary with the fatty acid composition. Thus the limiting area of dipal-
mitoylglycerol was shown to be about 40 Å^2 (Alexander, 1941), while
those of mixed acids gave limiting areas corresponding to the sum of the
component fatty acids. The fully saturated phosphatidylcholines also have
been found to occupy an area close to the limiting area of the sum of the
component fatty acids. Hence, the fatty chains must be almost vertically

packed (Rose, 1947). Van Deenen *et al.* (1962) have demonstrated that a progressive shortening of the chain length of the acids or introduction of double bonds greatly expands the estimated cross-sectional area. Chapman *et al.* (1966) showed that a replacement of cis by trans double bonds in fatty acyl chains of phosphatidylcholine causes condensation of monolayers and hence a decrease in the cross-sectional area as would be expected on the basis of the above considerations of the molecular shapes of the acids. Demel *et al.* (1972a) studied the force–area characteristics of phosphatidylcholines containing one to six double bonds per molecule. The area per molecule increased stepwise with increasing unsaturation although the most significant increase was observed after the introduction of the first double bond.

Tinoco and McIntosh (1970) separated the phosphatidylcholines of rat liver according to unsaturation (one to six double bonds) and found that these species possessed areas much greater than the dipalmitoyl species, although all fractions had areas per molecule within 10% of each other at a given pressure. These authors also observed that the total liver phosphatidylcholine occupied a larger area than any of the fractions studied and proposed that a wide variety of molecular shapes prevents compact packing in the monolayer. For a series of 1-saturated, 2-unsaturated phosphatidylcholines, Ghosh and Tinoco (1972) observed the 1-palmitoyl homologues to have a significantly greater area per molecule than the corresponding 1-stearoyl species when these acids were paired with linoleic, linolenic, or arachidonic acids at the 2 position. Subsequent work by Ghosh *et al.* (1973) suggested that the orientation of the polar group in monolayers can vary between different molecular species of phosphatidylcholine.

Stoffel and Pruss (1969) have determined the molecular areas of selected species of choline and ethanolamine phosphatides and of the corresponding 1,2-diacyl-*sn*-glycerols. Table IX gives the values of the collapse point of the lipids at temperatures between 10 and 40°C. The molecular areas at the collapse point of the lipids were influenced by the polar head group and tended to become larger with increasing temperature except in the case of the 1,2-diacyl-*sn*-glycerols which were present in a condensed state. Most of the other lipid species reach the collapse point at relatively loose packing. Extensive data have been provided by Ghosh *et al.* (1973) on pressure–area curves for monolayers of 10 different molecular species of phosphatidylcholine.

In the liquid monolayer state under low compression, the fatty acyl chains are in the liquid form and can oscillate, rotate, and vibrate (Shah, 1970). Because of the thermal motion, the fatty acyl chains are believed to occupy a volume represented by a cone with its apex at the interface

Table IX

MOLECULAR AREAS OF MIXED FATTY ACID 1,2-DIACYL-*sn*-GLYCEROLS,
PHOSPHATIDYLETHANOLAMINES, AND PHOSPHATIDYLCHOLINES
AT DIFFERENT TEMPERATURES [a]

Molecular species		Molecular area ($Å^2$/molecule)			
1-	2-	10°C	20°C	30°C	40°C
Diacylglycerols					
18:0	18:0	36.5	36.3	36.3	35.5
18:0	18:1	42.0	42.0	44.0	44.0
18:1	18:1	55.8	57.0	69.5	60.0
18:0	18:2	52.8	62.0	65.5	69.8
18:0	20:4	57.5	59.5	61.0	65.0
Phosphatidylcholines					
18:0	18:1	40.0	52.5	57.0	59.5
18:0	18:2	50.5	56.3	58.8	60.0
18:0	18:3	47.0	55.5	57.5	59.5
Phosphatidylethanolamines					
18:0	18:1	37.0	36.8	32.5	46.3
18:0	18:3	45.8	50.5	55.0	57.8
18:0	20:4	51.0	52.5	55.8	57.5

[a] Abbreviated from Stoffel and Pruss (1969).

and base at the terminal of the fatty acyl chain. (Shah and Schulman, 1967a). The true shape of the molecules at the aqueous interface depends on the surrounding environment and the pressure. There is some controversy about the orientation of the polar head group in the monolayer (see Shah and Schulman, 1967b; Standish and Pethica, 1968; Pethica, 1969; de Titta and Craven, 1973; Gally *et al.*, 1975).

2. Monolayer and Bulk-Phase Properties

The density of packing of the molecular species of diacylglycerophospholipids in a monolayer or bilayer depends on both the fatty acid composition of the lipid esters, which is reflected in the cross-sectional area of the molecules, and the degree of hydration and charge of the polar head groups which determine the force required for the compression to the limiting area. Thus the monolayers of dimyristoylglycerophosphorylethanolamine are condensed when compared to those of dimyristoylglycerophosphorylcholine (Cadenhead *et al.*, 1967). These two types of molecules differ only in the structure of the polar groups and the degree of their hydration.

Stoffel and Pruss (1969) have shown that the energy of compression is a function of the hydrophilic group. The hydration of the polar phosphorylethanolamine is much stronger than that of the hydroxy group of the respective diacylglycerol, but less than that of the bulky trimethylammonium group of the corresponding phosphatidylcholine. Only a small change in the energy of compression is produced by a change in the number of cis double bonds in the hydrophobic part of the lipids according to Stoffel and Pruss (1969). The rate of change in the area of a lipid molecule with a change in pressure (i.e., compressibility) could prove to be a much more meaningful concept in estimating the potential fluidity of phospholipids in biological membranes than the measurement of molecular areas at one or two selected pressures.

Glycerophospholipids, either in the anhydrous condition or in the presence of water, exhibit thermotropic mesomorphism, which is a property of forming a liquid crystalline phase (Chapman, 1975). Each phosphatide or group of phosphatides possesses a transition temperature below which it exists in a liquid-crystalline type of organization. At the transition point, a marked absorption of heat occurs. Chapman et al. (1967) have recorded the temperature curves for various synthetic 1,2-diacylphosphatidylcholine monohydrates and for egg yolk phospholipids. As the hydrocarbon chain length of the fatty acid residue becomes shorter the principal endothermic transition temperature steadily decreases. The presence of cis unsaturated acid groups in the hydrocarbon chains also causes a decrease of the main endothermic transition temperature. The presence of water causes the transition temperature to fall until it reaches a limiting value, which is characteristic for each particular phospholipid. According to Chapman and Leslie (1970), the temperature of transition from crystalline to liquid crystalline phase depends also upon the branching of the chain, the class of phospholipid and the presence of cations.

The transition temperature for fully saturated species of glycerophospholipids was high even in the presence of water. Thus, distearoylphosphatidylcholine in water had a phase transition temperature of 60°C, while dipalmitoylphosphatidylcholine in water had a transition temperature of 41°C (Chapman et al., 1967). Highly unsaturated phosphatidylcholines gave transition temperatures below 0°C. Natural phosphatidylcholines, which contain a mixture of chain lengths, gave a much broader endotherm at the solid-to-liquid crystal transition than those of a single, discrete chain length. The solid-state properties of both acylglycerols and acylglycerophospholipids in the bulk state are affected by the presence of each other as well as of cholesterol and other lipids. The latter effects are considered below under monolayer properties and in a special section reserved for interaction with cholesterol (see Section II,B,3).

It should be noted that a specific relationship has been suggested to exist between the bulk phase transformations and the biological functions of glycerophospholipids. Thus, thermal phase transitions have been demonstrated in isolated membranes by means of differential scanning calorimetry (Steim .*et al.,* 1969) and X-ray diffraction studies (Engelman, 1970; Esfahani *et al.,* 1971). The temperature of these transitions has been related in part to the growth of microorganisms and to the state of the fatty acyl chains of membrane glycerophospholipids, which depends upon the fluidity of the fatty acids present. It is now generally accepted that natural cell membranes contain crystalline or gel-state lipids in addition to fluid liquid crystalline domains (Oldfield, 1973; Singer, 1973). Phase transitions of membrane lipids·have been correlated with marked alterations in the function of membrane associated enzymes (Esfahani *et al.,* 1971; Overath *et al.,* 1970; Fox, 1972).

The effects of mixing synthetic phosphatidylcholines having different chain lengths have been studied by differential scanning calorimetry and monolayer techniques, and their phase behavior in excess water has been investigated by Phillips *et al.* (1970). The compounds were the pure 1,2-dimyristoyl, dipalmitoyl, distearoyl and dibehenoyl, dioleoyl and stearoelaidoyl 3-phosphorylcholines. It was shown that, when the chain lengths of the two components were similar, cocrystallization and ideal mixing occurred. When the chain length or unsaturation of the two components was very different, monotectic behavior was observed. In the latter case, the liquid crystalline transition of the higher melting component became broader and was at a reduced temperature. This effect has been attributed to the highly disordered liquid hydrocarbon chains of one component causing an increase in the kinetic motions of the ordered chains of the second component. Such effects also occurred within natural lipid extracts.

In biological systems there is a further complication because of intramolecular mixing of chains. Phillips *et al.* (1970) have shown that 1-stearoyl-2-elaidoyl phosphatidylcholine gives an endothermic transition at 26°C. The peak was as sharp as that obtained with a phosphatidylcholine containing two identical chains which indicated that the two chains melt simultaneously and the behavior of inter- and intramolecularly mixed chains is different.

Phillips *et al.* (1970) showed that, when dioleoyl phosphatidylcholine is mixed with distearoyl phosphatidylcholine which forms condensed monolayers (Phillips and Chapman, 1968), an expansion or positive deviation from the additivity line occurs. In the dioleoyl-dipalmitoyl phosphatidylcholine system, ideal mixing occurs at low pressures where the dipalmitoyl species gives liquid-expanded films, whereas an expansion at high pressures is observed where the dipalmitoylphosphatidylcholine is condensed. The dipalmitoyl-distearoyl phosphatidylcholine system was found to be ideal at all pressures.

The highly mobile oleoyl chains in the proximity of crystalline saturated chains require an expanded lattice in order to undergo the kinetic motions characteristic of the phosphatidylcholine liquid crystals (Phillips *et al.,* 1969). This decrease in chain packing density allows increased configurational freedom for the saturated chains. From the preceding data, it is possible to envisage that not all combinations of fatty acids or molecular species of diacylglycerophospholipids will mix or melt together at the temperatures of the appropriate living systems where they are found.

3. Interaction with Metal Ions and Cholesterol

Diacylglycerophospholipids are major lipid components of the cell membrane, which is generally regarded as being composed of a bimolecular lipid leaflet containing dispersed protein molecules or, alternatively, of lipoprotein subunits. In these membranes the glycerophospholipids interact with divalent ions, cholesterol, and protein in a manner that is characteristic of the molecular species. The phosphatide interactions with metal ions, cholesterol, and to a lesser extent proteins, have been investigated by surface techniques. Thus, Shah and Schulman (1967a) have reported that the binding of calcium to phosphatidylcholine monolayers is significantly reduced by increasing unsaturation in the fatty acyl chains. For yeast phosphatidylcholine, the unsaturation in both hydrocarbon chains (1-palmitoleoyl 2-oleoyl and 1-oleoyl 2-palmitoleoyl) prevented the interaction of calcium ion with the phosphate groups, whereas in diphosphatidylglycerol the unsaturated hydrocarbon chains (linoleoyl) did not prevent such interaction (Shah and Schulman, 1965). This could be explained by the fact that in the latter, the two phosphate groups involved in Ca^{2+} binding are in the same molecule and the unsaturation of the hydrocarbon chains of diphosphatidylglycerol does not affect the proximity or orientation of the two phosphate groups. The surface pressure–area curves of diacyl and 1-alkyl 2-acyl glycero-3-phosphorylcholine were not affected by the presence of divalent ions in the subsolution, whereas the surface pressure–area curve of diphosphatidylglycerol showed 10–13% contraction of the film in their presence (Shah and Schulman, 1965).

Synthetic dipalmitoylphosphatidylcholine showed a higher surface potential in the presence of divalent metal ions than in the presence of monovalent ions; the increase was greatest for the fully saturated dipalmitoyl species and smallest for the fully unsaturated (yeast) species. In fact, yeast phosphatidylcholine did not show Ca^{2+} binding at all at low surface pressures. It was suggested that the interaction of the divalent metal ions with phosphatidylcholine in monolayers is dependent on the packing of the hydrocarbon chains (Shah and Schulman, 1965).

Anderson and Pethica (1956) measured the surface potentials of synthetic dipalmitoylphosphatidylcholine monolayers as a function of the ionic composition of the aqueous subphase. They found that, in dilute solutions of potassium, sodium, and lithium chloride, the surface potential is independent of the concentration and the same for each electrolyte, and concluded that no ion binding to the monolayers occurs. At high NaCl concentrations (above 1 M), the potential became more positive, which suggested sodium binding. These results were confirmed by Standish and Pethica (1968). The monolayers of dipalmitoylphosphatidylethanolamine, however, were much more sensitive to salt effects than the phosphatidylcholine film. Furthermore, the phosphatidylethanolamine monolayers differentiate between sodium and potassium, giving greater expansion effects with potassium. The surface potentials of the phosphatidylethanolamine layers are also different for subsolutions containing sodium or potassium, although the differences are not large. Some of these effects have also been observed in liposomes (Ohki, 1972).

Many of the ion effects are controversial and need to be reinvestigated using purified salts and synthetic phosphatides as well as standardized spreading techniques for the preparation of the monolayers (Papahadjopoulos, 1968, 1973). In all instances, there has been insufficient emphasis on the role of the polyunsaturated species in the binding processes, except in the case of Ca^{2+} binding where at least the mono- and diunsaturated fatty acid esters have been tested.

The apparent condensation of mixed monolayers of certain phosphatidylcholine species when cholesterol is added is explained by a consideration of molecular cavities or vacancies caused by thermal motion of the fatty acyl chains, the size of these cavities being influenced by the length and degree of saturation (especially the proportion of monounsaturation) of the fatty acyl chains and the extent of compression of the monolayer (Shah and Schulman, 1967a). The cholesterol molecules occupy these cavities and therefore cause no proportional increase in area per molecule in the mixed monolayers. Monolayers are liquefied by the presence of cholesterol as well as of unsaturated fatty acyl chains; in contrast, Ca^{2+} ions tend to solidify phosphatidylcholine monolayers.

The average area per molecule for mixed monolayers of dipalmitoylphosphatidylcholine and cholesterol varies with the surface pressure. At low surface pressures, the average area per molecule shows a deviation from additivity, whereas at a surface pressure of 30 dyn/cm it follows the additivity rule (Shah and Schulman, 1967a). That is, the molecules of both compounds in mixed monolayers occupy the same molecular area as in their individual monolayers. The maximum condensation at low surface pressures occurs at a phosphatidylcholine/cholesterol molar ratio of 1:1, which signifies a geometrical arrangement of these molecules for optimum packing in a mixed monolayer. Since the fatty acyl chains of dipalmitoylphosphatidylcholine are symmetrical, the number of cavities formed is the same as the number of phosphatidylcholine molecules in the monolayer. In contrast to the dipalmitoyl phosphatidylcholine–cholesterol monolayers, egg phosphatidylcholine–cholesterol monolayers showed a deviation from the additivity rule at a surface pressure of 30 dyn/cm. The deviation in this case could be explained by the presence of molecular cavities caused by the kink in the oleoyl chain of egg phosphatidylcholine, which would reduce the average area per molecule at low as well as at high surface pressures. The same concept explains the condensation of monolayers of dioleoylphosphatidylcholine by cholesterol reported by van Deenen (1965). The optimum condensation observed at the molar ratios of 3:1 and 1:3 between egg phosphatidylcholine and cholesterol agrees with the results reported by de Bernard (1958), and presumably represents the fraction (one-third) of oleoyl chains of egg phosphatidylcholine. Mixed monolayers of 1-stearoyl 2-oleoyl phosphatidylcholine–cholesterol show optimum condensation at molar ratio 1:1 (Demel *et al.,* 1967). It has been shown by van Deenen (1965) that the mixed monolayers of 1-palmitoyl 2-linolenoyl phosphatidylcholine–cholesterol follow the additivity rule, even though this forms more expanded monolayers than those of egg phosphatidylcholine. This has been explained by Shah and Schulman (1967a) on the basis of molecular cavities as follows. At low surface pressures, the large area per molecule in 1-palmitoyl 2-linolenoyl phosphatidylcholine monolayers would correspond to a large intermolecuar spacing with a molecular cavity, but one of decreased height, into which cholesterol cannot fit. At high surface pressures, the linolenoyl chain does not form a molecular cavity and therefore addition of cholesterol causes a proportional increase in the area of the film. Chapman *et al.* (1966) have reported that the mixed monolayers of rac-1,2-dielaidoyl glycerophosphorylethanolamine and cholesterol show maximal condensation at a molar ratio of 1:1 at low surface pressures but follow the additivity rule at high pressures. This behavior is identical to that of dipalmitoylphosphatidylcholine and cholesterol and can be related to the known similarities in shape (Schneider *et al.,* 1949) between a fatty acyl chain with a trans double bond and a saturated acyl chain. The interactions of other glycerophospholipids with cholesterol may therefore also be explained on the basis of molecular cavities, and the concept of Shah and Schulman (1967a) may be used to anticipate the behavior of other systems not yet subjected to experimental testing. Interestingly, the naturally occurring glycerophospholipid molecule, 1-stearoyl 2-linoleoyl glycerophosphorylcholine, condenses with cholesterol whereas the rare homologue, 1-linoleoyl 2-stearoyl glycerophosphorylcholine, does not (Tinoco and McIntosh, 1970; Demel *et al.,* 1967).

In later work, Demel *et al.* (1972a) studied the interaction of cholesterol with individual phosphatidylcholine species containing one to six double bonds per molecule of fatty acid in the 2 position and observed a condensation with all species although only a slight effect was observed for 1-palmitoyl 2-docosahexaenoyl species. No effect was observed for dilinoleoyl and dilinolenoylphosphatidylcholine. The behavior of the mixed cholesterol–phosphatidylcholine films was attributed in part to van der Waals interactions which varies with different molecular species. Ghosh *et al.* (1973) found the condensation by cholesterol to occur with those molecular species that form expanded films, and most strongly with molecules having a segment of saturated hydrocarbon chain extending nine or more carbons from the carboxyl group. Ghosh and Tinoco (1972) also considered the structural requirements of sterols in this interaction with individual phosphatidylcholine species. Of the sterols tested by Ghosh and Tinoco (1972), all condensed strongly with dipalmitoylphosphatidylcholine at low pressures, while cholesterol and β-sitosterol produced the greatest condensation with films prepared from eight other synthetic species. The results suggested that a B ring with a double bond at C_5 favors condensation much more than either a saturated B ring or one with double bonds at C_5 and C_7. Demel *et al.* (1972b) found that the interaction of 1-oleoyl 2-stearoyl phosphatidylcholine with sterols depended upon a planar steroid nucleus, a 3-β-hydroxy group, and an intact side chain.

Calorimetric studies by Ladbrooke *et al.* (1968) have shown that cholesterol has a marked effect upon the transition temperature of different diacylglycerophospholipids. When cholesterol is present in equal molar ratios with phospholipid, the transition between gel and liquid crystalline phase is removed. Hinz and Sturtevant (1972) have reexamined the dependence of the cooperative transition and have noted that the transition enthalpy decreases linearly with increasing mole percentage of cholesterol and vanishes at 33%. This indicates that each molecule of added cholesterol removes two molecules of glycerolipid from the hexagonal phase which undergoes the cooperative transition to liquid crystal phase. An interesting explanation of this stoichiometry is proposed by Engelman and Rothman (1972) who observed a similar relationship by means of low-angle X-ray scattering. By model building, these authors demonstrated that under the lamellar phase conditions, each molecule of cholesterol is surrounded by seven molecules of phosphatidylcholine. In such a case there are no cholesterol–cholesterol contacts. These observations may be pertinent to the finding that in plasma lipoproteins and in certain other systems (Shah, 1970), the phosphatidylcholine–cholesterol molar ratio frequently approaches 2:1.

Cholesterol also affects the chain mobility. In nature, there is a rough correlation between chain length, unsaturation, and cholesterol content in the membranes of various subcellular fractions. The mitochondrial membranes contain little cholesterol, and have much more unsaturation in the hydrocarbon chains. In myelin, the cholesterol is present to a much higher degree and the hydrocarbon chains are more saturated. Ladbrooke *et al.* (1968) have suggested that one of the purposes for cholesterol in cell membranes may be to prevent the lipid chains from crystallizing.

By means of spin labeling, Marsh and Smith (1973) observed that the condensing effect of cholesterol arises from molecular interactions with the fatty acyl chains of the phosphatidylcholine and the existence of molecular cavities within the acyl chain region of the lipid bilayer. However, the general use of ESR probes should be carefully controlled since such probes as 3-nitroxide cholestane do not behave with a phosphatidylcholine film as does cholesterol or dihydrocholesterol (Tinoco *et al.*, 1972).

A relatively new technique which should provide further insight into the properties of molecular species of diacylglycerophospholipids in natural membranes is fluorescence polarization which gives the microviscosity of the hydrocarbon region of glycerophospholipid dispersions (Cogan *et al.*, 1973). As expected, egg phosphatidylcholine gives a much lower viscosity than dipalmitoylphosphatidylcholine and both have greatly increased viscosity when cholesterol is added.

4. *Protein–Acylglycerophospholipid Interaction*

The critical physical factors and the theoretical possibilities in glycerophospholipid-protein interaction have been reviewed by several authors (Morrisett *et al.*, 1975; Chapman, 1975; Scanu and Wisdom, 1972; Jackson *et al.*, 1976). The occurrence of characteristic molecular species of acylglycerols and diacylglycerophospholipids in natural lipoproteins and membrane complexes agrees best with models of the type put forward by Benson (1966), Wallach *et al.* (1975), and Singer and Nicolson (1972), in which a membrane peptide is envisaged to be located on both of the membrane surfaces and also within the apolar core of the membrane. Protein located on the surface is considered to be coiled irregularly while any segments penetrating the apolar core are predominantly helical rods, with a hydrophobic surface packed to form subunit assemblies, the exterior of which is lipophilic. The apolar amino acid residues which make up the external surfaces of the subunit assemblies are considered to comprise specific binding sites for the hydrocarbon residues of tightly retained molecular species of membrane lipids, whose head groups can also participate in polar associations with the protein side chains located in the surface (Morrisett *et al.*, 1975). Furthermore, any glycerophospholipid located more distant from the protein would be bound less tightly and less specifically and would provide a bridge between adjacent lipoprotein units. Any bilayer regions would probably be confined to the latter areas of the membrane.

Indirect support for the Wallach-Benson type of lipid–protein association comes from studies of the binding between diacylglycerophospholipids and delipidated lipoproteins. Thus, it has been claimed (Scanu, 1969; Scanu and Wisdom, 1972) that the linkages between plasma apo-HDL and phospholipids are predominantly nonpolar in nature, and that the binding between apo-HDL and phospholipids is greatly influenced by the chain length and nature of the fatty acid esters. Collins *et al.* (1971) have provided evidence that the rate and extent of binding were dependent upon the fatty acid composition of the phosphatidylcholine molecule.

Recent work has shown that the glycerophospholipid–protein interaction is restricted to specific binding sites, which do not appear to be uniformly distributed along the length of the polypeptide chain (Jackson *et al.*, 1976; Morrisett *et al.*, 1975). Thus certain fragments of plasma apo LP-Ala, apo LP-Gln-1, and apo LP-Gln-11 preferentially bind diacylglycerophospholipid as compared to other fragments. It has been found that the binding of the glycerophospholipid is accompanied by circular dichroism changes that are consistent with an increase in the α-helical content of the protein or peptide. Under identical conditions, peptide fragments that do not bind glycerophospholipids show no change in circular dichroism. Segrest *et al.* (1974) have reexamined the known sequences of the plasma apoproteins to determine whether there are any structural features which might account for both the helical transitions and the binding of phospholipids. Based on the findings, they have proposed a new theory suggesting that the apoproteins contain specific amino acid sequences with amphipathic regions that can assume the α-helical conformation and which possess a relatively large apolar face for the association with the fatty acid chains of diacylglycerophospholipids and a polar face in which side chains of aspartate, glutamate, lysine, and arginine are disposed so that negatively charged groups are at the center and positively charged groups at the periphery of this face. This configuration allows interaction of the carboxyl terminal position of the fatty acid chain with the hydrophilic face of the helix. The model for glycerophospholipid–protein interaction suggested by Segrest *et al.* (1974) is one in which a helical region of the apoprotein is half buried at the surface of the glycerophospholipid structure, such as in a micelle. This permits close steric contact between a charged amino acid side chain and the oppositely charged groups of the glycerophospholipid. The amphipathic model proposed is consistent with binding studies between glycerophospholipids and peptide fragments and exhibits an impressive topographical fit.

There are several other potentially important aspects that are not covered by this theory including the effects of adding neutral lipid, lipid–lipid interactions, and the influence of long-range forces within an apoprotein. No specific role is envisaged for the different molecular species of the diacylglycerophospholipids although glycerophospholipid classes differing in charge and configuration could conceivably be accommodated under the same general rules.

The concepts incorporated in this model are consistent with the evidence for a boundary lipid in membranes. Studies with membranous cytochrome c oxidase by means of spin label and electron spin resonance have shown that a single layer of diacylglycerophospholipid may surround the protein complex (Jost et $al.$, 1973). The amount of phospholipid bound to the protein was independent of the extent of the fluid bilayer region. It is conceivable that only certain phosphatide classes or indeed specific molecular species are suitable for optimum binding to the associated proteins, but this aspect has not received experimental attention.

Because of technical difficulties in obtaining purified lipid-free proteins in their natural state, little information is available on the interaction of membrane protein with various molecular species of natural glycerophospholipids. The early work of Collins et $al.$ (1971), which suggested that such interactions are likely dependent upon the fatty acid composition of the phosphatidylcholine, has been supported in recent studies with synthetic phosphatidylcholines (Barratt et $al.$, 1974). Barratt et $al.$ (1974) demonstrated the influence of the acyl chain length of phosphatidylcholines and lysophosphatidylcholines on the interaction with casein by means of density gradient centrifugation and electrophoresis. Dicaproyl and dilauroyl phosphatidylcholines both formed lipid–protein complexes with α_{s1}-casein but not with β-casein. Also, dicaproylphosphatidylcholine did not interact with κ-casein. Dimyristoylphosphatidylcholine, however, showed no interaction with α_{s1}-casein. The interactions between synthetic lysophosphatidylcholines (C_{10}–C_{20}) and α_s-casein showed that the short–chain lysophosphatidylcholines (C_{10}–C_{12}) formed complexes which had a tendency to dissociate under the experimental conditions used. The C_{14}, C_{16}, and C_{18} lysophosphatidylcholines formed stable lipid–protein complexes, while C_{20} formed complexes with some difficulty. The observation that the complex formation between the short-chain lysophosphatidylcholines and α_{s1}-casein is not quantitative is consistent with the expectation that hydrophobic interactions with proteins should be weaker with glycerolipids of shorter acyl chains. The protein presumably provides binding sites of limited size or accessibility (see Wishnia and Pinder, 1966). Barratt *et al.* (1974) have pointed out that the free energy of transfer of lipid to protein will decrease with lipid chain length until the binding site is filled. After that, any further increase in lipid chain length merely results in lowering the free energy of the lipid phase with the ultimate result that lipid–protein interaction becomes unfavorable.

Pawnall *et al.* (1977) have studied the interaction of apoC III with pure dimyristoyl phosphatidylcholine and dipalmitoylphosphatidylcholine, and with mixtures of the two phosphatide species, in which the two lipids are in the same vesicle or in separate vesicles. Depending on the ratio of the dimyristoyl and dipalmitoyl species of phosphatidylcholine recovered in the lipoprotein complexes, it was concluded that the apoC III interacts with large lipid domains within a vesicle and does not selectively bind the low-melting dimyristoyl species. The apoC III binding to the dimyristoyl/ dipalmitoyl phosphatidylcholine bilayer mixtures was temperature dependent. Although the generality of such relationships remains to be shown, such mechanisms are considered important in lipoprotein formation and in the interaction of proteins with membranes. Jonas *et al.* (1977) have shown that apo A-I proteins interact stoichiometrically with dimyristoyl phosphatidylcholine vesicles above the gel-to-liquid–crystalline transition temperature of the lipid, promoting the destruction of vesicles and the formation of well-defined particles of the general size of high density serum lipoproteins. The interaction appeared to be a highly cooperative, all or none, process, resulting in the average binding of 90 ± 20 lipid molecules per protein monomer, regardless of the initial concentration or ratios of components.

Stoffel *et al.* (1974) have claimed on the basis of ^{13}C nuclear magnetic resonance studies that in human HDL hydrophobic binding of the fatty acid residues of glycerophospholipids to apoproteins takes place, not the ionic interactions of these molecules. On this basis the authors have proposed a model for HDL structure in which the predominantly unsaturated long-chain fatty acyl residues are bound to the apolipoproteins.

The work of Kamp *et al.* (1977) has sought to establish which components of the phosphatidylcholine molecule are essential to the specific interaction with the phosphatidylcholine exchange protein from bovine liver, which stimulates the specific transfer of this phospholipid from rat liver microsomes to mitochondria or phospholipid vesicles (Wirtz *et al.*, 1970; Wirtz *et al.*, 1976). Radiochemically labeled analogues of phosphatidylcholine were synthesized with modifications in the polar and apolar moieties, and the transfer measured between donor and acceptor vesicles.

Relative to 1-palmitoyl-2-oleoyl phosphatidylcholine, the transfer is inhibited or abolished when the distance between phosphorus and nitrogen is increased or decreased, and when a methyl group on the quaternary nitrogen is removed or substituted by an ethyl or propyl group. The transfer was much less affected when the ester bonds were replaced by either carbon–carbon bonds, when the phosphatide molecules contain saturated fatty acids, or when the D-stereoisomer was used. It was concluded that the protein has a binding site which interacts specifically with the phosphorylcholine head group and that substantial configurational changes cannot be accommodated. Interaction with the apolar moiety of the phosphatidylcholine was less specific, but the dipalmitoyl derivative was transferred at one-third the rate of the 1-palmitoyl-2-oleoyl species. Replacing the ester bond at the 1 position for an ether bond gives an alkyl analogue of phosphatidylcholine, which was also transferred at a reduced rate.

There is evidence (van Deenen, 1969) that the monolayer properties of the glycerophospholipid mixture from a given lipoprotein or membrane display fairly characteristic behavior and that environmentally induced changes in the molecular species are compensated for by the organism in a way which preserves the lipid-expanded character of the monolayer. At the present time, it is impossible to extrapolate this behavior to the nature and function of biological membranes and lipoproteins. This may be due to the fact that the membrane glycerophospholipids do not act alone but in conjunction with other organic and inorganic components as well as on enzymes. It is anticipated that the determinations of amino acid sequences in the apoproteins of lipoproteins and of membrane proteins along with any covalent secondary structure will help to recognize the critical areas of interaction.

III. Evidence for Specific Metabolic Functions of Individual Molecular Species of Diacylglycerophospholipids

Except for a few isolated instances, the evidence of a specific metabolic action of individual molecular species of glycerophospholipids is indirect. Changes in acyl chain composition of selected acylglycerolipids affecting both chain length and the unsaturation have been shown to bring about changes in function when assays of adequate sensitivity have been employed. In the absence of suitable assays, it is necessary to rely upon circumstantial evidence such as that derived from a high degree of correlation between the molecular species composition of specific tissues or organelles and their physiological function. Frequently, the significance of these correlations is reinforced by the generality of their distributions in different animal species and the physicochemical properties of the molecules in question.

A. ANALYTICAL BASIS

A great variety in lipid composition is observed both in kind and in relative abundance at the level of species, genus, and family of mammals. Both tissue and subcellular differences exist which encompass the total lipid content as well as the proportions of the lipid classes, members of these classes, fatty acid chain length, unsaturation, and molecular associations within various acylglycerolipids.

1. *Variation in Tissue Composition among Animal Species*

By combined application of complementary chromatographic techniques and specific enzyme hydrolyses (reviewed by Kuksis, 1972), it has been possible to isolate and quantitate the individual diacylglycerophospholipid species that occur in corresponding tissues of different animals. Although the documentation is incomplete, there is no doubt about the wide discrepancies in composition which exist regardless of which tissues or membranes are selected for comparison. Many of these differences are anticipated from simple comparisons of fatty acid composition (see Section II,A).

Several groups of investigators have determined the molecular species of phosphatidylcholine in the plasma and red blood cells of rat (Kuksis *et al.,* 1968), man (Van Golde *et al.,* 1967; Marai and Kuksis, 1969), and rabbit (Van Golde *et al.,* 1967). A comparative examination of the data reveals both remarkable similarities and certain striking differences among the animal species. Thus, the rat contained about 25% saturated phosphatidylcholine in its erythrocytes while the erythrocytes of man and rabbit had only 4–13% of these species. The monoenes and dienes were present in the rat erythrocytes in proportionally smaller amounts, while the hexaenes were twice as high in the rat as in man, with the tetraenes accounting for almost equal proportions of the total in both. The dienoic and tetraenoic phosphatidylcholines of plasma occurred in about the same proportions in both man and rat while the proportions of the hexaenoic phosphatidylcholine were three times as high in rat as in human plasma. The percentage of monoenoic phosphatidylcholines in rat plasma was about one-half that in the plasma of man. Both plasma and cells of the rabbit contained significant amounts of l-oleoyl 2-linoleoyl phosphatidylcholine as did the sample of human blood analyzed by Van Golde *et al.* (1967). Marai and Kuksis (1969), however, detected only relatively small amounts of this particular triene in either cells or plasma of man. The lack of agreement between the results obtained for the red blood cells and plasma of man by the two groups of workers could be due in part to dietary differences which are known to influence the composition of the lipids of both plasma and cells (see Section V,A).

Montfort *et al.* (1971) have observed striking differences among the molecular species of phosphatidylcholines from corresponding tissues of different animals. Thus, in all animal species relatively high levels of dipalmitoylphosphatidylcholine (up to 30% of the total) were identified in the lung tissue in the order: pig > rat > rabbit > cow. The proportion of dipalmitoylphosphatidylcholine in the brain was nearly constant in all animal species. The 1-palmitoyl 2-oleoyl phosphatidylcholine, which is the major species in the brain, was present in increasing amounts in the order: rat, rabbit, pig, and cow. In all tissues of all animal species investigated by Montfort *et al.* (1971), a preference was seen for the combination of oleic with palmitic rather than stearic acid except for the phosphatidylcholine from cow liver. While the other animals contained only small amounts of dioleoyl and 1-oleoyl 2-linoleoyl species of phosphatidylcholine in their tissues, pig liver and rabbit kidney contained as much as 10% of the 1-oleoyl 2-linoleoyl homologue. Only in the liver of all species studied was arachidonate at the 2 position paired with stearate at the primary position.

Marked similarities along with certain differences have also been found for the phosphatidylcholines of the sarcoplasmic reticulum of the skeletal muscle of rat, rabbit, chicken, and man (Marai and Kuksis, 1973b). In all cases, the phosphatidylcholines contained largely combinations of palmitic acid with linoleic, oleic, and arachidonic acids. There were significant variations among the animal species in the contribution of stearic acid combined with unsaturated acids, but they never exceeded the contributions of the palmitoyl species. In striking contrast to the rabbit, the phosphatidylcholines from lobster sarcoplasmic reticulum were devoid of 1-palmitoyl 2-linoleoyl molecules but contained significant quantities of heptaenoic (1-oleoyl 2-docosahexaenoyl) and decaenoic (dieicosapentaenoyl) species (Madeira and Antunes-Madeira, 1976). The similarity in the molecular composition of the phosphatidylcholines among the homeothermic animal species is greater for the sarcoplasmic reticulum of skeletal muscle than for many of the other tissues thus far compared. It is exceeded only by the characteristic occurrence of dipalmitoylphosphatidylcholine in lung (Klaus *et al.,* 1961) and 1-palmitoyl 2-linoleoyl phosphatidylcholine in the bile (Balint *et al.,* 1965) of some animal species (see Section III,B).

Comparisons of the composition of the molecular species of phosphatidylethanolamines from corresponding tissues of different animals have also shown discrepancies. The most extensive data on animal species have been provided by Marai and Kuksis (1973b) who analyzed the phosphatidyl-enthanolamines of the sarcoplasmic reticulum of the skeletal muscle of man, rat, chicken, and rabbit. Differences were found in the proportions of the fatty acids and aldehydes, as well as in their composition. As a result, considerable variation was found in the relative proportions of the various molecular species that were identified. The rabbit contained most of the plasmalogenic type of phosphatidylethanolamine, while the chicken contained the least. Comparisons of the major molecular species of the diacyl phosphatidylethanolamines from rat (Holub and Kuksis, 1971c) and pig (Hunter *et al.*, 1973) liver show striking similarities in fatty acid associations but marked differences in the proportions of the various unsaturation classes.

Only a few analyses have been made of the molecular species of phosphatides other than those of choline and ethanolamine. Marai and Kuksis (1973b) compared the molecular species of phosphatidylinositols and phosphatidylserines in the rat, rabbit, man, and chicken, as isolated from the sarcoplasmic reticulum of skeletal muscle. Remarkable similarities were seen among the different animal species but significant discrepancies also occurred. In all cases, the phosphatide composition is extremely simple and reminiscent of the composition of the specialized glycerophospholipids found in the lung and bile secretions previously mentioned. Since much of the lipid in the sarcoplasmic reticulum of the skeletal muscle is contributed by the Ca^{2+}-dependent ATPase, it is possible that these similarities are due to some specific requirement of the ATPase system, and may be governed by the common nature of the enzyme proteins (MacLennan *et al.*, 1971). Interestingly, the composition of the molecular species of the phosphatidyl-inositols of the skeletal muscle of these animals is generally similar to that of rat liver (Holub and Kuksis, 1971c), pig liver (Hunter *et al.*, 1973), and bovine brain (Holub *et al.*, 1970). About 60–70% of the total was contributed by the 1-stearoyl 2-arachidonoyl species. However, only 17% of the lamb liver phosphatidylinositol consisted of tetraenoic species, while 60% were monoenoic (Luthra and Sheltawy, 1972a). Nevertheless, arachidonic acid was paired exclusively with stearic acid in this tissue while the oleic acid in the monoenes was paired with palmitic and stearic acids. The composition of the molecular species of phosphatidylserine of corresponding animal tissues also varied significantly between different animal species. These differences are seen from analyses of the phosphatidyl-serines of skeletal muscle (Marai and Kuksis, 1973b) of man, rat, rabbit, and chicken, and of the brain (Yeung *et al.*, 1977) of ox and pig. The molecular species of the phosphatidylserine in the erythrocytes of the pig and rat were rather alike (Yeung *et al.,* 1977) but markedly different from those of the skeletal muscle or the brain.

In summary, comparisons of the composition of molecular species among corresponding tissues of different animal species show striking similarities for some glycerophospholipids and marked differences for others. Some of the differences are probably due to discrepancies in dietary and environmental influences. Characteristically, the animal species differing most in their physiology and living habitats show the greatest differences in the composition of the molecular types of these lipids. The remaining differences, however, which cannot be accounted for by environment alone must be a result of genetic factors and metabolic regulation.

2. *Variation in Tissue Composition within Animal Species*

Further evidence for a specific metabolic function of individual (or small groups of) molecular species of glycerophospholipids may be obtained from comparisons among different tissues or organs of the same animal. Under such conditions, all tissues are subject to the same dietary influence. Although interlaboratory comparisons may still be difficult on account of variations in the age, sex, and the exact strain of the animal, the number of variables remaining is distinctly smaller than that involved in interspecies comparisons.

The molecular species composition of phosphatidylcholines from various tissues of the rat has been reported (Kuksis *et al.,* 1968; Marai and Kuksis, 1969; Montfort *et al.,* 1971). In general, only species representing more than 2% of the total phosphatidylcholines were measured directly. The phosphatidylcholines of the lung are seen to be highly saturated with 46% of the total being contributed exclusively by dipalmitoyl species (Kuksis *et al.,* 1968). The other tissues contain only small amounts of fully saturated species, although the red blood cells of the rat are also relatively rich in this phosphatidylcholine (Marai and Kuksis, 1969). The lung contains about 30% of its phosphatidylcholine as the 2-oleoyl derivative, while the liver and intestine have only about one-third as much of this species. Monoenoic species of phosphatidylcholine containing oleic acid were found predominantly in brain which contained little linoleic acid species as reported by Montfort *et al.* (1971). The phosphatidylcholines containing one saturated and one diunsaturated acid were abundant in the intestine and plasma, while the heart and liver were richest in species containing one saturated and one tetraunsaturated fatty acid. The plasma phosphatidylcholines contained about twice as much of the species with one saturated and one hexaunsaturated fatty acid than heart and kidney, which were the next richest tissues in polyunsaturated species. The data show that, in all tissues, palmitic acid is favored above stearic acid as a pairing partner for oleic acid and for linoleic acid except in heart. Other workers (Van Golde and van Deenen, 1966; Montfort *et al.,* 1971) have reported an even more specific pairing of palmitic and oleic, and palmitic and linoleic acids in phosphatidylcholine. In contrast to oleic and linoleic acid, arachidonic acid seems to be preferentially combined with stearic acid except in the intestine and kidney where palmitic acid again is favored. The stearic acid was favored as a pairing partner for docosahexaenoic acid in heart and intestinal phosphatidylcholines, and palmitic acid in kidney and plasma, while the liver contained both saturated acids in about equal proportions in the hexaenoic phosphatidylcholine.

These differences in the composition of the molecular species of phosphatidylcholine must be largely due to a selectivity in uptake and utilization, as well as to chemical modification of the acids prior to or subsequent to their incorporation into the phosphatide molecules. The data appear to provide a good basis for claiming the existence of a tissue specificity as suggested previously by Veerkamp *et al.* (1962). This claim is supported by the common patterns seen for the molecular species of lung phosphatidylcholines from rat, rabbit, pig, cow, and sheep and of brain phosphatidylcholines of various animals.

Characteristic differences have also been noted in the molecular species of phosphatidylethanolamines of different tissues in the same animal. However, only a limited number of such studies has been made and seldom more than one tissue has been analyzed at a time. A comparison of the analyses of the molecular species of the phosphatidylethanolamines of rat liver (Holub and Kuksis, 1971c) and of the sarcoplasmic reticulum of rat skeletal muscle (Marai and Kuksis, 1973b) shows significant differences due to the presence of plasmalogenic species in the muscle preparation. However, readily discernible discrepancies are also seen in the proportions of the various species of the diacylglycerophosphorylethanolamines. There are lesser differences in the molecular species of the phosphatidylethanolamines of rat skeletal muscle and red blood cells, which also contain significant amounts of plasmalogenic species (Yeung *et al.,* 1977).

In summary, comparison of the composition of molecular species reveals dramatic differences for some glycerophospholipids and marked similarities for others among different tissues within an animal species. The differences probably reflect variations in the structure and function of the lipid membranes of the cells found at different levels of differentiation in these tissues. Since all tissues or organs contain more than one cell type, it is possible that further differences and/or similarities could have been detected if comparisons of molecular species of glycerophospholipids had been made among individual cell types.

3. *Variations in Subcellular Distribution*

As would be expected from the fatty acid compositions presented in Section II,A, striking differences as well as similarities are evident when comparisons are made among molecular species of glycerophospholipids from different subcellular fractions such as microsomes, mitochondria, plasma membranes, and other cellular organelles. These discrepancies may be due to differences in the synthetic capacities of the various cell organelles and/or to incomplete equilibration of the lipid classes and molecular species among the cell lipoproteins and membranes. The latter exchange is mediated by specific carrier proteins which can transport most phospholipids from their site of synthesis (e.g., endoplasmic reticulum) to other sub-cellular sites (Dawson, 1973). Theoretically, the differences in molecular compositions of the glycerolipids between the cell organelles could reflect specific functions of molecular species at different intracellular sites as components of either membranes or lipoproteins. Unfortunately, very few attempts have been made to characterize the molecular species of individual glycerolipids from different subcellular fractions.

O'Brien and Geison (1971) studied the molecular species of phospha-tidylcholines present in the myelin, nerve endings, mitochondria, and the 15,000 g supernatant. The results indicated that at least three distinct populations of the choline phosphatides existed in brain. Nerve endings and the supernatant had similar patterns of molecular species with dipal-mitoylphosphatidylcholine representing over 30% of the total. The phos-phatidylcholine from myelin was greatly enriched in 1-palmitoyl 2-oleoyl species whereas mitochondria contained molecules with relatively more long-chain polyunsaturated fatty acids, such as 1-stearoyl 2-arachidonoyl phosphatidylcholine. Luthra and Sheltawy (1972b) characterized the molecular species composition of phosphatidylinositol from three non-myelinic and two myelinic fractions of ox cerebral hemispheres. The trienoic species constituted approximately 20% of the phosphatidylinositol from the two myelinic fractions (large and small) but less than 14% of the nonmyelinic fractions. The nuclear and nerve ending plus mitochondrial fractions were enriched in the monoenoic and tetraenoic species of phos-phatidylinositol when compared to the myelinic fractions. Only the post-mitochondrial supernatant contained significant quantities of fully saturated species of this glycerophospholipid.

Parkes and Thompson (1973) separated the phosphatidylcholines from the mitochondrial and microsome fractions of guinea pig liver into eight different classes according to their degree of unsaturation. The dienoic and monoenoic molecules accounted for some 60% and 15%, respectively, of the total phosphatidylcholine in both fractions. No statistically significant difference was found between the distribution of molecular classes, or their fatty acid compositions, when mitochondria were compared with microsomes. The data on fatty acid composition of glycerophospholipids from microsomal and mitochondrial membranes (see Section II,A) also indicate similar complements of phosphatidylethanolamine and phosphatidylinositol species in these organelles. Thus, the dienes and tetraenes constituted 50% and 20%, respectively, of the total phosphatidylethanolamines in these two organelles from guinea·pig liver, and no significant difference in the proportions of the various molecular classes was found between them (Parkes and Thompson, 1975). The latter data suggest that in liver, but possibly not in brain, the molecular classes of the common glycerophospholipids are transferred to mitochondria in approximately the proportions in which they are found in the endoplasmic reticulum. In support of this concept, both *in vivo* (Parkes and Thompson, 1973, 1975) and *in vitro* (Wirtz *et al.,* 1970; Taniguchi *et al.,* 1973) studies have shown no significant selectivity for the exchange of individual molecular classes of choline or ethanolamine phosphatides between liver mitochondria and microsomes.

Other workers have shown significant differences in the composition of the phosphatidylcholines of liver, plasma, and bile, all of which are presumably synthesized in hepatic microsomes. Thus, Balint *et al.* (1967) showed that while rat bile contained significant amounts of palmitoyl linoleoyl species, the plasma and liver phosphatidylcholines were rich in linoleoyl and arachidonoyl species. There is evidence that the various plasma lipoproteins differ in their composition of phosphatidylcholines although the differences observed in rats have been minor (Mookerjea *et al.,* 1975). In the laying hen, however, the plasma can be shown to contain at least two general types of choline and ethanolamine phosphatides: one type being transferred to the egg yolk, while the other is retained in plasma or transferred to another tissue (Gornall and Kuksis, 1973). The species that are transferred to the yolk are more unsaturated than those retained in the plasma.

Arvidson and Nilsson (1972) have reported upon the molecular species of phosphatidylcholines found in lymph chylomicrons during the absorption of safflower oil (rich in linoleic acid) or triolein. They recognized four subfractions of molecular species. A combined fraction of saturates, monoenes, and monoenoic acid-containing dienes made up only a small proportion during sunflower oil absorption, but became significant after feeding triolein which caused a sharp increase in the proportion of the dioleoyl lecithins in the chylomicrons. Another fraction, which was major in all cases, contained linoleic acid in combination with saturated and monounsaturated acids. The third fraction contained linoleic acid almost exclusively and was present only after feeding safflower oil. It was identified as dilinoleoylphosphatidylcholine. Fraction four was rich in arachidonic acid and saturated acids and accounted for 15–20% of the total chylomicron phosphatidylcholine with both kinds of fat meals. These were largely palmitoyl and stearoyl arachidonates. Other workers (Kuksis *et al.*, 1968; Yurkowski and Walker, 1971) have shown that the phosphatidylcholines normally present in the mucosa are largely the palmitoyl and stearoyl linoleates and arachidonates.

B.   PHYSIOLOGICAL BASIS

The enrichment of some animal tissues and subcellular fractions in certain molecular species of glycerophospholipids has provided circumstantial evidence for specific physiological functions of these lipids. This specialization in the composition of the molecular species may be traced to the production of characteristic secretions, lipoproteins, and membranous structures which apparently require a specific hydrophobic environment.

1.   *Natural Surfactants*

The evidence for a particular physiological function of a given molecular species of glycerophospholipid is best documented in the case of dipalmitoylphosphatidylcholine and its role as a surfactant in lungs. Intensive investigations have shown that pulmonary surfactant is the material that lines the alveoli and stabilizes air spaces at small lung volumes by maintaining a low surface tension (Pattle, 1965; Clements *et al.*, 1961). The reduction in alveolar surface forces during respiration prevents alveolar collapse (Pattle, 1965). Dipalmitoylphosphatidylcholine is generally accepted to be the major active component of lung surfactant (King and Clements, 1972; Goerke, 1974). The high concentration of dipalmitoyl species in phosphatidylcholine of lung of various animal species was pointed out in Section III,A,1.

Watkins (1968) investigated the surface potential of thin films of dipalmitoylphosphatidylcholine in relation to the surface properties exhibited by lung extracts. It was suggested that a conformational change of the choline moiety from a coplanar to a coaxial arrangement occurs during compression of saturated phosphatidylcholines which may contribute to the surface pressure and surface potential characteristics of monolayers of this glycerophospholipid and of lung lipid extracts. Subsequent physicochemical studies by Frosolono *et al.* (1970) on a surface active fraction from dog lung, which contained lipid, protein, and carbohydrate, indicated that the surface properties of this fraction could not be explained solely from a consideration of the properties of dipalmitoylphosphatidylcholine. Furthermore, Munden and Swarbrick (1973) have shown that the surface films of lung alveolar surfactant consistently demonstrate a greater stability than those of dipalmitoylphosphatidylcholine even though the latter is a major component of lung alveolar surfactant.

Recently, much attention has been attached to the occurrence of phosphatidylglycerol as a minor component of lung surfactant lipids isolated from a number of animal species including man (Pfleger and Thomas, 1971; Rooney *et al.*, 1974; Saunders and Longmore, 1975). From the positional distribution of fatty acids in rat lung surfactant glycerophospholipids provided by Saunders and Longmore (1975), it can be calculated that dipalmitoyl molecules represent approximately 58% and 72%, respectively, of the total phosphatidylglycerol and phosphatidylcholine. Dipalmitoylphosphatidylcholine is highly surface active (Rooney *et al.*, 1974) and appears to be tightly bound to surfactant apoprotein (Hallman and Gluck, 1974; King *et al.*, 1973). On the basis of its physical properties, it has been suggested that phosphatidylglycerol may play a role in stabilization of the surfactant lipoprotein complex (Godinez *et al.*, 1975) and modification of surfactant function (Hallman and Gluck, 1976). The role of the alveolar cells and specific lipid-synthesizing enzymes in the production of the surfactant glycerophospholipids is discussed in Section IV,B.

2. Micellar Solubilizers

The various glycerophospholipids differ in their ability to form micelles and to solubilize other substances. Only certain molecular species of specific glycerophospholipids have been shown to possess pronounced micellar properties under physiological ranges of concentration, pH, and ionic strength. Although micelle formation may be one of the major results of the physiological action of glycerophospholipids, such a function for these molecules in living systems has been specifically recognized in only a few instances.

It is well established that the bile from all animal species is rich in phosphatidylcholine which exists in micellar solution and functions as a detergent. Thus, biliary phosphatidylcholine plays a part in the solubilization of the cholesterol present in bile (Bourges *et al.*, 1967; Neiderhiser and Roth, 1968). Table X gives the molecular species of phosphatidylcholine present in the more common animal biles. Whereas the 1-palmitoyl 2-linoleoyl species predominate in the bile of man, dog, rat, and swine, the 1-palmitoyl 2-oleoyl species was the major component in sheep and cow bile. In all instances only very minor amounts of arachidonoyl species were found in the bile despite their high proportion in the hepatic phosphatidylcholines. It is obvious, therefore, that either a preferential selection of certain species from a mixed pool takes place during bile formation or there is a random drainage of a highly compartmentalized pool of hepatic glycerophospholipids. Recent findings indicate that the bile canalicular membrane has little capacity for the formation of phosphatidylcholine which suggests that the endoplasmic reticulum is the site of synthesis of the phosphatidylcholine for subsequent release into the bile (Gregory *et al.*, 1975; Yousef *et al.*, 1977).

On the basis of *in vitro* studies, there appears to exist a well-defined molar ratio of phosphatidylcholine to cholesterol and bile salt in these complexes which is required for complete aqueous solubility and stability. In the absence of phosphatidylcholine, approximately 97 molecules of bile salt are necessary to solubilize 3 molecules of cholesterol. As the proportion of phosphatidylcholine increases, progressively more cholesterol is solubilized to a maximum of about 10 molecules per 60 of bile salt and 30 molecules of phosphatidylcholine (Admirand and Small, 1968). Small (1968) has proposed a disk-shaped micelle model in which an outer perimeter of bile salt molecules encloses a small disk of phosphatidylcholine molecules. These micelles are capable of partial expansion as a result of taking up cholesterol. As yet there has been no physicochemical basis suggested for the relatively specific finding of the 1-palmitoyl 2-linoleoyl and 1-palmitoyl 2-oleoyl phosphatidylcholines in most animal biles (Christie, 1973). However, a specific functional role for the linoleoyl phosphatidylcholines is suggested by the observation that essential fatty acid deficiency in hamsters leads to impaired biliary excretion of taurocholate, phosphatidylcholine, and water, which results in the supersaturation of bile with respect to the cholesterol (Sarfeh *et al.*, 1974).

A possible micellar function for bile phosphatidylcholine may be recognized also in the duodenum and the upper jejunum where it would act in conjunction with the bile salts. Both diacyl and monoacylphosphatidylcholines have been shown to be prominent components of the micellar phase of the gut contents during active fat absorption (Hofmann and Borgström, 1962). Furthermore, monoacylphosphatidylcholines are readily absorbed by the mucosal cells and reacylated in the mucosal cell (Parthasarathy *et al.*, 1974). It has been suggested that they subsequently serve to maintain the micellar dispersions of the lipids during the initial stages of triacylglycerol resynthesis and it is known that they eventually participate in the stabilization of the chylomicron surface (Zilversmit, 1969). There is experimental evidence which shows that much of the bile phosphatidylcholine is transferred to the chylomicron membranes and eventually appears in the lymph (Scow *et al.*, 1967). Furthermore, bile fistula rats are unable

Table X

PRINCIPAL MOLECULAR SPECIES OF BILE PHOSPHATIDYLCHOLINES FROM
PIG, SHEEP AND COW [a]

Molecular species	Proportion (%)		
	Pig bile	Sheep bile	Cow bile
16:0–16:0	—	2.8	—
16:0–18:0	—	1.2	—
16:0–16:1	0.9	1.0	3.0
16:0–18:1	22.6	39.7	37.6
18:0–18:1	3.6	7.3	9.9
16:1–18:1	1.1	2.1	2.5
18:1–18:1	1.5	1.9	3.6
16:0–18:2($n-6$)	26.9	9.6	11.3
18:0–18:2($n-6$)	13.1	2.9	7.9
16:0–18:2conj [b]	—	9.0	1.4
18:0–18:2conj [b]	—	2.1	tr
16:0–18:3($n-3$)	tr	6.7	3.5
18:0–18:3($n-3$)	tr	2.2	1.6
16:0–18:3conj [c]	—	2.3	—
18:0–18:3conj [c]	—	0.6	—
16:0–18:3($n-6$)	0.8	—	1.3
18:3	0.5	—	1.4
18:0– ($n-6$) 20:3			
16:1–18:2	0.8	—	0.4
18:1–18:2	2.7	—	1.4
16:0–20:4($n-6$)	7.9	0.9	1.8
18:0–20:4($n-6$)	3.6	0.7	0.9
18:4 16:0– ($n-3$) 20:4	—	—	1.2
18:4 18:0– ($n-3$) 20:4	—	—	1.3
18:1–18:3	—	0.7	—
18:2–18:2($n-6$)	1.5	—	—
16:0–20:5/22:5	2.2	0.5	3.0
18:0–20:5/22:5	0.8	3.1	1.5
16:0–22:6	2.3	1.5	0.6
18:0–22:6	0.5	0.5	0.2

[a] Modified from Christie (1973).

[b] *cis*-9, *trans*-11-Octadecadienoic acid.

[c] *cis*-9, *trans*-11,*cis*-15-Octadecatrienoic acid.

to secrete chylomicrons effectively and thus are unable to clear the gut of dietary lipid (Gallagher *et al.,* 1965; O'Doherty *et al.,* 1973). The fatty gut can be readily cleared by the fistula rat following the supplementation of the dietary fat with phosphatidylcholine or choline, but not with phosphatidylethanolamine or inositol (O'Doherty *et al.,* 1973). In addition, Van den Berg and Hulsman (1971) have claimed that maximum rates of chylomicron formation and secretion are not obtained unless specific molecular species of 1,2-diacylglycerols can be formed. The optimum rates of fat absorption are obtained in the presence of palmitoyl linoleoyl and palmitoyl oleoyl and to a lesser extent palmitoyl arachidonoyl phosphatidylcholines. Arvidson and Nilsson (1972) have demonstrated that the composition of the major molecular species of chylomicron phosphatidylcholines remains largely unaltered regardless of whether unsaturated or saturated fats are fed.

3. *Mediators of Immune and Humoral Responses*

There is evidence which implicates various glycerophospholipids in immune response (Kinsky, 1972; Lauf, 1975). Among the immunologically active lipids are a few glycerophospholipids with haptenic properties such as diphosphatidylglycerol (Rapport and Graf, 1969) and phosphatidylinositol (Kataoka and Nojima, 1970). Antisera against diphosphatidylglycerol and phosphatidylinositol have been shown to combine specifically with the polar head groups of the reactive phospholipids (Inoue and Nojima, 1967, 1969; Kataoka and Nojima, 1970). However, according to Faure and Coulon-Morelec (1963) the phosphatides derived from diphosphatidylglycerol by loss of one or two fatty acids are active but less active than the original molecule itself; the molecules which have lost three and four fatty acids are deprived of any serological activity. Furthermore, the diphosphatidylglycerols containing unsaturated fatty acids are more active than analogous compounds containing saturated fatty acids. In addition, Faure and Coulon-Morelec (1963) have recognized that the loss of activity on storage of phosphatidylcholine is due to the peroxidation of its unsaturated fatty acids, although the activity was also lost as a result of alcoholysis of the phosphatide. De Bruijn (1966) has presented a review of the literature on the structure of phosphatidylcholine and the serological activity of similar synthetic compounds. The obtained results suggested that synthetic diphosphatidylglycerol containing equimolar amounts of stearic and oleic acids was as active as natural ox heart diphosphatidylglycerol which is made up largely of linoleic acid. Subsequent work by Inoue and Nojima (1967, 1969) has shown the importance of the hydrophobic moiety since an analogue which has benzyl groups instead of diacylglycerol residues has no reactivity.

Phosphatidylcholine is generally required for the serologic reaction of most of the glycerolipid haptens as an auxiliary lipid. Kataoka and Nojima (1970) have found that the entire phosphtidylcholine molecule is required when haptens are prepared by mixing their lipid components, and the diacylglycerol structure of phosphatidylcholine rather than the phosphorylcholine moiety is important in preserving the haptenic structure. Following the formation of micelles, the phosphorylcholine moiety may be removed by means of phospholipase C without distortion of the active diphosphatidylglycerol micelle. Tonks and Allen (1953) examined several synthetic phosphatidylcholines for their activity as the auxiliary lipids in serological tests with tetramyristoyldiphosphatidylglycerol and found that except for distearoylphosphatidylcholine which was rather insoluble, all the others gave about the same activity as the beef heart phosphatidylcholine used as a control.

There is some evidence to indicate that specific molecular species of glycerolipids may play a role in enhancing host resistance to a variety of infectious agents, modulating inflammation and neoplasia, as well as altering transplantation events (diLuzio, 1972). Only a few systematic studies, however, have been made with different molecular species. It has been theorized (diLuzio, 1972) that the macrophage cell itself may be regulated in part through the carbon chain length of the fatty acid radical, the exact nature of the fatty acid, and the particle size of specific lipid moieties which exist in the environment of the macrophage.

4. *Others*

There are numerous other physiological responses which are considered to be mediated by glycerophospholipids, but the information available on the role of specific molecular species is limited. Thus, a role for glycerophospholipids in epinephrine binding to protein receptors is indicated although it is not clear whether the phospholipids play a specific role in the complexing process or a nonspecific role in helping to maintain a particular conformation of the adenylate cyclase in the membrane (Tomasi *et al.,* 1970; Marinetti *et al.,* 1972; Lesko and Marinetti, 1975). Birnbaumer (1973) has claimed that phospholipids play a specific role in coupling the hormone-receptor interaction to adenylate cyclase activation. There are also data to support the role of glycerophospholipids in the receptor for thyrotropin-releasing hormone in the plasma membranes of bovine anterior pituitary gland (Barden and Labrie, 1973). Likewise, a specific glycerophospholipid requirement is indicated in the binding of glucocorticoids to receptors of fibroblasts and thymic lymphocytes (Schulte *et al.,* 1976).

There is evidence to suggest that the physiological reactions of platelets are mediated by the constituent glycerophospholipids, presumably phosphatidylcholines (Schick and Yu, 1974). An increase in the activity of platelet glycerophospholipids has been associated with an increase in the content of stearic and oleic at the expense of the polyunsaturated acids (Renaud and Gautheron, 1975).

Endoperoxides, thromboxanes (Samuelsson *et al.,* 1975; Kolata, 1975), and prostacyclin, which are derived from polyunsaturated fatty acids, are now recognized to be of great importance in the platelet aggregation and release reactions. Phosphatidylethanolamine has been reported to be a principal source of arachidonic acid released by human platelet membranes (Jesse and Cohen, 1976), but phosphatidylcholine and phosphatidylinositol may also release it (Rittenhouse-Simmons *et al.,* 1977). Lapetina *et al.* (1977) have concluded that the intracellular concentration of cyclic AMP may regulate the thrombin-induced stimulation of phospholipase release of the polyunsaturated acids. This action of cyclic AMP could at least partially explain the inhibitory effect of prostacyclin on platelet aggregation since the availability of arachidonic acid necessary for the formation of endoperoxides and thromboxanes would be restricted.

Glycerophospholipids are also thought to play an important role in the physiological function of the nervous system (Ansell, 1973). Thus, the phosphatidylinositols and phosphatidic acids have been implicated in synaptic transmission whereas the polar head groups of glycerophospholipids are believed to be involved in axonal conduction (Hawthorne, 1973). The association of specific molecular species with particular functions of the nervous system has not been extensively studied. However, the quantitative analyses of O'Brien and Geison (1971) on the subcellular distribution of various phosphatidylcholines in brain (see Section III,A) and the finding of high concentrations of docosahexaenoyl species of phosphatidylethanolamine and phosphatidylserine in synaptosomal plasma membranes (Breckenridge *et al.,* 1972) indicate that such investigations may provide important clues to the understanding of the structure–function relationship of these glycerophospholipids.

C. BIOCHEMICAL BASIS

In the following section, an effort has been made to assemble information on established biochemical reactions of molecular species of diacylglycerophospholipids. These observations have provided evidence for defined metabolic functions of molecular species differing in their fatty acid composition. Many of the biochemical functions of the various species of the glycerophospholipids are mediated by their structural association with biological membranes and lipoproteins, while others are known to take place in micellar solutions.

1. Structural Role in Membranes and Lipoproteins

Although a large number of models of membrane structure have been proposed and discussed (Danielli and Davson, 1935; Stein and Danielli, 1956; Robertson, 1958; Benson, 1966; Stoeckenius and Engelman, 1969; Deamer, 1970; Vandenheuvel, 1971; Singer and Nicolson, 1972; Finean, 1973), none have accounted for differences in the fatty acid composition of the diacylglycerophospholipid molecules. It is outside the scope of this review to consider the merits and shortcomings of the individual models. For the present purpose, it is sufficient to acknowledge that protein–glycerophospholipid interaction is of utmost importance for maintaining the structure and function of biological membranes and that this feature is emphasized in all the current models of natural membranes. On the basis of studies with isolated systems (see Section II,B), it is anticipated that such lipid–protein interactions will be different for different molecular species of the glycerophospholipids, which in turn will influence membrane structure and function. Direct evidence for the effect of individual molecular species of glycerophospholipids on the structure of intact membranes is limited. However, it is well established that the activities of membrane-bound enzymes as well as assorted transport processes are dependent upon the acyl chain composition of the membrane glycerophospholipids.

Extensive studies have been made on the possible relationship between the fatty acid composition of the membrane glycerophospholipids and mitochondrial structure in animal systems made deficient in essential fatty acids. This results in an increase in the proportion of hepatic oleoyl and eicosatrienoylphosphatidylcholines and a decrease in linoleoyl and arachidonoylphosphatidylcholines in the rat (Van Golde and van Deenen, 1966; Van Golde *et al.*, 1968). It has been observed that liver mitochondria from essential fatty acid-deficient mice show enlargement and a central stacking of elongated cristae (Wilson and Leduc, 1963). In contrast to the mouse, liver mitochondria from essential fatty acid-deficient rats were enlarged although no extra cristae were apparent (Smithson, 1969). The spontaneous swelling of mitochondria from essential fatty acid deficient animals has been widely reported (Houtsmuller *et al.*, 1969; Guarnieri and Johnson, 1970). Earlier work of de Pury and Collins (1966) had indicated that the phosphatidylcholines from essential fatty acid deficient rats are bound more rapidly to delipidated liver mitochondria. Subsequent studies have shown that the fatty acid composition of the various phosphatidylcholines greatly influences their binding to mitochondrial proteins with the arachidonoyl species of phosphatidylcholine interacting significantly more slowly than those of eicosatrienoyl or mixtures of oleoyl and linoleoyl species (Collins *et al.*, 1971).

Further indication of the possible biochemical importance of the molecular species of glycerophospholipids comes from studies on the association, binding, and exchange of these lipids with the plasma lipoproteins of different density classes. There is evidence that the plasma lipoproteins possess an optimum spectrum of molecular species of glycerophospholipids under normal physiological conditions and that alterations in this spectrum are associated with abnormalities in lipid metabolism and possible disease conditions (Spritz and Mishkel, 1969; de Pury and Collins, 1972). A substitution of polyunsaturated for saturated fats in the diet results in a marked decrease in the total plasma glycerolipids and cholesterol, which is also accompanied by a fourfold increase in the proportion of the 1-saturated 2-linoleoyl species of phosphatidylcholine (Spritz and Mishkel, 1969). Spritz and Mishkel (1969) have proposed that the linoleoylphosphatidylcholines occupy a larger surface area in the lipoprotein which reduces the glycerolipid carrying capacity of the apoprotein of the low density lipoprotein and produces a lower lipid/protein ratio during unsaturated fat feeding.

Detailed studies by de Pury and Collins (1972) have revealed a close similarity in the fatty acid composition of the phosphatidylcholines from the various serum lipoproteins of essential fatty acid deficient rats, whereas phosphatidylcholines from the high density lipoprotein of control rats were greatly depleted in arachidonate and enriched in oleate relative to the very low and low density lipoproteins. Discrepancies in the molecular species composition of the glycerophospholipids of plasma lipoproteins have also been observed by Mookerjea *et al.* (1975). The chylomicron phosphatidylcholines reflected the dietary fat and obviously did not equilibrate with the phosphatidylcholines of other plasma lipoproteins. The differences between the glycerophospholipids of high and low density lipoproteins were somewhat smaller but still significant. The most extensive investigations of the composition of glycerolipids of plasma lipoproteins have been performed in the laying hen (Gornall and Kuksis, 1973). Detailed comparisons among the molecular species of the triacylglycerols and the choline and ethanolamine phosphatides of the plasma and yolk lipoproteins of corresponding densities revealed considerable similarities, along with minor but significant differences, which could be correlated with the existence in the plasma of lipoproteins of distinctly different glycerolipid composition; those destined for deposition in the egg yolk and those in the normal plasma lipoproteins.

On the basis of *in vitro* work, it has been claimed (Rehnborg and Nichols, 1964) that a significant exchange of glycerolipids takes place among plasma lipoproteins, although more recent work has not supported as extensive an exchange of triacylglycerols as originally believed (Quarfordt *et al.*, 1971). On the basis of both *in vitro* and *in vivo* work (Illingworth and Portman, 1972a,b), it is known that an exchange of glycerophospholipids between the plasma lipoproteins occurs independently of protein exchange. The rates of exchange of four phosphatidylcholine subfractions (monoenes, dienes, tetraenes, and polyenes) between the low and high density lipoproteins of squirrel monkeys were found to be the same (Illingworth and Portman, 1972a). However, there remains some uncertainty about the extent and nature of equilibration of phosphatidylcholine among the plasma lipoprotein classes (Wirtz, 1974). Furthermore, these findings do not necessarily contradict the mass analyses referred to above.

The discrepancies in the composition of the molecular species of the glycerophospholipids in the plasma lipoprotein may reflect differences in the amino acid composition of the various apoproteins (Baker *et al.*, 1974; Brewer *et al.*, 1972a,b; Jackson *et al.*, 1976) and appropriate models for the glycerophospholipid–protein interaction have been proposed (Scanu and Wisdom, 1972; Jackson *et al.*, 1976). The binding and degree of interaction of various phosphatidylcholines with the apoprotein are known to depend on the chain length and unsaturation of the fatty acid esters (Camejo *et al.*, 1970; Scanu and Wisdom, 1972). In such a case, the exchange of glycerophospholipids among lipoproteins would be expected to be largely restricted to like molecules.

2. Regulators of Enzyme Activity and of Transport Processes

It was pointed out in Section III,B that membrane glycerophospholipids play an important role in mediating the physiological action of various hormones. In addition, it is now well recognized that glycerophospholipids can regulate the activity of membrane-bound enzymes and membrane transport in a manner which is dependent on their fatty acid composition. Direct evidence of the importance of the hydrophobic fatty acyl chains in the regulation of the activity of various enzymes is derived from experiments on activation of delipidated enzyme preparations by exogenous glycerophospholipids. Indirect evidence comes from studies where manipulation of the dietary fat has resulted in changes in the fatty acid composition of membrane glycerophospholipids, which correlate with alterations in the activity of membrane-bound enzymes. Although recent reviews have acknowledged the importance of lipid composition in various enzyme systems (Coleman, 1973; Finean, 1973; Fourcans and Jain, 1974; Farias *et al.*,

1975), the role of specific molecular species of glycerophospholipids in such membrane processes has only recently begun to become unraveled. Much of the earlier work on the activation of lipid-depleted enzyme systems has disregarded the fatty acid composition of the exogenously added glycerophospholipid.

The mitochondrial enzyme β-hydroxybutyric acid dehydrogenase is known to have a specific requirement for phosphatidylcholine with unsaturated fatty acids (Jurtshuk et al., 1961). The level of enzyme activation is influenced by the length and degree of unsaturation of the aliphatic chains in the added phosphatidylcholine (Levy et al., 1976). However, Grover et al. (1975) have observed that monoenic phosphatidylcholines containing one molecule of oleate gave higher maximal activation than dioleoyl or dilinoleoyl species. It has now been demonstrated that the binding of NADH to the dehydrogenase is dependent upon the formation of an enzyme–phosphatidylcholine complex and that the complex formed with dioleoylphosphatidylcholine permits better binding of NADH than those with dilauroylphosphatidylcholine (Gazotti et al., 1974).

Das et al. (1962) have reported that the activating properties of the glycerophospholipid–cytochrome C complex depend upon the presence of unsaturated fatty acids in the added phosphatidylethanolamine. No activation was observed with dimyristoylphosphatidylethanolamine. The presence of glycerophospholipids with unsaturated fatty acyl groups also appeared to be essential for reconstitution of the activity of oxidative phosphorylation in the mitochondrial membrane (Kagawa et al., 1973).

Purification and delipidation of the microsomal glucose-6-phosphatase has revealed that dioleoyl and egg phosphatidylcholine are almost equally effective in the enzyme reactivation, whereas dipalmitoyl phosphatidylcholine is inactive under all conditions tested (Garland and Cori, 1972). O'Doherty et al. (1974) have observed that dilinoleoyl and dioleoylphosphatidylcholines are more effective than dimyristoyl or dipalmitoylphosphatidylcholines in restoring the activity of mono- and diacylglycerol acyltransferases in phosphatidylcholine-depleted microsomes from rat intestinal mucosa. Kimelberg and Papahadjopoulos (1972) report that maximal reactivation of the $(Na^+ + K^+)$-dependent ATPase from rabbit kidney is obtained only when the fatty acyl chains of the glycerophospholipids are in their fluid state since the relative effectiveness of dipalmitoyl and egg phosphatidylglycerol is a function of the assay temperatures and appears to be related to their transition temperatures. The same authors have later shown that the temperature at which the Arrhenius plot discontinuities occur is from 1 to 8°C lower than the initial rise of the main endothermic peak as measured by differential scanning calorimetry for the following series: dimyristoyl, dipalmitoyl, and distearoyl phosphatidylglycerols

(Kimelberg and Papahadjopoulos, 1974). Dioleoylphosphatidylglycerol, which did not undergo a phase transition within the experimental temperature range, was found to activate the enzyme at much lower concentrations than the saturated phosphatidylglycerols, and the Arrhenius plot did not show discontinuities. Pure complexes of synthetic phosphatidylcholines (dimyristoyl, dipalmitoyl, and diolcoyl species) with the Ca^{2+}-dependent ATPase derived from sarcoplasmic reticulum gave evidence for a critical effect of the chain conformation on the activity of the enzyme (Warren *et al.*, 1974). The activity of ATPase complexes with saturated phosphatidylcholines was completely inhibited below temperatures which correspond to a phase transition of the glycerophospholipids.

Alterations in the type of dietary fat have provided the opportunity for correlating the fatty acid composition of membrane glycerophospholipids with changes in the activity of membrane-bound enzymes. For many of these studies, essential fatty acid-deficient diets have been employed to produce membrane glycerophospholipids with increased levels of oleoyl and eicosatrienoyl and decreased proportions of linoleoyl and arachidonoyl species (Van Golde *et al.*, 1968). Thus, recent studies have indicated that the specific activity of 5'-nucleotidase from liver plasma membranes of deficient rats was lower than for controls (Brivio-Haugland *et al.*, 1976). However, the activity and apparent K_m for total $(Na^+ + K^+ + Mg^{2+})$-ATPase were higher in the deficient liver plasma membranes; supplementation of deficient rats with a source of essential fatty acids restored the latter kinetic parameters to normal. By estimating transition temperatures from Arrhenius plots, Solomonson *et al.* (1976) concluded that the effect of dietary lipid on the changes in activity of the plasma membrane $(Na^+ + K^+)$-ATPase was mediated by induced changes in the fatty acid composition of the glycerophospholipids in the plasma membrane. Many other enzymes have been shown to require glycerophospholipids for optimal activity, but the role of the individual molecular species has not been investigated (Coleman, 1973). It is possible that the effect of different species as well as the relative contributions of hydrophilic and hydrophobic moieties of the phosphatides vary with each enzyme.

In addition to the active movement of Na^+ and K^+ across plasma membranes, the fatty acid composition of membrane glycerophospholipids has been implicated in other cellular transport processes. Thus, Imai *et al.* (1970) have shown that the parameters measuring the slow step of transport of a neutral solute such as α-methyl-D-glucoside were all reduced about 30% in evert sacs of intestinal segments from essential fatty acid deficient rats. Ahmed and Walker (1972) observed that the accumulation of phenylalanine, leucine, and lysine was significantly greater in some intestinal sections from essential fatty acid-deficient rats than from control rats when the data were expressed on a tissue dry weight basis. These findings were related to alterations in the glycerophospholipids of the mucosal cell membrane. A dietary deficiency of essential fatty acids resulted in the partial replacement of arachidonoyl by eicosatrienoyl, and of linoleoyl by oleoylphosphatidylcholines in the intestinal mucosa of rats (Yurkowski and Walker, 1971). More recently, Johns and Bergen (1974) concluded that the major effect of an essential fatty acid deficiency was to induce membrane alterations of intestinal mucosa which lowered the ability of mucosal cells to retain amino acids. The formation of an amino acid–glycerophospholipid complex has been proposed which allows an amino acid to traverse the epithelial cell membrane (Reiser and Christiansen, 1968). Glycerol and phosphate permeability of red blood cells from various mammals have also been correlated with the ratio of poly-/mono-unsaturated fatty acids in the constituent glycerophospholipids (Deuticke and Gruber, 1970; Wessels and Veerkamp, 1973; van Deenen and De Gier, 1974). In addition, studies with phospholipid vesicles (Papahadjopoulos, 1973; van Deenen and De Gier, 1974) and bacterial mutants (Oxender, 1972) have supported the importance of the fatty acid chains in the transport of inorganic ions, amino acids, and various sugars.

3. Metabolic Substrates

In addition to having an important structural and functional role in cell membranes and lipoproteins, the various molecular species of glycerophospholipids have been demonstrated to serve as specific substrates in a variety of metabolic transformations. It is well established that different phosphatidylcholines can serve as substrates for the plasma enzyme, phosphatidylcholine–cholesterol acyl transferase, which transfers the acyl chains from the 2 position of phosphatidylcholine to cholesterol thereby forming the corresponding cholesterol ester (Glomset, 1968). This reaction appears to take place on or within the high density lipoproteins, predominantly the lower molecular weight subfractions (Glomset et al., 1966). The work of Portman and Sugano (1964) has indicated that cholesteryl arachidonate and cholesteryl linoleate are the major products of this reaction in rat and human plasma, respectively. These authors also proposed that the pattern of the cholesteryl esters formed during the incubations were related to the specificity of the enzyme rather than the fatty acid composition of the available phosphatidylcholines. Sugano (1971) studied the specificity of the enzyme in the residual protein fraction from ultracentrifugation of rat plasma and found the following specificities towards different molecular species of phosphatidylcholines labeled in the fatty acid at the 2 position: arachidonoyl > linoleoyl > oleoyl > palmitoyl. Sgoutas (1972) found the enzyme from human plasma to have a much different selectivity towards phosphatidylcholines with different acyl chains at the 2 position: linoleoyl > oleoyl > arachidonoyl > palmitoyl; the specificity was not influenced by the nature of the fatty acid at the *sn*-1 position of the phosphatidylcholine molecule. Studies on whole plasma from rabbit and bovine plasma have also indicated a specificity of the acyltransferase towards phosphatidylcholines with linoleate at the 2 position (Stefanovich, 1969; Noble *et al.,* 1972). Sugano (1973) has pointed out that the availability of different molecular species of plasma phosphatidylcholines and the specificity of the enzyme may directly or indirectly regulate the uptake of circulating phosphatidylcholine by the liver and peripheral tissues. Earlier, Holub and Kuksis (1971b) had shown that the utilization of the arachidonoyl phosphatidylcholine as substrate for the acyl transferase could provide in the rat for the net transfer of cholesterol from plasma to liver in the form of its arachidonoyl ester. The lysophosphatidylcholine released into plasma by the enzyme is reacylated in liver with arachidonic acid so as to regenerate the substrate for the plasma phosphatidylcholine-cholesterol acyl transferase.

Shohet (1970) has demonstrated that certain species of phosphatidylcholine of red blood cells donate their unsaturated fatty acids to the 2 position of lysophosphatidylethanolamine which is also present in these cells. Shohet *et al.* (1971) have described a defect in the transfer of fatty acids from phosphatidylcholine to lysophosphatidylethanolamine in a hereditary intercorpuscular hemolytic anemia. This reaction normally accounts for about one-third of the fatty acid turnover within the cell.

Unsaturated species of both phosphatidylcholine and phosphatidylethanolamine have been reported to be involved as substrates for the formation of glycerophospholipid-bound peroxides (May and McCay, 1968a). The experiments of May and McCay (1968a,b) have demonstrated that the unsaturated species of both choline and ethanolamine phosphatides are altered due to a TPNH oxidase activity in rat liver microsomes. From a study of the unsaturated fatty acids associated with the glycerophospholipids that became consumed during the reaction, it was established that the arachidonoyl glycerophospholipids were utilized at a higher rate than the linoleoyl and docosahexaenoyl species. The production of malondialdehyde accounted for only a small proportion of the polyunsaturated glycerophospholipids which were consumed (May and McCay, 1968b). Niehaus and Samuelsson (1968) have also demonstrated that the malonaldehyde produced during microsomal lipid peroxidation is derived from arachidonoyl-glycerophospholipids.

An important potential role for the polyunsaturated species of glycerophospholipids as substrates for the biosynthesis of prostaglandins lies in the fact that phosphatides are the major sources of arachidonic and eicosatrienoic acids, the immediate precursors of the fatty acid-like hormones. Work with synthetic 1-palmitoyl [2-^{14}C]eicosatrienoyl phosphatidylcholine and 1-stearoyl [2-^{3}H]arachidonoyl phosphatidylcholine as substrates with sheep vesicular gland preparations demonstrated that unesterified prostaglandins were formed from the added glycerophospholipids. No appreciable amount of radioactive prostaglandin was found esterified to glycerophospholipid (Lands and Samuelsson, 1968; Vonkeman and Van Dorp, 1968). It was also observed that a supernatant fraction, which was itself incapable of synthesizing prostaglandins, stimulated the synthesis by releasing fatty acids from labeled glycerophospholipids (Lands and Samuelsson, 1968). Added phospholipase A$_2$ was also found to stimulate prostaglandin formation in the particulate fraction of sheep vesicular glands (Vonkeman and Van Dorp, 1968). Therefore, it has been suggested that the activity of tissue phospholipases could be a key factor regulating prostaglandin biosynthesis (Kunze and Vogt, 1971). Subsequently, arachidonoylphosphatidylinositol has been implicated as a specific donor of arachidonic acid for the biosynthesis of prostaglandins in the thyroid gland of pig (Haye et al., 1973). Furthermore, since arachidonic acid has been shown to be preferentially retained in the ethanolamine plasmalogens of rat testes during essential fatty acid deficiency, it has been speculated that the plasmalogens might serve as the reservoir of prostaglandin precursors (Blank et al., 1973).

There is considerable evidence to support the concept that oleoylglycerophospholipids may serve as substrates for the desaturases which produce linoleate in yeasts, algae, and fungi (Talamo et al., 1973; Pugh and Kates, 1975; Gurr and Brawn, 1970; Baker and Lynén, 1971). Few analogous studies have been conducted in animals although experiments with lower microorganisms suggest that oleoylglycerophospholipids are not substrates in linoleate formation (Vijay and Stumpf, 1971; Holloway and Holloway, 1974). Recently, Pugh and Kates (1977) have reported that 1-acyl 2-eicosatrienoyl phosphatidylcholine could serve as a substrate for arachidonate formation via a desaturation reaction in rat liver microsomes. In an analogous fashion, it has been demonstrated that ethanolamine plasmalogen is synthesized by dehydrogenation of the corresponding 1-0-alkyl-2-acylglycerophosphorylethanolamine (Wykle et al., 1972; Paltauf and Holasek, 1973). Also, Soodsma et al. (1976) have observed a doubling of the dipalmitoylphosphatidylcholine in fetal rabbit lung during the last week of gestation and have suggested that it may be derived by biohydrogenation of the palmitoyl-palmitoleoyl phosphatidylcholine when breathing begins. However, the interconversion of the molecules by deacylation-reacylation cycles is a distinct possibility as well (see Section IV). Finally, some of the major glycerophospholipids can be specifically interconverted via modification of their nitrogenous bases through methylation and decarboxylation reactions. The latter transformations which also favor specific molecular species will be discussed in a later section on glycerophospholipid biosynthesis (see Section IV).

IV. Biosynthesis of Molecular Species of Diacylglycerophospholipids

The biosynthesis of the common glycerophospholipids is known to involve phosphatidic acids, 1,2-diacyl-*sn*-glycerols, and CDP-diacylglycerols as intermediates. A comparison of the mass composition of molecular species of the phosphatidylcholines, phosphatidylethanolamines, and phosphatidylinositols with their presumed precursors (see Section II,A) indicates marked discrepancies which are not consistent with any simple precursor–product relationship. These differences apparently reflect the modifying effect of different pathways in the metabolism of various molecular species of the glycerophospholipids. *In vitro* experiments on the individual reactions involved in glycerolipid synthesis have shown that enzyme specificity towards precursors of certain fatty acid composition contributes to the pattern of molecular species associated with a particular type of glycerophospholipid. *In vivo* experiments with isotopic precursors have supported this concept and have indicated that enzyme selectivity as well as substrate availability control the pattern of molecular species of glycerophospholipids formed.

A. Biosynthesis of Phosphatidic Acids, 1,2-Diacyl-*sn*-Glycerols, and CDP-Diacylglycerols

It is now well established that the initial step in the *de novo* biosynthesis of the glycerophospholipids involves the acylation of glycerol-3-phosphate or dihydroxyacetone phosphate with an intermediate formation of phosphatidic acid (Hill and Lands, 1970; Hubscher, 1970; Van Den Bosch *et al.*, 1972). The glycerol phosphate and dihydroxyacetone phosphate acyltransferase activities may represent dual functions of a single enzyme (Schlossman and Bell, 1976). The various molecular species of phosphatidic acids can give rise to the corresponding 1,2-diacyl-*sn*-glycerols and CDP-diacylglycerols in the presence of phosphatidate phosphohydrolase (Hubscher,

1970) and CTP: phosphatidate cytidylyltransferase, respectively (Carter and Kennedy, 1966).

1. *Biosynthesis of Phosphatidic Acids*

The phosphatidic acid from rat liver and other tissues examined is known to contain a preponderance of monoenoic and dienoic species (mainly *sn*-1 16:0, 2 18:1 and *sn*-1 16:0, 2 18:2) with lesser amounts of polyenoic species (mainly *sn*-1 18:0, 2 20:4) being present (see Section II,A). The evidence to date suggests that 1-acyl glycerol-3-phosphate is the likely intermediate in the formation of phosphatidic acid (Lamb and Fallon, 1970; Yamashita and Numa, 1972; Tamai and Lands, 1974), although the involvement of a 2-acyl derivative cannot be completely excluded (Okuyama *et al.*, 1971; Tamai and Lands, 1974). Okuyama *et al.* (1971) showed that the 2-acyl (unsaturated) isomer was acylated with saturated and unsaturated acyl-CoAs at one-fifth to one twenty-fourth the rate of the 1-acyl isomer in rat liver microsomes. Studies on the partially purified glycerophosphate acyltransferase from rat liver microsomes revealed that the rate of formation of 1-acyl glycerol-3-phosphate from palmitoyl-CoA was greater than that from stearoyl-CoA and all unsaturated fatty acyl-CoAs tested (Yamashita and Numa, 1972). Although glycerophosphate acylation has been reported by some authors to occur almost exclusively in the microsomal fraction of liver (Eibl *et al.*, 1969; Davidson and Stanacev, 1972), others have found the highest specific activity in the mitochondria (Zborowski and Wojtczak, 1969; Daae and Bremer, 1970). Studies with mitochondria and with a partially purified enzyme preparation from this subcellular fraction have shown 1-acyl glycerol-3-phosphate as the product of glycerol-3-phosphate acylation with palmitoyl-CoA and the order of effectiveness of various acyl-CoA donors was $16:0 > 18:0 >>$ $18:1 = 18:2$ (Monroy *et al.*, 1972, 1973; Daae, 1972). The acylation of dihydroxyacetone phosphate, the activity of which predominates in mitochondria (La Belle and Hajra, 1972), has been found to occur at highest rates with palmitoyl-CoA when various saturated and unsaturated acyl-CoA preparations are tested (Hajra, 1968). Subsequent reduction of the monoacyl product by NADPH in mitochondria provides 1-acyl glycerol-3-phosphate (Hajra and Agranoff, 1968). Thus, the fatty acid specificity of the acyl transferases in monoacyl glycerol-3-phosphate formation would be expected to provide phosphatidic acid which is greatly enriched in palmitate at the 1 position. These expectations are consistent with the composition of natural phosphatidate from rat liver (Possmayer *et al.*, 1969; Akesson *et al.*, 1970a).

The specific activity of the acyl transferases which convert 1-acyl glycerol-3-phosphate to phosphatidic acid is reported to be higher in microsomes as compared to mitochondria (Eibl *et al.,* 1969; Sarzala *et al.,* 1970) in contrast to earlier findings (Stoffel and Schiefer, 1968), although significant activity exists in the mitochondria as well (Sarzala *et al.,* 1970). Numerous studies have been reported on the fatty acid preference in the acylation of the 1-monoacylglycerolphosphate. Using mixed 16- and 18-carbon 1-monoacylglycerolphosphates, Lands and Hart (1965) showed that the rate of incorporation varied with the nature of the acyl-CoA used and the source of the microsomes. While the guinea pig preparations showed only marginal differences among the precursor 16- and 18-carbon acyl-CoAs, the rat liver microsomes greatly preferred oleoyl- and linoleoyl-CoA while the pig liver microsomes favored oleoyl-CoA above all others. In contrast to the above studies, Stoffel *et al.* (1967) found little specificity for the fatty acid component of the acyl-CoA in the acylation of 1-acylglycerolphosphate by saturated and unsaturated fatty acids when using rat liver microsomes. In a later study, Hill and Lands (1968) found that, with the exception of the stearoyl derivative, the acyl-CoAs containing 16 and 18 carbon atoms were readily esterified to the 2 position of mixed 1-palmitoyl and 1-stearoyl lysophosphatidic acids by rat and guinea pig liver microsomes regardless of the degree of unsaturation while the acyl-CoAs containing 20 or 22 carbons were not. In a study conducted with both substrates at levels below the critical micelle concentration, Barden and Cleland (1969) found that the fatty acids of the acylglycerol-3-phosphate were not very important in determining reaction rates, but that the oleoyl-CoA was the preferred donor of acyl groups of all the CoA esters tested. Subsequent work by Okuyama and Lands (1972) revealed that the selectivity of the acyltransferases depends upon 1-acylglycerol-3-phosphate concentrations since palmitate and arachidonate tended to be excluded at very low concentrations of the acyl acceptor. Using a purified enzyme preparation from rat liver, Yamashita *et al.* (1973) have shown that a marked preference exists for oleoyl-CoA over all saturated and unsaturated donors in the acylation of 1-acylglycerophosphate. The arachidonoyl-CoA was almost completely ineffective. On the basis of these specificities, one would predict that the biosynthesis of phosphatidic acid would yield molecular species which would be enriched in 16:0 at the 1 position and 18:1 at the 2 position as shown by compositional data.

Only a few studies have been made on extrahepatic tissues. In rabbit heart mitochondria (Liu *et al.,* 1974) and microsomes (Zaror-Behrens and Kako 1976), the preference for saturated and unsaturated fatty acids at the 1 and 2 positions, respectively, was found to be less pronounced than in liver mitochondria and microsomes, and the positional specificity in the rat lung microsomal fraction was different from that in the liver microsomes

(Hendry and Possmayer, 1974). The incorporation of fatty acids into rat brain phosphatidate *in vivo* has shown a different positional specificity from that in rat liver (Baker and Thompson, 1972). The recent work of Bjerve *et al.* (1976) confirms that the mitochondrial acyltransferases are different from the microsomal ones, but also indicates that the concentrations of both acyl-CoA and lysophosphatidic acid influence the pattern of fatty acid incorporation into phosphatidic acid. Whether these differences reflect the presence of particle-specific acyltransferases or differences in the phospholipid composition of the membranes where the substrates and enzymes are embedded is not yet known. Fleming and Hajra (1977) have found 1-alkyl-*sn*-glycerol-3-phosphate:acyl-CoA acyltransferase in rat heart, spleen, brain, kidney, liver, and lung. The enzyme in rat brain showed the highest specific activity in the microsomal fraction. Comparison of the acyl-CoA specificity of 1-alkyl-*sn*-glycero-3-phosphate acyltransferase and ether-glycerolipid acyl composition suggests that this acyltransferase could partially determine the composition of acyl groups in ether lipids.

The nature of the molecular species of phosphatidate formed by *de novo* synthesis has been estimated by the use of radioactive glycerol as the glycerolipid precursor. Thus, Hill *et al.* (1968a) found, from experiments with [^{14}C]glycerol, that 70–80% of the newly synthesized phosphatidates in rat liver slices were monoenoic plus dienoic species whereas less than 25% of the total radioactivity was associated with species containing three or more double bonds. Since the 2-monoacylglycerols derived from the phosphatidic acids gave similar distributions of radioactivities, it was concluded that the newly formed product contained almost exclusively saturated acids in the 1 position and unsaturated acids in the 2 position. Similar distributions of radioactive glycerol among the various species of phosphatidates have been reported in rat liver microsomes using [^{14}C]glycerol-3-phosphate as the radioactive precursor (Holub and Piekarski, 1976). Akesson *et al.* (1970a) studied the incorporation *in vivo* of labeled glycerol into various phosphatidates in rat liver; [2-^{3}H]glycerol was employed in order to exclude the possible formation of radioactive phosphatidates by the acylation of dihydroxyacetone phosphate. The distributions of radioactivity among the unsaturation classes of phosphatidates were similar to those obtained in previous work in liver slices (Hill *et al.*, 1968a). At least 95% of the label in the monoenoic and dienoic species was associated with the 1-palmitoyl homologue (Akesson *et al.*, 1970a). In contrast to results in liver, the most extensively labeled classes of phosphatidic acid in rat brain were the disaturates, monoenes, and the polyenes containing more than four double bonds (MacDonald *et al.*, 1975). Although a significant portion of the glycerol which enters tissue phosphatidate under physiological conditions is thought to do so by the acylation of dihydroxyacetone phosphate in addition to glycerol-3-phosphate (Manning and Brindley, 1972; Rognstad *et al.*, 1974;

Pollock *et al.*, 1975), the experiments of Okuyama and Lands (1970) indicate that both pathways produce a similar pattern of molecular species of phosphatidic acids; but isotopic effects have been reported in work with [2-³H]glycerol (Manning and Brindley, 1972). Thus, isotopic studies *in vitro* and *in vivo* provide a very close approximation of the known composition of molecular species of phosphatidate in rat liver (see Section II,A) which supports the concept that they are derived primarily by established metabolic sequences for the *de novo* biosynthesis of phosphatidic acid. Discrepancies between expected and observed compositions of tissue phosphatidates might reflect deacylation–reacylation reactions at the level of phosphatidic acid (Possmayer *et al.*, 1969), subcellular compartmentation of precursors and enzymes involved in phosphatidate synthesis, preferential utilization of certain molecular species of phosphatidate, as well as its derivation from other sources such as diglyceride kinase activity (Hokin and Hokin, 1959; Prottey and Hawthorne, 1967; Lapetina and Hawthorne, 1971) or by reversal of the pathway leading to phosphatidyl-inositol synthesis (Jungalwala *et al.*, 1971).

2. Biosynthesis of 1,2-Diacyl-sn-Glycerols

The action of phosphatidate phosphohydrolase yields the various molecular species of 1,2-diacyl-*sn*-glycerols from the corresponding phosphatidates. The enzyme activity has been reported in most subcellular fractions derived from tissue homogenates and appears in membrane-bound, readily solubilized, and soluble forms although the cytosol enzyme is of prime importance in providing 1,2-diacylglycerols as substrates for glycerolipid synthesis in the endoplasmic reticulum (Smith *et al.*, 1967; Johnston *et al.*, 1967; Mitchell *et al.*, 1971). Studies on phosphatidate phosphohydrolase from brain tissue revealed that reaction rates with added phosphatidates prepared from natural phosphatidylcholines (mainly dilinoleoyl, dipalmitoyl, or 1-palmitoyl 2-oleoyl) were about twice those observed with synthetic *rac*-dioleoylphosphatidates. Mitchell *et al.* (1971) found the soluble enzyme from rat liver to show greatest activity with dimyristoyl and palmitoyl-oleoyl phosphatidates as membrane-bound substrates whereas dilauroyl and distearoylphosphatidate were poor substrates; the particulate enzyme had activities which were highest with distearoyl and dioleoylphosphatidate.

Studies with radioactive glycerol in rat liver slices or *in vivo* gave distributions of radioactivity among the various classes of 1,2-diacylglycerols which were very similar to those in the corresponding phosphatidic acids. This indicated that the phosphatidate phosphohydrolase does not exert selectivity toward substrates of different fatty acid composition under physiological conditions (Hill *et al.*, 1968a,b; Akesson *et al.*, 1970a). Such similarities in isotopic distributions were not realized in rat brain (Mac-Donald *et al.,* 1975). A close similarity in the molecular species composition of phosphatidic acids and 1,2-diacylglycerols might be anticipated in liver if the latter glycerolipids are all derived directly by way of phosphatidate phosphohydrolase activity. To a considerable extent this is the case, although significant differences in composition between these two classes of glycerolipids do exist (see Section II,A). These discrepancies probably reflect the contribution of other metabolic pathways for the production of intermediary 1,2-diacylglycerols. Thus, 1,2-diacylglycerols could arise in liver and other tissues by reversal of the corresponding phosphotransferase reactions which form phosphatidylcholine and phosphatidylethanolamine (Bjornstad and Bremer, 1966; Kanoh and Ohno, 1973a), partial lipolysis of triacylglycerols (Waite and van Deenen, 1967), acylation of 2-monoacylglycerol (Sundler and Akesson, 1970), or by the action of phosphodiesterase on phosphatidylinositol and its mono- and diphosphate derivatives (Keough and Thompson, 1972; Lapetina and Michell, 1973; Tou *et al.,* 1973). The reversal of the cholinephosphotransferase reaction in rat liver microsomes is known to produce a complement of molecular species of 1,2-diacylglycerols in proportion to their abundance in the phosphatidylcholines (Kanoh and Ohno, 1973b; Sundler *et al.,* 1974a) and it has been estimated that these diacylglycerols contribute about 26% and 13% of the total pool of diacylglycerols incorporated into the phosphatidylethanolamines and phosphatidlycholines, respectively (Sundler *et al.,* 1974a). In contrast to findings in liver, the composition of molecular species in the free, 1,2-diacylglycerol pool in brain is greatly enriched in arachidonoyl species and drastically different from that in phosphatidic acid (MacDonald *et al.,* 1975). In addition, isotopic studies with [14C]glycerol *in vivo* have revealed low rates of synthesis of tetraenoic diacylglycerols relative to other species which suggests that they may be derived from sources other than the hydrolysis of phosphatidate by phosphatidate phosphohydrolase (MacDonald *et al.,* 1975). One such source may be the brain phosphodiesterase which can hydrolyze phosphatidylinositol and its mono- and diphosphate derivatives to 1,2-diacylglycerols with fatty acid compositions similar to those of its substrates and to the physiological pool of 1,2-diacylglycerols (Keough *et al.,* 1972; MacDonald, *et al.,* 1975).

3. *Biosynthesis of CDP-Diacylglycerols*

It is known that intact phosphatidic acid enters directly into CDP-diacylglycerol by reacting with CTP in the presence of the enzyme, CTP phosphatidate cytidylyltransferase (Paulus and Kennedy, 1960; Thompson *et al.,* 1963; Carter and Kennedy, 1966; Petzold and Agranoff, 1967).

The endoplasmic reticulum appears to be the main subcellular site for CDP-diacylglycerol synthesis in liver from phosphatidic acid (Carter and Kennedy, 1966; Hostetler and Van Den Bosch, 1972; Van Golde *et al.,* 1974; Davidson and Stanacev, 1974), but significant synthesis of this lipo-nucleotide has also been reported in isolated mitochondria (Vorbeck and Martin, 1970; Hostetler and Van Den Bosch, 1972). Although rat liver mitochondria are capable of synthesizing deoxy-CDP-diacylglycerol (ter Schegget *et al.,* 1971), this latter liponucleotide was not detected in bovine liver or brain (Thompson and MacDonald, 1975, 1976).

A few reports have appeared in the literature on the enzymic formation of different molecular species of CDP-diacylglycerols in mammalian tissue preparations from the corresponding phosphatidic acids. Synthetic saturated rac-phosphatidic acids were found to be inferior substrates relative to natural phosphatidic acid, prepared from egg lecithin, for the formation of CDP-diacylglycerol in a particulate fraction from embryonic chick brain (Petzold and Agranoff, 1967). Holub and Piekarski (1976) studied the possible selectivity of the cytidylyltransferase towards different unsaturation classes of phosphatidates by preparing rat liver microsomes in which the various molecular species of phosphatides were endogenously labeled with [^{14}C]glycerol. Since the distributions of radioactivity among the molecular species of newly formed CDP-diacylglycerols were similar to those among the corresponding phosphatidates, little selectivity of the cytidylyltransferase towards different molecular species of phosphatidate was apparent. The microsomal cytidylyltransferase produced mainly monoenoic plus dienoic species of CDP-diacylglycerol from phosphatidate which was derived from the acylation of glycerol-3-phosphate (Holub and Piekarski, 1976). Bishop and Strickland (1976) have reported on the formation by rat brain preparations of CDP-diacylglycerols from CTP and 10 different molecular species of exogenously added phosphatidic acids. The disaturated species with fatty acids of 10 to 18 carbons and the diarachidonoyl phosphatidate were less than one-sixth as active as dioleoyl phosphatidate. The 1-palmitoyl 2-oleoyl and 1-stearoyl 2-oleoyl species showed greater activity than the 1-stearoyl 2-arachidonoyl species. Thus, the failure of the transferase to show any preference for tetraenoic phosphatidates in liver and in brain microsomes indicates that this enzyme alone cannot account for the high proportion of 1-stearoyl 2-arachidonoyl CDP-diacylglycerols found in mammalian tissues *in vivo* (Thompson and MacDonald, 1975; Thompson and MacDonald, 1976). The metabolic origin of the poly-unsaturated species of the CDP-diacylglycerol therefore has not been demonstrated, but Thompson and MacDonald (1975) have speculated that this liponucleotide could be derived *in vivo* from an atypical pool of phosphatidic acids, such as that potentially generated by the back reaction of CDP-diacylglycerol: inositol phosphatidyltransferase in the presence of CMP (Petzold and Agranoff, 1967) or by deacylation-reacylation reactions at the level of the lipo nucleotide.

B. Biosynthesis of Phosphatidylcholines and Phosphatidylethanolamines

The major metabolic pathways responsible for entry of long-chain fatty acids into the phosphatidylcholines and phosphatidylethanolamines have been well established. Thus, the characteristic pattern of molecular species in these two glycerophospholipids arise by *de novo* synthesis from the 1,2-diacylglycerols (Kennedy, 1961), acylation of lysophosphatides (Lands, 1965), stepwise methylation of phosphatidylethanolamine to form phosphatidylcholine (Bremer *et al.*, 1960), and decarboxylation of phosphatidylserine to form phosphatidylethanolamine (Borkenhagen *et al.*, 1961). Current evidence suggests that base exchange reactions (Dils and Hubscher, 1961; Borkenhagen *et al.*, 1961) are not of quantitative significance for the interconversion and biosynthesis of the choline and ethanolamine phosphatides under physiological conditions (Bjerve, 1971; Sundler, 1973). It is now well recognized that the various pathways produce distinctly different complements of molecular species of phosphatidylcholines and phosphatidylethanolamines. In some cases, it has been possible to quantitate the contribution of these pathways to the biogenesis of individual molecular species of glycerophospholipids using appropriate isotopic markers.

1. Utilization of 1,2-Diacyl-sn-Glycerols

A number of *in vitro* studies have been performed in liver and other tissues in order to test the possible selectivity of the microsomal choline- and ethanolamine-phosphotransferases towards certain molecular species of 1,2-diacyl-*sn*-glycerols. Such studies are of particular interest since they permit rough estimates of the molecular species of glycerophospholipids which may be formed by these pathways under physiological conditions and the proportion of the naturally-occurring molecular species which may be derived from these reactions. Isotopic experiments *in vivo* provide more definitive information on both counts but do not allow firm conclusions on enzyme specificity.

a. Formation of Phosphatidylcholines.   There is general agreement from studies on liver preparations from various animal species that the *de novo* synthesis of phosphatidylcholine via cholinephosphotransferase activity resides in the microsomal fraction (Wilgram and Kennedy, 1963) with no significant activity in the Golgi complex, mitochondria, plasma membranes, and nuclei (McMurray and Dawson, 1969; Sarzala *et al.,* 1970; Victoria *et al.,* 1971; Van Golde *et al.,* 1971). The cholinephosphotransferase has also shown highest specific activities in the microsomal fraction of brain and lung (McCaman and Cook, 1966; Rooney *et al.,* 1975). Using a microsomal fraction from chicken liver, Weiss *et al.* (1960) observed that rac-palmitoyloleoyl diacylglycerols were less effective than 1,2-dioleoylglycerol in stimulating phosphatidylcholine biosynthesis from CDP-choline whereas disaturated substrates with fatty acids of 10, 12, and 16 carbons were inactive. Comparable observations were made by Strickland *et al.* (1963), who found that added 1,2-dimyristoyl, 1,2-dipalmitoyl, and 1,2-distearoylglycerol as well as 2,3-dioleoylglycerol did not significantly stimulate phosphatidylcholine synthesis in rat brain microsomes although a large and nearly equal stimulation was obtained with 1,2-dioleoylglycerol and 1,2-diacylglycerols prepared from egg phosphatidylcholine. The failure of fully saturated diacylglycerols to serve as substrates was attributed to enzyme specificity and not merely problems in their solubilization. Studies with mixtures of 1,2-diacylglycerols prepared from natural phosphatidylcholines suggested the following order of selectivity of brain cholinephosphotransferase towards different substrates: 1,2-dipalmitoleoyl > 1,2-dilinoleoyl > 1-palmitoyl 2-oleoyl diacylglycerol (McCaman and Cook, 1966).

Subsequent studies on the cholinephosphotransferase from rat liver microsomes have included the use of natural 1,2-diacylglycerols with up to six double bonds per molecule as potential substrates for the enzyme. Thus, Mudd *et al.* (1969) found the rate of phosphatidylcholine synthesis to be the same with monoenoic, dienoic, and tetraenoic diacylglycerols containing oleic, linoleic, and arachidonic acids, respectively, in the 2 position and mixtures of palmitic and stearic acids in the 1 position. These results have been confirmed by Holub (1977) who observed only a moderate discrimination by the cholinephosphotransferase against hexaenoic (1-saturated 2-docosahexaenoyl) diacylglycerols when compared to the monoenoic and dienoic species at low but not at high concentrations of substrate. The findings suggested that the selectivity of the enzyme for certain molecular species could be mediated by enzyme substrates (CDP-ethanolamine, acyl-CoA) which compete for common diacylglycerol precursors. Kanoh (1970) had claimed that tetraenoic were incorporated to a greater extent than dienoic species in experiments with diacylglycerols added to hepatic microsomes. However, the rates of phosphatidylcholine synthesis given in the latter study may not be reliable since they were based on results with different molecular species labeled *in vivo* with radioactive glycerol and it was not possible to ensure equal specific activities for all homologues.

Experiments with rat liver microsomes enriched in endogenous 1,2-diacyl-glycerols have revealed no marked selectivity towards specific molecular species (Kanoh and Ohno, 1975), although this approach also does not permit normalization of substrate concentration for each molecular species tested. From the preceding studies it would be expected that the unsaturation of classes of phosphatidylcholine produced by the cholinephosphotransferase would be similar to the relative abundance of the corresponding unsaturation classes in the free 1,2-diacylglycerol pool of rat liver. As discussed below, such an expectation has been realized to considerable extent by tracer experiments with radioactive phosphate, glycerol, and choline *in vivo*. More detailed analyses of the phosphatidylcholine biosynthesis *in vitro* have shown (Holub, 1978) that a distinct preference exists for the 1-palmitoyl homologues when mixtures of various 1-saturated 2-unsaturated (2-oleoyl, 2-linoleoyl, 2-arachidonoyl, and 2-docosahexaen-oyl) diacylglycerols are tested as substrates of cholinephosphotransferase.

The pioneering work of Rowe (1959, 1960), Collins (1960), and Harris *et al.* (1960) with [32]P *in vitro* showed that phosphatidylcholines with different fatty acid compositions had strikingly different specific activities. These experiments led to the concept that individual molecular species of phosphatidylcholine from a given tissue exhibit a metabolic as well as a structural heterogeneity. Subsequent work by Isozaki *et al.* (1962) and Collins (1963) indicated that following administration of ^{32}P, the specific activity of hepatic phosphatidylcholine fractions enriched in stearic and arachidonic acids was much lower than that of fractions containing palmitic, oleic, and linoleic acids. The development of argentation thin-layer chromatography for separating intact phosphatidylcholines according to degree of unsaturation (Arvidson, 1965) provided a more feasible approach to studying metabolic heterogeneity of these glycerolipids than was possible by adsorption column chromatography (Isozaki *et al.*, 1962) or countercurrent distribution (Collins, 1963). Balint *et al.* (1967) applied argentation thin-layer chromatography to show that the arachidonoyl phosphatidylcholines from rat liver had lower specific activities than linoleoyl species up to 4 hours following an intravenous injection of ^{32}P into rats. These results were confirmed by Arvidson (1968a), who obtained the following order of specific activities for various chemical classes of hepatic phosphatidylcholines: monoenoic = dienoic > total > hexaenoic > tetraenoic. These latter results were interpreted to reflect differences in substrate specificity of the cholinephosphotransferase towards different molecular species of 1,2-diacylglycerols. At least a partial entry of isotope into phosphatidylcholine by methylation of phosphatidylethanolamine (Bremer *et al.*, 1960) is also possible in such experiments. Similar results to those of Arvidson (1968a) have been reported in analogous experiments with radioactive phosphate *in vivo* in rats (Trewhella and Collins, 1969) and rat liver slices (Kanoh, 1969). By means of argentation TLC and countercurrent distribution, Trewhella and Collins (1969) were able to show that the specific activity of the 1-palmitoyl homologue was 6, 11, and 12 times greater than that of the 1-stearoyl homologue for phospatidylcholines with oleate, linoleate, and arachidonate in the 2 position, respectively. Thus, the *in vivo* studies in liver with labeled phosphate, which enters phosphatidylcholine mainly by way of CDP-choline, indicate that the cholinephosphotransferase produces a complement of molecular species that consists predominantly of monoenoic (mainly 1-palmitoyl 2-oleoyl) and dienoic (mainly 1-palmitoyl 2-linoleoyl) species as predicted from *in vitro* studies and the known composition of hepatic 1,2-diacylglycerols (see Section II,A,4).

Shamgar and Collins (1975a) have determined the specific radioactivities of individual molecular species of the phosphatidylcholines and phosphatidylethanolamines of rat skeletal muscle after intraperitoneal injection of ortho [^{32}P]phosphate. Under these conditions the specific radioactivities of the species present in rat muscle were found to be measures of the relative turnover of these molecules. The specific radioactivity of phosphatidylcholine was approximately three times that of phosphatidylethanolamine. The 1-palmitoyl 2-oleoyl and 1-oleoyl 2-linoleoyl phosphatidylcholines had the fastest turnover and the 1-oleoyl 2-arachidonoyl the slowest. The results indicate that the phosphoacylglycerols in rat muscle turn over more slowly and more uniformly than do rat liver phosphoacylglycerols.

A number of comparable studies on the labeling of individual molecular species of phosphatidylcholines have been conducted in liver and other tissues both *in vitro* and *in vivo* after the introduction of radioactive glycerol. The use of radioactive glycerol allows an estimate of the relative rates of synthesis of the individual species of phosphatidylcholine via the 1,2-diacylglycerols which are being derived directly from the corresponding phosphatidic acids. The latter glycerolipids can incorporate the labeled glycerol by the acylation of glycerol-3-phosphate or dihydroxyacetone phosphate. Hill *et al.* (1968a) determined the distribution of added [^{14}C]glycerol among the newly synthesized phosphatidylcholines in a rat liver slice system. After an incubation period of 1 hour, the saturated, monoenoic, dienoic, trienoic, tetraenoic, and polyenoic (> tetraenoic) species contained 4%, 17%, 43%, 10%, 13%, 10%, respectively, of the total radioactivity in the phosphatidylcholines. These latter findings have been confirmed by Kanoh (1969) in rat liver slices. Similar distributions among hepatic phosphatidylcholines *in vivo* were observed by Akesson *et al.* (1970a) and others (Holub and Kuksis, 1971c; Vereyken *et al.*, 1972) up to 5 minutes following the administration of labeled glycerol. By conducting reversed-phase partition thin-layer chromatography (Arvidson, 1967), it was possible to demonstrate that 97% of the radioactive glycerol in the monoenoic and dienoic phosphatidylcholines was associated with the 1-palmitoyl homologues (Akesson *et al.,* 1970a). Thus, the studies with labeled glycerol indicate that the 1,2-diacylglycerols derived from the corresponding phosphatidic acids give rise to the production of phosphatidylcholines *in vivo* which consist largely of 1-palmitoyl 2-oleoyl and 1-palmitoyl 2-linoleoyl species. This is in general agreement with results obtained using labeled phosphate. Estimations of synthetic rates *in vivo* based on the assumption that the 1,2-diacylglycerols, labeled with [^{3}H]glycerol from the corresponding phosphatidic acids, equilibrate with the total hepatic pool of diacylglycerols have indicated the rate of formation of arachidonoylphosphatidylcholines to be considerably greater than each of the other molecular fractions (Sundler and Akesson, 1975). In general, experiments with labeled phosphate have also resulted in a somewhat higher proportion of the radioactivity appearing in the 1-stearoyl homologues (Trewhella and Collins, 1969; Akesson *et al.,* 1970a) than found with labeled glycerol. These small discrepancies in labeling patterns may reflect the reactions of radioactive CDP-choline, derived from ^{32}P, with 1,2-diacylglycerols which are derived from sources other than phosphatidic acid hydrolysis (see Section IV,A).

The biosynthesis of different molecular species of phosphatidylcholines from [^{3}H]glycerol has more recently been studied in isolated rat hepatocytes by addition of different albumin-bound fatty acids to the incubation medium (Sundler *et al.,* 1974b). The utilization of diacylglycerols for the synthesis of phosphatidylcholine varied with the structure of the added acid which was attributed to the substrate specificity of the cholinephosphotransferase. Unsaturated diacylglycerols were well utilized for phosphatidylcholine synthesis, while dimyristoylglycerol was better utilized than other saturated diacylglycerols with fatty acids of increasing or decreasing chain length. Somewhat similar results have been obtained also in isolated pig hepatocytes (Akesson *et al.,* 1976a).

The entry of radioactive choline into individual molecular species of hepatic phosphatidylcholines has been monitored in both the *in vitro* and *in vivo* studies. The use of labeled choline can provide information on the molecular products due to cholinephosphotransferase activity because of its entry into CDP-choline which can react with the available 1,2-diacylglycerols (Sundler *et al.,* 1972; Sundler and Akesson, 1975). It has been estimated that almost all of the free choline which enters phosphatidylcholine *in vivo* does so by CDP-choline rather than through base exchange (Bjerve, 1971; Sundler *et al.,* 1972). It is not surprising to find, therefore, that the *in vivo* entry of labeled choline into phosphatidylcholine produces a pattern of molecular species similar to that obtained with ^{32}P. The work of Balint *et al.* (1967) with ([^{3}H]methyl)-choline *in vivo* gave rise to a higher specific activity in the hepatic linoleoylphosphatidylcholines as compared to the corresponding arachidonoyl species. The elaborate work of Arvidson (1968b) showed that 27%, 53%, 14%, and 5% of the incorporated radioactivity was associated with monoenoic, dienoic, tetraenoic, and hexaenoic species, respectively, at 0.5 hour following the intraperitoneal injection of [^{14}C]choline. In all studies conducted with labeled choline both *in vivo* and in rat liver slices, the specific activities of the monoenoic and dienoic phosphatidylcholines are much higher than those of the tetraenoic and hexaenoic species for the first few hours following exposure to the radioactive precursor (Arvidson, 1968b; Rytter *et al.*, 1968; Kanoh, 1969; Spitzer *et al.*, 1969; Treble *et al.*, 1970; Salerno and Beeler, 1973). A higher labeling of the arachidonoyl and docosahexaenoyl species relative to other species has been observed with ([^{8}H]methyl-)choline as compared to (1,2-[^{14}C])-choline which was attributed to the entry of a methyl group from choline into products by phosphatidylethanolamine methylation (Spitzer *et al.*, 1969). The much higher labeling of 1-stearoyl 2 arachidonoyl and docosapentaenoyl species relative to less unsaturated phosphatidylcholines in liver observed with (methyl-[^{8}H])-choline as compared to ^{32}P (Trewhella and Collins, 1973b) is consistent with this interpretation. Arvidson (1968b) also showed the specific activity of the 1-palmitoyl 2-oleoyl and 1-palmitoyl 2-linoleoyl species in liver to be 5–13 times greater than that of the corresponding 1-stearoyl homologues 30 minutes after injecting [^{14}C]choline into rats. Subsequent work by Sundler *et al.* (1972) gave 1-palmitoyl 2-linoleoyl and 1-palmitoyl 2-arachidonoyl species with specific activities that were seven- and threefold greater, respectively, than those of the corresponding 1-stearoyl homologues 5 minutes after [^{14}C]choline administration. Table XI gives the rates of biosynthesis of individual molecular species of rat liver phosphatidylcholines from CDP-choline and their turnover times based on studies with [^{14}C]choline (Sundler and Akesson, 1975). The importance of the CDP-choline pathway in the formation of 1-palmitoyl 2-linoleoyl phosphatidylcholine, as indicated by the data in Table XI, is consistent with the preferred association of linoleate at the 2 position with palmitate at the 1 position in hepatic phosphatidylcholines (Holub and Kuksis, 1971c). The very active synthesis of the 1-palmitoyl 2-linoleoyl species may partly reflect the need to supply this important constituent of the biliary phosphatidylcholines (see Section III,B) which all appear to be derived from the same pool in liver (Curstedt, 1974). It is evident from both *in vitro* and *in vivo* studies that under physiological conditions the hepatic cholinephosphotransferase produces a complement of molecular species which is strikingly different

Table XI

RATES OF BIOSYNTHESIS AND TURNOVER TIMES
FOR RAT LIVER PHOSPHATIDYLCHOLINES [a]

Molecular species	Synthetic rate (μmoles/min/liver)	Turnover time (hours)
1-Palmitoyl 2-oleoyl	} 0.26 [b]	} 0.92 [b]
1-Stearoyl 2-oleoyl		
1-Palmitoyl 2-linoleoyl	0.47	0.87
1-Stearoyl 2-linoleoyl	0.027	6.5
1-Palmitoyl 2-arachidonoyl	0.13	3.9
1-Stearoyl 2-arachidonoyl	0.037	11.3
1-Palmitoyl 2-docosahexaenoyl	} 0.071 [b]	} 4.8 [b]
1-Stearoyl 2-docosahexaenoyl		

[a] Abbreviated from Sundler and Akesson (1975).
[b] Data for mixtures of the indicated species.

from the known composition of liver phosphatidylcholines (see Section II, A). The total hepatic phosphatidylcholines are known to be much richer in all major 1-stearoyl as well as 2-arachidonoyl and 2-docosahexaenoyl species (Holub and Kuksis, 1971c) than those produced by the reaction of CDP-choline with 1,2-diacylglycerols (Sundler and Akesson, 1975). These discrepancies substantiate claims that enzymes other than cholinephosphotransferase produce a considerable portion of the various molecular species of liver phosphatidylcholines. It should be noted, however, that the pattern of molecular species of phosphatidylcholines formed by cholinephosphotransferase may be different in livers from animals other than the rat. Thus, a much heavier labeling of the tetraenoic and polyenoic relative to the monoenoic and dienoic classes in guinea pig liver was observed after [³H]-glycerol administration (Parkes and Thompson, 1973).

Only a few studies have been conducted in tissues other than liver on the labeling of individual molecular species of phosphatidylcholine with radio-active glycerol. Unfortunately, the specific activities of the 1-palmitoyl and 1-stearoyl homologues have not been determined separately which limits estimations on the rates of synthesis of individual phosphatidylcholines by the cholinephosphotransferase. Vereyken *et al.* (1972) found the specific activity of the fully saturated phosphatidylcholines in rat lung to be much less than that for all other chemical classes after the intravenous injection of [³H]glycerol. The CDP-choline pathway was considered to contribute significantly to the formation of dienoic species but could not readily account for the high proportion of dipalmitoylphosphatidylcholine in lung tissue. Comparable experiments in rat lung slices had given similar results (Akino *et al.,* 1971). These latter findings are consistent with observations that 1,2-dipalmitoylglycerol is a poor substrate for the cholinephosphotransferase in mouse and rat lung microsomes (Sarzala and Van Golde, 1976; Possmayer *et al.,* 1977). O'Brien and Geison (1974) have followed the *in vivo* entry of infused [^{3}H]glycerol into rat brain phosphatidylcholines and provided evidence for an active *de novo* synthesis of highly unsaturated species in this tissue. The incorporation into species with polyunsaturated fatty acids of 20 or 22 carbon atoms was greater than into species containing only saturated and/or monounsaturated fatty acids. More recently, Sprecher and Duffy (1975) observed that the percent of radioactivity incorporated in the oleoyl and linoleoylphosphatidylcholines exceeded the molar contribution of these fractions at early time periods after the intratesticular injection of [^{14}C]glycerol into rats suggesting an active synthesis of these species by the reaction of CDP-choline with 1,2-diacylglycerols. The much lower labeling at early times of the tetraenes and pentaenes, which were major contributors to the total phosphatidylcholines, did not support a predominant role for cholinephosphotransferase in their formation.

b. *Formation of Phosphatidylethanolamines.* Approaches similar to those described for the phosphatidylcholines have been utilized in studying the *de novo* biosynthesis of individual molecular species of phosphatidylethanolamines from the corresponding 1,2-diacylglycerols. In comparison, a relatively smaller number of *in vitro* and *in vivo* studies have been conducted on the ethanolaminephosphotransferase. Nevertheless, there is evidence that *de novo* synthesis alone cannot account for the molecular species composition of tissue phosphatidylethanolamines.

The most extensive investigations into the activity of the ethanolaminephosphotransferase have been conducted in brain. Thus, the studies of Porcellati *et al.* (1970) and Ansell and Metcalfe (1971) in chick and rat brain, respectively, have revealed that the specific activity of this enzyme in the microsomal fraction is much higher than that in the whole homogenate or any other subcellular fraction. The recent work of Coleman and Bell (1977) suggests that the ethanolaminephosphotransferase from adipose tissue or fat cells is a separate microsomal enzyme from the cholinephosphotransferase. De Kruyff *et al.* (1970) compared the utilization of mixtures of 1-palmitoyl 2-oleoyl, 1-palmitoyl 2-linoleoyl, and 1-saturated 2-arachidonoyl diacylglycerols, which contained labeled fatty acids in the 2 position, for the synthesis of phosphatidylethanolamine in rat liver microsomes in the presence of both CDP-ethanolamine and CDP-choline. The results indicated that the ethanolaminephosphotransferase showed no specificity with respect to the different molecular species of diacylglycerols that were tested. Using as substrates 1,2-diacylglycerols obtained from biosynthetically labeled phosphatidylcholines, Kanoh (1970) reported comparable utilization of the various species for phosphatidylethanolamine formation, when each species was incubated separately. A relatively higher utilization of the hexaenoic species was observed when mixtures of 1,2-di-acylglycerols were employed. Recently Holub (1978) has found distinctly higher reaction rates with the combined 1-saturated 2-docosahexaenoyl diacylglycerols than with the corresponding monoenoic, dienoic, or tetra-enoic substrates. Kanoh and Ohno (1975) have also examined the substrate selectivity of the ethanolamine phosphotransferase using rat liver micro-somes enriched in endogenous 1,2-diacylglycerols from the back reaction of the cholinephosphotransferase. Under these conditions, a marked prefer-ence was seen for the utilization of the hexaenoic diacylglycerols. In another experiment Kanoh and Ohno (1975) prepared rat liver micro-somes containing 1,2-diacylglycerols labeled in the 1 position with [^{3}H]-palmitate or [^{3}H]stearate following the injection of rats with the correspond-ing 1-acyl lysophosphatidyl-cholines. Using such microsomes these workers were able to demonstrate preferential utilization of 1-stearoyl over 1-pal-mitoyl diacylglycerols by the ethanolaminephosphotransferase. A pref-erential utilization of the 1-stearoyl 2-arachidonoyl over the 1-palmitoyl 2-arachidonoyl diacylglycerol by the ethanolaminephosphotransferase has now been demonstrated by Holub (1978) using exogenously added sub-strates of known specific activity. The phosphatidylethanolamines generated by the ethanolamine phosphotransferase, therefore, would tend to resemble the species of the endogenous pool of 1,2-diacylglycerols, although an enrichment in 1-stearoyl and 2-docosahexaenoyl species would be an-ticipated. *In vivo* studies with radioactive phosphate, glycerol, and ethanol-amine have generally supported the relative rates of synthesis of the various molecular species anticipated from the results of *in vitro* studies.

The work of Arvidson (1968a) with ^{32}P administered intraperitoneally to rats showed the following order of specific activities in liver phosphatidyl-ethanolamines after 30 minutes: monoenes > hexaenes > dienes > tetra-enes. These labeling patterns were attributed to the substrate specificity of the ethanolaminephosphotransferase towards different molecular species of 1,2-diacylglycerols as also demonstrated *in vitro* (see above). The findings of Arvidson (1968a) have been confirmed and extended by Trewhella and Collins (1969, 1973a,b). The latter workers found the specific activity of the 1-palmitoyl 2-linoleoyl and 1-palmitoyl 2-arachidonoyl species to be two to three times greater than that of the corresponding 1-stearoyl homo-logues. Unlike *in vivo* studies, the entry of ^{32}P into molecular species of phosphatidylethanolamines following incubation with rat liver slices has produced highest specific activities in the hexaenoic species (Kanoh, 1969).

A determination of the specific activities of the individual molecular species of the phosphatidylethanolamines of rat skeletal muscle 3 hours after intraperitoneal injection of ortho [^{32}P]phosphate by Shamgar and Collins (1975a) has shown that the linoleoyl and the docosahexaenoyl species possessed the fastest turnover and 1-stearoyl-2-arachidonoyl the slowest. The specific radioactivity of phosphatidylethanolamine was approximately three times lower than that of phosphatidylcholine.

The *de novo* biosynthesis of hepatic phosphatidylethanolamines from the reaction of 1,2-diacylglycerols with CDP-ethanolamine has also been studied with radioactive glycerol. Thus, Akesson *et al.* (1970a) found 9%, 18%, 8%, 5%, and 60% of the radioactivity incorporated into the liver phosphatidylethanolamines to be associated with the monoenoic, dienoic, trienoic, tetraenoic, and hexaenoic species, respectively, within 5 minutes after the intraportal injection of [^{3}H]glycerol into rats. Hexaenoic phosphatidylethanolamines were more heavily labeled *in vivo* relative to other species than found in rat liver slices with [^{14}C]glycerol (Hill *et al.*, 1968a; Kanoh, 1969). A very active *de novo* synthesis of hexaenoic, dienoic, and monoenoic species via liver ethanolaminephosphotransferase has been reported in other experiments (Holub and Kuksis, 1971c; Vereyken *et al.*, 1972) analogous to those of Akesson *et al.* (1970a). The somewhat heavier labeling of tetraenoic relative to other species that is often observed with labeled phosphate as compared to glycerol might reflect the reaction of CDP-ethanolamine with diacylglycerols derived from sources other than phosphatidate (see Section IV,A). Experiments with isolated hepatocytes from the rat and pig, which were incubated with added fatty acids and [^{3}H]glycerol, have revealed that unsaturated diacylglycerols are well utilized for phosphatidylethanolamine synthesis (Sundler *et al.*, 1974b; Akesson *et al.*, 1976a). The very low utilization of saturated diacylglycerols was attributed to the substrate specificity of the ethanolaminephosphotransferase.

The incorporation of [^{14}C]ethanolamine into individual molecular species of hepatic phosphatidylethanolamines at relatively early times following its administration to rats has provided results similar to those obtained with ^{32}P. This is in keeping with the common entrance of ethanolamine into phosphatidylethanolamine via CDP-ethanolamine and not to any significant extent by base exchange (Sundler, 1973). Thus, Arvidson (1968a) and Trewhella and Collins (1973b) have found the relative specific activities of the various phosphatidylethanolamines following [^{14}C]ethanolamine injection to be very similar to those obtained using ^{32}P (see the preceding discussion). In other studies with [^{14}C]ethanolamine *in vivo* (Rytter *et al.*, 1968; Salerno and Beeler, 1973; Sundler, 1973) and in rat liver slices (Kanoh, 1969), it has been shown that the hexaenoic fraction is most extensively labeled of all unsaturation classes of phosphatidylethanolamines. Sundler (1973) has also determined the distribution of radioactivity among the hepatic 1-palmitoyl and 1-stearoyl homologues of dienoic, tetraenoic, and hexaenoic species 5 minutes after the intraportal injection of [^{14}C]-ethanolamine. The percent distribution of radioactivity among these two homologues for the various unsaturation classes was similar to their relative abundance in the corresponding 1,2-diacylglycerols (Akesson, 1969). It was concluded, therefore, that the ethanolaminephosphotransferase does not discriminate *in vivo* between diacylglycerols containing palmitate or stearate at the 1 position (Sundler, 1973). This latter conclusion contrasts somewhat with that reported from work on rat liver microsomes (Kanoh and Ohno, 1975). The ethanolamineophosphotransferase appears to be less sensitive to the fatty acid (palmitate versus stearate) in the 1 position of the 1-saturated 2-unsaturated diacylglycerol precursors as compared to the cholinephosphotransferase from rat liver (Holub, 1978). From studies with [^{3}H]ethanolamine *in vivo,* Sundler and Akesson (1975) have calculated the rates of biosynthesis of individual rat liver phosphatidylethanolamines from CDP-ethanolamine and diacylglycerols. The synthetic rates are given in Table XII. It is apparent that the hepatic ethanolaminephosphotransferase gives rise to a pattern of molecular species which is quite different from that of the mass composition of phosphatidylethanolamines in rat liver (see Section II,A). The hepatic phosphatidylethanolamines are more enriched in 1-stearoyl and 2-arachidonoyl species (Holub and

Table XII

RATES OF BIOSYNTHESIS OF RAT LIVER
PHOSPHATIDYLETHANOLAMINES [a]

Molecular species	Synthetic rate (μmoles/min/liver)
Saturated	0.000
Monoenoic	0.020
Monoenoic-monoenoic	0.005
1-Palmitoyl 2-linoleoyl	0.035
1-Stearoyl 2-linoleoyl	0.010
Monoenoic-dienoic	0.007
Dienoic-dienoic	0.010
1-Palmitoyl 2-arachidonoyl	0.023
1-Stearoyl 2-arachidonoyl	0.049
Pentaenoic	0.020
1-Palmitoyl 2-docosahexaenoyl	0.134
1-Stearoyl 2-docosahexaenoyl	0.023

[a] Abbreviated from Sundler and Akesson (1975).

Kuksis, 1971c) than can be accounted for by *in vitro* or *in vivo* activity of the ethanolaminephosphotransferase. The remaining discrepancies likely reflect the role of other enzymic reactions in the biogenesis of certain molecular species of phosphatidylethanolamine. The data in Table XII are consistent, however, with the preferential association of linoleate and docosahexaenoate with palmitate at the 1 position of phosphatidylethanol-amine (Holub and Kuksis, 1971c) which is consistent with the role of the CDP-ethanolamine pathway in their biosynthesis.

Akesson (1977) has assessed the incorporation of diethylethanolamine into the unnatural phosphatidyldiethylethanolamine by primary cultures of rat hepatocytes. Most of the diethylethanolamine appeared to be taken up by *de novo* synthesis via phosphatidate, as indicated by the high labeling of phosphatidyldiethylethanolamine by [^{3}H]glycerol. In addition, its fatty acid composition with high proportions of palmitate, oleate, and linoleate is similar to the fatty acids incorporated into glycerolipids via phosphatidate. The low proportions of stearate and arachidonate also indicated that this phospholipid was less prone to undergo deacylation-reacylation reactions than other phospholipids. The pronounced accumulation of phosphatidyl-diethylethanolamine was attributed to the fact that it is not efficiently methylated although it may be dealkylated. Such a conversion has also been suggested for phosphatidylisopropylethanolamine (Lee *et al.*, 1975).

2. Acylation of Lysophosphatides

Since the original recognition by Lands (1960, 1965) that mammalian tissues contain acyltransferases which are capable of converting monoacyl glycerophospholipids to their diacyl forms, numerous studies have been conducted to determine the role of these enzymes in the generation of natural glycerophospholipids. Evidence from both *in vitro* and *in vivo* studies has indicated that these reactions may be important in the formation of molecular species with characteristic fatty acid compositions in different tissues from various animal species. The occurrence of phospholipases A_1 and A_2 (McMurray and Magee, 1972), as well as of the acyltransferases, provides the basis for a deacylation–reacylation cycle whereby molecular species of diacylglycerophospholipids are interconverted by alteration of the fatty acids at the 1 or 2 positions. It has not yet been established whether different acyltransferases exist for different fatty acids.

The most extensive investigation into the subcellular distribution of the monoacyl glycerophospholipid acyltransferases which acylate the 1 and 2 positions of the acceptor glycerolipid was conducted by Eibl *et al.* (1969) in rat liver. The 1- and 2-acyl-*sn*-glycero-3-phosphorylcholine and 1-acyl-*sn*-glycero-3-phosphorylethanolamine acyltransferases were found by these workers to be located almost exclusively in the microsomal fraction and no activity in the mitochondria was detected. The earlier work of Stoffel and Schiefer (1968) had indicated the presence of significant 1-acyl-*sn*-glycero-3-phosphorylcholine acyltransferase activity in the outer mitochondrial membrane. These latter findings have been supported by Sarzala *et al.* (1970) who reported the presence of 1- and 2-acyl-*sn*-glycero-3-phosphorylcholine acyltransferase activity in outer membranes of mitochondria. The specific activities in this fraction were less than one-half that for rat liver microsomes. Significant 1-acyl-*sn*-glycero-3-phosphorylcholine acyltransferase activity has been found in the plasma membrane from rat liver (Stein *et al.*, 1968) and in the Golgi complex of bovine liver but not in that of rat liver (Van Golde *et al.*, 1971).

   a. Formation of Phosphatidylcholines.   The marked differences in the fatty acid selectivities of the 1- and 2-acyl-*sn*-glycero-3-phosphorylcholine acyltransferases towards acyl-CoA derivatives was shown by Lands and Merkl (1963) to be consistent with the positional distribution of saturated and unsaturated acids in natural phosphatidylcholines (see Section II,A). Thus, linoleate was preferred over stearate for acylation of the 2 position in the acyl acceptor with a microsomal system from rat liver whereas the converse selectivity was true for acylation of the 1 position. Lands and Hart (1965) conducted an extensive survey of the selectivity of the 1- and 2-acyl-*sn*-glycero-3-phosphorylcholine acyltransferases towards lauroyl-, palmitoyl-, stearoyl-, oleoyl-, and linoleoyl-CoA using liver microsomal preparations from the rat, guinea pig, ox, and pig. The characteristic general pattern of selectivity noted was a greater rate of esterification of saturated and unsaturated fatty acids at the 1 and 2 positions, respectively, although the guinea pig and ox appeared to be somewhat less discriminating than the other two animal species. The observations of Lands and colleagues were subsequently confirmed by other investigators (Stoffel *et al.*, 1967; Van Den Bosch *et al.*, 1967, 1968). It was suggested by Van Den Bosch *et al.* (1968) that the selectivity of the acyl transferases may serve to maintain the asymmetric distribution of saturated and unsaturated fatty acids in the diacylglycerophospholipids which may have been introduced at the level of *de novo* biosynthesis.

   Brandt and Lands (1967) also tested the possibility of obtaining a specific pairing of unsaturated fatty acids with either palmitate or stearate at the 1 position in hepatic phosphatidylcholines (see Section IV,A) as a result of acyltransferase activity. The nature of the acyl group in the six different species of 1-acyl-*sn*-glycero-3-phosphorylcholines had little effect on the acyl transferase rates for the various unsaturated acyl-CoA derivatives. Thus, the pairing of acids in various molecular species of phosphatidylcholines could not be explained by 1-acyl-*sn*-glycero-3-

phosphorylcholine selectivity. By measuring 1-acyl-*sn*-glycero-3-phosphorylcholine acyl transferase activity in human erythrocyte stroma with various acyl-CoA derivatives, Waku and Lands (1968a) were able to predict the composition of the 2 position in the erythrocyte phosphatidylcholine from the relative abundance of the corresponding acyl moieties in the plasma free fatty acid pool. The excellent agreement between the predicted and actual compositions led these authors to conclude that the stromal acyl transferases could be the significant enzymatic factor controlling the complement of acids at the 2 position in the phosphatidylcholine. Later studies by Hill and Lands (1968) included polyunsaturated acyl-CoA derivatives as substrates for the 1-acyl-*sn*-glycero-3-phosphorylcholine acyl transferases using microsomes from rat liver. The reaction rates with rat liver microsomes and the various acyl-CoA preparations were as follows in decreasing order of magnitude: $20:5(n-3) = 20:3(n-6) > 20:4(n-6) = 18:2(n-6) > 20:2(n-9) > 18:3(n-3) > 18:1(n-9) > 22:6(n-3) > 16:0 > 18:0$. More recently, Okuyama *et al.* (1975) have found a much greater selectivity for arachidonate relative to oleate at very low concentrations of the 1-acyl-*sn*-glycero-3-phosphorylcholine acceptor. Waku and Lands (1968b) found that enzymes from erythrocytes, muscle, and testes could acylate 1-0-alk-1-enylglycero-3-phosphorylcholine and showed highest reaction rates with linoleoyl- and arachidonoyl-CoA. Using a partially purified preparation of 1-acyl-*sn*-glycero-3-phosphorylcholine acyltransferase from rat liver microsomes, Yamashita *et al.* (1973) reported reaction rates with arachidonoyl-CoA to be sixfold those for all other saturated and unsaturated acyl donors. The aforementioned studies indicate, therefore, that the hepatic 1-acyl-*sn*-glycero-3-phosphorylcholine acyltransferase could be of importance for the entry of arachidonate into phosphatidylcholine.

A number of isotopic studies *in vivo* with labeled phosphate, glycerol, and choline have provided support for the role of deacylation–reacylation reactions in the biogenesis of certain molecular species of phosphatidylcholines in liver and other tissues. In earlier work Arvidson (1968b) had observed that following the injection of [1,2-14C]choline into rats the specific activity of the hepatic monoenoic and dienoic phosphatidylcholines decreased while that of the tetraenoic species increased with time. Although these changes in specific activities could be attributed to the release of phosphatidylcholines into plasma, the results were also consistent with a precursor–product relationship between the monoenoic plus dienoic, and tetraenoic species mediated via deacylation–reacylation reactions. A decrease in the relative specific activity of the monoenoic and dienoic concomitant with an increase in the tetraenoic phosphatidylcholines has been observed with labeled glycerol in liver as well (Kanoh, 1970;

Holub and Kuksis, 1971c). The very low specific activity of the hepatic 1-stearoyl 2-arachidonoyl phosphatidylcholine as compared to other molecular species following ^{32}P administration to rats supports the hypothesis that the stearate and arachidonate in the molecule are both introduced by a deacylation–reacylation mechanism (Trewhella and Collins, 1973b). The specific activity relationships further suggest that the 1-stearoyl 2-arachidonoyl phosphatidylcholine is formed by such a mechanism from 1-stearoyl 2-oleoyl, 1-stearoyl 2-linoleoyl, or 1-palmitoyl 2-arachidonoyl species. The latter three species, in turn, were presumably derived by deacylation–reacylation reactions from 1-palmitoyl 2-oleoyl, and 1-palmitoyl 2-linoleoyl phosphatidylcholines which are major products of the cholinephosphotransferase *in vivo*. At later time periods following the intratesticular injection of [^{14}C]glycerol, Sprecher and Duffy (1975) reported that the percent of phosphatidylcholine radioactivity in the oleoyl and linoleoyl species decreased concomitant with an increase in that found in the arachidonoyl and docosapentaenoyl species which suggested that the monoenoic and dienoic phosphatidylcholines formed by *de novo* synthesis were giving rise to the highly unsaturated species by way of a deacylation–reacylation cycle.

Somewhat more definitive studies on the role of acyl transferase activity in the biogenesis of various molecular species of phosphatidylcholines have been realized in experiments with radioactive fatty acids and lysophosphatidylcholines. The early work of Elovson (1965) with [^{14}C]stearate indicated a rapid entry of this acid into hepatic diacylglycerophospholipids, predominantly into the arachidonoyl species, within 5 seconds after its intraportal injection to rats. Since only a very minor percentage of the radioactivity in the free 1,2-diacylglycerols was associated with the arachidonoyl species, it was concluded that almost all the stearic acid was entering the diacylglycerophospholipids by direct acylation as proposed by Lands and Merkl (1963). Van Golde *et al.* (1969) performed dual-labeling experiments with [^{14}C]stearate and [^{3}H]glycerol in rat liver slices and found the $^{3}H/^{14}C$ ratio in the tetraenoic phosphatidylcholines to be less than one-half that in the corresponding phosphatidic acids whereas lesser differences in ratios were found between these glycerolipids in the case of monoenoic and dienoic species. These authors suggested that *de novo* synthesis via phosphatidic acid is highly operative for the formation of monoenoic and dienoic molecular species of phosphatidylcholine whereas the tetraenoic molecules are synthesized mainly by acylation of lysophosphatidylcholines. By comparing data on the entry of [^{3}H]palmitate into individual molecular species of liver phosphatidylcholines following its injection into rats (Akesson *et al.*, 1970b) with that derived from studies with [^{3}H]glycerol (Akesson *et al.*, 1970a), these workers have calculated the relative importance of acyl transferase reactions for palmitate entry into the diacylglycerophospholipid. These estimates do not include the formation of phosphatidylcholine by methylation of phosphatidyletha-nolamine. Thus, approximately 13%, 22%, 64%, and 54% of the palmitic acid entering the monoenoic, dienoic, tetraenoic, and hexaenoic species, respectively, was found to do so by acylation of the corresponding 2-acyl-*sn*-glycero-3-phosphorylcholines (Akesson *et al.*, 1970b). Using a similar approach with [^{14}C]linoleic acid, Akesson (1970) calculated that 30% of the linoleate entering the 1-palmitoyl 2-linoleoyl phosphatidylcholine did so by acylation and the remaining 70% entered by *de novo* biosynthesis via the CDP-choline pathway. Thus, 58% of the 1-palmitoyl 2-linoleoyl phos-phatidylcholine was formed *de novo* from the corresponding 1,2-diacylglyc-erol (Akesson, 1970). Acylation reactions accounted for 97% of linoleate entry into 1-stearoyl 2-linoleoyl phosphatidylcholine. Holub *et al.* (1971) determined the specific activities of the 1-palmitoyl 2-linoleoyl and 1-stearoyl 2-linoleoyl phosphatidylcholines in rat liver by means of radio gas-liquid chromatography following the intravenous injection of [^{14}C]linoleate as an albumin complex. In direct contrast to studies with isotopic choline and phosphate (Arvidson, 1968b; Trewhella and Collins, 1969), a much heavier labeling of the 1-stearoyl relative to the 1-palmitoyl homologue was observed. These authors (Holub *et al.*, 1971) were able to estimate that most of the 1-palmitoyl 2-linoleoyl phosphatidylcholine was derived by *de novo* synthesis whereas at least 75% of the linoleate entering the 1-stearoyl 2-linoleoyl species did so via acyltransferase activity. By an iden-tical approach, the injection of [^{14}C]-arachidonate was found to result in the 1-palmitoyl 2-arachidonoyl and 1-stearoyl 2-arachidonoyl phosphatidyl-cholines having nearly identical specific activities (Holub *et al.*, 1971) whereas ^{32}P administration showed the 1-palmitoyl homologue to have a specific activity some 12-fold that of the corresponding 1-stearoyl species (Trewhella and Collins, 1969). It was estimated that the [^{14}C]arachidonate was incorporated into the 1-stearoyl 2-arachidonoyl species almost entirely by acyl transferase activity. Akesson (1970) studied the relative incorpora-tion of labeled arachidonic acid into hepatic diacylglycerophospholipids, phosphatidic acids, and diacylglycerols after its formation from [^{41}C]lino-leate *in vivo*. This latter author concluded that the entry of arachidonic acid into phosphatidylcholine occurred mainly by acylation of 1-acyl-*sn*-glycero-3-phosphorylcholine. It is difficult to assess to what extent the newly formed arachidonate associated with the phosphatidylcholine in the experiments of Akesson (1970) was actually derived from an acyl transfer reaction since Pugh and Kates (1977) have reported the desaturation of eicosatrienoic to arachidonic acid on the glycerolipid molecule itself.

The entry of free arachidonic acid into hepatic phosphatidylcholine by

acyltransferase activity has been supported in experiments using radioactive lysophosphatides as the labeled precursor. A study *in vitro* with a
rat liver slice system has shown that 1-acyl-*sn*-glycero-3-phosphorylcholine
labeled with [^{14}C]choline is incorporated preferentially into tetraenoic phosphatidylcholines (Kanoh, 1969). Holub and Kuksis (1971b) studied the
incorporation of ^{14}C-labeled 1-acyl-*sn*-glycero-3-phosphorylcholine into
the chemical classes of hepatic phosphatidylcholines following its intravenous injection into rats as an albumin complex. The monoenoic, dienoic,
tetraenoic, and polyenoic species contained 6%, 24%, 51%, and 20%,
respectively, of the total radioactivity incorporated into the phosphatidylcholines. These results suggest an active entry of arachidonic acid into
phosphatidylcholine by acylation of 1-acyl-*sn*-glycero-3-phosphorylcholine.
Subsequent *in vivo* experiments using other radioactive 1-acyl-*sn*-glycero-
3-phosphorylcholines (Kanoh and Ohno, 1975; MacDonald and Thompson,
1975) have yielded comparable results. Thus, both kinetic studies on the
acyl transferases, and tracer studies *in vivo* and *in vitro,* have indicated
that arachidonic acid enters rat liver phosphatidylcholine mainly by acylation of 1-acyl-*sn*-glycero-3-phosphorylcholine and not by *de novo* biosynthesis from reaction of CDP-choline with 1,2-diacylglycerols. Furthermore,
the 1-stearoyl 2-linoleoyl and 1-stearoyl 2-arachidonoyl species which constitute 30% of the total phosphatidylcholines (Holub and Kuksis, 1971c)
are formed almost entirely by acyl transferase activity. From data available
on the formation of the 1-palmitoyl 2-unsaturated species, it can be estimated that acylation reactions account for about 50% of the total phosphatidylcholine synthesis in rat liver. Akesson *et al.* (1976b) have provided
in vivo evidence to support the preferential acylation of labeled 2-linoleoyl-
sn-glycero-3-phosphorylcholine with stearic acid in rat liver.

Erbland and Marinetti (1965a,b) reported the formation of phosphatidylcholine by transacylation between two molecules of lysophosphatidylcholine
in the presence of a high-speed supernatant from rat liver. Since the
endogenous lysophosphatidylcholines in rat liver contain mainly palmitic
and stearic acids (Van Den Bosch and van Deenen, 1965), the presence
of only 1% of the total phosphatidylcholines as fully saturated species in
this tissue (Holub and Kuksis, 1971c) does not indicate any quantitative
significance for this pathway. This latter conclusion is supported by studies
in rat liver with 1-acyl-*sn*-glycero-3-phosphorylcholine containing radioactive fatty acids as previously discussed. The experiments of Van Den
Bosch *et al.* (1965) in rat liver homogenates also indicate the intermolec-
ular transesterification reaction to be of minor importance under normal
physiological conditions.

Unlike the findings discussed for rat liver, studies in guinea pig liver with radioactive 1-acyl-*sn*-glycero-3-phosphorylcholine, dual labeled with [^{14}C]palmitate and [^{3}H]glycerol, have shown an active entry of the precursor into fully saturated phosphatidylcholines (Thompson and MacDonald, 1975). The failure to find significant radioactivity in the fatty acids released from the 2-position following hydrolysis with phospholipase A$_2$ did not support the origin of these species from transesterification between two molecules of lysophosphatide (Erbland and Marinetti, 1965 a,b). Since the 1-acyl-*sn*-glycero-3-phosphorylcholine acyl transferase in the microsomes of guinea pig liver discriminates against saturated acids (Hill and Lands, 1968), the mechanism for biosynthesis of the fully saturated species could not be explained.

Experiments comparable to those performed in the liver have also been conducted in other tissues. Baker and Thompson (1972) studied the simultaneous uptake of [^{3}H]arachidonate or [^{3}H]stearate and [^{14}C]glycerol into the glycerolipids of rat brain following intracerebral injections. At early times, the ^{3}H/^{14}C ratios in the phosphatidylcholine greatly exceeded those in the phosphatidate which suggested a rapid incorporation of arachidonate as well as a partial entry of stearate by acyl transfer. Subsequent experiments in 1-acyl-*sn*-glycero-3-phosphorylcholine acyl transferase in rat brain microsomes revealed a preference for unsaturated over saturated thioesters, although the reaction rates with arachidonoyl-CoA were similar to those with linoleoyl-, linolenoyl-, and eicosatrienoyl-CoA (Baker and Thompson, 1973). Wykle *et al.* (1973) have shown that rat testes microsomes incorporate arachidonic acid into the 2 position of alkylacylglycerophosphorylcholine by acyltransferase activity, which supports the importance of deacylation–reacylation reactions demonstrated with these ether lipids *in vivo*.

There has been some controversy in regard to the relative importance of 1-acyl-*sn*-glycero-3-phosphorylcholine acyl transferase activity (Lands, 1960) and the lysophosphatidylcholine interesterification pathway (Erbland and Marinetti, 1965a,b) in the biogenesis of dipalmitoylphosphatidylcholine in lung. The early work of Wolfe *et al.* (1970) with rabbit lung slices suggested that the entry of ^{32}P-labeled 1-acyl-*sn*-glycero-3-phosphorylcholine into phosphatidylcholine was occurring by the Erbland-Marinetti pathway since [^{3}H]palmitate uptake into the glycerolipid was not enhanced by addition of the lysophosphatide. The importance of the Lands pathway for the biosynthesis of dipalmitoylphosphatidylcholine in lung was supported by Frosolono *et al.* (1971) who showed that, in contrast to liver, the 1-acyl and 2-acyl-*sn*-glycero-3-phosphorylcholine acyl transferases in dog lung microsomes showed equal reactivity with palmitoyl-CoA. Vereyken *et al.* (1972) also found that the 1-acyl-*sn*-glycero-3-phosphorylcholine acyltransferase in lung microsomes had higher reaction rates with palmitoyl-CoA as compared to the enzyme in liver microsomes whereas the converse was true with oleoyl-CoA. In dual-labeling experiments in rat lung slices with [³H]glycerol and [¹⁴C]palmitate, Akino et al. (1971) found the ratio of ¹⁴C/³H to be much higher in phosphatidylcholine than in either phosphatidic acid or 1,2-diacylglycerol which suggested that palmitate was being incorporated into phosphatidylcholine by pathways other than de novo biosynthesis. Using 1-acyl-sn-glycero-3-phosphorylcholine labeled with [³H]glycerol and [¹⁴C]palmitate at position 1, the ratio of ¹⁴C/³H approached 2 in the saturated species. Since 60% and 40% of the ¹⁴C activity was found in the 1 and 2 positions, respectively, it was suggested that the Erbland-Marinetti pathway may be the principal pathway responsible for the production of dipalmitoylphosphatidylcholine. The experiments of Kyei-Aboagye et al. (1973) in rabbit lung homogenates allowed these authors to suggest that 1-palmitoyl 2-oleoyl phosphatidylcholine was converted into the dipalmitoyl species by a deacylation–reacylation reaction at the 2 position which might involve the reaction of 1-palmitoyl-sn-glycero-3-phosphorylcholine with endogenously synthesized palmitoyl-CoA (Lands, 1960). More recently, Hasegawa-Sasaki and Ohno (1975) have provided kinetic data on the palmitoyl-CoA: 1-acyl-sn-glycero-3-phosphorylcholine acyl transferase in rat lung microsomes and concluded that this enzymic reaction is not an important pathway for the synthesis of dipalmitoylphosphatidylcholine in rat lung as previously suggested (Frosolono et al., 1971; Vereyken et al., 1972). Tansey and Frosolono (1975) have questioned these latter findings (Hasegawa-Sasaki and Ohno, 1975) and have provided kinetic data to support the role of acyl-CoA: 1-acyl-sn-glycero-3-phosphorylcholine acyl transferase in dipalmitoylphosphatidylcholine synthesis.

Abe et al. (1974) have shown that the lysolecithin–lysolecithin acyl transferase in the soluble fraction from rat lung is also a lysolecithin acylhydrolase. This enzyme, provisionally denoted as lysophospholipase-transacylase, has been partially purified and shown to be capable of synthesizing disaturated phosphatidylcholine (Bromley and Van den Bosch, 1977). Baranska and Van Golde (1977) have shown that the lamellar bodies of mouse lung lack the capacity to synthesize phosphatidylcholine de novo but that they contribute to the activity of microsomal lysophosphatidylcholine acyl transferase by a cooperative effect, which may promote the biosynthesis of 1,2-dipalmitoyl-sn-glycero-3-phosphorylcholine. Baranska and Van Golde (1977) suggest that this cooperation between lamellar bodies and microsomes may explain the finding of lysophosphatidylcholine acyltransferase activity in lamellar bodies from rat lung which could not be simply accounted for by the degree of microsomal contamination (Engle et al., 1976).

b. Formation of Phosphatidylethanolamines. The work of Lands and colleagues (Merkl and Lands, 1963; Lands and Hart, 1965) indicated that the 1- and 2-acyl-*sn*-glycero-3-phosphorylethanolamine acyl transferases have fatty acid selectivities that are somewhat similar to those just described for the lysophosphatidylcholine acyltransferases. De Tomas and Brenner (1970) found a close similarity in the K_m values for selected polyunsaturated acyl-CoA derivatives when the activities of the 1-acyl-*sn*-glycero-3-phosphorylethanolamine and 1-acyl-*sn*-glycero-3-phosphorylcholine acyl transferases in rat liver microsomes were compared. The physiological importance of the 1-acyl and 2-acyl-*sn*-glycero-3-phosphorylethanolamine acyl transferases in the biosynthesis of certain molecular species of phosphatidylethanolamines in rat liver has been indicated by isotopic studies both *in vitro* and *in vivo*. By incubating rat liver slices with both [³H] glycerol and [¹⁴C]stearate, Van Golde *et al.* (1969) found the ³H/¹⁴C ratio in the tetraenoic phosphatidylethanolamines to be only one-third that of the corresponding phosphatidic acids whereas the differences in ratios were much less pronounced in the case of monoenoic and dienoic species. These authors suggested that *de novo* synthesis was highly operative for the production of monoenoic and dienoic phosphatidylethanolamines whereas the polyunsaturated molecules were derived mainly by acylation reaction. In support of this concept, Kanoh (1969) found 1-acyl-*sn*-glycero-3-phosphorylethanolamine labeled with [¹⁴C]ethanolamine to be incorporated mainly into tetraenoic phosphatidylethanolamines in a rat liver slice system. By determining the specific activities of individual molecular species of phosphatidylethanolamine *in vivo* following the administration of ³²P, Trewhella and Collins (1973b) concluded that the 1-stearoyl 2-arachidonoyl species was derived from the 1-palmitoyl 2-arachidonoyl, 1-stearoyl 2-oleoyl, and 1-stearoyl 2-linoleoyl species by a deacylation–reacylation mechanism. The latter three species were considered to be derived from the 1-palmitoyl 2-oleoyl and 1-palmitoyl 2-linoleoyl phosphatidylethanolamines by a similar mechanism. Akesson *et al.* (1970a,b) followed the early entry of labeled palmitate and glycerol into the hepatic glycerolipids *in vivo* and were able to calculate that 18%, 70%, and 11% of the palmitate entering the dienoic, tetraenoic, and hexaenoic phosphatidylethanolamines, respectively, did so by acyltransferase activity rather than by *de novo* synthesis. Subsequent studies with [¹⁴C]linoleic acid (Akesson, 1970) indicated that 29% and 97% of the acid which entered the 1-palmitoyl 2-linoleoyl and 1-stearoyl 2-linoleoyl phosphatidylethanolamine, respectively, *in vivo* did so by acyltransferase activity. Thus, only 61% of the 1-palmitoyl 2-linoleoyl species was derived directly by *de novo* synthesis from the corresponding 1,2-diacylglycerol. This worker was also able to calculate that the arachidonic acid derived from linoleic acid was entering the phosphatidylethanolamine almost exclusively by acylation of 1-acyl-*sn*-glycero-3-phosphorylethanolamine (Akesson, 1970). The studies conducted to date indicate that the 1-stearoyl 2-linoleoyl and 1-stearoyl 2-arachidonoyl species, which constitute at least 40% of the total phosphatidylethanolamines in rat liver (Holub and Kuksis, 1971c), are derived almost entirely by acyl-transferase activity. If data on the formation of the 1-palmitoyl 2-unsaturated species are included, it can be estimated that approximately one-half the total pool of phosphatidylethanolamines are derived by acylation of lysophosphatidylethanolamines. A highly preferential acylation of 2-linoleoyl-*sn*-glycero-3-phosphorylethanolamine in rat liver with stearic acid is indicated by *in vivo* experiments of Akesson *et al.* (1976b).

Good evidence for the role of acylation reactions in the biogenesis of the phosphatidylethanolamines has also been provided in tissues other than liver. Baker and Thompson (1972) compared the $^3H/^{14}C$ ratios in phosphatidylethanolamine and phosphatidic acid in rat brain following the intracerebral injection of [^{14}C]glycerol with [^{3}H]arachidonate or [^{3}H]stearate. In the first hour after injection, much higher ratios in the phosphatidylethanolamine were found which suggested a partial entry of these acids independent of phosphatidic acid precursors. Studies by Wykle *et al.* (1973) with microsomes from rat testes have shown that arachidonic acid is incorporated into the 2 position of alk-1-enylacylglycero-3-phosphorylethanolamine by deacylation–reacylation reaction. A similar conclusion has been reached by Rittenhouse-Simmons *et al.* (1977) for human platelets.

In summary, the acylation of lysophosphatides and the operation of a deacylation–reacylation cycle is of considerable importance for the synthesis of characteristic molecular species of phosphatidylcholines and phosphatidylethanolamines in liver and other tissues. Such reactions produce a complement of molecular species of diacylglycerophospholipids which cannot be accounted for by *de novo* biosynthesis from precursor 1,2-diacylglycerols.

3.   *Methylation of Phosphatidylethanolamine*

The stepwise methylation of phosphatidylethanolamine by the transfer of three methyl groups from *S*-adenosyl methionine has been shown to provide an alternative pathway for the *de novo* biosynthesis of phosphatidylcholine in liver and other tissues (Bremer *et al.,* 1960; Gibson *et al.,* 1961). It has also been established that the phosphatidylethanolamine *N*-methyltransferase produces a complement of molecular species of phosphatidylcholine which differs markedly from that derived by cholinephos-photransferase activity or by acylation of lysophosphatidylcholines.

It is now recognized that the *N*-methylation pathway is primarily localized in the microsomal fraction of liver (Bremer and Greenberg, 1961; Gibson *et al.*, 1961; Rehbinder and Greenberg, 1965) with no significant activity being present in the mitochondria, Golgi complex, or plasma membranes (Van Golde *et al.*, 1974). LeKim *et al.* (1973) studied the activity of the *N*-methyltransferase in rat liver microsomes by addition of different molecular species of radioactive phosphatidyl-*N,N*-dimethylethanolamines. The methylation rates were found to increase with increasing degree of unsaturation of the species tested: dilinoleoyl > 1-stearoyl 2-linoleoyl > 1-stearoyl 2-oleoyl.

Isotopic studies *in vivo* and in rat liver slices with labeled ethanolamine and methionine have allowed the characterization of the molecular species of phosphatidylcholine formed by the *N*-methylation pathway. These studies are consistent with highly unsaturated phosphatidylcholines being the major products of the *N*-methylation pathway. Arvidson (1968a) followed the incorporation of [^{14}C]ethanolamine among the molecular fractions of liver phosphatidylcholines up to 4 hours after its administration to female rats. Since 50–60% of the radioactivity in the phosphatidylcholines was associated with hexaenoic species, it was suggested that the latter molecules were the major products of *N*-methylation of phosphatidylethanolamine. The much heavier labeling of hexaenoic relative to other molecular species of phosphatidylcholine has been confirmed by others in comparable experiments with radioactive ethanolamine (Rytter *et al.*, 1968; Tinoco *et al.*, 1970; Salerno and Beeler, 1973). Trewhella and Collins (1973b) found [^{14}C]ethanolamine to give the highest specific activity in the docosapentaenoyl phosphatidylcholines in rat liver and claimed the *N*-methylation pathway to be of considerable importance for the formation of this as well as the 1-stearoyl 2-arachidonoyl molecular species.

Isotopic experiments which have employed methyl-labeled methionine to monitor the products of *N*-methylation have given distributions of radioactivity among the molecular species of phosphatidylcholine which differ to some extent from those found with labeled ethanolamine. Studies with radioactive methionine are somewhat easier to interpret since the use of labeled ethanolamine results in molecular species of precursor phosphatidylethanolamines having different specific activities. The early *in vivo* studies in rat liver showed that the phosphatidylcholine fraction enriched in arachidonic acid had the highest specific activity following the administration of methyl-labeled methionine (Isozaki *et al.*, 1962; Balint *et al.*, 1967; Tinoco *et al.*, 1967). It was suggested, therefore, that methylation of phosphatidylethanolamine preferentially leads to arachidonoyl phosphatidylcholine. In comparable experiments, however, Arvidson (1968b) found the specific activity of the hexaenoic phosphatidylcholines to be 2–5 times greater than that of the tetraenoic species. The highest specific activities in the hexaenoic species of phosphatidylcholine were subsequently confirmed by other investigators working *in vivo* and with rat liver slices after a more complete separation of the tetraenoic and the hexaenoic phosphatidylcholines (Kanoh, 1969; Lyman *et al.,* 1969; Treble *et al.,* 1970; Salerno and Beeler, 1973). It has been reported that the tetraenoic and polyenoic (tetraenoic) fractions each contained 35–50% of the radioactive methyl groups from ([^{14}C]methyl)-methionine which enters the rat liver phosphatidylcholines *in vivo* (Arvidson, 1968b; Fex, 1971; MacDonald and Thompson, 1975). It has also been shown that the majority of the radioactivity which enters the arachidonoyl and docosahexaenoyl phosphatidylcholines of the livers of male rats was associated with the 1-palmitoyl species (Arvidson, 1968b). Comparison of the labeling patterns with the mass compositions of molecular species of hepatic phosphatidylethanolamines suggested that the 1-palmitoyl 2-docosahexaenoyl species is preferentially methylated compared to other polyenoic substrates. The data of Arvidson (1968b) permitted the conclusion that 1-stearoyl 2-arachidonoyl phosphatidylethanolamine is less rapidly methylated of all the potential polyunsaturated substrates. The studies performed to date indicate that the methylation pathway produces a pattern of phosphatidylcholines enriched in 1-palmitoyl 2-docosahexaenoyl, 1-palmitoyl 2-arachidonoyl, and 1-stearoyl 2-arachidonoyl species. This pathway appears to be quantitatively important only in the liver (Bjornstad and Bremer, 1966).

Unlike the results from experiments in rat liver, the *in vivo* work of MacDonald and Thompson (1975) with ([^{14}C]methyl)-methionine suggested that the N-methylation pathway produces mainly dienoic species of phosphatidylcholine in guinea pig liver. The work of Morgan *et al.* (1965) showed the phosphatidyl-N,N-dimethylethanolamine from dog lung tissue to have a similar fatty acid composition to that of phosphatidylcholine which led to the suggestion that dipalmitoylphosphatidylcholine may be formed mainly by the N-methylation pathway. Subsequent studies in rabbit and dog lung indicated a slow rate of methylation of phosphatidylethanolamine (Bjornstad and Bremer, 1966; Spitzer *et al.,* 1968; Weinhold, 1968; Wolfe *et al.,* 1970). Furthermore, the rapid entry of [^{3}H]palmitate into phosphatidylcholine could not be attributed to the N-methylation pathway (Wolfe *et al.,* 1970) which did not support its quantitative importance in the formation of dipalmitoylphosphatidylcholine. The failure of Vereyken *et al.* (1972) to detect disaturated species in phosphatidylethanolamine from rat lung supported the concept that the N-methylation pathway does not play an important role in the formation of dipalmitoyl-phosphatidylcholine.

4. Base Exchange Reactions

The work of Dils and Hubscher (1961) and Borkenhagen *et al.* (1961) indicated that the presence of Ca^{2+} in liver preparations could stimulate the entry of free choline and ethanolamine into phosphatidylcholine and phosphatidylethanolamine, respectively, by way of base exchange reactions. Phosphatidylcholine and phosphatidylserine can serve as substrates for the exchange with both choline and ethanolamine; phosphatidylethanolamine can exchange with ethanolamine but not choline (Bjerve, 1973b). Experiments with rat liver subcellular particles revealed that the Ca^{2+}-dependent incorporation of choline and ethanolamine was located exclusively in the microsomal fraction (Bjerve, 1973a).

Based on isotopic experiments *in vivo,* Treble *et al.* (1970) proposed that the rate of choline entry into liver phosphatidylcholine by base exchange is several fold higher than that by way of phosphorylcholine and CDP-choline. However, studies on the complement of molecular species of phosphatidylcholine which are labeled by base exchange reactions have made doubtful its physiological significance (Bjerve, 1971; Sundler *et al.,* 1972). Thus, Bjerve (1971) studied the Ca^{2+}-stimulated entry of radioactive choline in rat liver microsomes and found the specific activity of the hexaenoic phosphatidylcholines to be 12 times higher than that of the monoenes. Since *in vivo* studies with labeled choline gave highest specific activities in the monoenoic and dienoic species (Arvidson, 1968b), it was concluded by Bjerve (1971) that the base exchange reaction for choline incorporation was quantitatively unimportant *in vivo.* From *in vivo* studies with [^{14}C]choline, Sundler *et al.* (1972) were able to calculate that at least 20 times more choline is incorporated into hepatic phosphatidylcholines via phosphorylcholine and CDP-choline than through the exchange mechanism. These latter authors found a high proportion of the radioactivity incorporated through base exchange to be in the arachidonoyl phosphatidylcholines.

By means of analogous experiments *in vitro* and *in vivo* with labeled ethanolamine, Bjerve (1973a) and Sundler (1973) have assessed the physiological importance of base exchange reactions for ethanolamine entry into phosphatidylethanolamine. Thus, the Ca^{2+}-dependent entry of free ethanolamine in rat liver microsomes gave tetraenoic species with specific activities greater than those of the monoenoic and dienoic but less than those of the hexaenoic phosphatidylethanolamines in contrast to *in vivo* results (Arvidson, 1968a . The Ca^{2+}-stimulated incorporation of ethanola-

mine was considered, therefore, not to play a major role in phosphatidylethanolamine biosynthesis *in vivo* (Bjerve, 1973a). Sundler (1973) found
the distributions of radioactive ethanolamine among hepatic phosphatidylethanolamines, up to 5 minutes following injection, to closely resemble
patterns obtained using labeled glycerol and phosphate (see Section
IV,B,1). It was concluded that ethanolamine entry occurred mainly via
CDP-enthanolamine and not to any significant extent by base exchange
(Sundler, 1973). The quantitative significance of the base exchange reactions for the biosynthesis of phosphatidylcholine and phosphatidylethanol⁻
amine requires additional evaluation is liver as well as in brain and other
tissues (Porcellati *et al.,* 1971; Kanfer, 1972.

5. *Decarboxylation of Phosphatidylserine*

The report by Borkenhagen *et al.* (1961) on the ability of rat liver
homogenates to decarboxylate phosphatidylserine to form phosphatidylethanolamine provided an alternate pathway for the biosynthesis of the
latter diacylglycerophospholipid. Studies on subcellular particles from rat
and mouse livers have revealed that the phosphatidylserine decarboxylase
is localized almost exclusively in the mitochondria (Dennis and Kennedy,
1972; Van Golde *et al.,* 1974; Suda and Matsuda, 1974). However, there
are no reports to date on the molecular species of phosphatidylethanolamines which are derived by this reaction in mammalian tissues. Because of
the marked differences in fatty acid compositions of phosphatidylethanolamines and phosphatidylserines from the same tissues (see Section II,A),
studies along these lines should prove to be most fruitful.

In summary, the formation of the molecular species of tissue phosphatidylcholines and phosphatidylethanolamines has been shown to involve
a number of biosynthetic mechanisms. Each of these pathways gives rise
to a characteristic pattern of molecular species of diacylglycerophospholipids. The quantitative significance of these metabolic pathways in the
formation of diacylglycerophospholipids, however, varies considerably
among individual molecular species. The phosphatidylcholines and phosphatidylethanolamines which are synthesized in the endoplasmic reticulum
can be exchanged with those in the mitochondria in the presence of appropriate carrier proteins (Wirtz and Zilversmit, 1968; McMurray and
Dawson, 1969; Dawson, 1973; Wirtz, 1974). No significant selectivity
has been found towards specific molecular species of phosphatidylcholine
and phosphatidylethanolamine in the exchange process (see Section
III,A,3).

The metabolic heterogeneity of the molecular species of the choline and
ethanolamine phosphatides demonstrated with radioactive and mass tracers

has been confirmed and extended by studies with stable isotopes, which have permitted the differentiation between old and new molecules (Kuksis and Myher, 1976). Curstedt and Sjovall (1974a,b) have determined the incorporation of deuterium into different positions of individual molecular species of biliary phosphatidylcholines in bile fistula rats given [1,1-²H₂]ethanol at a constant rate for 24 hours. The rate of deuterium incorporation indicated the presence of at least two pools of phosphatidylcholines with widely different turnover rates. The apparent half-life times of the glycerol moiety of molecular species in the pool having a rapid turnover varied between 1 hour (dipalmitoyl species) and about 8 hours (1-stearoyl 2-linoleoyl species). The apparent half-life times of 1-palmitoyl residues in the different molecular species were about 4 and 10 hours in rats given glucose and fructose, respectively. The values were the same for all species studied, indicating that labeled palmitoyl residues in different molecular species were derived from the same palmitic acid pool. Kuksis *et al.* (1975a) have determined the metabolic utilization of the newly synthesized palmitic and stearic acids during the perfusion of isolated rat livers with deuterium oxide-containing buffers. Evidence was obtained for an extensive utilization of newly formed palmitic acid in the *de novo* synthesis of glycerolipids while the newly formed stearic acid entered the glycerolipid molecules largely by deacylation–reacylation reactions. This mode of utilization appeared to be similar to that demonstrated for exogenous palmitic and stearic acids. A determination of the percent replacement of old by new molecules of palmitic and stearic acid in the various molecular species of phosphatidylcholine and phosphatidylethanolamine (Kuksis *et al.,* 1975b) confirmed the earlier postulated differential utilization of these acids in glycerolipid biosynthesis as well as supported the hypothesis of a precursor–product relationship between the oligoenoic and tetraenoic species of both phosphatides. Calculation of half-lives gave values of 14–19 hours for palmitoyl oligoenes, 40–50 hours for palmitoyl tetraenes, and 22–28 hours for palmitoyl hexaenes of both choline and ethanolamine phosphatides. The corresponding stearoyl species had half-lives which ranged from 89 to 200 hours. Evidence was also obtained for a metabolic heterogeneity among subunits of molecular species recognized on the basis of combinations of new and old glycerol and fatty acids in the same glycerolipid molecule (Kuksis and Myher, 1976).

C. Biosynthesis of Phosphatidylinositol

Phosphatidylinositol is known to be greatly enriched in 1-stearoyl 2-arachidonoyl species as compared to other diacylglycerophospholipids present in liver and brain of the rat, pig, and ox (see Section III,A). Thus, considerable interest has been attached to the biosynthetic pathways by which phosphatidylinositol from various tissues attains its unique fatty acid composition. The role of *de novo* synthesis via CDP-diacylglycerols and deacylation–reacylation reactions in the formation of characteristic molecular species of phosphatidylinositol has been investigated both at the enzymatic level *in vitro* and with isotopic precursors *in vivo*.

The exchange of phosphatidylinositol between subcellular structures has been demonstrated (Dawson, 1973; Zborowski and Wojtczak, 1975; Brammer and Sheltawy, 1975).

1.   *Utilization of CDP-Diacylglycerols*

It has been well established in various mammalian tissues that the reaction of CDP-diacylglycerol with free inositol accounts for the *de novo* biosynthesis of phosphatidylinositol in the presence of the enzyme CDP-diacylglycerol: inositol phosphatidyltransferase (Agranoff *et al.,* 1958; Paulus and Kennedy, 1960; Thompson *et al.,* 1963). The specific activity of this enzyme has been found to be highest in the microsomal fraction of brain and liver cells (Benjamins and Agranoff, 1969; Bishop and Strickland, 1970; Van Golde *et al.,* 1974) with no significant activity present in mitochondria, plasma membranes, and the Golgi complex from rat liver (Van Golde *et al.,* 1974). Benjamins and Agranoff (1969) have tested the effect of CDP-diacylglycerols with different fatty acid compositions on enzyme activity using microsomal fractions from guinea pig brain. *Rac*-CDP-didecanoylglycerol was a better substrate than *rac*-CDP-dipalmitoylglycerol or CDP-diacylglycerol prepared from egg phosphatidylcholine. No reaction was observed with synthetic CDP-diacylglycerols containing C_{20} or C_{22} fatty acids under the assay conditions employed. Subsequently, Bishop and Strickland (1970) observed the following relative activities for various molecular species of CDP-diacylglycerols with rat brain microsomes: 1,2-dioleoyl > 1-stearoyl   2-oleoyl > 1-oleoyl   2-stearoyl = 1-palmitoyl   2-oleoyl > 1,2-distearoyl > 1,2-dipalmitoyl. Recently, Bishop and Strickland (1976) have referred to an unpublished study in which the 1-stearoyl 2-arachidonoyl species was not as active as the corresponding CDP-diacylglycerol in which oleic acid replaced arachidonic acid. Thus, it has been concluded that the selectivity imposed at the final enzymic step in the *de novo* biosynthesis of phosphatidylinositol is not sufficient to account for its natural fatty acid composition (Bishop and Strickland, 1976).

Recently, CDP-diacylglycerol has been isolated from bovine liver and brain and has been found to have a predominantly 1-stearoyl-2-arachidonoyl composition (Thompson and MacDonald, 1975; Thompson and MacDonald, 1976). Its composition was more closely related to that of phosphatidylinositol from this source than to phosphatidic acid. Thompson and MacDonald (1975) suggested that one way of accounting for this structure would be the formation of CDP-diacylglycerol by the back-reaction of phosphatidylinositol synthetase, as claimed by Petzold and Agranoff (1967). It has now been shown by Hokin-Neaverson *et al.* (1977) that this reaction takes place readily with 1-stearoyl-2-arachidonoyl phosphatidylinositol as an exogenous source in dialyzed microsomal preparations from mouse pancreas.

Using a rat liver slice system, Akino and Shimojo (1970) found that the entry of [^{14}C]glycerol into phosphatidylinositols produced monoenoic and dienoic species with specific activities that were much greater than those of the tetraenoic molecules. Holub and Kuksis (1971a) reported that the monoenoic plus dienoic, trienoic, tetraenoic, and polyenoic species contained 65%, 7%, 17%, and 11%, respectively, of the radioactivity associated with the hepatic phosphatidylinositols within 5 minutes after giving [^{14}C]glycerol intravenously. Comparable experiments, in which ^{32}P was administered intraperitoneally, resulted in monoenoic plus dienoic species with specific activities approximately 17 times higher than the tetraenes at 1 hour following injection (Holub and Kuksis, 1971a). These tracer studies indicate that the intact phosphatidic acids which enter directly into phosphatidylinositol during *de novo* biosynthesis are enriched in monoenoic plus dienoic species. However, significant quantities of tetraenoic phosphatidylinositols are also produced. In other experiments, a somewhat heavier labeling of the tetraenoic species relative to other phosphatidylinositols from rat liver was obtained soon after the intraperitoneal injection of [^{3}H]inositol (Holub and Kuksis, 1972). This latter phenomenon likely reflects the reaction of free inositol with an endogenous pool of CDP-diacylglycerol enriched in arachidonoyl molecular species which are not derived directly from the corresponding phosphatidic acids (see Section IV,A,3). The *in vivo* studies with [^{3}H]inositol (Holub and Kuksis, 1972) indicate that in rat liver the reaction of inositol with CDP-diacylglycerols, in the presence of the CDP-diacylglycerol: inositol phosphatidyltransferase, produces monoenoic plus dienoic, trienoic, tetraenoic, and hexaenoic species which represent 37%, 4%, 41%, and 18%, respectively, of the newly formed phosphatidylinositols. Thus, the preponderance by mass of the 1-stearoyl-2-arachidonoyl relative to monoenoic and dienoic phosphatodylinositols in the liver (Holub and Kuksis, 1971c) cannot be explained solely on the basis of *de novo* biosynthesis.

Similar studies have been reported on the *de novo* biosynthesis of individual molecular species of phosphatidylinositol in brain. MacDonald *et al.* (1975) monitored the distribution of radioactivity among the various molecular classes of phosphatidylinositol soon after the intraventricular injection of [^{14}C]glycerol. The data suggested a preferential synthesis of disaturated, monoenoic, and polyenoic (> tetraenoic) phosphatidylinositols from phosphatidic acid precursors even though the tetraenoic species predominate on a mass basis. Comparable studies with ^{32}P and [^{14}C]glucose in guinea pig cerebral hemispheres have indicated that part of the tetraenoic and probably all of the saturated phosphatidylinositol may be formed by transacylation reactions (Luthra and Sheltawy, 1976).

2. Acylation of Lysophosphatidylinositol

There is evidence that the high level of 1-stearoyl 2-arachidonoyl species in phosphatidylinositol from various tissues can arise from the activity of the lysophosphatidyl acyl transferases. Keenan and Hokin (1964) were the first to report upon the presence of 1-acyl-sn-glycero-3-phosphorylinositol acyl transferase in animal tissues. These workers reported the greatest total activity and the highest specific activity to be present in the microsomal fraction of pigeon pancreas although significant activity was also found in the mitochondria. The initial velocities obtained with oleoyl-CoA were more than twice those observed with palmitoyl-CoA (Keenan and Hokin, 1964). The selectivity of the 1-acyl-sn-glycero-3-phosphorylinositol acyl transferase has been studied in rat brain microsomes by testing the suitability of eight different acyl-CoA derivatives as substrates (Baker and Thompson, 1973). The most striking feature was that rates with arachidonoyl-CoA were 2 to 5 times higher than with linoleoyl-CoA and 5 to 10 times higher compared with oleoyl- and docosahexaenoyl-CoA. The acyltransferase from rat liver also showed a marked preference for arachidonoyl-CoA over saturated and other unsaturated acyl-CoA derivatives (Holub, 1976a). Holub (1976a) also studied the incorporation of radioactive 1-acyl-sn-glycero-3-phosphorylinositol into the molecular species of phosphatidylinositol using rat liver homogenate or microsomal preparations supplemented with cofactors for the activation of endogenous fatty acids. Some 56–74% of the newly incorporated lysophosphatidylinositol was associated with the arachidonoyl species. Thus, the preceding results indicate that the acylation of lysophosphatidylinositol in liver is of considerable importance for the formation of arachidonoyl phosphatidylinositols. The selectivity of the 1-acyl-sn-glycero-3-phosphorylinositol acyl transferase is consistent with the preponderance of arachidonic acid at the 2 position of phosphatidylinositol (see Section II,A,2).

Tracer experiments in vivo and in tissue homogenates have demonstrated that the acylation of lysophosphatidylinositols is of physiological importance for the synthesis of tetraenoic species of phosphatidylinositol. Holub and Kuksis (1971a) provided evidence for the interconversion of monoenoic plus dienoic into tetraenoic phosphatidylinositols in rat liver by monitoring the specific activities of the various molecular species for extended times following the administration of ^{32}P or [^{14}C]glycerol. The specific activity of the monoenes plus dienes exceeded that of the arachidonoyl tetraenes by 17-fold 1 hour after injection of ^{32}P whereas the specific activities of all the fractions were about equal within 4 days. From 3 hours to 4 days, the specific activity of the total phosphatidylinositols changed little, while there was a striking decrease in the specific activity of the monoenes plus dienes concomitant with an increase in that of the tetraenes. These experiments suggest that the monoenoic plus dienoic phosphatidylinositols, which are derived from *de novo* biosynthesis via phosphatidic acid, are subsequently converted into arachidonoyl species by a deacylation–reacylation cycle (Holub and Kuksis, 1971a). These findings were also supported by *in vivo* experiments using [^{3}H]inositol as the precursor for the various phosphatidylinositols (Holub and Kuksis, 1972).

Experiments with radioactive glycerol and fatty acids in rat brain have supported conclusions from work in liver. Thus, MacDonald *et al.* (1975) observed a rapid fall in the relative specific activities of the disaturated and monounsaturated species of phosphatidylinositol after the intraventricular injection of [^{14}C]glycerol as those of the tetraunsaturated species increased. These labeling patterns were considered to be consistent with acyl transferase reactions regulating the formation of arachidonic acid-containing species. In dual-labeling experiments with [^{3}H]arachidonate and [^{14}C]glycerol, Baker and Thompson (1972) found the $^{3}H/^{14}C$ ratios in the tetraenoic phosphatidylinositol to be much greater than those in the corresponding phosphatidic acids. The high initial incorporation of arachidonate was attributed to an independent acyl exchange mechanism rather than to *de novo* synthesis via phosphatidic acid.

3. Base Exchange Reactions

An alternative route for the entry of free inositol into phosphatidylinositol was reported by Paulus and Kennedy (1960) using microsomes from chicken livers. This route involves an exchange reaction of free inositol for certain nitrogenous bases in endogenous diacylglycerophospholipids. In rat liver microsomes, this exchange reaction was found to require the addition of Mn^{2+} (Hubscher, 1962) but not Ca^{2+}, which stimulates the exchange with choline, ethanolamine, and serine (see Section IV,B,4). The experiments of Holub (1975) indicate that microsomal phosphatidylinositol is the preferred substrate for the Mn^{2+}-stimulated entry of free inositol into diacylglycerophospholipid in rat liver microsomes when the exchange reaction is enhanced by the addition of CTP or CDP-choline.

Holub (1974) has studied the entry of [³H]inositol by the exchange reaction into the various molecular species of phosphatidylinositol of rat liver microsomes. The monoenoic plus dienoic and tetraenoic species contained 4% and 82%, respectively, of the radioactivity incorporated into the total phosphatidylinositols. In contrast, these same two chemical fractions each contained 35–50% of the radioactivity in the phosphatidylinositols from whole livers or the microsomes after intraperitoneal injection of [³H]inositol (Holub and Kuksis, 1972; Holub, 1974). On the basis of this discrepancy in the labeling pattern it may be concluded that the inositol exchange reaction is only of minor importance for inositol entry into phosphatidylinositol under physiological conditions.

D. BIOSYNTHESIS OF OTHER DIACYLGLYCEROPHOSPHOLIPIDS

In contrast to the diacylglycerophospholipids already discussed, little information is available on the biogenesis of the individual molecular species of phosphatidylserine, phosphatidylglycerol, diphosphatidylglycerol, and the mono- and diphosphates of phosphatidylinositol. This section summarizes the current knowledge in this area of investigation of molecular species of glycerophospholipids.

1. *Formation of Phosphatidylserines*

The work of Borkenhagen et al. (1961) showed that the *de novo* biosynthesis of phosphatidylserine in mammalian tissues could occur by the Ca^{2+}-dependent exchange reaction between L-serine and phosphatidylethanolamine. Studies on the subcellular distribution of phosphatidylethanolamine-L-serine phosphatidyltransferase have shown the activity to be almost entirely associated with the microsomal fraction in rat liver (Dennis and Kennedy, 1972; Bjerve, 1973a). Van Golde et al. (1974) found the rough microsomes to have a much greater capacity for phosphatidylserine synthesis than the smooth microsomes. It is important to note that Bjerve (1973b) has concluded on the basis of chase experiments in rat liver microsomes that phosphatidylcholine can also serve as a substrate for the Ca^{2+}-stimulated entry of L-serine into diacylglycerophospholipid. Although endogenous phosphatidylserine can also serve as a substrate for base exchange with L-serine, such a reaction does not provide for the net synthesis of this diacylglycerophospholipid (Bjerve, 1973b). Saito and Kanfer (1973) reported that added phosphatidylethanolamine as well as phosphatidylcholine could stimulate [¹⁴C]serine incorporation into diacylglycerophospholipid with a membrane-bound enzyme from rat brain. The complement of molecular species of phosphatidylserine which are derived from the exchange reactions already described have not yet been elucidated, although Yeung and Kuksis (1976) have observed a heavy labeling of tetraenoic species in liver soon after the administration of radioactive serine to rats. An efficient transfer of phosphatidylserine from rat liver microsomes, its site of synthesis, to the mitochondria has been demonstrated (Butler and Thompson, 1975).

Kiss (1976) has investigated the incorporation of ^{32}P-labeled phosphate into the glycerophospholipids of rat heart slices in pulse chase experiments. The comparison of the specific activities of individual phospholipids suggested that phosphatidic acid can be a ^{32}P precursor for phosphatidylserine. Studies with L-serine revealed the full calcium dependence of phosphatidylserine formation in heart homogenates. Chasing experiments with radioactive ethanolamine and choline proved the precursor role of phosphatidylethanolamine and phosphatidylcholine and indicated a base exchange mechanism. Among phospholipids, phosphatidic acid was the most potent in stimulating phosphatidylserine formation in homogenates. The conclusion was reached that phosphatidic acid can also be regarded as a precursor of phosphatidylserine. Yeung and Kuksis (1976) have reexamined the utilization of L-serine in the *in vivo* biosynthesis of glycerophospholipids by rat liver. It was noted that the rate of biosynthesis of phosphatidylserine in rat liver compared closely to the rates of biosynthesis of other glycerophospholipids in this tissue. However, decarboxylation to phosphatidylethanolamine appeared to account for only about one-half of the degradation of phosphatidylserine, the rest being possibly subject to base exchange with choline and ethanolamine. Further insight into the metabolism of phosphatidylserine and its conversion into other glycerophospholipids has been obtained by analyses of the molecular species of these phosphatides (Yeung and Kuksis, 1978).

2. *Formation of Phosphatidylglycerols*

The biosynthesis of phosphatidylglycerol in mammalian tissues involves the reaction of CDP-diacylglycerol with *sn*-glycero-3-phosphate to form phosphatidylglycerophosphate which is subsequently dephosphorylated to liberate the end product (Kiyasu *et al.,* 1963; Davidson and Stanacev, 1970). The CDP-diacylglycerol: *sn*-glycero-3-phosphate phosphatidyltransferase is localized mainly in the mitochondria of liver (Kiyasu *et al.,* 1963; Dennis and Kennedy, 1972; Davidson and Stanacev, 1974) although significant synthesis has been found in the endoplasmic reticulum, Golgi apparatus, and plasma membranes (Van Golde *et al.,* 1971; Victoria *et al.,* 1971). The enzymic dephosphorylation of phosphatidylglycerophosphate also appears to occur in the mitochondria (Davidson and Stanacev, 1971). Possibly, CDP-diacylglycerol can be transported from the endoplasmic reticulum, its major site of synthesis (see Section IV,A,3), to the mitochondria by specific carrier proteins (Dawson, 1973) before it serves in phosphatidylglycerol synthesis.

Hostetler *et al.* (1975) tested the suitability of various CDP-diacylglycerols as substrates for the synthesis of phosphatidylglycerol in rat liver mitochondria. The CDP-diacylglycerols with short-chain saturated acids, dilauroyl and dimyristoyl, were better substrates than the dipalmitoyl and distearoyl homologues. The 1-palmitoyl 2-oleoyl CDP-diacylglycerol was more effective than the dioleoyl and dilinoleoyl species although all three unsaturated substrates were preferred over the distearoyl homologue. These enzyme studies and the known fatty acid composition of natural CDP-diacylglycerol (Thompson and MacDonald, 1975, 1976) do not allow for a simple account of the fatty acid composition of phosphatidylglycerol from mammalian tissues (White, 1973). It remains to be investigated whether the CDP-diacylglycerols from different subcellular fractions show heterogeneity and their fatty acid compositions. It should be noted, also, that 1-acyl-*sn*-glycero-3-phosphorylglycerol acyl transferase activity has been reported in rat liver microsomes (Wittels, 1973) which could be of importance for the formation of specific molecular species of phosphatidylglycerol.

3. *Formation of Diphosphatidylglycerols*

The *de novo* biosynthesis of diphosphatidylglycerol from phosphatidylglycerol and CDP-diacylglycerol is known to occur in the mitochondrial fraction of rat liver (Davidson and Stanacev, 1971; Hostetler *et al.,* 1971). Hostetler *et al.* (1975) did not find exogenously added dilinoleoyl CDP-diacylglycerol to be an especially preferred substrate for diphosphatidylglycerol synthesis in liver mitochondria although it was a better substrate than the dipalmitoyl and distearoyl species. Highest reaction rates were observed with dilauroyl, dimyristoyl, and 1-palmitoyl 2-oleoyl CDP-diacylglycerols whereas lower reaction rates were obtained with dioleoyl and dilinoleoyl species. Thus, the high linoleic acid content of diphosphatidylglycerol from liver and other tissues (see Section II,A) cannot be readily explained on the basis of enzyme selectivity or the fatty acid composition of tissue CDP-diacylglycerols (Thompson and MacDonald, 1975, 1976).

The presence of significant di(1-acyl-lysophosphatidyl)glycerol acyltransferase activity in rat liver microsomes has been reported by Eichberg (1974) who observed the formation of phosphatidyllysophosphatidylglycerol. However, linoleoyl-CoA was the least effective of all saturated and unsaturated acyl-CoA derivatives that were tested as substrates. Therefore, the selectivity of the reacylating enzymes also does not account for the preponderance of dilinoleoyl species in diphosphatidylglycerol from mammalian tissues.

4. Formation of Polyphosphoinositides

The enzymic phosphorylation of phosphatidylinositol first at the 4 and subsequently at the 5 position results in the biosynthesis of its mono- and diphosphate derivatives. The kinases which form these latter two diacylglycerophospholipids in the presence of ATP and Mg^{2+} or Mn^{2+} appear to reside predominantly in the plasma membrane of mammalian cells (Colodzin and Kennedy, 1965; Kai *et al.*, 1966). These phosphorylation reactions have not yet been studied with substrates of different fatty acid compositions although all three inositol phosphatides from bovine brain have shown very similar complements of molecular species (Holub *et al.*, 1970). The possible acylation of the lyso derivatives of the mono- and diphosphate derivatives of phosphatidylinositol remains to be investigated.

E. DEGRADATION OF DIACYLGLYCEROPHOSPHOLIPIDS

There are several hydrolytic enzymes which degrade the various diacylglycerophospholipids in mammalian tissues. Such catabolic reactions may provide the necessary precursors for the biosynthesis of the characteristic molecular species associated with different diacylglycerophospholipids. A selective destruction of certain molecular species of diacylglycerophospholipids could also contribute to the differences in the mass composition between these glycerolipids and their presumed precursors. The hydrolytic enzymes make available such substrates as lysophosphatides, 1,2-diacylglycerols, and phosphatidic acids. It is unfortunate that studies on individual catabolic enzymes have seldom tested the suitability of different molecular species of a given diacylglycerophospholipid as substrates for the corresponding enzymes. Such omissions have not allowed a firm assessment of the relative importance of anabolic and catabolic reactions in controlling the molecular species composition of tissue diacylglycerophospholipids. Experiments with bacterial and snake venom phospholipases have shown very pronounced selectivity towards different molecular species of phosphatidylcholines (Moore and Williams, 1963; Nutter and Privett, 1966). Extensive reviews of the enzymes which degrade diacylglycerophospholipids in mammalian tissues are available (McMurray and Magee, 1972; Van Den Bosch *et al.*, 1972; Thompson, 1973; Brockerhoff and Jensen, 1974).

1. Release of Lysophosphatides

The occurrence and subcellular distribution of phospholipases A_1 and A_2 as well as the lysophospholipases have been discussed in several review articles (Van Den Bosch *et al.*, 1972; McMurray and Magee, 1972; Thompson, 1973; Brockerhoff and Jensen, 1974). An elaborate study on membrane-confined phospholipases in the rat hepatocyte has been conducted by Nachbaur *et al.* (1972). McMurray and Magee (1972) have also summarized the metabolic role of phospholipase activity in providing 1-acyl and 2-acyl lysophosphatides which serve as intermediates in deacylation–reacylation cycles. Such cycles are thought to provide for the biosynthesis of characteristic molecular species of diacylglycerophospholipids. Waite and Sisson (1971) have reported that phospholipase A_2 from rat liver mitochondria discriminates against molecular species of diacylglycerophospholipids which have highly unsaturated fatty acids in the 2 position. Solubilized mitochondrial phospholipase A_2 released oleic acid preferentially to arachidonic acid from rat liver phosphatidylethanolamine. Woelk *et al.* (1973) studied the activity of phospholipase A_1 from the neurons of rabbit brain towards phosphatidylcholines which were specifically labeled with radioactive palmitic, oleic, or linoleic acid at the 1 position. The relative rates of hydrolysis were as follows: $16:0 > 18:1 > 18:2$. The possibility that phospholipases from different subcellular fractions show heterogeneity in their fatty acid specificities remains to be investigated further.

Waite and Sisson (1973, 1976) have described a heparin-solubilized phospholipase A_1 in the plasma membrane of rat liver cells which can catalyze the hydrolysis of mono- and diacylglycerols and mono- and diacyl phosphatidylethanolamine as well as a transacylation of the acyl group from position 1 of these lipids to an acceptor monoacylglycerol. Experiments of Kanoh and Akesson (1977) using isolated rat hepatocytes have suggested that the degradation of dilinoleoyl phosphatidylcholine could be accounted for by the action of phospholipase A_1 while the degradation of the dipalmitoyl species could have proceeded through the action of phospholipase A_2.

2. Release of 1,2-Diacyl-sn-Glycerols

Although a wide distribution of phospholipase C activity in bacterial systems is well recognized, little information is available on the hydrolysis of diacylglycerophospholipids to 1,2-diacylglycerols in mammalian tissues. The inositol phosphatides are the only well-documented diacylglycerophospholipid substrates for such phospholipase C activity in animal tissues.

Thus, both soluble and particulate forms of phosphodiesterase from various tissues have been shown to release free 1,2-diacylglycerols from phosphatidylinositol as well as its mono- and diphosphate derivatives (Atherton and Hawthorne, 1968; Friedel *et al.*, 1969; Keough and Thompson, 1972; Tou *et al.*, 1973; Lapetina and Michell, 1973). Keough *et al.* (1972) found that ox brain phosphodiesterase showed no significant selectivity towards different molecular species of phosphatidylinositol diphosphate. In view of the molecular species composition of the three inositol phosphatides in ox brain (Holub *et al.*, 1970), the phosphodiesterase would be expected to release a high proportion of 1-stearoyl 2-arachidonoyl diacylglycerols. The presence of phosphomonoesterase activity in mammalian tissues gives rise to phosphatidylinositol and its monophosphate derivative from phosphatidylinositol mono- and diphosphate, respectively (Dawson and Thompson, 1964; Chang and Ballou, 1967; Lee and Huggins, 1968; Sheltawy *et al.*, 1972). Subcellular fractionation of homogenates from rat kidney cortex has revealed that the phosphatases which attacked phosphatidylinositol mono- and diphosphate were associated with the Golgi membranes and the supernatant fraction (Cooper and Hawthorne, 1975). The role of phosphatidate phosphohydrolase activity in the formation of 1,2-diacylglycerols has already been discussed, as has been the biogenesis of diacylglycerols by a reversal of phosphatidylcholine synthesis (see Section IV,C,1).

3. *Release of Phosphatidic Acids*

Enzymes with phospholipase D activity are known to be widely distributed in bacteria and higher plants although information on their presence in animal tissues is almost nonexistent. The occurrence of phospholipase D activity has been reported in studies using mouse liver microsomes (Taki and Matsumoto, 1973). Saito and Kanfer (1975) recently demonstrated the formation of phosphatidic acid from phosphatidylcholine using a solubilized preparation from a rat brain particulate fraction. Phosphatidic acid can also be derived by reversal of the pathway leading to phosphatidylinositol synthesis (see Section IV,A,1).

V. Alterations in Metabolism of Molecular Species of Diacylglycerophospholipids

It is well documented that natural or experimentally induced changes in the metabolic state of an animal are frequently associated with dramatic changes in the fatty acid composition of individual diacylglycerophospholipids. Thus, a corresponding change in the composition and metabolism of the individual molecular species would be anticipated under such conditions. This section will summarize research which has demonstrated a shift in the composition and metabolism of individual molecular species with dietary, physiological, and pharmacological stresses and disease.

A. DIETARY INFLUENCES

Alterations in the pattern of molecular species associated with various diacylglycerophospholipids have been realized by different forms of nutritional manipulation. Extensive investigations have been directed towards a comparison of the molecular species of hepatic phosphatidylcholines in essential fatty acid deficient versus control animals. Van Golde *et al.* (1968) studied the qualitative and quantitative changes in the molecular species pattern of the phosphatidylcholines as a function of time when corn oil was added to the diet of deficient rats. Within 3 days of corn oil feeding, the increase in 1-palmitoyl 2-arachidonoyl and 1-stearoyl 2-arachidonoyl phosphatidylcholine had already reached their maximum level. During a 9-day feeding period, a very rapid replacement of 1-palmitoyl 2-eicosatrienoyl and 1-stearoyl 2-eicosatrienoyl species by the corresponding 2-arachidonoyl homologues was observed. The dioleoyl species decreased much quicker than the 1-palmitoyl 2-oleoyl and 1-stearoyl 2-oleoyl phosphatidylcholines over the 9-day period. Lyman *et al.* (1969) found that the dienes and tetraenes contributed 28% and 54%, respectively, to the total hepatic phosphatidylcholines in control rats but only about 10% each in deficient animals. The monoenes and trienes represented 41% and 38%, respectively, of the total phosphatidylcholines in essential fatty acid deficient rats. Yurkowski and Walker (1971) have shown that a dietary deficiency of essential fatty acids results in the partial replacement of arachidonic acid-containing species by 1-palmitoyl 2-eicosatrienoyl and 1-stearoyl 2-eicosatrienoyl phosphatidylcholines and of linoleic acid-containing species by 1-palmitoyl 2-oleoyl and 1-stearoyl 2-oleoyl molecules in the intestinal mucosa of rats. In comparable studies conducted over extended time intervals with swine fed fat-free diets, Shaw and Bottino (1974) found the molecular species of hepatic phosphatidylethanolamines to be more sensitive to dietary change than those of the phosphatidylcholines. The effect of dietary fat on the composition of molecular species of diacylglycerophospholipids has sometimes been studied using chow as the control diet (Beeler *et al.,* 1970). Such studies are somewhat difficult to interpret since these diets differ in essentially all nutrients. The molecular species composition of the biliary phosphatidylcholines is also known to change with an alteration in the type of dietary fat (Christie *et al.,* 1975).

The data of Beeler *et al.* (1970) suggest that the 1-palmitoyl 2-oleoyl phosphatidylcholine predominates in the bile of essential fatty acid deficient hamsters whereas the 2-linoleoyl homologue is the major species in control animals. Recently, Kyriakides *et al.* (1976) found a significant reduction of dipalmitoylphosphatidylcholine in lung tissue and lavage fluid from essential fatty acid deficient rats, while the total phosphatidylcholine content remained unchanged. On feeding a diet containing linoleate to the deficient rats, a reversal of these changes was nearly complete by 7–14 days.

Several investigators have studied the effect of dietary fat on the biosynthesis of individual molecular species of diacylglycerophospholipids. It has been shown in studies with ^{32}P in rats and hamsters (Collins, 1962; Beeler *et al.*, 1970) that hepatic phosphatidylcholines from essential fatty acid deficient animals have higher specific activities than controls. The enhanced turnover of phosphatidylcholine in deficient animals was attributed mainly to the presence of the 1-palmitoyl 2-oleoyl species (Trewhella and Collins, 1973a). Beeler *et al.* (1970) found the ^{3}H/^{14}C and ^{14}C/^{32}P ratios to be very similar in the phosphatidylcholines of both deficient and normal animals soon after injection mixtures of ^{33}P, ([^{14}C]methyl)-methionine, and ([^{3}H]methyl)-choline into hamsters. They suggested that the oleoyl species in liver substitutes for the linoleoyl and that the eicosatrienoyl phosphatidylcholine takes over the metabolic role of the arachidonoyl species. Trewhella and Collins (1973a) also concluded that the 1-stearoyl 2-eicosatrienoyl phosphatidylcholine had the slowest turnover rate in the livers of essential fatty acid-deficient rats based on its low specific activity following the intraperitoneal injection of ^{32}P. Lyman *et al.* (1970) claimed a more rapid turnover of the hepatic phosphatidylcholine from deficient rats since the specific activities of the individual molecular species in the latter animals reached equilibrium sooner than controls following injection of ([^{14}C]methyl)-methionine.

Shamgar and Collins (1975b) have determined the specific radioactivities of individual molecular species of the choline and ethanolamine phosphatides in the skeletal muscle of control rats and rats deficient in essential fatty acids 3 hours after intraperitoneal injection of ortho [^{32}P]phosphate. These workers demonstrated that the high average specific radioactivity of these phosphoacylglycerols in muscle of rats deficient in essential fatty acids was due to both increased amounts and increased turnover of 1-palmitoyl-2-oleoyl phosphatidylcholine and phosphatidylethanolamine. The 1-stearoyl-2-arachidonoyl phosphatidylcholine was found to turn over faster than the 1-palmitoyl-2-arachidonoyl species. In rats deficient in essential fatty acids, the 1-stearoyl-2-(5,8,11-eicosatrienoyl)phosphatidylcholine turned over more rapidly than the 1-palmitoyl-2-(5,8,11-eicosatrienoyl) species. Both of these findings for the rat skeletal muscle are in contrast with the results of similar analysis for rat liver (Trewhella and Collins, 1973a). The differences may be due at least in part to the fact that muscle phosphoacylglycerols, in contrast to those of liver, are not exported, and therefore the phosphoacylglycerol metabolism in muscle reflects the synthesis and degradation of these compounds solely within the tissue.

Blank *et al.* (1973) have demonstrated that arachidonic acid is metabolized more rapidly in the diacyl phospholipids and is retained to a greater extent in the plasmalogens of testicular lipids of rats fed an essential fatty acid-deficient diet. It was concluded that the buildup of labeled arachidonic acid in the plasmalogens from animals fed the fat-free diet is explained by an acyl exchange reaction since the quantity of ethanolamine plasmalogens in the testes remained constant. The fact that arachidonate at the 2 position of the ethanolamine plasmalogens was retained to a greater degree than in the diacyl analog was taken to indicate that the two lipids served different functions in the testicular tissue, and that plasmalogens were important reservoirs for prostaglandin precursors in animals deficient in essential fatty acids.

Mendenhall *et al.* (1969) have reported a significant increase in 1-acyl-*sn*-glycero-3-phosphorylcholine acyl transferase activity with arachidonoyl-CoA as substrate in liver microsomes of rats fed diets containing corn oil relative to those containing coconut oil. Acyl transferase activities with other acyl-CoA derivatives were not significantly affected by the type of dietary fat.

A number of studies have been conducted on the effect of choline deficiency on the composition and metabolism of individual molecular species of diacylglycerophospholipids in liver. Research in this area has been directed towards an understanding of the lipotropic action of choline. Lyman *et al.* (1973) found a slight increase in the concentration of phosphatidylethanolamine in livers from choline deficient rats coupled with a marked reduction in the proportion of the tetraenoic and a doubling of the hexaenoic species. The relative abundance of palmitate and stearate among the various phosphatidylcholine fractions was not greatly altered by a deficiency of dietary choline. Glenn and Austin (1971) had observed quite different shifts in the pattern of molecular species of phosphatidylethanolamine in earlier studies on choline deficiency, but an inappropriate control diet was employed in their experiments. In later work, Lyman *et al.* (1975) reported a decrease in the level of hepatic phosphatidylcholine in deficient rats which was accounted for mainly by a drop in the linoleoyl species. Interestingly, the concentration of the total phosphatidylcholines in plasma from the deficient animals was much less than controls; the drop was accounted for by large decreases in linoleoyl and arachidonoyl species. Tracer studies with ([14C]methyl)-methionine showed that deficient rats incorporated less radioactivity into their linoleoyl and arachidonoyl phosphatidylcholine in liver than did the supplemented animals (Lyman *et al.*, 1975). It was suggested that a deficiency of labile methyl groups in choline deficiency may reduce the formation of arachidonoyl phosphatidylcholine from methylation of the corresponding phosphatidylethanolamine. A reduction in transmethylation may impair normal lipid transport from liver. Using different experimental conditions, Chen and Lombardi (1973a) concluded that the synthesis of phosphatidylcholine via stepwise methylation of phosphatidylethanolamine may be increased in choline deficiency. The same workers also found that the selectivity of the 1-acyl-*sn*-glycero-3-phosphorylcholine acyl transferase in rat liver microsomes toward different acyl-CoA derivatives was not influenced by choline deficiency (Chen and Lombardi, 1973b). The acyl transferases do not appear to be responsible for the change in fatty acid composition of liver phosphatidylcholines in choline deficiency.

Lands and Hart (1966) have studied the effect of starvation, and starvation and refeeding on the molecular species of hepatic phosphatidylcholines as compared to control rats. Although the phosphatidylcholines from the starved animals did not differ appreciably from those in the normal, the results with refed animals showed a large decrease in the saturated-dienoic and saturated-tetraenoic species. Sugano (1973) observed that plasma from fasted rats had only one-half the concentration of 1-saturated 2-linoleoyl phosphatidylcholine as compared to fed rats whereas the tetraenoic and hexaenoic species were not markedly changed. Arvidson (1968b) also observed that the monoenoic, dienoic, and hexaenoic phosphatidylcholines from livers of starved male rats were reduced almost twofold in concentration as compared to fed rats. Imaizumi *et al.* (1973) found the *in vivo* entry of labeled palmitic acid into all molecular species of phosphatidylcholine to be markedly decreased in fasted rats; the incorporation of [14C]-stearic acid into the monoenoic and dienoic species was decreased by fasting while that into the tetraenoic and hexaenoic species was not. It was concluded that specific changes in the turnover of individual fatty acids in hepatic glycerolipids cause the fasting-induced changes in fatty acid composition. Ellingson *et al.* (1970) did not find a significant change in the fatty acid selectivity of the 1-acyl-*sn*-glycero-3-phosphorylcholine acyl transferase in rat liver microsomes with fasting. Arvidson (1968b) did, however, observe an enhanced labeling of the hexaenoic relative to the dienoic phosphatidylcholines in liver following ([14C]methyl)-methionine injection into rats. These results suggest a possible effect of fasting on the *N*-methylation pathway which may be partly responsible for the altered pattern of molecular species in rat liver.

B. Physiological and Pharmacological Factors

Numerous analytical studies have revealed that various physiological and pharmacological factors influence the fatty acid composition of glycerolipids in a variety of tissues. However, only a few of these studies have dealt specifically with individual molecular species of diacylglycerophospholipids.

Wood (1973) has determined the changes in the fatty acid composition of glycerophospholipids of developing chick brain, heart, and liver 10–53 days after incubation. The fatty acid composition of brain phosphoacylglycerols showed the least change, while liver showed the greatest fluctuations. Docosahexaenoic acid and, in most cases, arachidonic acid decreased in the glycerophospholipids with increased development. The decrease in docosahexaenoic acid correlated well with the decreasing mitotic indices of heart and liver cells as development progressed. Comparison of observed lipid patterns between mature and neoplastic tissue with embryonic tissue lipid profiles suggests that some of the observed abnormalities of neoplasma are probably due to changes in lipid metabolism associated with rapidly proliferating cells, whereas other abnormalities appear to be associated with neoplasma. Abad *et al.* (1976) have investigated differences in the composition of the molecular species of the phosphatidylcholines during development of the chick embryo liver and have obtained results comparable to those of Wood (1973). The relative amounts of 1-palmitoyl 2-arachidonoyl species decreased while the 1-stearoyl 2-linoleoyl species increased during embryo development. These changes were attributed to an alteration of the membrane properties of the hepatocyte during this period of growth.

A further indication of tissue specificity and of a hormonal or metabolic regulation of tissue lipid composition comes from studies of sex differences. Arvidson (1968a) compared the distribution of the molecular species of phosphatidylcholines and phosphatidylethanolamines in the livers of male and female rats. The tetraene and hexaene fractions together accounted for 60–65% of the total phosphatidycholine in both males and females, but the proportions between them were different. The livers of the female rats contained more hexaenes and less tetraenes than those of the male rats. Furthermore, the tetraenoic phosphatidylcholines of female rats contained much more stearic than palmitic acid, while in the males there were about equal proportions of the two saturated acids in this fraction.

Lyman *et al.* (1967) also showed that female rats consistently had higher proportions of stearic and arachidonic acids in the phosphatidylcholine from liver. The relative specific activity of this fraction was also higher in females than in males after the intraperitoneal injection of ([^{14}C]-methyl)-methionine (Lyman *et al.,* 1967). It was suggested, therefore, that the higher proportion of stearoyl-arachidonoyl phosphatidylcholine in females might result from methylation of phosphatidylethanolamine which is also enriched in this species in female rats. A significantly higher proportion of the labeled methyl group from methionine found by Arvidson (1968b) in the arachidonoyl and docosahexaenoyl phosphatidylcholines was associated with the 1-stearoyl homologues in females than in males. In subsequent work, Lyman *et al.* (1968) treated castrated male rats with testosterone or estradiol prior to administering ([^{14}C]methyl)-methionine. Estradiol, but not testosterone, was found to increase the contribution of stearoyl-arachidonoyl species to the hepatic phosphatidylcholines. Estradiol also increased the proportion of label from ([^{14}C] methyl)-methionine which entered the tetraenoic species of phosphatidylcholine. It was concluded that estradiol had enhanced the methylation of the corresponding phosphatidylethanolamines. An increased activity of the *N* methyltransferase has been reported in rat liver microsomes following the treatment of castrated male rats with estradiol (Young, 1971).

A few studies have considered the effect of various chemical agents, both foreign and natural, on the structure and metabolism of individual molecular species of diacylglycerophospholipids. Sugano *et al.* (1970) have examined the composition of molecular species of phosphatidylcholines and phosphatidylethanolamines from the livers of control and carbon tetrachloride-treated female rats. An increase in the monoenoic phosphatidylcholines from 6% up to 11% and in the monoenoic phosphatidylethanolamines from 2% up to 9% was observed due to treatment with the chemical agent. Significant decreases in the palmitate/stearate ratio were found with treatment in the monoenoic and hexaenoic classes of both diacylglycerophospholipids. Cho *et al.* (1975) found an increased incorporation of [^{14}C]choline and ([^{14}C]methyl)-methionine into the monoenoic relative to other phosphatidylcholines of treated rats using liver slices. Thus, alterations in the biosynthetic pathways may be partly responsible for the alterations in the molecular species of diacylglycerophospholipids in animals exposed to carbon tetrachloride. B. J. Holub and A. Kuksis (unpublished results, 1970) have studied the effect of ethionine treatment on the composition of the molecular species of the phosphatidylcholines and phosphatidylethanolamines from the livers of female rats. The proportions of monoenoic, dienoic, and trienoic species in both glycerolipids showed increases of two- to threefold with treatment as compared to controls whereas a corresponding reduction was found in the pentaenoic plus hexaenoic molecules of the stressed group. The increase in the monoenoic and dienoic species was due primarily to the 1-stearoyl homologues.

Schacht and Agranoff (1974) have studied the incorporation of ^{32}P into the molecular classes of phosphatidylinositol in guinea pig synaptosomes in the presence of the cholinergic agent carbamylcholine. Whereas the tetraenoic and trienoic species showed a similar stimulation of labeling by this agent, the monoenoic and dienoic species appeared to be much less responsive. Recently, Geison *et al.* (1976) studied the effect of acetylcholine on phosphatidylinositol metabolism in mouse pancreas. Their results indicated that the 1-stearoyl 2-arachidonoyl diacylglycerol backbone of phosphatidylinositol appears in phosphatidic acid during acetylcholine stimulation and is transformed back to phosphatidylinositol on reversion to the unstimulated state.

C. DISEASE STATES

In addition to dietary physiological and pharmacological factors, changes in the composition and metabolism of the diacylglycerophospholipids have been associated with liver regeneration and various disease states. Fex (1971) reported that regenerating rat livers had higher percentages of the monoenoic plus dienoic and lower of the polyenoic species of phosphatidylcholines and phosphatidylethanolamines after partial hepatectomy. However, the fatty acid composition of the isolated subfractions was not greatly affected. A higher incorporation of radioactivity into the monoenoic and dienoic species of the diacylglycerophospholipids was observed in regenerating relative to control livers after the injection of [^{14}C]choline, [^{14}C]ethanolamine, and ([^{14}C]methyl)-methionine. The altered composition of the diacylglycerophospholipids from the regenerating livers was attributed to changes in the composition of the acyl-CoA pool.

It is now well documented that the composition of molecular species of various diacylglycerophospholipids isolated from tumors is markedly different from that of normal tissues of the host animals (reviewed by Wood, 1973; Ruggieri and Fallani, 1973; Bergelson and Dyatlovitskaya, 1973). Examples of these compositional differences are given in Table XIII. The phosphatidylcholines from the Yoshida and Morris hepatomas showed much higher levels of the dioleoyl species as well as the reverse isomers, such as the 1-oleoyl 2-palmitoyl and 1-linoleoyl 2-palmitoyl species, when compared to the host livers.

Table XIII

MAJOR MOLECULAR SPECIES OF PHOSPHATIDYLCHOLINES FROM YOSHIDA HEPATOMA AH130 AND MORRIS HEPATOMA 5123C IN COMPARISON WITH THOSE FROM LIVERS OF TUMOR-BEARING RATS [a]

Molecular species	Fatty acids		Yoshida hepatoma	Host liver [b]	Morris hepatoma	Host liver [c]
	1 Pos.	2 Pos.				
Saturated	14:0	16:0	0.2	—	—	—
	16:0	16:0	2.7	1.9	1.1	1.0
	18:0	16:0	2.2	0.7	0.3	0.3
Monoenes	16:0	18:1	9.1	5.7	21.9	10.5
	16:0	16:1	0.8	0.3	1.4	0.7
	18:0	18:1	4.9	1.7	3.5	2.8
	16:1	16:0	0.7	—	0.2	—
	18:1	16:0	6.9	1.4	5.2	1.6
Dienes	16:0	18:2	13.9	11.8	13.6	14.6
	18:0	18:2	7.5	9.9	5.4	12.6
	18:2	16:0	5.8	1.6	3.6	1.6
	18:1	18:1	5.1	0.7	2.2	1.1
Trienes	18:1	18:2	8.0	1.6	2.3	1.5
	18:2	18:1	3.7	0.9	1.7	0.7
Tetraenes	16:0	20:4	4.4	11.0	10.2	11.0
	18:0	20:4	4.0	13.8	4.0	11.8
	20:4	16:0	—	1.8	—	—
	20:4	18:0	1.1	1.2	0.5	—
Polyenes	16:0	22:polyuns.	1.6	9.2	7.8	6.1
	18:0	22:polyuns.	0.9	9.8	2.1	5.7
	22:polyuns.	16:0	0.6	2.4	1.6	0.9

[a] Reproduced with permission from Ruggieri and Fallani (1973).
[b] Obtained from rats of Wistar strain which were used to maintain Yoshida hepatoma AH130.
[c] Obtained from rats of Buffalo strain which were used to maintain Morris hepatoma 5123C.

Wood (1975) has compared the molecular species composition of hepatoma, host liver and normal rat liver phospholipids on chow and fat-free diets. Diacylglycerols from normal liver phosphatidylcholines of animals fed the fat-free diet contained a higher percentage of lower molecular weight species than liver phosphatidylcholines of chow-fed animals. Host liver phosphatidylcholine of both chow- and fat-free diet fed rats contained a higher percentage of higher molecular weight species than either normal liver or hepatoma phosphatidylcholines. The carbon number distribution of hepatoma phosphatidylcholine was not affected by diet and agreed more closely with that of normal liver phosphatidylcholine than with that of host liver phosphatidylcholine. Determined and calculated (random) carbon number percentages of liver phosphatidylcholine did not agree, although a close agreement was observed for hepatoma phosphatidylcholine. The carbon number distribution of diacylglycerols from phosphatidylethanolamine was dramatically different from phosphatidylcholine diacylglycerols of both liver and hepatoma. In contrast to liver phosphatidylcholine, the fat-free diet caused an elevation in the higher molecular weight species of both normal and host liver phosphatidylethanolamine. Hepatoma phosphatidylethanolamine was not affected by diet and exhibited a carbon number distribution very different from that of liver phosphatidylethanolamine. Again the determined and calculated carbon number distributions for liver phosphatidylethanolamine were not comparable. In contrast, hepatoma phosphatidylethanolamine showed agreement between experimental and random carbon number percentages. Clearly, the hepatoma cell contains less of the molecular species of 20- and 22-carbon polyunsaturated fatty acids in their glycerolipids. In addition, the hepatoma cell glycerolipids are made up of a largely 1-random-2-random distribution of fatty acids, which further reduces the proportion of the molecular species characteristic of normal rat liver cells. The biochemical basis of these changes in the molecular species composition of the tumor and normal cells remains to be investigated as does the influence of such alterations on membrane structure and function.

Since the neoplastic process is believed to be associated with abnormalities in the physical structure of cell membranes, Burns et al. (1977) have investigated the effect of dietary lipids of various degrees of saturation on the composition of L1210 murine leukemia cells. The results indicate that the fatty acid saturation and turnover of the cell phospholipids can be altered appreciably. Although the molecular species of the glycerophospholipids were not specifically analyzed it was obvious that it may be possible to alter the physical properties and function of tumor cell membranes by dietary modification of the phospholipid composition. On the basis of these studies and a review of the literature, Burns et al. (1977)

have concluded that it would be worthwhile to explore the possible therapeutic implications of fatty acid modifications using this experimental tumor
system.

VI. Summary and Conclusions

Recent advances in analytical methods have permitted complete determinations of the molecular composition of the natural diacylglycerophospholipids. Extensive analyses have revealed a highly specific pairing of
certain fatty acids within most diacylglycerophospholipid classes as isolated
from different animal species, tissues, and subcellular fractions. Analytical
data on the molecular compositions of diacylglycerophospholipids from
corresponding tissues of different animal species have provided indirect
evidence for a specific physiological role of individual or small groups of
molecular species of glycerophospholipids. The selective participation of
certain molecular species of diacylglycerophospholipids in a number of
biochemical reactions has also become well recognized. Furthermore,
individual molecular species of the glycerophospholipids have been shown
to possess striking differences in their physicochemical properties and
much effort has been directed towards correlating the lipid composition of
membranes with various physiological functions. A clear understanding of
the biological function of phospholipids based on their physicochemical
properties, however, is not yet possible although such factors as membrane
fluidity, compressibility, and permeability would appear to be clearly involved. It is unfortunate that many of the physicochemical investigations
have been conducted with mixtures of molecular species or with molecular
species which are not major constituents of natural membranes or lipoproteins.

Detailed investigations of the metabolism of the molecular species of
different glycerophospholipid types have revealed remarkable differences
in the biochemical pathways involved in their formation and in the rates
at which they are subsequently utilized. Each of the pathways would appear
to give rise to a characteristic complement of molecular species of diacylglycerophospholipids. The quantitative contribution of each pathway to the
total turnover of each molecular species shows tissue and animal species
differences. The physiological and metabolic significance of these transformations, however, remains obscure. Furthermore, much of the work on
the metabolism of the molecular species of glycerophospholipids has been
done with rat liver and the results obtained may not apply fully to other

tissues and other animal species. Nevertheless, there is clear-cut evidence that the metabolism of the molecular species of the glycerophospholipids is intimately involved with the activity of the acyl transferases. Their potential involvement in the control of membrane fluidity is obvious as is their role in the retention of the essential fatty acids in the diacylglycerophospholipid molecules. However, a special metabolic role for the lysoglycerophospholipids also appears to be emerging and the acyl transferases are involved in controlling their levels.

It would appear that promising approaches for further work in this area would lie in the identification of the mechanisms responsible for the control of the composition and turnover of the various molecular species of the glycerophospholipids. The isolation and characterization of fatty acid requiring mutants of cultured mammalian cells should be helpful in identifying the biological role of specific molecular species. Furthermore, work with uniform cultures of mammalian cells should allow a better experimental and statistical control of the results. Likewise, studies with synchronized cell cultures would permit the assessment of the effect of the cell cycle on the metabolism of molecular species of the glycerophospholipids. Hopefully such studies could be combined with the use of stable isotopes so that the exact structure, distribution, and pool size of the newly synthesized molecules can be simultaneously determined along with the structure, distribution, and pool size of the old molecules. Computer analyses of the data currently provided by combined applications of gas–liquid or liquid chromatography and mass spectrometry would appear adequate for this purpose, provided these methods are preceded by appropriate subcellular fractionations. Such studies would vastly expand our knowledge and hopefully our understanding of the metabolism of molecular species of glycerolipids and of their role in the biology of the cell.

The practical significance of detailed analyses of the molecular species of the diacylglycerophospholipids rests with the biological importance of the structure and function of the lipid phase of cell membranes and lipoproteins. There is good evidence that the glycerolipid composition of cell membranes and lipoproteins is metabolically adjusted to meet specific requirements and that it does not merely reflect the supply of different fatty acids in the diet or in the cell culture medium. Adequate adjustment, however, may not always be possible, and under such conditions the cellular activity would presumably take place in a suboptimal physicochemical environment, and characteristic symptoms of a disease state may appear. Since the cellular lipid composition is subject to considerable dietary and pharmacological manipulation, the possibility must be considered that therapeutic alterations in the composition of the molecular species of the glycerolipids may be feasible and may yield beneficial results in the treatment of membrane diseases.

ACKNOWLEDGMENTS

The authors' research described here was supported by grants from the Medical Research Council of Canada and the Ontario Heart Foundation. The Department of Nutrition, University of Guelph, provided partial assistance in typing of the manuscript.

References

Abad, C., Basch, M. A., Municio, A. M., and Ribera, A. (1976). *Biochim. Biophys. Acta* **431**, 62.

Abe, M., Ohno, K., and Sato, R. (1974). *Biochim. Biophys. Acta* **369**, 361.

Abrahamson, S., and Ryderstedt-Nahringbauer, I. (1962). *Acta Crystallogr.* **15**, 1261.

Admirand, W. H., and Small, D. M. (1968). *J. Clin. Invest.* **47**, 1043.

Agranoff, B. W., Bradley, R. M., and Brady, R. O. (1958). *J. Biol. Chem.* **233**, 1077.

Ahmed, S., and Walker, B. L. (1972). *Biochim. Biophys. Acta* **255**, 815.

Akesson, B. (1969). *Eur. J. Biochem.* **9**, 463.

Akesson, B. (1970). *Biochim. Biophys. Acta* **218**, 57.

Akesson, B. (1977). *Biochem. Biophys. Res. Commun.* **76**, 93.

Akesson, B., Elovson, J., and Arvidson, G. (1970a). *Biochim. Biophys. Acta* **210**, 15.

Akesson, B., Elovson, J., and Arvidson, G. (1970b). *Biochim. Biophys. Acta* **218**, 44.

Akesson, B., Sundler, R., and Nilsson, A. (1976a). *Eur. J. Biochem.* **63**, 65.

Akesson, B., Arner, A., and Sundler, R. (1976b). *Biochim. Biophys. Acta* **441**, 453.

Akino, T., and Shimojo, T. (1970). *Biochim. Biophys. Acta* **210**, 343.

Akino, T., Abe, M., and Arai, T. (1971). *Biochim. Biophys. Acta* **248**, 274.

Alexander, A. E. (1941). *Trans. Faraday Soc.* **37**, 426.

Anderson, P. J., and Pethica, B. A. (1956). *Trans. Faraday Soc.* **52**, 1.

Anonymous (1967). *J. Lipid Res.* **8**, 523.

Ansell, G. B. (1973). *In* "Form and Function of Phospholipids" (G. B. Ansell, R. M. C. Dawson, and J. N. Hawthorne, eds.), 2nd ed., p. 377. Elsevier, Amsterdam.

Ansell, G. B., and Metcalfe, R. F. (1971). *J. Neurochem.* **18**, 647.

Arvidson, G. A. E. (1965). *J. Lipid Res.* **6**, 574.

Arvidson, G. A. E. (1967). *J. Lipid Res.* **8**, 155.

Arvidson, G. A. E. (1968a). *Eur. J. Biochem.* **4**, 478.

Arvidson, G. A. E. (1968b). *Eur. J. Biochem.* **5**, 415.

Arvidson, G. A. E., and Nilsson, A. (1972). *Lipids* **7**, 344.

Atherton, R. W., and Hawthorne, J. N. (1968). *Eur. J. Biochem.* **4**, 68.

Baer, E. (1963). *Prog. Chem. Fats Other Lipids* **6**, 33.

Baer, E., and Fischer, H. O. L. (1939). *J. Biol. Chem.* **123**, 475.

Baker, H. N., Delahaunty, T., Gotto, A. M., and Jackson, R. L. (1974). *Proc. Natl. Acad. Sci. U.S.A.* **71**, 3631.

Baker, N., and Lynén, F. (1971). *Eur. J. Biochem.* **19**, 200.

Baker, R. R., and Thompson, W. (1972). *Biochim. Biophys. Acta* **270**, 489.

Baker, R. R., and Thompson, W. (1973). *J. Biol. Chem.* **248**, 7060.

Balint, J. A., Kyriakides, E. C., Spitzer, H. L., and Morrison, E. S. (1965). *J. Lipid Res.* **6,** 96.

Balint, J. A., Beeler, D. A., Treble, D. H., and Spitzer, H. L. (1967). *J. Lipid Res.* **8,** 486.

Bangham, A. D. (1972). *Annu. Rev. Biochem.* **41,** 753.

Baranska, J., and Van Golde, L. M. G. (1977). *Biochim. Biophys. Acta* **488,** 285.

Barden, N., and Labrie, F. (1973). *J. Biol. Chem.* **248,** 7601.

Barden, R. E., and Cleland, W. W. (1969). *J. Biol. Chem.* **244,** 3677.

Barratt, M. D., Austin, J. P., and Whitehurst, R. J. (1974). *Biochim. Biophys. Acta* **348,** 126.

Beeler, D. A., Treble, D. H., Kyriakides, E. C., and Balint, J. A. (1970). *Biochim. Biophys. Acta* **218,** 112.

Benjamins, J. A., and Agranoff, B. W. (1969). *J. Neurochem.* **16,** 513.

Benson, A. A. (1966). *J. Am. Oil Chem. Soc.* **43,** 265.

Bergelson, L. D., and Dyatlovitskaya, E. V. (1973). *In* "Tumor Lipids: Biochemistry and Metabolism" (R. Wood, ed.), p. 111. Am. Oil Chem. Soc. Press, Champaign, Illinois.

Birnbaumer, L. (1973). *Biochim. Biophys. Acta* **300,** 129.

Bishop, H. H., and Strickland, K. P. (1970). *Can. J. Biochem.* **48,** 269.

Bishop, H. H., and Strickland, K. P. (1976). *Can. J. Biochem.* **54,** 249.

Bjerve, K. S. (1971). *FEBS Lett.* **17,** 14.

Bjerve, K. S. (1973a). *Biochim. Biophys. Acta* **296,** 549.

Bjerve, K. S. (1973b). *Biochim. Biophys. Acta* **306,** 396.

Bjerve, K. S., Daae, L. N. W., and Bremer, J. (1976). *Biochem. J.* **158,** 249.

Bjornstad, P., and Bremer, J. (1966). *J. Lipid Res.* **7,** 38.

Blank, M. L., Wykle, R. L., and Snyder, F. (1973). *Biochim. Biophys. Acta* **316,** 28.

Borkenhagen, L. F., Kennedy, E. P., and Fielding, L. (1961). *J. Biol. Chem.* **236,** PC28.

Bottino, N. R., Vandenburg, G. A., and Reiser, R. (1967). *Lipids* **2,** 489.

Bourges, M., Small, D. M., and Dervichian, D. G. (1967). *Biochim. Biophys. Acta* **144,** 189.

Brammer, M. J., and Sheltawy, A. (1975). *J. Neurochem.* **25,** 699.

Brandt, A. E., and Lands, W. E. M. (1967). *Biochim. Biophys. Acta* **144,** 605.

Breckenridge, W. C., Gombos, G., and Morgan, I. G. (1972). *Biochim. Biophys. Acta* **266,** 695.

Bremer, J., and Greenberg, D. M. (1961). *Biochim. Biophys. Acta* **46,** 205.

Bremer, J., Figard, P. H., and Greenberg, D. M. (1960). *Biochim. Biophys. Acta* **43,** 477.

Brewer, H. B., Lux, S. E., Ronan, R., and John, K. M. (1972a). *Proc. Natl. Acad. Sci. U.S.A.* **69,** 1304.

Brewer, H. B., Shulman, R., Herbert, P., Ronan, R., and Wehrly, K. (1972b). *Adv. Exp. Biol. Med.* **26,** 280.

Brivio-Haugland, R. P., Louis, S. L., Musch, K., Waldeck, N., and Williams, M. A. (1976). *Biochim. Biophys. Acta* **433,** 150.

Brockerhoff, H. (1965). *J. Lipid Res.* **6,** 10.

Brockerhoff, H. (1975). *In* "Methods in Enzymology" (J. M. Lowenstein, ed.), Vol. 35, Part B, p. 315. Academic Press, New York.

Brockerhoff, H., and Jensen, R. G. (1974). *In* "Lipolytic Enzymes" (H. Brockerhoff and R. G. Jensen, eds.), p. 197. Academic Press, New York.

Bromley, G., and Van Den Bosch, H. (1977). *J. Lipid Res.* **18,** 523.

Burns, C. P., Luttenegger, D. G., Wei, S-P. L., and Spector, A. A. (1977). *Lipids* **12,** 747.
Butler, M. M., and Thompson, W. (1975). *Biochim. Biophys. Acta* **388,** 52.
Cadenhead, D. A., Demchak, R. J., and Phillips, M. C. (1967). *Kolloid Z. & Z. Polym.* **22,** 59.
Camejo, G., Suarez, Z. M., and Muñoz, V. (1970). *Biochim. Biophys. Acta* **218,** 155.
Carter, J. R., and Kennedy, E. P. (1966). *J. Lipid Res.* **7,** 678.
Chang, M., and Dalluu, C. E. (1967). *Biochem. Biophys. Res. Commun.* **26,** 199.
Chapman, D. (1973). In "Form and Function of Phospholipids" (G. B. Ansell, R. M. C. Dawson, and J. N. Hawthorne, eds.), 2nd ed., p. 117. Elsevier, Amsterdam.
Chapman, D. (1975). *Q. Rev. Biophys.* **8,** 185.
Chapman, D., and Leslie, R. B. (1970). In "Membranes of Mitochondria and Chloroplasts" (E. Racker, ed.), p. 91. Van Nostrand-Reinhold, Princeton, New Jersey.
Chapman, D., Owens, N. F., and Walker, D. A. (1966). *Biochim. Biophys. Acta* **120,** 148.
Chapman, D., Williams, R. M., and Ladbrooke, B. D. (1967). *Chem. Phys. Lipids* **1,** 445.
Chen, S., and Lombardi, B. (1973a). *Nutr. Rep. Int.* **8,** 95.
Chen, S., and Lombardi, B. (1973b). *Lipids* **8,** 163.
Cho, S., Sugano, M., and Wada, M. (1975). *J. Agric. Chem. Soc. Jpn.* **49,** 21.
Christie, W. W. (1973). *Biochim. Biophys. Acta* **316,** 204.
Christie, W. W., and Moore, J. H. (1970). *Biochim. Biophys. Acta* **210,** 46.
Christie, W. W., Moore, J. H., Noble, R. C., and Vernon, R. G. (1975). *Lipids* **10,** 645.
Clements, J. A., Husted, R. F., Johnson, R. P., and Gribetz, I. (1961). *J. Appl. Physiol.* **16,** 444.
Cogan, U., Shinitzky, M., Weber, G., and Hishida, T. (1973). *Biochemistry* **12,** 521.
Colbeau, A., Nachbaur, J., and Vignais, P. M. (1971). *Biochim. Biophys. Acta* **249,** 462.
Coleman, R. (1973). *Biochim. Biophys. Acta* **300,** 1.
Coleman, R., and Bell, R. M. (1977). *J. Biol. Chem.* **252,** 3050.
Collins, F. D. (1960). *Nature (London)* **186,** 366.
Collins, F. D. (1962). *Biochem. Biophys. Res. Commun.* **9,** 289.
Collins, F. D. (1963). *Biochem. J.* **88,** 319.
Collins, F. D. (1964). In "New Biochemical Separations" (A. T. James and L. J. Morris, eds.), p. 379. Van Nostrand-Reinhold, Princeton, New Jersey.
Collins, F. D., de Pury, G. G., Havlicek, M., and Lim, C.-S. (1971). *Chem. Phys. Lipids* **7,** 144.
Colodzin, M., and Kennedy, E. P. (1965). *J. Biol. Chem.* **240,** 3771.
Cooper, P. H., and Hawthorne, J. N. (1975). *Biochem. J.* **150,** 537.
Courtade, S., Marinetti, G. V., and Stotz, E. (1967). *Biochim. Biophys. Acta* **137,** 121.
Craven, B. M. (1959). *J. Phys. Chem.* **63,** 1296.
Curstedt, T. (1974). *Biochim. Biophys. Acta* **369,** 196.
Curstedt, T., and Sjovall, J. (1974a). *Biochim. Biophys. Acta* **360,** 24.
Curstedt, T., and Sjovall, J. (1974b). *Biochim. Biophys. Acta* **369,** 173.
Daae, L. N. W. (1972). *Biochim. Biophys. Acta* **270,** 23.
Daae, L. N. W., and Bremer, J. (1970). *Biochim. Biophys. Acta* **210,** 92.
Danielli, J. F., and Davson, H. (1935). *J. Cell. Comp. Physiol.* **5,** 495.
Das, M. L., Hiratsuka, H., Machinist, J. M., and Crane, F. L. (1962). *Biochim. Biophys. Acta* **60,** 433.

Davidson, J. B., and Stanacev, N. Z. (1970). *Can. J. Biochem.* **48,** 633.
Davidson, J. B., and Stanacev, N. Z. (1971). *Biochem. Biophys. Res. Commun.* **42,** 1191.
Davidson, J. B., and Stanacev, N. Z. (1972). *Can. J. Biochem.* **50,** 936.
Davidson, J. B., and Stanacev, N. Z. (1974). *Can. J. Biochem.* **52,** 936.
Dawson, R. M. C. (1973). *Sub-Cell. Biochem.* **2,** 69.
Dawson, R. M. C., and Thompson, W. (1964). *Biochem. J.* **91,** 244.
Deamer, D. W. (1970). *Bioenergetics* **1,** 237.
de Bernard, L. (1958). *Bull. Soc. Chim. Biol.* **40,** 161.
De Bruijn, J. H. (1966). *Br. J. Vener. Dis.* **42,** 125.
de Haas, G. H., Daemen, F. J. M., and van Deenen, L. L. M. (1962). *Biochim. Biophys. Acta* **65,** 260.
De Kruyff, B., Van Golde, L. M. G., and van Deenen, L. L. M. (1970). *Biochim. Biophys. Acta* **210,** 425.
Demel, R. A., van Deenen, L. L. M., and Pethica, B. A. (1967). *Biochim. Biophys. Acta* **135,** 11.
Demel, R. A., Geurts Van Kessel, W. S. M., and van Deenen, L. L. M. (1972a). *Biochim. Biophys. Acta* **266,** 26.
Demel, R. A., Bruckdorfer, K. R., and van Deenen, L. L. M. (1972b). *Biochim. Biophys. Acta* **255,** 311.
Dennis, E. A., and Kennedy, E. P. (1972). *J. Lipid Res.* **13,** 263.
de Pury, G. G., and Collins, F. D. (1966). *Chem. Phys. Lipids* **1,** 1.
de Pury, G. G., and Collins, F. D. (1972). *Lipids* **7,** 225.
Dervichian, D. G., and Joly, M. (1939). *J. Phys. Radium* **10,** 375.
de Titta, G. T., and Craven, B. M. (1973). *Acta Crystallogr., Sect. B* **29,** 1354.
De Tomas, M. E., and Brenner, R. R. (1970). *Biochim. Biophys. Acta* **202,** 184.
Deuticke, B., and Gruber, W. (1970). *Biochim. Biophys. Acta* **211,** 369.
Dils, R. R., and Hubscher, G. (1961). *Biochim. Biophys. Acta* **46,** 505.
diLuzio, N. R. (1972). *Adv. Lipid Res.* **10,** 43.
Eibl, H., Hill, E. E., and Lands, W. E. M. (1969). *Eur. J. Biochem.* **9,** 250.
Eichberg, J. (1974). *J. Biol. Chem.* **249,** 3423.
Ellingson, J. S., Hill, E. E., and Lands, W. E. M. (1970). *Biochim. Biophys. Acta* **196,** 176.
Elovson, J. (1965). *Biochim. Biophys. Acta* **106,** 291.
Engelman, D. M. (1970). *J. Mol. Biol.* **47,** 115.
Engelman, D. M., and Rothman, J. E. (1972). *J. Biol. Chem.* **247,** 3694.
Engle, M. J., Saunders, R. L., and Longmore, W. J. (1976). *Arch. Biochem. Biophys.* **173,** 586.
Erbland, J. F., and Marinetti, G. V. (1965a). *Biochim. Biophys. Acta* **106,** 128.
Erbland, J. F., and Marinetti, G. V. (1965b). *Biochim. Biophys. Acta* **106,** 139.
Esfahani, M., Limbrick, A. R., Knuttons, S., Oka, T., and Wakil, S. J. (1971). *Proc. Natl. Acad. Sci. U.S.A.* **68,** 3180.
Farias, R. N., Bloj, B., Morero, R. D., Sineriz, F., and Trucco, R. E. (1975). *Biochim. Biophys. Acta* **415,** 231.
Faure, M., and Coulon-Morelec, M.-J. (1963). *Ann. Inst. Pasteur, Paris* **104,** 246.
Fex, G. (1971). *Biochim. Biophys. Acta* **231,** 161.
Finean, J. B. (1973). *In* "Form and Function of Phospholipids" (G. B. Ansell, R. M. C. Dawson, and J. N. Hawthorne, eds.), 2nd ed., p. 171. Elsevier, Amsterdam.
Fischer, H. O. L., and Baer, E. (1941). *Chem. Rev.* **29,** 287.
Fleming, P. J., and Hajra, A. K. (1977). *J. Biol. Chem.* **252,** 1663.

Fourcans, B., and Jain, M. K. (1974). *Adv. Lipid Res.* **12**, 147.
Fox, C. F. (1972). *In* "Membrane Molecular Biology" (C. F. Fox and A. D. Keith, eds.), p. 345. Sinauer Assoc., Stamford, Connecticut.
Friedel, R. O., Brown, J. D., and Durrell, J. (1969). *J. Neurochem.* **16**, 371.
Frosolono, M. F., Charms, B. L., Pawlowski, R., and Slivka, S. (1970). *J. Lipid Res.* **11**, 439.
Frosolono, M. F., Slivka, S., and Charms, B. L. (1971). *J. Lipid Res.* **12**, 96.
Fütter, J. H., and Shorland, F. B. (1957). *Biochem. J.* **65**, 689.
Gallagher, N., Webb, J., and Dawson, A. M. (1965). *Clin. Sci.* **29**, 73.
Gally, H.-U., Niederberger, W., and Seelig, J. (1975). *Biochemistry* **14**, 3647.
Garland, R. C., and Cori, C. F. (1972). *Biochemistry* **11**, 4712.
Gazzotti, P., Bock, H. G., and Fleischer, S. (1974). *Biochem. Biophys. Res. Commun.* **58**, 309.
Geison, R. L., Banschbach, M. W., Sadeghian, K., and Hokin-Neaverson, M. (1976). *Biochem. Biophys. Res. Commun.* **68**, 343.
Ghosh, D., and Tinoco, J. (1972). *Biochim. Biophys. Acta* **266**, 41.
Ghosh, D., Williams, M. A., and Tinoco, J. (1973). *Biochim. Biophys. Acta* **291**, 351.
Gibson, K. D., Wilson, J. D., and Udenfriend, S. (1961). *J. Biol. Chem.* **236**, 673.
Gitler, C. (1972). *Annu. Rev. Biophys. Bioeng.* **1**, 51.
Glenn, J. L., and Austin, W. (1971). *Biochim. Biophys. Acta* **231**, 153.
Glomset, J. A. (1968). *J. Lipid Res.* **9**, 155.
Glomset, J. A., Janssen, E. T., Kennedy, R., and Dobbins, J. (1966). *J. Lipid Res.* **7**, 638.
Godinez, R. I., Sanders, R. L., and Longmore, W. J. (1975). *Biochemistry* **14**, 830.
Guerke, J. (1974). *Biochim. Biophys. Acta* **344**, 241.
Gornall, D. A., and Kuksis, A. (1971). *Can. J. Biochem.* **49**, 51.
Gornall, D. A., and Kuksis, A. (1973). *J. Lipid Res.* **14**, 197.
Gray, G. M., and MacFarlane, M. G. (1961). *Biochem. J.* **81**, 480.
Gregory, D. H., Vlahcevic, Z. R., Schatzki, P., and Swell, L. (1975). *J. Clin. Invest.* **55**, 105.
Grigor, M. R., Blank, M. L., and Snyder, F. (1971). *Lipids* **6**, 965.
Grover, A. K., Slotboom, A. J., de Haas, G. H., and Hammes, G. G. (1975). *J. Biol. Chem.* **250**, 31.
Guarnieri, M., and Johnson, R. M. (1970). *Adv. Lipid Res.* **8**, 115.
Gurr, M. I., and Brawn, P. (1970). *Eur. J. Biochem.* **17**, 19.
Hagen, P.-O. (1971). *Lipids* **6**, 935.
Hajra, A. K. (1968). *J. Biol. Chem.* **243**, 3458.
Hajra, A. K., and Agranoff, B. W. (1968). *J. Biol. Chem.* **243**, 3542.
Hallman, M., and Gluck, L. (1974). *Biochem. Biophys. Res. Commun.* **60**, 1.
Hallman, M., and Gluck, L. (1976). *J. Lipid Res.* **17**, 257.
Hanahan, D. J., Brockerhoff, H., and Barron, E. J. (1960). *J. Biol. Chem.* **235**, 1917.
Harris, P. M., Robinson, D. S., and Getz, G. (1960). *Nature (London)* **188**, 742.
Hasegawa, K., and Suzuki, T. (1975). *Lipids* **10**, 667.
Hasegawa-Sasaki, H., and Ohno, K. (1975). *Biochim. Biophys. Acta* **380**, 486.
Hawke, J. C. (1959). *Biochem. J.* **71**, 588.
Hawthorne, J. N. (1973). *In* "Form and Function of Phospholipids" (G. B. Ansell, R. M. C. Dawson, and J. N. Hawthorne, eds.), 2nd ed., p. 423. Elsevier, Amsterdam.
Haye, B., Champion, S., and Jacquemin, C. (1973). *FEBS Lett.* **30**, 253.
Hendry, A. T., and Possmayer, F. (1974). *Biochim. Biophys. Acta* **369**, 156.

Hilditch, T. P. (1940). "The Chemical Constitution of Natural Fats," 1st ed. Chapman & Hall, London.
Hill, E. E., and Lands, W. E. M. (1968). *Biochim. Biophys. Acta* **152**, 645.
Hill, E. E., and Lands, W. E. M. (1970). *In* "Lipid Metabolism" (S. J. Wakil, ed.), p. 185. Academic Press, New York.
Hill, E. E., Husbands, D. R., and Lands, W. E. M. (1968a). *J. Biol. Chem.* **243**, 4440.
Hill, E. E., Lands, W. E. M., and Slakey, S. P. M. (1968b). *Lipids* **3**, 411.
Hinz, H.-J., and Sturtevant, J. M. (1972). *J. Biol. Chem.* **247**, 3697.
Hofmann, A. F., and Borgström, B. (1962). *Fed. Proc., Fed. Am. Soc. Exp. Biol.* **21**, 43.
Hokin, M. R., and Hokin, L. E. (1959). *J. Biol. Chem.* **234**, 1381.
Hokin-Neaverson, M., Sadeghian, K., Harris, D. W., and Merrin, J. S. (1977). *Biochem. Biophys. Res. Commun.* **78**, 364
Holloway, C. T., and Holloway, P. W. (1974). *Lipids* **9**, 196.
Holub, B. J. (1974). *Biochim. Biophys. Acta* **369**, 111.
Holub, B. J. (1975). *Lipids* **10**, 483.
Holub, B. J. (1976). *Lipids* **11**, 1
Holub, B. J. (1977). *Can. J. Biochem.* **55**, 700.
Holub, B. J. (1978). *J. Biol. Chem.* **253**. (In press).
Holub, B. J., and Kuksis, A. (1969). *Lipids* **4**, 466.
Holub, B. J., and Kuksis, A. (1971a). *J. Lipid Res.* **12**, 699.
Holub, B. J., and Kuksis, A. (1971b). *Can. J. Biochem.* **49**, 1005.
Holub, B. J., and Kuksis, A. (1971c). *Can. J. Biochem.* **49**, 1347.
Holub, B. J., and Kuksis, A. (1972). *Lipids* **7**, 78.
Holub, B. J., and Piekarski, J. (1976). *Lipids* **11**, 251.
Holub, B. J., Kuksis, A., and Thompson, W. (1970). *J. Lipid Res.* **11**, 558.
Holub, B. J., Breckenridge, W. C., and Kuksis, A. (1971). *Lipids* **5**, 307.
Hostetler, K. Y., and Van Den Bosch, H. (1972). *Biochim. Biophys. Acta* **260**, 380.
Hostetler, K. Y., Van Den Bosch, H., and van Deenen, L. L. M. (1971). *Biochim. Biophys. Acta* **239**, 113.
Hostetler, K. Y., Galesloot, J. M., Boer, P., and Van Den Bosch, H. (1975). *Biochim. Biophys. Acta* **380**, 382.
Houtsmuller, U. M. T., Van Der Beek, A., and Zaalberg, J. (1969). *Lipids* **4**, 571.
Hubscher, G. (1962). *Biochim. Biophys. Acta* **57**, 555.
Hubscher, G. (1970). *In* "Lipid Metabolism" (S. J. Wakil, ed.), p. 279. Academic Press, New York.
Hunter, M. L., Christie, W. W., and Moore, J. H. (1973). *Lipids* **8**, 65.
Husbands, D. R. (1970). *Biochem. J.* **120**, 365.
Illingworth, D. R., and Portman, O. W. (1972a). *J. Lipid Res.* **13**, 220.
Illingworth, D. R., and Portman, O. W. (1972b). *Biochim. Biophys. Acta* **280**, 281.
Imai, R. H., Reiser, S., and Christiansen, P. A. (1970). *J. Nutr.* **100**, 101.
Imaizumi, K., Yamamoto, M., and Sugano, M. (1973). *J. Nutr. Sci. Vitaminol.* **19**, 419.
Inoue, K., and Nojima, S. (1967). *Biochim. Biophys. Acta* **144**, 409.
Inoue, K., and Nojima, S. (1969). *Chem. Phys. Lipids* **3**, 70.
Isozaki, M., Yamamoto, A., Amako, T., Sakai, Y., and Okita, H. (1962). *Med. J. Osaka Univ.* **12**, 285.
Jackson, R. L., Morrisett, J. D., and Gotto, A. M., Jr. (1976). *Physiol. Rev.* **56**, 259.
Jesse, R. L., and Cohen, P. (1976). *Biochem. J.* **158**, 283.
Johns, J. T., and Bergen, W. G. (1974). *J. Nutr.* **104**, 300.

Johnston, J. M., Rao, G. A., Lowe, P. A., and Schwartz, B. E. (1967). *Lipids* **2**, 14.
Johnston, J. M., Paultauf, F., Schiller, C. M., and Schultz, L. D. (1970). *Biochim. Biophys. Acta* **218**, 124.
Jonas, A., Krajnovich, D. J., and Patterson, B. W. (1977). *J. Biol. Chem.* **252**, 2200.
Jost, P. C., Griffith, O. H., Capaldi, R. A., and Vanderkooi, G. (1973). *Proc. Natl. Acad. Sci. U.S.A.* **70**, 480.
Jungalwala, F. B., Freinkel, N., and Dawson, R. M. C. (1971). *Biochem. J.* **123**, 19.
Jurtshuk, P., Sekuzu, I., and Green, D. E. (1961). *Biochem. Biophys. Res. Commun.* **6**, 76.
Kagawa, Y., Kandrach, A., and Racker, E. (1973). *J. Biol. Chem.* **248**, 676.
Kai, M., White, G. L., and Hawthorne, J. N. (1966). *Biochem. J.* **101**, 328.
Kamp, H. H., Wirtz, K. W. A., Baer, P. R., Slotboom, A. J., Rosenthal, A. F., Paltauf, F., and van Deenen, L. L. M. (1977). *Biochemistry* **16**, 1310.
Kanfer, J. N. (1972). *J. Lipid Res.* **13**, 468.
Kanoh, H. (1969). *Biochim. Biophys. Acta* **176**, 756.
Kanoh, H. (1970). *Biochim. Biophys. Acta* **218**, 249.
Kanoh, H., and Akesson, B. (1977). *Biochim. Biophys. Acta* **488**, 311.
Kanoh, H., and Ohno, K. (1973a). *Biochim. Biophys. Acta* **306**, 203.
Kanoh, H., and Ohno, K. (1973b). *Biochim. Biophys. Acta* **326**, 17.
Kanoh, H., and Ohno, K. (1975). *Biochim. Biophys. Acta* **380**, 199.
Kataoka, T., and Nojima, S. (1970). *J. Immunol.* **105**, 502.
Keenan, R. W., and Hokin, L. E. (1964). *J. Biol. Chem.* **239**, 2123.
Keenan, R. W., and Morré, P. J. (1970). *Biochemistry* **9**, 19
Kennedy, E. P. (1961). *Fed. Proc., Fed. Am. Soc. Exp. Biol.* **20**, 934.
Kennedy, E. P., and Weiss, S. B. (1956). *J. Biol. Chem.* **222**, 193.
Keough, K. M. W., and Thompson, W. (1972). *Biochim. Biophys. Acta* **270**, 324.
Keough, K. M. W., MacDonald, G., and Thompson, W. (1972). *Biochim. Biophys. Acta* **270**, 337.
Kimelberg, H. K. and Papahadjopoulos, D. (1972). *Biochim. Biophys. Acta* **282**, 277.
Kimelberg, H. K., and Papahadjopoulos, D. (1974). *J. Biol. Chem.* **249**, 1071.
King, R. J., and Clements, J. A. (1972). *Am. J. Physiol.* **223**, 715.
King, R. J., Klass, D. J., Gikas, E. G., and Clements, J. A. (1973). *Am. J. Physiol.* **224**, 788.
Kinsky, S. C. (1972). *Biochim. Biophys. Acta* **265**, 1.
Kiss, Z. (1976). *Eur. J. Biochem.* **67**, 557.
Kiyasu, J. Y., Pieringer, R. A., Paulus, H., and Kennedy, E. P. (1963). *J. Biol. Chem.* **238**, 2293.
Klaus, M. H., Clements, J. A., and Havel, R. J. (1961). *Proc. Natl. Acad. Sci. U.S.A.* **47**, 1858.
Klenk, E., and Bohm, P. (1951). *Hoppe Seyler's Z. Physiol. Chem.* **288**, 98.
Kolata, G. B. (1975). *Science* **190**, 770.
Kuksis, A. (1965). *J. Am. Oil Chem. Soc.* **42**, 269.
Kuksis, A. (1972). *Prog. Chem. Fats Other Lipids* **12**, 1.
Kuksis, A. (1978). *In* "Handbook of Lipid Research" (D. J. Hanahan, ed.), Vol. 1 (A. Kuksis, ed.). Plenum Press, New York (in press).
Kuksis, A., and Marai, L. (1967). *Lipids* **2**, 217.
Kuksis, A., and Myher, J. J. (1976). *In* "Lipids" (R. Paoletti, G. Porcellati, and G. Jacini, eds.), Vol. 1, pp. 23–38. Raven Press, New York.
Kuksis, A., Marai, L., Breckenridge, W. C., Gornall, D. A., and Stachnyk, O. (1968). *Can. J. Physiol. Pharmacol.* **46**, 511.

Kuksis, A., Myher, J. J., Marai, L., Yeung, S. K. F. Steiman, I., and Mookerjea, S. (1975a). *Can. J. Biochem.* **53,** 509.

Kuksis, A., Myher, J. J., Marai, L., Yeung, S. K. F., Steiman, I., and Mookerjea, S. (1975b). *Can. J. Biochem.* **53,** 519.

Kunze, H., and Vogt, W. (1971). *Ann. N.Y. Acad. Sci.* **180,** 123.

Kyei-Aboagye, K., Rubinstein, D., and Beck, J. C. (1973). *Can. J. Biochem.* **51,** 1581.

Kyriakides, E. C., Beeler, D. A., Edmonds, R. H., and Balint, J. A. (1976). *Biochim. Biophys. Acta* **431,** 399.

La Belle, E. F., Jr., and Hajra, A. K. (1972). *J. Biol. Chem.* **247,** 5835.

Ladbrooke, B. D., Williams, R. M., and Chapman, D. (1968). *Biochim. Biophys. Acta* **150,** 333.

Lamb, R. G., and Fallon, H. J. (1970). *J. Biol. Chem.* **245,** 3075.

Lands, W. E. M. (1960). *J. Biol. Chem.* **235,** 2233.

Lands, W. E. M. (1965). *Annu. Rev. Biochem.* **34,** 313.

Lands, W. E. M., and Hart, P. (1965). *J. Biol. Chem.* **240,** 1905.

Lands, W. E. M., and Hart, P. (1966). *J. Am. Oil Chem. Soc.* **43,** 290.

Lands, W. E. M., and Merkl, I. (1963). *J. Biol. Chem.* **238,** 898.

Lands, W. E. M., and Samuelsson, B. (1968). *Biochim. Biophys. Acta* **164,** 426.

Langmuir, I. (1917). *J. Am. Chem. Soc.* **39,** 1848.

Lapetina, E. G., and Hawthorne, J. N. (1971). *Biochem. J.* **122,** 171.

Lapetina, E. G., and Michell, R. H. (1973). *Biochem. J.* **131,** 433.

Lapetina, E. G., Schmitges, C. J., Chandrabose, K., and Cuatrecasas, P. (1977). *Biochem. Biophys. Res. Commun.* **76,** 828.

Lauf, P. K. (1975). *Biochim. Biophys. Acta* **415,** 173.

Lee, T. C., and Huggins, C. G. (1968). *Arch. Biochem. Biophys.* **126,** 206.

Lee, T. C., Blank, M. L., Piantodosi, C., Ishaq, K. S., and Snyder, F. (1975). *Biochim. Biophys. Acta* **409,** 218.

LeKim, D., Betzing, H., and Stoffel, W. (1973). *Hoppe-Seyler's Z. Physiol. Chem.* **354,** 437.

Lesko, L., and Marinetti, G. V. (1975). *Biochim. Biophys. Acta* **382,** 419.

Levy, M., Joncourt, M., and Thiessard, J. (1976). *Biochim. Biophys. Acta* **424,** 57.

Liu, M. S., Brooks, P. J., and Kako, K. J. (1974). *Lipids* **9,** 391.

Luthra, M. G., and Sheltawy, A. (1972a). *Biochem. J.* **126,** 1231.

Luthra, M. G., and Sheltawy, A. (1972b). *Biochem. J.* **128,** 587.

Luthra, M. G., and Sheltawy, A. (1973). *Biochem. Soc. Trans.* **1,** 461.

Luthra, M. G., and Sheltawy, A. (1976). *J. Neurochem.* **27,** 1503.

Lyman, R. L., Tinoco, J., Bouchard, P., Sheehan, G., Ostwald, R., and Miljanich, P. (1967). *Biochim. Biophys. Acta* **137,** 107.

Lyman, R. L., Hopkins, S. M., Sheehan, G., and Tinoco, J. (1968). *Biochim. Biophys. Acta* **152,** 197.

Lyman, R. L., Hopkins, S. M., Sheehan, G., and Tinoco, J. (1969). *Biochim. Biophys. Acta* **176,** 86.

Lyman, R. L., Fosmire, M. A., Giotas, C., and Miljanich, P. (1970). *Lipids* **5,** 583.

Lyman, R. L., Sheehan, G., and Tinoco, J. (1973). *Lipids* **8,** 71.

Lyman, R. L., Giotas, C., Medwadowski, B., and Miljanich, P. (1975). *Lipids* **10,** 157.

McCaman, R. E., and Cook, K. (1966). *J. Biol. Chem.* **241,** 3390.

MacDonald, G., and Thompson, W. (1975). *Biochim. Biophys. Acta* **398,** 424.

MacDonald, G., Baker, R. R., and Thompson, W. (1975). *J. Neurochem.* **24,** 655.

MacLennan, D. H., Seeman, P., Illes, G. H., and Yip, C. C. (1971). *J. Biol. Chem.* **246,** 2702.

McMurray, W. C., and Dawson, R. M. C. (1969). *Biochem. J.* **112**, 91.
McMurray, W. C., and Magee, W. L. (1972). *Annu. Rev. Biochem.* **42**, 786.
Madeira, V. M. C., and Antunes-Madeira, M. C. (1976). *Can. J. Biochem.* **54**, 516.
Manning, R., and Brindley, D. N. (1972). *Biochem. J.* **130**, 1003.
Marai, L., and Kuksis, A. (1969). *J. Lipid Res.* **10**, 141.
Marai, L., and Kuksis, A. (1973a). *Can. J. Biochem.* **51**, 1248.
Marai, L., and Kuksis, A. (1973b). *Can. J. Biochem.* **51**, 1365.
Marinetti, G. V., Shlatz, I., and Reilly, K. (1972). *In* "Insulin Action" (I. B. Fritz, ed.), p. 207. Academic Press, New York.
Marsh, D., and Smith, I. C. P. (1973). *Biochim. Biophys. Acta* **298**, 133.
Mattson, F. H., and Beck, L. W. (1956). *J. Biol. Chem.* **219**, 735.
May, H. E., and McCay, P. B. (1968a). *J. Biol. Chem.* **243**, 2288.
May, H. E., and McCay, P. B. (1968b). *J. Biol. Chem.* **243**, 2296.
Mendenhall, C. L., Bradford, R. H., and Furman, R. H. (1969). *Biochim. Biophys. Acta* **187**, 510.
Merkl, I., and Lands, W. E. M. (1963). *J. Biol. Chem.* **238**, 905.
Mitchell, M. P., Brindley, D. N., and Hubscher, G. (1971). *Eur. J. Biochem.* **18**, 214.
Monroy, G., Rola, F. H., and Pullman, M. E. (1972). *J. Biol. Chem.* **247**, 6884.
Monroy, G., Kelker, H. C., and Pullman, M. E. (1973). *J. Biol. Chem.* **248**, 2845.
Montfort, A., Van Golde, L. M. G., and van Deenen, L. L. M. (1971). *Biochim. Biophys. Acta* **231**, 335.
Mookerjea, S., Park, C. E., and Kuksis, A. (1975). *Lipids* **10**, 374.
Moore, J. H., and Williams, D. L. (1963). *Biochim. Biophys. Acta* **70**, 348.
Morgan, T. E., Finley, T. N., and Fialkow, H. (1965). *Biochim. Biophys. Acta* **106**, 403.
Morrisett, J. D., Jackson, R. L., and Gotto, A. M., Jr. (1975). *Annu. Rev. Biochem.* **44**, 183.
Mudd, J. B., Van Golde, L. M. G., and van Deenen, L. L. M. (1969). *Biochim. Biophys. Acta* **176**, 547.
Munden, J. W., and Swarbrick, J. (1973). *Biochim. Biophys. Acta* **291**, 344.
Muto, Y., and Gibson, D. M. (1970). *Biochem. Biophys. Res. Commun.* **38**, 9.
Myher, J. J., Kuksis, A., Marai, L., and Yeung, S. K. F. (1978). *Anal. Chem.* (in press).
Nachbaur, J., Colbeau, A., and Vignais, P. M. (1972). *Biochim. Biophys. Acta* **274**, 426.
Neiderhiser, D. H., and Roth, H. P. (1968). *Proc. Soc. Exp. Biol. Med.* **128**, 221.
Nicolaides, N., and Laves, F. (1958). *J. Am. Chem. Soc.* **86**, 5752.
Niehaus, W. G., and Samuelsson, B. (1968). *Eur. J. Biochem.* **6**, 126.
Noble, R. C., O'Kelly, J. C., and Moore, J. H. (1972). *Biochim. Biophys. Acta* **270**, 519.
Nutter, L. J., and Privett, O. S. (1966). *Lipids* **1**, 258.
O'Brien, J. F., and Geison, R. L. (1971). *J. Neurochem.* **18**, 1615.
O'Brien, J. F., and Geison, R. L. (1974). *J. Lipid Res.* **15**, 44.
O'Brien, J. S. (1967). *J. Theoret. Biol.* **15**, 307.
O'Doherty, P. J. A., Kakis, G., and Kuksis, A. (1973). *Lipids* **8**, 249.
O'Doherty, P. J. A., Yousef, I. M., and Kuksis, A. (1974). *Can. J. Biochem.* **52**, 726.
Ohki, S. (1972). *Biochim. Biophys. Acta* **255**, 57.
Okuyama, H., and Lands, W. E. M. (1970). *Biochim. Biophys. Acta* **218**, 376.
Okuyama, H., and Lands, W. E. M. (1972). *J. Biol. Chem.* **247**, 1414.

Okuyama, H., Eibl, H., and Lands, W. E. M. (1971). *Biochim. Biophys. Acta* **248,** 263.
Okuyama, H., Yamada, K., and Ikezawa, H. (1975). *J. Biol. Chem.* **250,** 1710.
Oldfield, E. (1973). *Science* **180,** 982.
Overath, P., Shairer, H. V., and Stoffel, W. (1970). *Proc. Natl. Acad. Sci. U.S.A.* **67,** 606.
Oxender, D. L. (1972). *Annu. Rev. Biochem.* **41,** 777.
Padley, F. B. (1966). *Chromatog. Rev.* **8,** 208.
Paltauf, F., and Holasek, A. (1973). *J. Biol. Chem.* **248,** 1609.
Papahadjopoulos, D. (1968). *Biochim. Biophys. Acta* **163,** 240.
Papahadjopoulos, D. (1973). *In* "Form and Function of Phospholipids" (G. B. Ansell, R. M. C. Dawson, and J. N. Hawthorne, eds.), 2nd ed., p. 143. Elsevier, Amsterdam.
Parkes, J. G., and Thompson, W. (1970). *Biochim. Biophys. Acta* **196,** 162.
Parkes, J. G., and Thompson, W. (1973). *J. Biol. Chem.* **248,** 6655.
Parkes, J. G., and Thompson, W. T. (1975). *Can. J. Biochem.* **53,** 698.
Parthasarathy, S., Subbaiah, P. V., and Ganguly, J. (1974). *Biochem. J.* **140,** 503.
Pattle, R. E. (1965). *Physiol. Rev.* **45,** 48.
Paulus, H., and Kennedy, E. P. (1960). *J. Biol. Chem.* **235,** 1303.
Pawnall, H. J., Morrisett, J. D., and Gotto, A. M., Jr. (1977). *J. Lipid Res.* **18,** 14.
Pethica, B. A. (1969). *In* "Structural and Functional Aspects of Lipoproteins in Living Systems" (E. Tria and A. M. Scanu, eds.), p. 37. Academic Press, New York.
Petzold, G. L., and Agranoff, B. W. (1967). *J. Biol. Chem.* **242,** 1187.
Pfleger, R. C., and Thomas, H. G. (1971). *Arch. Intern. Med.* **127,** 863.
Phillips, M. C., and Chapman, D. (1968). *Biochim. Biophys. Acta* **163,** 301.
Phillips, M. C., Williams, R. M., and Chapman, D. (1969). *Chem. Phys. Lipids* **3,** 234.
Phillips, M. C., Ladbrooke, B. D., and Chapman, D. (1970). *Biochim. Biophys. Acta* **196,** 35.
Pollock, R. J., Hajra, A. K., and Agranoff, B. W. (1975). *Biochim. Biophys. Acta* **380,** 421.
Porcellati, G., Biasion, M. G., and Pirotta, M. (1970). *Lipids* **5,** 734.
Porcellati, G., Arienti, G., Pirotta, M., and Giorgini, D. (1971). *J. Neurochem.* **18,** 1417.
Portman, O. W., and Sugano, M. (1964). *Arch. Biochem. Biophys.* **105,** 532.
Possmayer, F., Scherphof, G. L., Dubbelman, T. M. A. R., Van Golde, L. M. G., and van Deenen, L. L. M. (1969). *Biochim. Biophys. Acta* **176,** 95.
Possmayer, F., Duwe, G., and Buchnea, D. (1977). *Can. J. Biochem.* **55,** 609.
Prottey, C., and Hawthorne, J. N. (1967). *Biochem. J.* **105,** 379.
Pugh, E. L., and Kates, M. (1975). *Biochim. Biophys. Acta* **380,** 442.
Pugh, E. L., and Kates, M. (1977). *J. Biol. Chem.* **252,** 68.
Quarfordt, S. H., Boston, F., and Hilderman, H. (1971). *Biochim. Biophys. Acta* **231,** 290.
Rapport, M. M., and Graf, L. (1969). *Prog. Allergy* **13,** 273.
Rehbinder, D., and Greenberg, D. M. (1965). *Arch. Biochem. Biophys.* **109,** 110.
Rehnborg, C. S., and Nichols, A. V. (1964). *Biochim. Biophys. Acta* **84,** 596.
Reiser, S., and Christiansen, P. A. (1968). *J. Lipid Res.* **9,** 606.
Renaud, S., and Gautheron, P. (1975). *Atherosclerosis* **21,** 115.
Renkonen, O. (1965). *J. Am. Oil Chem. Soc.* **42,** 298.

Renkonen, O. (1966). *Biochim. Biophys. Acta* **125**, 288.
Renkonen, O. (1967). *Adv. Lipid Res.* **5**, 329.
Renkonen, O. (1968). *Biochim. Biophys. Acta* **152**, 114.
Rittenhouse-Simmons, S., Russell, F. A., and Deykin, D. (1977). *Biochim. Biophys. Acta* **488**, 370.
Robertson, J. D. (1958). *J. Biophys. Biochem. Cytol.* **4**, 349.
Rognstad, R., Clark, D. G., and Katz, J. (1974). *Biochem. J.* **140**, 249.
Rooney, S. A., Canavan, P. M., and Motoyama, E. K. (1974). *Biochim. Biophys. Acta* **360**, 56.
Rooney, S. A., Page-Roberts, B. A., and Motoyama, E. K. (1975). *J. Lipid Res.* **16**, 418.
Rose W. G. (1947). *J. Am. Chem. Soc.* **69**, 1384.
Rowe, C. E. (1959). *Biochem. J.* **73**, 438.
Rowe, C. E. (1960). *Biochem. J.* **76**, 471.
Ruggieri, S., and Fallani, A. (1973). *In* "Tumor Lipids: Biochemistry and Metabolism" (R. Wood, ed.), p. 89. Am. Oil Chem. Soc. Press, Champaign, Illinois.
Rytter, D. J., Miller, J. E., and Cornatzer, W. E. (1968). *Biochim. Biophys. Acta* **152**, 418.
Saito, M., and Kanfer, J. (1973). *Biochem. Biophys. Res. Commun.* **53**, 391.
Saito, M., and Kanfer, J. (1975). *Arch. Biochem. Biophys.* **169**, 318.
Salem, L. (1962). *Can. J. Biochem. Physiol.* **40**, 1287.
Salem, N., Jr., Abood, L. G., and Hoss, W. (1976). *Anal. Biochem.* **76**, 407.
Salerno, D. M., and Beeler, D. A. (1973). *Biochim. Biophys. Acta* **326**, 325.
Samuelsson, B., Granstrom, E., Green, K., Hamberg, M., and Hammarstrom, S. (1975). *Ann. Rev. Biochem.* **44**, 669.
Sarfeh, I. J., Beeler, D. A., Treble, D. H., and Balint, J. A. (1974). *J. Clin. Invest.* **53**, 423.
Sarzala, M. G., Van Golde, L. M. G., De Kruyff, B., and van Deenen, L. L. M. (1970). *Biochim. Biophys. Acta* **202**, 106.
Sarzala, M. G., and Van Golde, L. M. G. (1976). *Biochim. Biophys. Acta* **441**, 423.
Saunders, R. L., and Longmore, W. J. (1975). *Biochemistry* **14**, 835.
Savary, P., and Desnuelle, P. (1956). *Biochim. Biophys. Acta* **21**, 349.
Scanu, A. M. (1969). *In* "Structural and Functional Aspects of Lipoproteins in Living Systems" (E. Tria and A. M. Scanu, eds.), p. 425. Academic Press, New York.
Scanu, A. M. (1972). *Biochim. Biophys. Acta* **265**, 471.
Scanu, A. M., and Wisdom, C. (1972). *Annu. Rev. Biochem.* **41**, 703.
Schacht, J., and Agranoff, B. W. (1974). *J. Biol. Chem.* **249**, 1551.
Schick, P. K., and Yu, B. P. (1974). *J. Clin. Invest.* **54**, 1032.
Schlossman, D. M., and Bell, R. M. (1976). *J. Biol. Chem.* **251**, 5738.
Schneider, V. L., Holman, R. T., and Burr, G. O. (1949). *J. Phys. Colloid Chem.* **53**, 1016.
Schulte, H. G., Nielsen, C. J., Sando, J. J., and Pratt, W. B. (1976). *J. Biol. Chem.* **251**, 2279.
Scow, R. O., Stein, Y., and Stein, O. (1967). *J. Biol. Chem.* **242**, 4919.
Segrest, J. P., Jackson, R. L., Morrisett, J. D., and Gotto, A. M. (1974). *FEBS Lett.* **38**, 247.
Sgoutas, D. S. (1972). *Biochemistry* **11**, 293.
Shah, D. O. (1970). *Adv. Lipid Res.* **8**, 347.
Shah, D. O., and Shulman, J. H. (1965). *J. Lipid Res.* **6**, 341.

Shah, D. O., and Shulman, J. H. (1967a). *J. Lipid Res.* **8,** 215.
Shah, D. O., and Shulman, J. H. (1967b). *J. Lipid Res.* **8,** 227.
Shamgar, F. A., and Collins, F. D. (1975a). *Biochim. Biophys. Acta* **409,** 104.
Shamgar, F. A., and Collins, F. D. (1975b). *Biochim. Biophys. Acta* **409,** 116.
Shaw, J. M., and Bottino, N. R. (1974). *J. Lipid Res.* **15,** 317.
Sheltawy, A., Brammer, M., and Borrill, D. (1972). *Biochem. J.* **128,** 579.
Shohet, S. B. (1970). *J. Clin. Invest.* **49,** 1668.
Shohet, S. B., Livermore, B. M., and Nathan, D. G. (1971). *Blood* **38,** 445.
Singer, S. J. (1973). *Science* **180,** 983.
Singer, S. J., and Nicolson, G. L. (1972). *Science* **175,** 720.
Small, D. M. (1968). *J. Am. Oil Chem. Soc.* **45,** 108.
Smedley-MacLean, I. (1932). *Annu. Rev. Biochem.* **1,** 135.
Smith, M. E., Sedgwick, B., Brindley, D. N., and Hubscher, G. (1967). *Eur. J. Biochem.* **3,** 70.
Smith, S. W., Weiss, S. B., and Kennedy, E. P. (1957). *J. Biol. Chem.* **228,** 915.
Smithson, J. E. (1969). *Lab. Invest.* **20,** 207.
Snyder, F. L. (1969). *Prog. Chem. Fats Other Lipids* **10,** 287.
Snyder, F. L. (1972). *In* "Ether Lipids: Chemistry and Biology" (F. L. Snyder, ed.), p. 121. Academic Press, New York.
Solomonson, L. P., Liepkalns, V. A., and Spector, A. A. (1976). *Biochemistry* **15,** 892.
Soodsma, J. F., Mims, L. C., and Harlow, R. D. (1976). *Biochim. Biophys. Acta* **424,** 159.
Spitzer, H. L., Morrison, K., and Norman, J. R. (1968). *Biochim. Biophys. Acta* **152,** 552.
Spitzer, H. L., Norman, J. R., and Morrison, K. (1969). *Biochim. Biophys. Acta* **176,** 584.
Sprecher, H., and Duffy, M. P. (1975). *Biochim. Biophys. Acta* **380,** 21.
Spritz, N., and Mishkel, M. A. (1969). *J. Clin. Invest.* **48,** 78.
Standish, M. M., and Pethica, B. A. (1968). *Trans. Faraday Soc.* **64,** 1113.
Stefanovich, V. (1969). *Biochem. J.* **115,** 555.
Steim, J. M., Tourtellotte, M. E., Reinert, J. C., McElhaney, R. N., and Rader, R. L. (1969). *Proc. Natl. Acad. Sci. U.S.A.* **63,** 104.
Stein, W. D., and Danielli, J. F. (1956). *Discuss. Faraday Soc.* **21,** 238.
Stein, Y., Widnell, C., and Stein, O. (1968). *J. Cell Biol.* **39,** 185.
Stoeckenius, W., and Engelman, D. M. (1969). *J. Cell Biol.* **42,** 613.
Stoffel, W., and Michaelis, G. (1976). *Hoppe Seyler's Z. Physiol. Chem.* **357,** 7.
Stoffel, W., and Pruss, H.-D. (1969). *Hoppe Seyler's Z. Physiol. Chem.* **350,** 1385.
Stoffel, W., and Schiefer, H. G. (1968). *Hoppe Seyler's Z. Physiol. Chem.* **349,** 1017.
Stoffel, W., De Tomas, M. E., and Schiefer, H. G. (1967). *Hoppe Seyler's Z. Physiol. Chem.* **348,** 882.
Stoffel, W., Zierenberg, O., Tunggal, B., and Schreiber, E. (1974). *Proc. Natl. Acad. Sci. USA* **71,** 3696.
Strickland, K. P., Subrahmanyam, O., Pritchard, E. T., Thompson, W., and Rositter, R. J. (1963). *Biochem. J.* **87,** 128.
Suda, T., and Matsuda, M. (1974). *Biochim. Biophys. Acta* **369,** 331.
Sugano, M. (1971). *Biochem. J.* **122,** 469.
Sugano, M. (1973). *J. Biochem. (Tokyo)* **74,** 191.
Sugano, M., Cho, S., Imaizumi, K., and Wada, M. (1970). *Biochem. Pharmacol.* **19,** 2325.
Sundler, R. (1973). *Biochim. Biophys. Acta* **306,** 218.

Sundler, R., and Akesson, B. (1970). *Biochim. Biophys. Acta* **218,** 89.
Sundler, R., and Akesson, B. (1973). *J. Chromatogr.* **80,** 233.
Sundler, R., and Akesson, B. (1975). *Biochem. J.* **146,** 309.
Sundler, R., Arvidson, G., and Akesson, B. (1972). *Biochim. Biophys. Acta* **280,** 559.
Sundler, R., Arkesson, B., and Nilsson, A. (1974a). *Biochim. Biophys. Acta* **337,** 248.
Sundler, R., Akesson, B., and Nilsson, A. (1974b). *J. Biol. Chem.* **249,** 5102.
Taki, T., and Matsumoto, M. (1973). *Jpn. J. Exp. Med.* **43,** 219.
Talamo, B., Chang, C., and Bloch, K. (1973). *J. Biol. Chem.* **248,** 2738.
Tamai, Y., and Lands, W. E. M. (1974). *J. Biochem. (Tokyo)* **76,** 847.
Taniguchi, M., Hirayama, H., and Sakagami, T. (1973). *Biochim. Biophys. Acta* **296,** 65.
Tansey, F. A., and Frosolono, M. F. (1975). *Biochem. Biophys. Res. Commun.* **67,** 1560.
Tattrie, N. H. (1959). *J. Lipid Res.* **1,** 60.
Tattrie, N. H., Bennett, J. R., and Cyr, R. (1968). *Can. J. Biochem.* **46,** 819.
ter Schegget, J., Van Den Bosch, H., Van Baak, M. A., Hostetler, K. Y., and Borst, P. (1971). *Biochim. Biophys. Acta* **239,** 234.
Thompson, G. A., Jr. (1973). *In* "Phospholipids: Form and Function" (G. B. Ansell, R. M. C. Dawson, and J. N. Hawthorne, eds.), p. 67. Elsevier, Amsterdam.
Thompson, W. (1969). *Biochim. Biophys. Acta* **187,** 150.
Thompson, W., and MacDonald, G. (1975). *J. Biol. Chem.* **250,** 6779.
Thompson, W., and MacDonald, G. (1976). *Eur. J. Biochem.* **65,** 107.
Thompson, W., Strickland, K. P., and Rositter, R. J. (1963). *Biochem. J.* **87,** 136.
Tinoco, J., and McIntosh, D. J. (1970). *Chem. Phys. Lipids* **4,** 72.
Tinoco, J., Hopkins, S. M., McIntosh, D. J., Sheehan, G., and Lyman, R. L. (1967). *Lipids* **2,** 479.
Tinoco, J., Sheehan, G., Hopkins, S., and Lyman, R. L. (1970). *Lipids* **5,** 412.
Tinoco, J., Ghosh, D., and Keith, A. D. (1972). *Biochim. Biophys. Acta* **274,** 279.
Tomasi, V., Koretz, S., Ray, T. K., Dunnick, J., and Marinetti, G. V. (1970). *Biochim. Biophys. Acta* **211,** 31.
Tonks, D. B., and Allen, R. H. (1953). *Science* **118,** 55.
Tou, J.-S., Hurst, M. W., Baricos, W. H., and Huggins, C. G. (1973). *Arch. Biochem. Biophys.* **154,** 593.
Trauble, H., and Hayes, D. H. (1971). *Chem. Phys. Lipids* **7,** 324.
Treble, D. H., Frumkin, S., Balint, J. A., and Beeler, D. A. (1970). *Biochim. Biophys. Acta* **202,** 163.
Trewhella, M. A., and Collins, F. D. (1969). *Lipids* **4,** 304.
Trewhella, M. A., and Collins, F. D. (1973a). *Biochim. Biophys. Acta* **296,** 34.
Trewhella, M. A., and Collins, F. D. (1973b). *Biochim. Biophys. Acta* **296,** 51.
van Deenen, L. L. M. (1965). *Prog. Chem. Fats Other Lipids* **8,** 59.
van Deenen, L. L. M. (1969). *In* "The Molecular Basis of Membrane Function" (D. C. Tosteson, ed.), p. 47. Prentice-Hall, Englewood Cliffs, New Jersey.
van Deenen, L. L. M., and De Gier, J. (1974). *In* "The Red Blood Cell" (D. M. Surgenor, ed.), 2nd ed., Vol. 1, p. 147. Academic Press, New York.
van Deenen, L. L. M., and de Haas, G. H. (1963). *Biochim. Biophys. Acta* **70,** 538.
van Deenen, L. L. M., and de Haas, G. H. (1964). *Adv. Lipid Res.* **2,** 167.
van Deenen, L. L. M., Houtsmuller, U. M. T., de Haas, G. H., and Mulder, E. (1962). *J. Pharm. Pharmacol.* **24,** 429.
Van den Berg, J. W. O., and Hulsman, W. L. (1971). *Fed. Eur. Biochem. Soc. Abstr.* No. 539.

Van Den Bosch, H., and van Deenen, L. L. M. (1965). *Biochim. Biophys. Acta* **106**, 326.

Van Den Bosch, H., Bonte, H. A., and van Deenen, L. L. M. (1965). *Biochim. Biophys. Acta* **98**, 648.

Van Den Bosch, H., Van Golde, L. M. G., Eibl, H., and van Deenen, L. L. M. (1967). *Biochim. Biophys. Acta* **144**, 613.

Van Den Bosch, H., Van Golde, L. M. G., Slotboom, A. J., and van Deenen, L. L. M. (1968). *Biochim. Biophys. Acta* **152**, 694.

Van Den Bosch, H., Van Golde, L. M. G., and van Deenen, L. L. M. (1972). *Ergeb. Physiol., Biol. Chem. Exp. Pharmakol.* **66**, 13.

Vandenheuvel, F. A. (1971). *Adv. Lipid Res.* **9**, 161.

Van Golde, L. M. G., and van Deenen, L. L. M. (1966). *Biochim. Biophys. Acta* **125**, 496.

Van Golde, L. M. G., Tomasi, V., and van Deenen, L. L. M. (1967). *Chem. Phys. Lipids* **1**, 282.

Van Golde, L. M. G., Pieterson, W. A., and van Deenen, L. L. M. (1968). *Biochim. Biophys. Acta* **152**, 84.

Van Golde, L. M. G., Scherphof, G. L., and van Deenen, L. L. M. (1969). *Biochim. Biophys. Acta* **176**, 635.

Van Golde, L. M. G., Fleischer, B., and Fleischer, S. (1971). *Biochim. Biophys. Acta* **249**, 318.

Van Golde, L. M. G., Raben, J., Batenburg, J. J., Fleischer, B., Zambrano, F., and Fleischer, S. (1974). *Biochim. Biophys. Acta* **360**, 179.

Veerkamp, J., Mulder, I., and van Deenen, L. L. M. (1962). *Biochim. Biophys. Acta* **57**, 299.

Vereyken, J. M., Montfort, A., and Van Golde, L. M. G. (1972). *Biochim. Biophys. Acta* **260**, 70.

Victoria, E. J., Van Golde, L. M. G., Hostetler, K. Y., Scherphof, G. L., and van Deenen, L. L. M. (1971). *Biochim. Biophys. Acta* **239**, 443.

Vijay, I. K., and Stumpf, P. K. (1971). *J. Biol. Chem.* **246**, 2910.

Vonkeman, H., and Van Dorp, D. A. (1968). *Biochim. Biophys. Acta* **164**, 430.

Vorbeck, M. L., and Martin, A. P. (1970). *Biochem. Biophys. Res. Commun.* **40**, 902.

Waite, M., and Sisson, P. (1971). *Biochemistry* **10**, 2377.

Waite, M., and Sisson, P. (1973). *J. Biol. Chem.* **248**, 7985.

Waite, M., and Sisson, P. (1976). *Biochim. Biophys. Acta* **450**, 301.

Waite, M., and van Deenen, L. L. M. (1967). *Biochim. Biophys. Acta* **137**, 498.

Waku, K., and Lands, W. E. M. (1968a). *J. Biol. Chem.* **243**, 2654.

Waku, K., and Lands, W. E. M. (1968b). *J. Lipid Res.* **9**, 12.

Wallach, D. F. H., Bieri, V., Verma, S. P., and Schmidt-Ullrich, R. (1975). *Ann. N.Y. Acad. Sci.* **264**, 142.

Warren, G. B., Toon, P. A., Birdsall, N. J. M., Lee, A. G., and Metcalfe, J. C. (1974). *Biochemistry* **13**, 5501.

Watkins, J. C. (1968). *Biochim. Biophys. Acta* **152**, 293.

Weinhold, P. A. (1968). *J. Lipid Res.* **9**, 262.

Weiss, S. B., Kennedy, E. P., and Kiyasu, J. Y. (1960). *J. Biol. Chem.* **235**, 40.

Wessels, J. M. C., and Veerkamp, J. H. (1973). *Biochim. Biophys. Acta* **291**, 190.

White, D. A. (1973). *In* "Form and Function of Phospholipids" (G. B. Ansell, R. M. C. Dawson, and J. N. Hawthorne, eds.), p. 441. Elsevier, Amsterdam.

Wilgram, G. F., and Kennedy, E. P. (1963). *J. Biol. Chem.* **238**, 2615.

Wilson, J. W., and Leduc, E. H. (1963). *J. Cell Biol.* **16**, 281.

Wirtz, K. W. A. (1974). *Biochim. Biophys. Acta* **344**, 95.
Wirtz, K. W. A., and Zilversmit, D. B. (1968). *J. Biol. Chem.* **243**, 3596.
Wirtz, K. W. A., Van Golde, L. M. G., and van Deenen, L. L. M. (1970). *Biochim. Biophys. Acta* **218**, 176.
Wirtz, K. W. A., Geurts Van Kessel, W. S. M., Kamp, H. H., and Demel, R. A. (1976). *Eur. J. Biochem.* **61**, 515.
Wishnia, A., and Pinder, T. W., Jr. (1966). *Biochemistry* **5**, 1534.
Wittels, B. (1973). *J. Biol. Chem,* **248**, 2906.
Woelk, H., Goracci, G., Gaiti, A., and Porcellati, G. (1973). *Hoppe Seyler's Z. Physiol. Chem.* **354**, 729.
Wolfe, B. M. J., Anhalt, B., Beck, J. C., and Rubinstein, D. (1970). *Can. J. Biochem.* **48**, 170.
Wood, R. (1973). *In* "Tumor Lipids: Biochemistry and Metabolism" (R. Wood, ed.), p. 139. Am. Oil Chem. Soc. Press, Champaign, Illinois.
Wood, R. (1974). *Lipids* **9**, 429.
Wood, R. (1975). *Lipids* **10**, 736.
Wood, R., and Harlow, R. D. (1969a). *Arch. Biochem. Biophys.* **131**, 495.
Wood, R., and Harlow, R. D. (1969b). *Arch. Biochem. Biophys.* **135**, 272.
Wykle, R. L., Blank, M. L., Malone, B., and Snyder, F. (1972). *J. Biol. Chem.* **247**, 5442.
Wykle, R. L., Blank, M. L., and Snyder, F. (1973). *Biochim. Biophys. Acta* **326**, 26.
Yamashita, S., and Numa, S. (1972). *Eur. J. Biochem.* **31**, 565.
Yamashita, S., Hosaka, K., and Numa, S. (1973). *Eur. J. Biochem.* **38**, 25.
Yeung, S. K. F., and Kuksis, A. (1974). *Can. J. Biochem.* **52**, 830.
Yeung, S. K. F., and Kuksis, A. (1978). *Fed. Proc., Fed. Am. Soc. Exp. Biol.* (in press).
Yeung, S. K. F., Kuksis, A., Marai, L., and Myher, J. J. (1977). *Lipids* **12**, 529.
Young, D. L. (1971). *J. Lipid Res.* **12**, 590.
Yousef, I. M., Fisher, M. M., Piekarski, J., and Holub, B. J. (1977). *Lipids* **12**, 140.
Yurkowski, M., and Walker, B. L. (1971). *Biochim. Biophys. Acta* **231**, 145.
Zaror-Behrens, G., and Kako, K. J. (1976). *Biochim. Biophys. Acta* **441**, 1.
Zborowski, J., and Wojtczak, L. (1969). *Biochim. Biophys. Acta* **187**, 73.
Zborowski, J., and Wojtczak, L. (1975). *FEBS Lett.* **51**, 317.
Zilversmit, D. B. (1969). *In* "Structural and Functional Aspects of Lipoproteins in Living Systems" (E. Tria and A. M. Scanu, eds.), p. 329. Academic Press, New York.

Fatty Acids and Immunity

CHRISTOPHER J. MEADE AND JÜRGEN MERTIN

Transplantation Biology Section
Clinical Research Centre
Harrow, Middlesex
England

I. Introduction

The idea that fatty acids may play a role in immunity is new, and no comprehensive earlier review exists. Parts of the field, however, have been surveyed by other workers. Resch and Ferber (1975) wrote an excellent account of their studies on the role of fatty acids in lymphocyte stimulation, updated in a 1976 German review (Ferber and Resch, 1976). The 1972 volume of this series contained a detailed account by diLuzio of the effects of emulsions of fatty acid esters on the reticuloendothelial system. Recently, Pelus and Strausser (1977) reviewed prostaglandins and immunity. We have written this review in an attempt to gather together these and other threads from the fields of immunology, biochemistry, and nutrition. Our primary aim has been to provide a new perspective rather than to summarize an established field. It is early yet to know whether fatty acid research may finally find a niche in immunology. We expect most of our readers to be lipid biochemists who may be unfamiliar with much of the literature that has appeared in immunological journals. Readers with only an immunological background may find useful the chapter on fatty acids in Gurr and James (1975).

This review will consider its topic from three viewpoints. First we shall examine the role of fatty acids, both as membrane components and prostaglandin precursors, in the biochemistry of the cells of the immune system. Second, we shall describe the effects of altered fatty acid concentrations on the immune response *in vivo* and *in vitro*. Finally, we shall try to show that some of the existing data on the relationship between dietary essential fatty acids and disease can be interpreted, among other ways, in terms of effects on the immune system.

II. Biosynthesis and Uptake of Fatty Acids by Lymphocytes

Like all mammalian cells, lymphocytes contain a variety of fatty acids, some of which, the essential fatty acids, must be supplied to the cells since they are unable to synthesize them. Of the essential fatty acids, linoleic acid and the derivative arachidonic acid are major components of the phospholipids of lymphocyte membranes (see Table I), while α-linolenic and its derivatives are only minor components. Essential fatty acids are polyunsaturated (i.e., having more than one double bond in the carbon chain) and lymphocytes lack the ability to perform the particular desaturation necessary for their synthesis from saturated precursors. Thus, arachidonic acid cannot be synthesized *de novo*, although it can, in most species, be made from linoleic acid by chain elongation (Liljeqvist, 1973). Essential fatty acids must be present in the mammalian diet for health to be maintained. Changes in the proportion of dietary essential fatty acids lead to changes in the fatty acid composition of lymph nodes (Meade *et al.*, 1978) or spleen cells (Tsang *et al.*, 1976).

Lymphocytes can synthesize all their nonessential fatty acids. This is shown by their ability to incorporate appreciable quantities of radioactive label from acetate-1-^{14}C into all fatty acids except linoleic acid (Blomstrand

Table I
ALTERATIONS IN FATTY ACID CONTENT OF PHOSPHATIDYL CHOLINE
FROM RABBIT THYMUS CELLS FOLLOWING STIMULATION BY CONCANAVALIN A [a,b]

| | Moles % | | | | | | Polyunsaturated/ saturated |
	16:0	18:0	18:1	18:2	20:4	22:6	fatty acids
Position 1							
Control	50.6	17.9	22.5	4.9	—	—	0.072
Con A	58.1	16.0	20.7	5.2	—	—	0.070
Position 2							
Control	47.4	3.2	20.0	19.4	7.8	—	0.538
Con A	39.0	1.6	21.7	20.3	17.2	—	0.924

[a] The cells were cultured for 4 hours in Eagle's medium with 5 μg concanavalin A/ml.
[b] From Ferber and Resch (1976).

and Liljeqvist, 1972; Liljeqvist, 1973). When a lymphocyte is stimulated, either specifically by antigen or nonspecifically by plant lectins such as phytohaemagglutinin or concanavalin A, a variety of metabolic changes occur which may result in cell division, antibody production, or a number of other responses. In unstimulated lymphocytes very little label is incorporated from acetate-1-^{14}C into palmitic or myristic acids, suggesting that incorporation of label is achieved chiefly by chain elongation. However, in stimulated lymphocytes cultured in lipid-free media, appreciable radioactivity appears in palmitic acid, most of it in carbon atoms other than the terminal carboxyl, implying *de novo* synthesis.

Studies of *in vitro* stimulation often use plant lectins, which react with a higher proportion of lymphocytes than most antigens. Liljeqvist (1973) and Resch and Ferber (1972) agree in finding incorporation of label from acetate-1-^{14}C into fatty acids to be increased following stimulation of lymphocytes by phytohaemagglutinin. They disagree, however, on the fate of this label. Liljeqvist, using human thoracic duct lymphocytes, found ^{14}C in all lipid fractions, but less in phospholipid. Resch and Ferber, using rabbit mesenteric lymph node cells, found preferential incorporation into the phospholipid fraction. Any of a number of differences in experimental design might explain this discrepancy. One point we would like to mention is that incorporation of radioactive label depends not only on rates of biosynthesis but also on the size of the pool of "cold" fatty acids available to compete with fatty acids formed from acetate-1-^{14}C for enzymes incorporating fatty acids into phospholipid. An increase in the size of the cold pool will decrease the incorporation of labeled fatty acids into phospholipid. Liljeqvist incubated lymphocytes for 18 hours, adding labeled acetate 6 hours before the end of incubation, while Resch and Ferber had acetate-1-^{14}C present throughout. An early phytohaemagglutinin-stimulated increase in the size of the cold pool might explain the discrepancy.

III. Fatty Acids as Lymphocyte Components

A.   LIPID COMPOSITION OF LYMPHOCYTE MEMBRANE

The lymphocyte is, like other cells, surrounded by a membrane consisting chiefly of proteins and phospholipids such as phosphatidylethanolamine and phosphatidylcholine. Table I shows the main fatty acids at position 1 and position 2 of phosphatidylcholine from rabbit thymus lymphocytes. In resting lymphocytes (the "control" of Table I), the ratio of polyunsaturated to saturated fatty acids in position 2 is lower than in phosphatidylcholine from rat liver (a widely used phospholipid source). This is true for phosphatidylcholine from lymphocytes of a number of species (Ferber et al., 1975). Modern concepts of cell membranes see them not as rigid, but in a dynamic state in which parts of the membrane lipid are constantly passing from an ordered to a fluid state (Singer and Nicolson, 1972). Although many factors contribute to membrane fluidity, membranes having a lower ratio of polyunsaturated to saturated fatty acids are generally less fluid than those having a higher ratio (Overath and Träuble, 1973).

Of the proteins in the lymphocyte membrane, antigen receptors and histocompatibility antigens are of particular immunological importance. The latter, present also on many cell types other than the lymphocyte, determine whether a cell will elicit a specific immune reaction. Although there is, as yet, no evidence for modulation of the biological activity of antigen receptors or histocompatibility antigens by their lipid environment, in experiments on a variety of cell types it has been shown that the enzymic or receptor activity of membrane proteins can be modulated by the composition, including fatty acid composition, of surrounding lipid (see Table II).

According to the "fluid mosaic model" of Singer and Nicolson, proteins are distributed randomly, so that unless the ratio of protein/lipid is very high, long-range cooperative effects between proteins must be transmitted through the lipid phase. Immunologically important long-range cooperative effects might include those between two or more antigen receptors, between antigen receptors and membrane enzymes, and between viruses and histocompatibility antigens. A hint that one such interaction might be through the fluid phase is the finding of Pfizenmaier et al. (1977) that in vitro killing

Table II

EXAMPLES OF MODULATION OF MEMBRANE PROTEIN ACTIVITY
BY FATTY ACID COMPOSITION OF SURROUNDING LIPIDS

System	Membrane protein activity	Reference
Escherichia coli	β-Galactoside transport system	Schairer and Overath (1969)
3T3 cells (a mouse fibroblast line)	Agglutinability of lectin receptors	Horwitz *et al.* (1974)
Rat erythrocyte	Allosteric activation or inhibition of ATPase, acetylcholinesterase, and *p*-nitrophenylphosphatase	Farias *et al.* (1975)
Mouse LM (fibroblast) cells	Adenylate cyclase activity	Engelhard *et al.* (1976)
Tetrahymena periformis	Fatty acid desaturase activity	Kasai *et al.* (1976)

of cells treated with inactivated Sendai virus cannot occur when the target cells are held at 4°C prior to exposure to attacker lymphocytes. Such killing involves target cell histocompatability antigens, since it can only occur when such cells have histocompatibility antigens in common with the cells used to prime the attacker lymphocytes. One interpretation of these results is that ordering or "freezing" fluid membrane at 4°C interferes with virus-histocompatibility antigen interaction. Figure 1 speculates how a change in the lipid phase might interact with a histocompatibility protein to cause a cell to be sensitive to immunological attack.

B. CHANGES IN FATTY ACID COMPOSITION OF LYMPHOCYTE MEMBRANES FOLLOWING STIMULATION

Membrane phospholipid fatty acid composition alters when lymphocytes are stimulated, either by antigen or by mitogens such as phytohaemagglutinin or concanavalin A (Table I). Most marked is an increase in arachidonic acid at position 2 (Ferber *et al.*, 1975). There is a rapid turnover of the fatty acids in the phosphatidylcholine of phytohaemagglutinin stimulated lymphocytes (sufficient to replace total cell phosphatidylcholine fatty acids within less than 10 hours). The alteration in fatty acid composition of this phospholipid after stimulation is largely a result of such turnover, rather than of *de novo* synthesis of new phospholipid molecules. Evidence for this comes from studies in which incorporation of oleic acid-1-^{14}C into phosphatidylcholine was used as a measure of fatty acid turnover. Simultaneous measurement of the incorporation of [^{14}C]choline could be

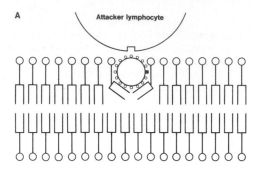

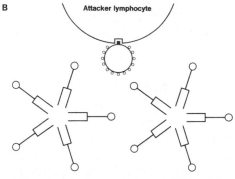

FIG. 1. How alterations in binding energies to lipid might cause a membrane protein to expose a certain antigenic determinant. In (A) the antigenic determinant is masked because attraction between hydrophobic parts of the protein molecule and membrane lipid places the antigenic determinant where it cannot be "seen" by a lymphocyte. In (B) as a result of, for example, interaction of the membrane with a virus, the phospholipid molecules are forced to adopt a new arrangement in which they can less easily interact with the protein molecule, which therefore alters its conformation to expose the determinant (hypothesis only).

used to assess *de novo* phosphatidylcholine biosynthesis, because there is only one pathway for putting a choline residue in the phosphatidylcholine molecule. That is from choline via cytidine diphosphatecholine (see Fig. 2). Resch and Ferber (1972) found that, under similar conditions, [^{14}C]-oleate incorporation into phosphatidylcholine could be 100-fold higher than [^{14}C]choline incorporation.

Ferber and Resch (1973) have described a plasma–membrane associated enzyme, catalysing incorporation of coenzyme A derivatives of fatty acids into phospholipid, and activated by phytohaemagglutinin or concanavalin A (Fig. 3). Affinity of this enzyme is greater for more highly unsaturated fatty acids, particularly arachidonic acid (Table III). Such a transferase enzyme can explain the preferential incorporation of arachidonate into the phospholipids of activated lymphocytes. It does not, however, explain why the arachidonic acid is preferentially incorporated into the 2 position since

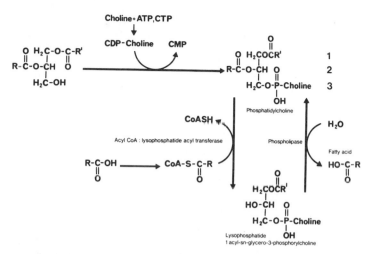

FIG. 2. Metabolism of phosphatidylcholine. The numbers 1, 2, and 3 identify the carbon atoms in the glyceryl backbone of the molecule.

the enzyme has similar affinity for lysophosphatide with either the 1 or 2 positions available for acylation by fatty acid.

Many enzyme activities are altered when lymphocytes are stimulated. There is evidence, however, that acyltransferase activation is a direct consequence of mitogen binding. First, neither mitogen binding nor enzyme activation is affected by puromycin, or by low temperature (0°C), suggesting enzyme activation requires neither protein biosynthesis nor energy metabolism. Second, both processes are complete within 30 min at 37°C.

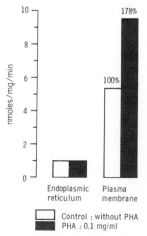

FIG. 3. Oleoyl CoA: 1 acyl-*sn*-glycero-3-phosphorylcholine acyltransferase in plasma membranes and endoplasmic reticulum from rabbit lymphocytes after 1 hour of stimulation with phytohaemagglutinin. From Ferber and Resch (1973).

Table III

Substrate Specificity of Microsomal Acyl CoA:1-Acyl-sn-Glycero-
3-Phosphorylcholine Acyltransferase of Concanavalin A-
Stimulated Thymus Cells [a]

	Oleoyl-CoA (18:1)		Arachidonyl-CoA (20:4)	
	V_{max} [b]	K_m M	V_{max}	K_m M
Control	3.9	1.0×10^{-5}	7.6	6.4×10^{-7}
Con A	7.9	1.2×10^{-5}	31.7	8.5×10^{-7}

[a] From Ferber and Resch (1976).
[b] V_{max} is given in nanomoles per milligram protein per minute.

Third, if within 30 min of first exposure binding of concanavalin A to its receptor is reversed by α-methylmannoside, a competitive ligand, the enzyme activation is also interfered with. Stepwise elution of membrane fractions from concanavalin A-sepharose using α-methylmannoside gives greatest specific activity of acyltransferase in the fraction most strongly able to bind concanavalin A (Ferber and Resch, 1976). There *are* differences in the kinetics of concanavalin A binding and acyltransferase activation. With increasing concanavalin A concentration, concanavalin binding increases with the usual hyperbolic kinetics associated with a simple, saturatable receptor. By contrast, activation of the transferase enzyme follows sigmoid kinetics. These differences do not, however, exclude the possibility that acyltransferase activation is a direct consequence of mitogen binding. The differences could, for example, be explained if, for transferase activation to occur, it was necessary not only for one concanavalin A receptor site to be occupied, but also for an interaction to occur between it and other occupied receptor sites. Such might be the case if aggregation of concanavalin A receptors was required for enzyme activation (Ferber and Resch, 1976).

C.   A Role for Fatty Acids in Lymphocyte Activation

One of the fundamental questions in immunology is how the occupation of a receptor by antigen causes a lymphocyte to divide, produce antibody, or engage in any of the multitude of other specific responses to antigen. This problem is important not only for immunology, but also for cell differentiation generally, for the ease with which the lymphocyte can be stimulated to differentiate by a simple experimental stimulus makes it a useful model. The problem is complicated by the existence of two major subclasses of lymphocytes, T and B cells. B cells produce antibody when stimulated by antigen. Sometimes the antigen alone is not sufficient stimulus and antibody will not be produced until there is "help" from a T cell, possibly via a soluble T cell product.

An important aspect of the problem is how a receptor–ligand interaction on the outer surface of the cell membrane alters activity of a wide variety of enzymes within the cell. Attention therefore centers on changes in the membrane, early after lymphocyte stimulation, which alter the internal environment in such a way as to affect many enzyme activities. One such change is an increased permeability to ions, particularly Ca^{2+} (Quastel and Kaplan, 1971; Whitney and Sutherland, 1972). Another is altered cyclic nucleotide levels (Smith *et al.*, 1971a; Hadden *et al.*, 1972). Resch and Ferber (1975) have suggested that changes in membrane fatty acid composition occurring shortly after lymphocyte stimulation might be the primary "signal" triggering the lymphocyte. Their hypothesis does not necessarily exclude a role either for solute fluxes or cyclic nucleotides, for both of these can be affected by the fatty acid composition of a membrane (Demel *et al.*, 1972; Engelhard *et al.*, 1976). Although most of their evidence comes from studies on lymphocyte stimulation by phytohaemagglutinin or concanavalin A, both of which only stimulate T cells, they have found that fatty acid turnover, as measured by incorporation of oleic acid-1-^{14}C into phosphatidylcholine, can also be stimulated by anti-immunoglobulin serum, a B cell mitogen (Resch and Ferber, 1972). Any theory involving fatty acid changes in B lymphocyte activation must also take into account the requirement of B cells for T cell help.

Resch and Ferber argue that the increased proportion of polyunsaturated fatty acids in lymphocyte phospholipids obtained early after stimulation is a sufficient explanation for the increased membrane fluidity which they (Ferber *et al.*, 1974) and others (Barnett *et al.*, 1974) report. As discussed earlier, membrane enzyme function and permeability can be altered by alterations in the lipid layer, and Resch and Ferber see the altered state of the lipid layer as being the underlying change which leads to those other changes that culminate in lymphocyte differentiation.

The technique Ferber *et al.* used to measure fluidity was the temperature dependence of the fluorescence polarization of perylene. If a fluorescent probe is excited by polarized light, it will reemit partially depolarized light, the degree of depolarization depending principally on the fluorescent lifetime of the probe and the fluidity of the probe environment. If the environment is very fluid, or if the fluorescent lifetime is long, the light will be completely depolarized. If it is assumed that the fluorescent lifetime is not affected by the membrane, then the temperature at which depolarization is complete gives an indication of the fluidity of the membrane. Using electron spin resonance, Barnett *et al.* (1974) also observed an increase in the fluidity of the membrane environment of their probe 6-(4'4'-dimethylox-azolidinyl-*N*-oxyl)heptadecanoate.

The principal problem about using probes in membranes is that they only provide information on their immediate environment, and it is often far from certain where this is (a discussion of this problem appears in the review by Nicolau *et al.*, 1977). The problem is particularly acute when whole cells are used, as in the study by Toyoshima and Osawa (1976). These workers followed changes in lymphocyte membrane fluidity using 1,6-diphenyl-1,3,5-hexatriene as their fluorescent probe. They found that the temporary increase in membrane fluidity following lectin binding was not accompanied by a particular incorporation of labeled polyunsaturated fatty acids. Sixty minutes after lectin binding, incorporation of [^{3}H]arachidonic acid [^{14}C]-1-linoleic acid was increased, but by this time membrane fluidity had virtually returned to normal. If the fluorescent probe and fatty acid incorporation measured were truly both in the lymphocyte plasma membrane, these results argue against an explanation of fluidity changes in terms of alterations in membrane fatty acid composition.

The concept that it is changes in the phospholipids which underlie lymphocyte triggering has intriguing implications for the control of lymphocyte function (Barton and Diener, 1975). As mentioned earlier, certain T cells appear to modulate the activity of B cells and, recent research suggests, of other T cell subpopulations, in part at least by means of soluble products. A triggering mechanism involving lipids implies that a molecule capable of interacting with the lipid layer would be particularly suitable as a modulator. One of the substances produced by T cells, and capable of specifically helping B cells to produce antibody, has been shown by Taussig and Munro (1974) to react with antiserum directed against certain histocompatibility antigens. Histocompatibility antigens exist on a very hydrophobic collection of proteins, which readily associate with lipids. Thus, one particular histocompatability antigen (HLA 7), when solubilized, occurs in the β-lipoprotein fraction of human serum (Charlton and Zmijewski, 1970). Normally, however, histocompatibility antigens are firmly anchored by hydrophobic forces within the lipid layer (Nathenson and Cullen, 1974). The presence of histocompatibility antigens as well as an antigen binding site on the soluble factor described by Taussig and Munro implies that such a factor might readily interact with the lipid layer.

IV. Role of Free Fatty Acids

Increased turnover of phospholipid fatty acids following lymphocyte stimulation requires not only a transferase to incorporate new fatty acids (as fatty acyl CoA's) but also a means of generating lysophosphatides and free fatty acids as substrates for this enzyme. Lysophosphatides can only be formed by cleavage of a fatty acid from phospholipid and radioisotope incorporation data suggest most of the free fatty acids incorporated into phospholipid are also derived in this way (Resch *et al.,* 1971). However, lymphocytes are not particularly rich in the cleaving enzymes and changes in phospholipase A activity on lymphocyte activation are only modest. Resch *et al.* (1971), using red cells containing labeled lecithin as substrate, found only a 30% increase in membrane associated phospholipase activity following phytohaemagglutinin stimulation of rabbit lymphocytes. In studies in which fatty acid release from [1-(1-^{14}C)]palmitoyl-*sn*-glycerol-3-phosphorylcholine was measured, no increased lysophospholipase activity could be observed at all (Ferber and Resch, 1973; Resch *et al.,* 1971). Possibly the lymphocyte membrane enzyme is not the only means of cleaving phospholipids. Is there another phospholipase involved? *In vitro* and *in vivo* stimulated lymphocytes are closely associated with macrophages or similar cells (McFarland *et al.,* 1966). Macrophages are required for optimal stimulation of T cells (Alter and Bach, 1970) as well as for the B cell response to T cell dependent antigens (Feldmann and Palmer, 1971). Macrophages have much more phospholipase activity than lymphocytes, and when stimulated can release this enzyme (Munder *et al.,* 1969). We speculate the macrophage may be a possible source of the enzyme generating lysophosphatides in the lymphocyte membrane, and phospholipase as one possible mediator of lymphocyte–macrophage interaction.

As well as lysophosphatide, the "turnover" biosynthesis of new phospholipid in stimulated lymphocytes requires a source of free fatty acids. There are marked differences between control and *in vivo Bacillus calmette guerin*-(BCG) stimulated rabbit lymphocytes with respect to the composition of their free fatty acid pool. In particular, arachidonic acid, which makes up 11% of the control free fatty acid pool, is not detectable in the free fatty acids of BCG stimulated lymphocytes (Ferber *et al.,* 1975). Nevertheless, the pool of free fatty acids utilized for phospholipid biosynthesis does not appear to exchange freely with the pool of free fatty acids within the lymphocyte. After phytohaemagglutinin or concanavalin A stimulation of rabbit lymph node cells in the presence of [1-^{14}C]acetate, ^{14}C incorporation into phosphatidylcholine is enhanced 30-fold, but into free fatty acids only threefold (Resch and Ferber, 1972). Cyong and Okada (1976) have demonstrated histochemically greatly increased quantities of free fatty acids between and on the surface of stimulated lymph node cells. Possibly this pool of fatty acids is also available to the transferase enzyme. To demonstrate *in vitro* that stimulated lymphocytes release free fatty acids, Cyong and Okada (1976) cultured a mixture of primed lymphocytes with other lymphocytes or tumor cells of a different histocompatability type. A soluble antigen, purified protein derivative of tuberculin (PPD), was also effective. In all these situations, T cells are of the predominant stimulated cell type.

Free fatty acids have a marked lytic action on cells of all types. This has led to the suggestion that release of free fatty acids during the immune response may be one of the mechanisms by which lymphocytes can kill other cells, including tumor cells (Kigoshi and Ito, 1973; Okada and Cyong, 1975). Lymphocytes, compared with other cell types, contain higher concentrations of free fatty acids. Resch and Ferber (1975) report free fatty acids to be about 9% of the total lipids of calf thymus lymphocytes. Guinea pig lymph nodes stimulated with complete Freund's adjuvant contain as much as 18% free fatty acids (Kigoshi and Ito, 1973). By contrast guinea pig liver, heart, lung, or kidney tissue contain only 2–3% free fatty acids. The figures for stimulated and unstimulated guinea pig spleen are 14% and 17%, respectively.

The measurement of free fatty acid levels in lymphoid tissues poses special problems, because endogenous phospholipase may be released when tissues are homogenized. Interest in a possible cytolytic role for free fatty acids was first aroused by attempts to identify a factor, present in extracts of normal lymph nodes and capable of killing a wide variety of cells, including tumor cell lines (Okudaira et al., 1970). This factor turned out to be free fatty acids generated during the extraction procedure. If the lymph nodes were first heat treated to destroy any lipases, then no killing activity could be demonstrated. However, later experiments showed that, even though no cytolytic activity was associated with lipid extracts of unsensitized cells, an ability to lyse red cells was present in a hexane extract of sensitized lymph node cells, incubated for 1 hour with the specific tumor line used for immunization. The control in which immune cells were incubated with a tumor cell line other than that against which they were immunized, was negative. The extracts were prepared in such a way that both intracellular and extracellular lipids were assayed (Okada and Cyong, 1975).

Two important mechanisms by which lymphoid cells kill other cells in vitro are direct action of a subpopulation of specifically immune T cells, and a mechanism involving specific antibody and a subpopulation of lymphoid cells termed K cells. During T cell killing, there is no killing of "bystander" cells bearing antigens other than those against which the T cells are sensitized (Berke et al., 1972). Similarly during K cell killing, there is no killing of bystanders not bearing antigens against which the specific antibody is directed (C. J. Sanderson, personal communication). These results make it unlikely that fatty acids, freely released into the medium surrounding tumor cell "targets," can have a role in tumor cell killing, at least by the mechanisms mentioned. They do not, however, exclude a transfer of free fatty acids (poorly soluble in aqueous media) during a contact between tumor cell and lymphocyte. Such contacts are essential for T cell killing, although cell death can occur after detachment of killer lymphocytes (Sanderson and Taylor, 1975).

The possible involvement of free fatty acids during the early events following lymphocyte stimulation and in the cytotoxic action of lymphocytes, together with recent evidence that prostaglandin biosynthesis can be affected by the availability of free fatty acid substrate (see next section) has led us to consider a possible regulatory function for free fatty acids either within the cell or in the local lymphatic microenvironment. Injected fatty acids, particularly arachidonic acid, can produce (with increasing total dosage) stimulation of lymphoid cell division, immune unresponsiveness, or lymphocytolysis (Meade and Mertin, 1976). The ability to produce these effects would be a suitable property for an immunoregulatory substance. Lymphocytes possess receptors for the major hormones involved in the regulation of fatty acid metabolism—insulin (Krug *et al.*, 1972) and corticosteroids (Turnell and Burton, 1975). They also have β-adrenergic receptors (Williams *et al.*, 1976). The physiological role of such hormone receptors is largely unknown, although corticosteroids have long been used clinically as immunosuppressants. Steroids are known both to stimulate and to inhibit phospholipase activity (Blackwell *et al.*, 1977). Could they, and perhaps other hormones, interact with the immune system by effects on fatty acid release?

Turnell and colleagues have suggested that glucocorticoid induced lymphocytolysis is mediated through a release of free fatty acids within the cell (Turnell *et al.*, 1973; Turnell and Burton, 1974, 1975). The evidence produced in support of this hypothesis is as follows:

1. The steroid dexamethasone raises the level of free fatty acids in thymic lymphocytes or in cells of a corticosteroid-sensitive mouse lymphosarcoma P1798S, but not in the steroid-resistant subline P1798R.

2. *In vitro*, relatively low concentrations of long-chain free fatty acids cause changes in P1798S cells or thymocytes similar to those produced by steroids, viz., disintegration of the nuclear membrane and ultimately karyolysis. The time sequences of the steroid and fatty acid induced effects are similar. However, the steroid-resistant P1798R subline requires 10-fold higher concentrations of added free fatty acids to show such effects.

3. "Naked" nuclei of either resistant or sensitive sublines are insensitive to doses of steroids similar to those which damage whole cells. Hence the basis of resistance in the P1798R subline lies outside the nucleus, although this is the first organelle to be damaged. However, nuclei from either subline are sensitive to free fatty acids.

4. Resistant subline cells, forced to accumulate free fatty acids by having their free fatty acid metabolism blocked by citral undergo lymphocytolysis. Turnell and colleagues visualize the source of free fatty acids being intracellular triglycerides, the level of which is higher in sensitive than resistant P1798 sublines.

Essential fatty acid deficiency potentiates the thymolytic activity of glucocorticoids in male mice, but the mechanism of this is unknown (C. J. Meade and J. Sheena, unpublished).

A second way in which lymphocyte fatty acid concentration might be regulated is via their interrelationship with cholesterol concentrations. Lymphoid cells have, compared with lung, liver, heart or kidney tissue a high level of sterol esters (Kigoshi and Ito, 1973). There is a good correlation between concentrations of free cholesterol and free fatty acids within lymphoid cells (Kigoshi et al., 1976). This might indicate (a) cholesterol esters are the major source of lymphoid cell free fatty acids (but cholesterol esters generally are less liable to hydrolysis than triglycerides), (b) free fatty acids control cholesterol levels, or (c) cholesterol levels control free fatty acid concentrations. Biosynthesis and uptake of cholesterol by lymphocytes are in turn regulated by a low density lipoprotein for which lymphocytes can develop a specific receptor (Ho et al., 1976, 1977). We still need to know (1) the relation of this lipoprotein to the low density lipoprotein which suppresses, even at low concentrations, immune function both in vitro (Curtiss and Edgington, 1976) and in vivo (Curtiss et al., 1977); (2) whether the ability of dietary linoleate to lower serum levels of some lipoproteins (Nichaman et al., 1967) extends to either the cholesterol binding or immunoregulatory lipoproteins; and (3) whether diets of different linoleate content, which alter plasma cholesterol concentrations (Alfin-Slater et al., 1954), also affect lymphoid tissue cholesterol levels.

A third way in which fatty acids might be involved in the regulation of immune responses is via their release from brown fat. Brown fat deposits are prominent in both very young and hibernating animals, both of which show poor immune responses (Brent, 1958; Sidky and Auerbach, 1968; Sidky et al., 1969; Sidky and Hayward, 1972). Removal of most of the brown fat in neonatal rats enhances T cell responses (e.g., rejection of a thyroid graft, the delayed skin reaction to bovine serum albumin, the severity of an autoimmune response to brain tissue), but only if the thymus is also present (Janković et al., 1975). There is no effect on B cell functions (e.g., production of antibodies against sheep red blood cells or bovine serum albumin). The active factor can be extracted with chloroform (Sidky et al., 1972). It is attractive to relate these results to the depression of thymus weight by arachidonic and other fatty acids (Meade and Mertin,

1976), but in the absence of any data on the effects of removal of brown fat on levels of different fatty acids in serum and lymphoid organs, we consider such an interpretation highly speculative. Other possibilities, e.g., that brown fat acts as a "reservoir" for corticosteroids, must also be considered (Ratsimamanga and Nigeon-Dureuil, 1959).

V. Fatty Acids in Macrophages

The fatty acid profile of macrophages has been little studied despite the importance of this cell type in phagocytosis and killing of microorganisms, and in the modulation of lymphocyte function. Analysis of the fatty acid composition of the macrophage plasma membrane is hampered by the difficulties that are involved in its separation from the relatively large quantities of endoplasmic reticulum characteristic of this cell type. However, the membranes of phagocytic vesicles can be separated. Most of their lipid is derived from the cell membrane. Arachidonic acid constitutes almost 20% of the total phospholipid fatty acid content of macrophages (Mason *et al.,* 1972). The phagocytic vesicles of rabbit alveolar macrophages also contain a high proportion (just less than 15%) of arachidonic acid, but the overall ratio of polyunsaturated to saturated fatty acids is slightly lower than that of the whole cell.

Macrophage membranes undergo profound morphologic changes when exposed to particulate matter, immune complexes, or nonantibody soluble T cell products (lymphokines). Macrophages, like lymphocytes and many other cell types, possess enzyme(s) capable of acylating lysophosphatides. Elsbach and Levy (1968) showed that phagocytosis of inert particles by rabbit alveolar macrophages tripled the formation of phosphatidylcholine or phosphatidylethanolamine from their respective labeled lyso-derivatives. It is not known, however, what part increased acylation of lysophosphatides by fatty acids plays in the phagocytosis process. However, alteration of the fatty acid composition of macrophage membranes by growth in media of different fatty acid compositions does affect phagocytic activity. Schroit *et al.* (1976) reported decreased uptake of ^{125}I-labeled Shigella by murine macrophages grown in medium containing elaidic acid (trans, 18:1) instead of oleic acid (cis, 18:1).

Macrophage lysosomes are rich in lipases, and during phagocytosis hydrogen peroxide is generated. There is evidence that peroxidation of polyunsaturated fatty acids such as arachidonic acid, occurs during phagocytosis. Assay of malondialdehyde, produced by the peroxidation of certain unsaturated fatty acids, is an easy way of quantifying this process. Alveolar macrophages produce malondialdehyde when ingesting polystyrene beads or emulsified paraffin oil (Mason *et al.,* 1972). Aldehydes such as those produced by lipid peroxidation may play a role in bacterial killing (Jacobs *et al.,* 1970).

The possibility that lysosomal lipases may act to release arachidonic acid from macrophage membranes has important implications, for example for the role of macrophages in prostaglandin production. These will be discussed in the next section.

Aluminium hydroxide and arlacel A enhance the breakdown by macrophages of phospholipids to free fatty acids and lysophosphatides, and it has been suggested that such breakdown may underlie the adjuvanticity of these substances (Munder *et al.,* 1969).

VI. Fatty Acids as Prostaglandin Precursors

Some derivatives of linoleic acid, notably di-homo-γ-linolenic acid and arachidonic acid, can undergo oxidation and cyclization to yield unstable endoperoxides which may be transformed either to other short-lived metabolites (thromboxanes, etc.) or to the more stable (but also short-lived) primary prostaglandins. The principal prostaglandins which have been used in immunological studies are those of the E and F series. Their major biosynthetic pathway is

There is a considerable literature on the effect of prostaglandins on immunity which, fortunately, has recently been reviewed in detail (Pelus and Strausser, 1977). The physiological significance of much of this work is difficult to evaluate. Prostaglandins are produced in a wide variety of nonimmunological as well as immunological situations and have many effects other than those on the immune system. Much of the experimental work describes effects of prostaglandins in tissue culture at concentrations several orders of magnitude larger than the nanogram levels normally found in tissues.

Bearing in mind these limitations, we may summarize the literature as follows.

A. PROSTAGLANDINS, ESPECIALLY THOSE OF THE E SERIES, INHIBIT THE IMMUNE RESPONSE

Inhibition of both T and B cell lymphocyte functions has been described, and different authors (using different experimental systems) have claimed the principal effect of prostaglandins is either on one or the other of the two major sets of lymphocytes.

Smith *et al.* (1971b), Offner and Clausen (1974), and Stockman and Mumford (1974) have all reported that E-type prostaglandins (and in some of these papers other prostaglandins) cause a reduction in the ability of phytohaemagglutinin to stimulate T cells. Prostaglandins have been reported also to inhibit *in vitro* T cell cytotoxicity (Lichtenstein *et al.*, 1972; Strom *et al.*, 1974, 1977) and *in vivo* graft rejection (Loose and diLuzio, 1973; Anderson *et al.*, 1975; Strom *et al.*, 1977). Stockman and Mumford found prostaglandin E_2 produced a more than 50% inhibition of phytohaemagglutinin stimulation of [^{3}H]thymidine or [^{3}H]uridine uptake, whereas there was no effect on the response to pokeweed mitogen (which preferentially stimulates B cells).

The opposite conclusion, that E-type prostaglandins inhibit B rather than T cells, was arrived at by two other groups of workers. Quagliata *et al.* (1973), though unable to demonstrate an effect of E-type prostaglandins alone, were able to demonstrate increased immunosuppression (prolonged allograft survival) in mice also treated with procarbazine hydrochloride which is a powerful T cell depressant. They concluded that the principal target of PGE_1 activity was the B cell, both from the preceding observation and a decrease in the numbers of B but not T cells in the spleens of PGE_1 treated animals. An effect on B rather than T cells was also implied by the observation of Zurier and Quagliata (1971) that E-type prostaglandins inhibited the antibody response to sheep red blood cells but not delayed hypersensitivity to PPD. Individual anti-sheep red blood cell antibody-producing lymphocytes (B cells) can be counted by suspending them in a red cell containing agar and measuring the number of lytic plaques formed as a result of antibody-mediated lysis. There are several reports of inhibition of "plaque cell" formation by prostaglandins (Melmon *et al.*, 1974; Plescia *et al.*, 1975a,b).

In the interpretation of all the experiments, possible cytotoxic effects of high ($> 10^{-3}M$) concentrations of prostaglandins *in vitro*, and stress-promoting effects *in vivo* must be carefully considered (Berenbaum *et al.,* 1976).

B. PROSTAGLANDINS CAN BE PRODUCED BY CELLS OF THE IMMUNE SYSTEM

Ferraris *et al.* (1974) found *in vitro* prostaglandin biosynthesis was increased following antigenic stimulation of spleen cells or unpurified human peripheral leucocytes. After glass-bead purification, known to deplete macrophages, no stimulation of peripheral leucocyte prostaglandin biosynthesis was observed, even though lymphocyte [^{3}H]thymidine uptake was still stimulated. Gordon *et al.* (1976) found that exudate cell populations (60–80% macrophages, 10% lymphocytes) were considerably better than lymph node cell populations ($> 90\%$ lymphocytes) in producing prostaglandin E_2. This suggests the macrophage activated, for example, by lymphokines is a major site of E-type prostaglandin biosynthesis. Since PGEs can also inhibit the activation of lymphocytes and the production of soluble mediators similar to those thought to cause macrophage activation, the possibility exists of a homeostatic mechanism (Morley, 1974):

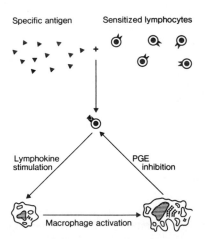

The existence of such a feedback cycle *in vivo* was supported by the studies of Osheroff *et al.* (1975) and Webb and Osheroff (1976). These workers found that formation of 19 S antibody against sheep red blood cells was enhanced by drugs blocking prostaglandin synthesis. Injection of sheep red blood cells caused, within a few minutes, a 20- to 80-fold,

T lymphocyte-dependent increase in splenic prostaglandin $F_{2\alpha}$. The increase in the prostaglandin $F_{2\alpha}$ content of the thymus (which contains few macrophages) was much smaller (twofold). The rate of increase in prostaglandin $F_{2\alpha}$ following challenge with a soluble antigen (bovine gamma globulin) was slower than following injection of sheep red blood cells, and was bimodal, the later increase occurring at 48 hours. Such timing is closer in order of magnitude to the time required *in vitro* for most macrophage activation processes to be stimulated by lymphocytes (Nath *et al.*, 1973; Meade *et al.*, 1974).

The evidence for this feedback cycle does not preclude the involvement of prostaglandins in other immunological feedback mechanisms. For example, Zimecki and Webb (1976) showed that drugs blocking prostaglandin biosynthesis could also enhance the *in vitro* antibody response to T-dependent antigens. This effect could still be demonstrated in cultures of highly purified B cells implying a regulatory mechanism involving B cells alone. The possibility of prostaglandin-mediated autoregulation of the macrophage must also be included in view of reports that prostaglandins can inhibit the release of lysosomal enzymes from this cell type (Zurier *et al.*, 1971; Ignarro *et al.*, 1973).

Studies on a variety of tissues have suggested that prostaglandin biosynthesis may be regulated by a number of factors including intracellular cyclic AMP levels. However, mitogenic agents capable of stimulating prostaglandin biosynthesis were found by Ferraris *et al.* (1974) not to significantly influence the cyclic AMP content of mouse spleen cells, while cholera toxin and epinephrine, both of which markedly increased the spleen cell cyclic AMP content, did not stimulate prostaglandin release. Another possible factor regulating prostaglandin biosynthesis is the availability for their fatty acid precursors. This is supported by increased prostaglandin biosynthesis by mouse neoplastic cells supplied with exogenous arachidonic acid (Hong *et al.*, 1976).

Activation of macrophages, which have membranes rich in arachidonic acid, leads to increased release of phospholipase A (Munder *et al.*, 1969). This enzyme can cleave phospholipids to release free fatty acids, which will be able to act as precursors for prostaglandin synthetase. Increased levels of extracellular free fatty acids have been demonstrated histochemically in populations of lymph node cells following immunological stimulation (Cyong and Okada, 1976). The cell populations used in these studies were not specifically purified to remove adherent (macrophage-type) cells, but clearly the major cell type was the lymphocyte, and Cyong and Okada (1976) suggested the lymphocyte as the major source of the free fatty acid generating enzyme(s) in their experiments.

Mertin *et al.* (1977) found that removal of the spleen considerably reduced the ability of linoleic acid to prolong allograft survival. One interpretation of this result is that injected linoleic acid, which increases arachidonic acid levels in the spleen acts, at least in part, by stimulating prostaglandin biosynthesis of splenic macrophages. Possibly prostaglandins are the major immunoinhibitory agent in these experiments.

VII. Modification of the Immune Response *in Vitro* and *in Vivo* by Exogenous Fatty Acids

In view of the importance of fatty acids as membrane constituents and prostaglandin precursors, discussed in previous sections of this review, it is not surprising that provision of exogenous fatty acids *in vitro* or *in vivo* should modify the immune response. Interpretation of observed effects of fatty acids in terms of what is known of their function at the cellular level is, however, difficult. In determining the particular effect of a fatty acid, not only the nature of that fatty acid but also the form of its administration is critical. Thus, for example, glycerol trioleate given as an emulsion by intravenous injection stimulates reticuloendothelial function, whereas given by mouth it is a reticuloendothelial depressant (Berken and Benacerraf, 1968).

Because fatty acids and their esters are insoluble in water, experiments designed to study the effects of fatty acids *in vitro* or *in vivo* must be carefully designed with respect to the presentation of the fatty acid. For example, fatty acids can be "dissolved" in water by first dissolving them in alcohol, then adding this alcoholic solution to the water. However, it cannot be assumed, even after this procedure, that all the fatty acid is in the aqueous phase without a subsequent analysis. For this reason, some workers have preferred to provide fatty acids *in vitro* bound to albumin, but using this form of presentation for fatty acids complicates analysis of results by adding the rate of dissociation of the albumin–fatty acid complex to those factors which might determine fatty acid activity.

A. EFFECT OF EXOGENOUS FATTY ACIDS ON *in Vitro* LYMPHOCYTE STIMULATION

The effect of added fatty acids on lymphocyte stimulation has been studied using dissolved free fatty acids by Mertin and Hughes (1975) and using albumin-bound fatty acids by Weyman *et al.* (1977).

Mertin *et al.* (1974) and Mertin and Hughes (1975) reported that linoleic acid and, to an even greater extent, arachidonic acid suppressed antigen- (PPD) or phytohaemagglutinin-induced increase in lymphocyte

[³H]uridine uptake, while palmitic, stearic, or oleic acid had very little specific activity. Mihas *et al.* (1975), following [³H]thymidine uptake, supported this finding and further showed that inhibitory doses of fatty acids did not affect cell viability. An inhibitory effect of linoleic and arachidonic acids was also reported by Offner and Clausen (1974), who observed an early event following lymphocyte stimulation, the increased incorporation of myo-(2-³H)inositol into phosphatidylinositol. Weyman *et al.* (1975, 1977), while confirming the ability of linoleic and arachidonic acids to inhibit phytohaemagglutinin-stimulated [¹⁴C]uridine uptake, did not agree that polyunsaturation was important in determining activity. They also showed appreciable inhibitory activity of the saturated fatty acids, heptadecanoic and stearic acids, as well as the mono-unsaturated oleic acid. In part, this may represent a difference in interpretation of results rather than in the results themselves. Mertin and Hughes (1975) had also reported inhibition of [³H]uridine uptake by stearic, palmitic, and oleic acids, but finding a similar percentage inhibition in unstimulated as well as stimulated lymphocytes had suggested that this inhibition might be nonspecific. Only with linoleic and arachidonic acid was inhibition of phytohaemagglutinin-stimulated uptake significantly different to that of unstimulated cells, and it was for these acids that they postulated an effect on the lymphocyte–antigen or lymphocyte–mitogen interaction. C. Weyman *et al.* were able to repeat this finding (personal communication), but when shorter culture times were employed (42 hours), there was no appreciable depression by any fatty acid of [³H]uridine uptake in unstimulated cells. Effects of saturated fatty acids on uptake in stimulated cells, however, could still be observed (Weyman *et al.*, 1977). It would thus seem that saturated fatty acids can, under appropriate conditions, also inhibit mitogen–lymphocyte interaction. Such an observation does not exclude a specific role for linoleic and arachidonic acid, because nonessential fatty acids can, possibly by acting as competitive substrates, influence the metabolism of essential fatty acids (Lowry and Tinsley, 1966; Dhopeshwarkar and Mead, 1961; Alfin-Slater and Aftergood, 1968). Furthermore, certain saturated fatty acids, particularly lauric and myristic acids, are inhibitors of the conversion of arachidonic acid to prostaglandin E_2 (Robak *et al.*, 1975).

Weyman *et al.* (1977) further reported that when saturated fatty acids were added to an incubation mixture containing unsaturated fatty acids, inhibition by the unsaturated fatty acids was markedly decreased. Myristic acid, which by itself had no effect on [³H]uridine uptake by phytohaemagglutinin-stimulated cells, was particularly effective at abrogating inhibition. Myristic acid also blocked inhibition by saturated fatty acids. This observation made it less likely that the effects of linoleic, arachidonic, and other fatty acids could be accounted for merely by a toxic action. Investigation of viability by trypan blue exclusion also supported this; Weyman *et al.* could not demonstrate any significant effect on cell viability of the concentrations of fatty acids they employed.

B. *In Vivo* EFFECTS OF FATTY ACIDS

In vivo, the fatty composition of the cells of the immune system can be altered by diet (Tsang *et al.,* 1976; Meade *et al.,* 1978) or by direct injection of fatty acids. Subcutaneous injection is a useful way of providing fatty acids *in vivo* without the toxicity sometimes associated with intraperitoneal administration (Ring *et al.,* 1974), but fatty deposits around the injection site suggest absorption is slow, and analysis is required to give an idea of the changes in serum and organ fatty acid levels which are being produced. Granulomae can also sometimes form at the site of injection, especially when larger quantities of fatty acid are employed. Dietary manipulation of fatty acid levels, while more physiological, has the disadvantage that some of the immunologically most interesting fatty acids are too rare and too expensive to be used as dietary supplements. Intravenous injection of fatty acid or fatty acid ester emulsions has also been used; in this case it appears that the reticuloendothelial system becomes the primary target. The point made earlier, that the same fatty acid can produce different effects depending on its mode of administration, must be emphasized.

The effects of subcutaneous injection of a variety of long-chain fatty acids were studied in mice by Meade and Mertin (1976). We found three types of effect produced following progressively longer periods of fatty acid administration. Initially there was immune activation, then a blocking of reactivity to antigen and finally lymphocytolysis. Most of these studies were made with linoleic acid, although the more expensive arachidonic acid was more effective.

One of the earliest effects of linoleic acid injection was stimulation of [^{125}I]udR uptake in thymus, spleen, and lymph nodes. [^{125}I]udR is an analogue of thymidine, and its uptake is a measure of DNA synthesis, which will be increased with an increased rate of cell division. Other changes associated with immune activation included increased cell division in the bone marrow, and changes in the spleen, such as increased proportion of red pulp and granulocyte precursors, similar to those seen after stimulation by a graft from a different strain of mouse. Autoradiographic analysis showed the lymphocyte was one of the cell types stimulated, although in the spleen other cell types also took up radioactive label following injection of an [^{125}I]udR/[^{3}H]methylthymidine "cocktail."

The idea that linoleic acid could activate the immune system was further supported by comparison between a skin graft from a different strain of mouse, and subcutaneous injection of linoleic acid in their influence on various organ weights. Just as lymph node and spleen weight was increased in skin grafted mice, while thymus weight was decreased, so the same pattern of changes was observed following subcutaneous linoleic acid treatment. The order of activity of fatty acids both in increasing spleen weight (Meade and Mertin, 1976) and decreasing thymus weight (C. J. Meade, unpublished) was arachidonic acid > linoleic acid > α-linolenic acid. Depression of thymus weight (which occurred also in adrenalec-tomized animals and was therefore not simply a stress effect) was par-ticularly easy to quantitate. Figure 4 shows five fatty acids compared: arachidonic acid, and those fatty acids closer to arachidonic acid along its biosynthetic pathway were most effective. Carbon clearance studies showed arachidonic and linoleic acid, injected subcutaneously, were potent activators of the reticuloendothelial system, while α-linolenic acid had no activity. This contrasts with diLuzio and Blickens' 1966 report of reticu-loendothelial system depression by the methyl esters of linoleic acid and arachidonic acid, injected as an intravenous emulsion, and may reflect once again the importance of mode of administration on the biological activity of fatty acids.

Subcutaneous injection of linoleic or (better) arachidonic acid, accord-ing to the schedules used in the Meade and Mertin studies, has been shown to raise the level of arachidonic acid in lymphoid tissues (M. Gurr, private communication). The stimulation of lymphocyte division by such injections is therefore compatible with the theories (discussed previously) which

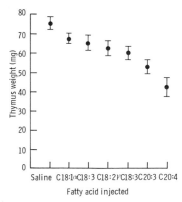

Fɪɢ. 4. Effect of different fatty acids on thymus weight. CBA mice received 100 μl of fatty acid spread over 10 days and four subcutaneous injections (C. J. Meade, unpublished).

suggest a role for a rise in membrane arachidonate in lymphocyte triggering. Of course, any antigen will stimulate lymphocyte division, but linoleic and arachidonic acids, being low-molecular-weight normal body constituents, are unlikely to serve as the good antigens, which their powerful *in vivo* activity would imply. Nevertheless, it must be emphasized that many substances not thought to have a role in lymphocyte triggering can also stimulate lymphocyte division *in vivo,* and our results are compatible with, rather than evidence for, the Ferber and Resch theories.

A second group of *in vivo* effects of subcutaneous linoleic or arachidonic acid may be summarized as interference in the interaction of the immune system with antigen. Longer treatment with subcutaneous linoleic acid was shown to reduce the ability of grafts to stimulate lymphocyte division (measured by [^{125}I]udR uptake) in the thymus and lymph nodes (Meade and Mertin, 1976). A parallel may be drawn to the inhibition by this fatty acid of lymphocyte stimulation, *in vitro* (referred to earlier). It has also been shown that certain fatty acids cause a small but significant prolongation of graft survival, the effectiveness again being in the following order: arachidonic > linoleic > α-linolenic acid (Mertin, 1976; Meade and Mertin, 1976). This effect is most readily seen in weak graft rejection systems (e.g., skin from a C3H strain mouse transplanted onto a CBA recipient) but some effect can be observed in strong systems (e.g., A strain skin on a CBA recipient).

It must always be taken into account that a nonspecific stress will also prolong graft survival. In the absence of antioxidants, linoleic and arachidonic acid readily oxidize to toxic peroxides. We were, therefore, careful to aliquot fatty acids used for our studies into small samples kept at $-20°C$. In our experiments, mice were treated with a mean daily dose of 10 μl of fatty acid, and for showing prolongation of graft survival, treatment was continued for 14 or 16 days. Using this regimen, the mortality associated with treatment was negligible and weight gain was similar to, or slightly less than, weight gain of saline-treated controls. By contrast, the grafting procedure itself was always associated with a significant weight loss, presumably resulting from the stress of surgery. It therefore seems that, in our hands, stress associated with treatment was likely to be negligible compared with the stress associated with the surgery of skin grafting.

Another example of inhibition of an immune response by subcutaneous linoleic acid is the reduced accumulation of T cells in the spleens of mice challenged by an intraperitoneal injection of ascitic tumor (Meade and Mertin, 1976). This may represent an abrogation of cell trapping or an effect on stimulation of cell division within the spleen. T cell killing by spleen cells was also reduced (Mertin, 1976).

How are the immunosuppressive effects of linoleic and arachidonic acid to be explained? These effects are preceded by effects associated with immune activation. Levey and Medawar (1966) suggested the concept of *sterile activation* to explain the action of antilymphocyte serum, and one suggestion is that linoleic and arachidonic acid might act similarly to forestall or supplant other immunological commitments. Phytohaemagglutinin, which also nonspecifically activates lymphocytes, also prolongs graft survival (Markley *et al.*, 1967).

Prolongation of allograft survival can also be produced by oral administration of linoleic acid (Ring *et al.*, 1974), and a diet poor in linoleic acid accelerates allograft rejection (Mertin and Hunt, 1976). Detailed studies of the effect of orally administered fatty acids on the lymphoreticular system have not, as yet, been made, and it is not known whether effects on immune organs similar to those seen following subcutaneous administration occur. Preliminary studies (C. J. Meade, unpublished) suggest that depression of thymus weight can also be produced by oral fatty acids, while splenomegaly is not seen.

Prolonged subcutaneous administration of linoleic or arachidonic acids caused damage to the lymphoid organs and particularly the spleen. Time-course experiments suggested that the immunosuppressive effects of these fatty acids could not be solely accounted for by this cytotoxic activity. There was a specificity of damage, severe splenic necrosis being observed without damage to liver tissue (Meade and Mertin, 1976). Free fatty acids are more toxic than the same fatty acids esterified in triglycerides (Morgenstern, 1968; Turnell *et al.*, 1973), and it is tempting to relate the sensitivity of lymphocytes to cytolysis to their high free fatty acid content (Kigoshi and Ito, 1973).

C. EFFECTS OF INTRAVENOUS FATTY ESTER EMULSIONS

Much of the earliest work on the role of fatty acids in immunity consisted of studies on the effects of injected fatty ester emulsions in experimental animals. Intravenous or intraperitoneal injection of a wide variety of fatty acid or fatty acid ester emulsions caused lymphoid organ necrosis (Shivas and Fraser, 1959). The spleen was a particular target for such emulsions, and this led Stuart (1960) to coin the term *chemical splenectomy* for the effects of intravenous ethyl palmitate emulsions. The dose of emulsion required to produce these effects was relatively large, and the physical form was critical to activity (Shivas and Fraser, 1959). It seems likely, therefore, that emulsified lipids act, in part, in the same way as other colloidal materials which, though chemically inert, can also produce lymphoid tissue necrosis, e.g., colloidal gold (Hahn *et al.*, 1956). The mechanism of the effect of all these colloids is thought to be via the reticuloendothelial system. Doses of ethyl palmitate able to produce splenic necrosis profoundly depressed reticuloendothelial system function, as measured by colloidal carbon clearance. Since carbon clearance is primarily a function of liver rather than splenic reticuloendothelial function, it is unlikely that changes in this parameter are only secondary to the splenic damage. Further, low doses of ethyl palmitate, too low to cause splenic necrosis, still affect reticuloendothelial function. Changes in macrophages must therefore be considered as possible causes of the changes in the lymphoid tissue.

Although the route and physical form of the injected material is important, the chemical nature of the lipid also appears to play some role. Thus, intravenous injection of 2-oleodistearin, glyceryl tricaprate, or glyceryl oleate produced a mild stimulation of reticuloendothelial function, while intravenous injection of emulsions of a wide variety of other methyl, ethyl, butyl, or cholesteryl esters of long-chain saturated or unsaturated fatty acids depress the reticuloendothelial system (Stuart *et al.,* 1960a,b; Stuart, 1962; Wooles and diLuzio, 1963; Stuart and Cooper, 1963; Stuart and Davidson, 1963; diLuzio and Wooles, 1964; diLuzio and Blickens, 1966; diLuzio, 1972). Therefore it is not enough to view the lipid particles just as an inert food for hungry macrophages which are inactive when they have "overeaten." Rather, the lipid must contribute to the biochemistry of the macrophage and its membrane. This idea is supported by Blickens and diLuzio's 1965 study on the metabolism of methyl palmitate, a potent reticuloendothelial depressant. Twenty-four hours after injection of radioactive methyl palmitate there was little storage of methyl palmitate in liver, lung, or spleen, nor was there a measurable alteration in tissue lipid levels. Therefore, saturation of the reticuloendothelial system by lipid was unlikely. Further, the distribution of radiolabeled methyl palmitate differed from most other colloids known to be cleared by phagocytosis by macrophages, and clearance was not competitively affected by prior injection of colloidal carbon. Hence, it appears phagocytosis is not even a major mechanism for methyl palmitate clearance. Quite how methyl palmitate or other fatty acid esters interact with the macrophage is not known. Structure activity studies made by Cooper (1964) in an attempt to relate stimulation of ^{131}I-labeled triolein clearance *in vitro* and *in vivo* to the chemistry of saturated triglycerides showed no simple relationships, except that *in vivo* activity was related to carbon chain length, deviations from a length of 10 atoms decreasing the ability to stimulate reticuloendothelial function.

Several of these fatty ester emulsions also suppress immune responsiveness. Formation of antibodies following challenge with sheep red blood cells has been shown to be lowered by intravenous injection of emulsions of methyl palmitate (diLuzio and Wooles, 1964; Wooles and diLuzio, 1963), ethyl palmitate, or cholesterol oleate (Stuart and Davidson, 1964), and a similar result has been obtained using methyl palmitate with a soluble antigen, bovine serum albumin (Ohbuchi, 1968). At the doses employed, these agents also depressed reticuloendothelial system function. The immunosuppressive effects could occur at doses of ester below those at which there was damage to lymphoid tissue and were not necessarily associated with lymphopenia. Morrow and diLuzio (1965) demonstrated an altered clearance of sheep red cell antigen in mice treated with methyl palmitate, so they suggested immunosuppression might be associated with altered processing of antigen by macrophages. Handling of an antigen by macrophages can alter its immunogenicity. The role of macrophages in immune responses is not, as yet, precisely known. Different theories have visualized the macrophage, for example, as an antigen concentration site, particularly for T cell dependent antigens (Lachmann, 1971), or as a site of production of a "super" (possibly RNA associated) antigen which might be transferred to potential antibody-forming cells by intercellular bridges (Cruchaud *et al.*, 1970). Emulsions of fatty esters such as methyl palmitate have been suggested as possible tools to throw light on this problem. For such a purpose it is important to know whether, at the dose level employed in an experiment, the reticuloendothelial system is the only system being affected, for example, by a methyl palmitate emulsion. Kauffman *et al.* (1967), using dogs, found that doses of methyl palmitate below those sufficient to cause reticuloendothelial depression were still able to cause depletion of the follicles of the lymph nodes and spleen. Further, this low dose could inhibit homograft sensitization as measured by second set rejection time of renal transplants following methyl palmitate treatment after first-set grafting. Caution should, perhaps, therefore be exercised before describing any process affected by methyl palmitate as being necessarily macrophage mediated.

VIII. Dietary Fatty Acids, Immunity, and Disease

In previous sections we have described the role of fatty acids in the biochemistry of immune cells and the modification of the immune response by fatty acids. In this section we shall discuss whether any of the work described before may have implications for human disease. Until now, there has been little published work relating to fatty acids, immunity, and disease. We shall therefore concentrate upon (1) identifying diseases in which it might be worthwhile to look for involvement of altered fatty acid levels in immune responses and (2) presenting alternative, immunological explanations for data relating to dietary fat and disease, usually interpreted without reference to immunology.

Important factors affecting the balance of fatty acids in serum and tissues are diet and the concentrations of hormones such as insulin, adrenalin, etc. Diet is particularly important in determining concentrations of those polyunsaturated fatty acids such as linoleic acid, which cannot be synthesized in the body (Beare and Kates, 1964). Recently, nutrition councils in a number of countries have encouraged the public to increase their consumption of polyunsaturated fats. Recommendations followed work associating diets rich in such fats with decreased incidence of atheroma (Boldingh, 1975). Implications of this recommended change in dietary pattern for long-term immunity to, for example, viruses and tumors remain to be explored. When, in experimental situations, dietary manipulation or injection has been used to alter fatty acid levels, the amounts of fatty acids required to produce immunological effects have been large, and the effects themselves small (Mertin, 1976; Meade and Mertin, 1976; Mertin and Hunt, 1976; Meade et al., 1978). It therefore only seems worthwhile to look for effects of altered fatty acid intake on immunity when there are considerable differences in intake. Patients participating in clinical trials of diets high in polyunsaturated fats for the prevention of cardiac disease may be a group suitable for additional immunological investigation. Another group liable to big differences in polyunsaturated fat intake are babies. Many artificial milks fed to babies are low in polyunsaturated fatty acids in comparison with mother's milk; some manufacturers supplement the milk with linoleate. In early life, when milk is the only source of nutriment, changes in milk composition can alter serum and tissue fatty acid composition. How does this affect the resistance of babies to infection, or, for example, their response to vaccination? Nagai et al. (1963) reported higher antimeasles antibody titer, and fewer febrile symptoms, in babies immunized with live measles vaccine and fed linoleate supplemented rather than ordinary artificial milk.

Nonspecific binding of measles virus to a subpopulation of T cells is enhanced by linoleic acid derivative, prostaglandin E_1 (Zurier et al., 1977). If there were an effect of linoleic acid levels on the response to measles virus, then this would be interesting not only because of the possibility of an altered response to vaccination but also because in a chronic disease of the central nervous system, multiple sclerosis, both impaired reactivity to measles virus (Zabriskie, 1975) and lowered serum and lymphocyte linoleate levels have been described (Thompson, 1975; Mahler, 1975). Lowered linoleate serum concentrations are not specific to multiple sclerosis; they occur to some extent in other neurological diseases (Love et al.,

1974; Mahler, 1975) and have been described in cystic fibrosis (Rosen-lund *et al.,* 1974). Wolfram *et al.* (1974) described a fall in serum choles-teryl linoleate in patients after major surgery. Sudo (1962) described an essential fatty acid deficiency in rats with an experimental streptococcal infection. Possibly lowered serum concentrations of essential fatty acid represent a response to prolonged stress.

In the following sections we shall discuss (in a deliberately one-sided way) whether any of the data accumulated on fatty acids and heart disease, tumor growth, or multiple sclerosis might be interpretable in an immuno-logical context.

A. CARDIOVASCULAR DISEASE

The increased levels of antimilk antibodies in the serum of patients recovering from myocardial infarction (Davies *et al.,* 1974) has led to suggestions of an involvement of autoimmune processes in atheroma. However, as yet there is no evidence that such increased antimilk titers are not an effect rather than a cause of cardiac disease (e.g., a result of increased permeability of the intestine to denatured milk antigens). It seems premature to involve such postulated autoimmune processes in ex-planations for protective effects of polyunsaturated acids. In patients with cardiovascular disease associated with increased fatty acid serum concen-trations, Dil'man (1976) has found decreased *in vitro* lymphocyte respon-siveness to phytohaemagglutinin; normalization of the serum fatty acid concentrations after treatment with phenformin resulted in restitution of the immune response.

B. TUMOR GROWTH

Influences on the immune system provide one explanation for the known effects of alterations in the dietary fatty acid content on the incidence of tumors in experimental animals following treatment with carcinogens. Carroll and Khor (1975) found that high-fat diets predisposed rats to mammary tumors after a single oral dose of 7,12-dimethylbenz-2-anthra-cene (DMBA). Unsaturated fats were more effective than saturated fats, a finding confirmed by Hopkins *et al.* (1976). The latter workers found that a diet rich in polyunsaturated fats was effective even when begun after DMBA administration but ineffective when fed before administration of the carcinogen with a switch to a saturated fat-rich diet afterwards. Carroll and Khor (1975) could obtain an enhanced yield of mammary tumors following DMBA administration when the switch to a corn oil-supplemented (i.e., polyunsaturated-fat-rich) diet was made as much as two weeks after administration of carcinogen. Rao and Abraham (1976) found enhanced growth of a mammary adenocarcinoma transplanted into mice fed a linoleate-rich diet. It is therefore likely that the effect of polyunsaturated fat-rich diets is on the survival and proliferation of tumor cells (in which immune mechanisms may be involved) rather than on the initial event of neoplastic transformation. The opposite effect, increased tumor resistance in mice fed an essential fatty acid-deficient diet, has been shown following methylcholanthrene treatment of mice by Mertin and Hunt (1976). However, the effects of high- or low-fat diets on tumor growth may merely reflect a more general effect of availability of nutrients, either to the tumor itself or to cells of the immune system. Other changes in nutritional status, such as protein–calorie malnutrition, have also been shown to alter the rate of growth of tumors, and immunological factors have been implicated in these effects (José and Good, 1973).

Chemically induced tumors are extremely antigenic in comparison with those which arise spontaneously, and their growth can be affected by agents which alter the immune response. There is doubt about the importance of immune mechanisms in the control of spontaneous tumor growth, despite the attractiveness of concepts of *immune surveillance* (Burnet, 1970). Except for the special cases of lymphoreticular or viral induced tumors, there is not a greatly increased tumor incidence either in patients immunosuppressed after transplantation, or in immunodeficient mice. Therefore, studies on the effect of diet on chemically induced carcinogenesis are not necessarily applicable to the different situation of "spontaneous" tumeriogenesis. Conclusive proof that dietary fats alter either morbidity or mortality from tumors in man has yet to be obtained. Epidemiological studies are complicated by associations between fat consumption and other factors such as obesity. Pearce and Dayton (1971) reported a slightly higher incidence of neoplasms in men eating a diet high in polyunsaturated fats as part of a trial for the prevention of heart disease. This result was on the borderline of significance ($p = 0.06$). No such increase has been observed in other, larger trials (Ederer *et al.,* 1971; Miettinen *et al.,* 1972). The Pearce and Dayton trial included elderly men who, if protected from atherosclerosis, were likely to die of some other cause, and cancer is the next most common cause of death in such a population.

C. MULTIPLE SCLEROSIS

Swank, on the basis of epidemiological data suggesting involvement of dietary factors in multiple sclerosis (Swank *et al.,* 1952), treated multiple sclerosis patients with a diet low in fat and high in oils (i.e., low in saturated but rich in polyunsaturated fats). He claimed his diet had, over

20 years' use, had a beneficial effect on the course of the disease (Swank, 1970). However, Swank's study made no comparison with a proper control group, only with relapse and survival rates reported in the literature. A better trial was the controlled double-blind trial reported by Millar *et al.* (1973). The diet of multiple sclerosis patients was supplemented with either linoleate-rich sunflower seed oil, or with a smaller quantity of oleate-rich olive oil. Relapses tended to be less severe and of shorter duration in the linoleate-supplemented group than in those receiving the oleate mixture, but clear evidence that treatment affected the overall rate of clinical deterioration was not obtained. Even this trial has been the subject of criticism (Vessey, 1975), and more double-blind trials are required to establish conclusively whether polyunsaturated fatty acids are beneficial in multiple sclerosis. There are many suggestions for the mechanism of the postulated beneficial effects of polyunsaturated fatty acids in this disease, and our recent review (Mertin and Meade, 1977) discusses these in detail. One possible mechanism is via the immune system. There is some evidence for involvement of autoimmunity in multiple sclerosis:

1. The presence of lymphocytes and other mononuclear cells in the early perivascular "cuffings" and at the edge of plaques in the central nervous system (Adams, 1977).
2. Similarities between the lesions in multiple sclerosis and iatrogenic allergic encephalomyelitis following injection of rabies vaccine contaminated with nervous tissue (Uchimara and Shiraki, 1957).
3. Presence of oligoclonal IgG in the cerebrospinal fluid (Link, 1973).
4. Increased frequency of multiple sclerosis in subjects having certain histocompatibility antigens on the surface of their lymphocytes, a feature of several autoimmune diseases (Batchelor, 1977).

There is no ideal animal model for multiple sclerosis. Injecting susceptible animals, together with an adjuvant, with homogenates of central nervous system tissue, or a protein extracted from such tissue, termed *myelin basic protein,* induces an allergic encephalomyelitis. This experimental autoimmune disease resembles multiple sclerosis in part clinically, and the observed demyelination in the central nervous system is here also associated with perivascular infiltration of mononuclear cells. Clausen and Møller (1969) showed a diet deficient in essential fatty acids potentiated the ability of injected brain homogenates to produce experimental allergic encephalomyelitis in rats. Selivonchick and Johnston (1975) confirming this also showed a protective effect of oral ethyl linoleate in rats fed a basic diet which was fat deficient. Meade *et al.* (1978) were able to show a protective effect on linoleic acid in guinea pigs fed a standard diet that was adequate in essential fatty acids, but which was sufficiently low for it to be possible to significantly raise serum linoleate levels by feeding.

These experiments can be interpreted in many ways. Clausen and Møller considered their observations largely in terms of altered myelin fatty acid composition affecting myelin stability. Unfortunately, the fatty acid analyses they use to support their hypothesis disagree with other reported figures for brain lipid composition. Selivonchick and Johnston (1975) found the lipid composition of myelin was little changed by their dietary treatment; Meade *et al.* (1978) reported their feeding schedule produced little change in brain fatty acid composition in normal animals, although serum and lymph node composition were altered. It therefore seems difficult to explain the effect of dietary fats on experimental allergic encephalomyelitis in terms of gross changes in myelin composition, although changes in particular membranes forming a small proporton of the total lipid (e.g., those forming the blood brain barrier) cannot be excluded. One alternative

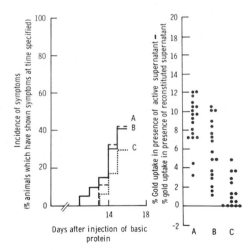

Fig. 5. Effect of linoleic acid on the clinical signs of experimental allergic encephalomyelitis, and the ability of isolated lymph node cells to produce macrophage-activating lymphokines on incubation with basic protein. Each spot represents one animal. Macrophage activation is assayed by the capacity of a macrophage monolayer to take up radioactive colloidal gold. The "active" supernatant is prepared by incubating lymphocytes with basic protein. The reconstituted supernatant is a control. Lymphocytes are incubated without basic protein, which is added only at the end of the culture. Group A = guinea pigs fed linoleic acid from 7 days before until 7 days after injection of basic protein in complete Freund's adjuvant. Group B = guinea pigs injected with basic protein in adjuvant but not fed a dietary supplement. Group C = guinea pigs fed linoleic acid from day 7 until they were killed on day 15. Comparison of groups B and C; significant difference in gold uptake $0.001 > p$. From Meade *et al.* (1978).

hypothesis sees the protective effect of linoleate resulting from an effect on the immune system. In support of this, Meade *et al.* (1978) found that feeding guinea pigs linoleic acid according to a schedule which reduced clinical and histological signs of experimental allergic encephalomyelitis also reduced the ability of isolated lymph node cells to respond to basic protein *in vitro* by production of macrophage-activating substances (Fig. 5).

IX. Summary

Since diLuzio's 1972 review on lipids and immunity in this series, new perspectives have opened. In biochemistry, the importance of fatty acids as membrane components and as prostaglandin precursors is becoming increasingly recognized. Ferber and Resch (1976) have provided a coherent and testable model for lymphocyte activation based on alterations in membrane fatty acid composition that has to be submitted to further investigations applying also, for example, inhibitors of lymphocyte activation. Lipids as lymphocyte membrane components have, up to now, been neglected by immunologists in favor of the protein components. One reason for this is the difficulty in preparing specific antisera against lipids. This contrasts to the relative ease with which immunological methods can be applied to the investigation of membrane proteins, for it was, above all, the use of fluorescent and cytotoxic antisera that allowed their detailed investigation. By contrast, the techniques of lipid analysis are rarely available in immunology laboratories.

We have described the effects of fatty acids on immune cells *in vitro* and *in vivo,* but it is clear we are still largely at the stage of describing phenomena rather than understanding them. We may summarize by saying that a wide variety of fatty acids produce effects on both the lymphoid and reticuloendothelial systems, the actual effects produced depending on the method of administration as well as the chemical nature of the fatty acid. Only when examining the effects of subcutaneously injected unsaturated fatty acids is a pattern discernible, increasing dosages of polyunsaturated fatty acids producing successively immune activation, immune inhibition, and lymphocytolysis, and arachidonic acid and its precursors being more active than other fatty acids tested. Arachidonic acid is also an immediate prostaglandin precursor, and plays a central role, according to the hypothesis of Ferber and Resch (1976), in lymphocyte activation.

With regard to fatty acids, diet, and disease, we consider it too early yet to say whether a role for fatty acids in the biochemistry of immune cells, or effects of fatty acids *in vivo,* have any relevance to human disease. The reticuloendothelial-suppressing and chemical splenectomizing actions of fatty acid ester emulsions have led to suggestions for their therapeutic use in acquired hemolytic anemia (Stuart and Davidson, 1963). The effect of fatty acid esters on reticuloendothelial function may be relevant if these esters are employed to form part of the liposomes used to entrap therapeutic drugs (Gregoriadis, 1977).

Prostaglandins are at present under investigation as suppressors of transplant rejection (Strom *et al.,* 1977). In other fields, natural prostaglandins (as well as thromboxanes and other intermediates) have, until now, frequently proven too unstable and possessing too wide a spectrum of actions to be useful drugs themselves. Research is moving toward the use of more stable synthetic prostaglandins, and as an alternative approach, to prostaglandin precursors (i.e., essential fatty acids) and the relevant biosynthetic mechanisms. The immunosuppressive action of polyunsaturated fatty acids alone is probably too limited to make them useful drugs in, for example, the treatment of transplant rejection, although they may be useful as additional—and nontoxic—constituents in a conventional immunosuppressive therapy (McHugh *et al.,* 1977). They also may find application where their ability to pass through membranes impermeable to water soluble drugs is of advantage. Such barriers include the skin (Press *et al.,* 1974; Friedman *et al.,* 1976) and the blood brain barrier.

To conclude, we hope that we have shown in this review that immunology may have a place in fatty acid research. We only hope that, in making this point, we do not blind the reader to the reality that effects on immunity represent only one of many ways in which fatty acids might be relevant to disease.

References

Adams, C. W. M. (1977). *Br. Med. Bull.* **33,** 15–20.
Alfin-Slater, R. B., and Aftergood, L. (1968). *Physiol. Rev.* **48,** 758–784.
Alfin-Slater, R. B., Aftergood, L., Wells, A. F., and Deuel, H. J. (1954). *Arch. Biochem. Biophys.* **52,** 180–185.
Alter, B. J., and Bach, F. H. (1970). *Cell. Immunol.* **1,** 207–218.
Anderson, C. B., Newton, W. T., and Jaffe, B. M. (1975). *Transplantation* **19,** 527–528.
Barnett, R. E., Scott, R. E., Furcht, L. T., and Kersey, J. H. (1974). *Nature (London)* **249,** 465–466.
Barton, M. A., and Diener, E. (1975). *Transplant. Rev.* **23,** 5–22.
Batchelor, J. R. (1977). *Br. Med. Bull.* **33,** 72–77.
Beare, J. L., and Kates, M. (1964). *Can. J. Biochem.* **42,** 1477–1486.
Berenbaum, M. C., Purves, E. C., and Addison, I. E. (1976). *Immunology* **30,** 815–823.
Berke, G., Sullivan, K. A., and Amos, B. (1972). *J. Exp. Med.* **135,** 1334–1350.
Berken, A., and Benacerraf, B. (1968). *Proc. Soc. Exp. Biol. Med.* **128,** 793–795.

Blackwell, G. J., Flower, R. J., Nijkamp, F. P., and Vane, J. R. (1977). *Br. J. Pharmacol.* **59**, 441 P.

Blickens, D. A., and diLuzio, N. R. (1965). *J. Reticuloendothel. Soc.* **2**, 60–74.

Blomstrand, R., and Liljeqvist, L. (1972). *Acta Chem. Scand.* **26**, 397–399.

Boldingh, J. (1975). *Chem. Ind. (London)* **23**, 984–993.

Brent, L. (1958). *Prog. Allergy* **5**, 271–348.

Burnet, F. M. (1970). *Prog. Exp. Tumor Res.* **13**, 1–27.

Carroll, K. K., and Khor, H. T. (1975). *Prog. Biochem. Pharmacol.* **10**, 308–353.

Charlton, R. K., and Zmijewski, C. M. (1970). *Science* **170**, 636–637.

Clausen, J., and Møller, J. (1969). *Int. Arch. Allergy Appl. Immunol.* **36**, Suppl., 224–233.

Cooper, G. N. (1964). *J. Reticuloendothel. Soc.* **1**, 50–67.

Cruchaud, A., Despont, J. P., Girard, J. P., and Mach, B. (1970). *J. Immunol.* **104**, 1256–1261.

Curtiss, L. K., and Edgington, T. S. (1976). *J. Immunol.* **116**, 1452–1458.

Curtiss, L. K., deHeer, D. H., and Edgington, T. S. (1977). *J. Immunol.* **118**, 648–652.

Cyong, J., and Okada, H. (1976). *Immunology* **30**, 763–767.

Davies, D. F., Rees, B. W. G., Johnson, A. P., Elwood, P. C., and Abernethy, M. (1974). *Lancet* **1**, 1012–1014.

Demel, R. A., Geurts van Kessel, W. S. M., and van Deenen, L. L. M. (1972). *Biochim. Biophys. Acta* **266**, 26–40.

Dhopeshwarkar, G. A., and Mead, J. F. (1961). *J. Am. Oil Chem. Soc.* **38**, 297–301.

Dil'man, V. M., Nemirovsky, V. S., Ostroumova, M. N., L'vovich, E. G., Blagosklonnaya, Ya. V., Uskova, A. L., Mar'enko, A. I., Kondrat'ev, V. B., Semiglazov, V. F., Bershtein, L. M., Bobrov, Ju. F., Vasil'eva, I. A., Tsveibah, A. S., and Gelfond, M. Z. (1976). *Vopr. Onkol.* **12**, 13–17.

diLuzio, N. R. (1972). *Adv. Lipid. Res.* **10**, 43–88.

diLuzio, N. R., and Blickens, D. A. (1966). *J. Reticuloendothel. Soc.* **3**, 250–270.

diLuzio, N. R., and Wooles, W. R. (1964). *Am. J. Physiol.* **206**, 939–943.

Ederer, F., Leren, P., Turpeinen, O., and Frantz, I. D., Jr. (1971). *Lancet* **2**, 203–206.

Elsbach, P., and Levy, S. (1968). *J. Clin. Invest.* **47**, 2217–2229.

Engelhard, V. H., Esko, J. D., Storm, D. R., and Glaser, M. (1976). *Proc. Natl. Acad. Sci. U.S.A.* **73**, 4482–4486.

Farias, R. N., Bloj, B., Morero, R. D., Faustino, S., and Trucco, R. E. (1975). *Biochim. Biophys. Acta* **415**, 231–251.

Feldmann, M., and Palmer, J. (1971). *Immunology* **21**, 685–699.

Ferber, E., and Resch, K. (1973). *Biochim. Biophys. Acta* **296**, 335–349.

Ferber, E., and Resch, K. (1976). *Naturwissenschaften* **63**, 375–381.

Ferber, E., Reilly, C. E., de Pasquale, G., and Resch, K. (1974). *Proc. Leucocyte Cult. Conf.* **8**, 529–534.

Ferber, E., de Pasquale, G. G., and Resch, K. (1975). *Biochim. Biophys. Acta* **398**, 364–376.

Ferraris, V. A., DeRubertis, F. R., Hudson, T. H., and Wolfe, L. (1974). *J. Clin. Invest.* **54**, 378–386.

Friedman, Z., Schochat, S. J., Maisels, M. J., Marks, K. H., and Lamberth, E. L. (1976). *Pediatrics* **58**, 650–654.

Gordon, D., Bray, M. A., and Morley, J. (1976). *Nature (London)* **262**, 401–402.

Gregoriadis, G. (1977). *Nature (London)* **265**, 407–411.

Gurr, M. I., and James, A. T. (1975). "Lipid Biochemistry: An Introduction," 2nd ed. Chapman & Hall, London.

Hadden, J. W., Hadden, E. M., Haddox, M. K., and Goldberg, N. D. (1972). *Proc. Natl. Acad. Sci. U.S.A.* **69**, 3024–3027.

Hahn, P. F., Jackson, A. H., Staggers, F. E., Jackson, M. A., and Carothers, E. L. (1956). *Am. J. Roentgenol., Radium Ther. Nucl. Med.* [N.S.] **75**, 1139–1143.

Ho, Y. K., Brown, M. S., Bilheimer, D. W., and Goldstein, J. L. (1976). *J. Clin. Invest.* **58**, 1465–1474.

Ho, Y. K., Faust, J. R., Bilheimer, D. W., Brown, M. S., and Goldstein, J. L. (1977). *J. Exp. Med.* **145**, 1531–1549.

Hong, S. L., Polsky-Cynkin, R., and Levine, L. (1976). *J. Biol. Chem.* **251**, 776–780.

Hopkins, G. J., West, C. E., and Hard, G. C. (1976). *Lipids* **11**, 328–333.

Horwitz, A. F., Hatten, E., and Burger, M. M. (1974). *Proc. Natl. Acad. Sci. U.S.A.* **71**, 3115–3119.

Ignarro, L. J., Oronsky, A. L., and Perper, R. J. (1973). *Life Sci.* **12**, 193–201.

Jacobs, A. A., Paul, B. B., Strauss, R. R., and Sbarra, A. J. (1970). *Biochem. Biophys. Res. Commun.* **39**, 284–289.

Janković, B. D., Janežić, A., and Popesković, L. (1975). *Immunology* **28**, 597–609.

José, D. G., and Good, R. A. (1973). *Cancer Res.* **33**, 807–812.

Kasai, R., Kitajima, Y., Martin, C. E., Nozawa, Y., Skriver, L., and Thompson, G. A. (1976). *Biochemistry* **15**, 5228–5233.

Kauffman, H. M., Humphrey, L. J., Hanback, L. D., Davis, F., Madge, G. E., and Rittenbury, M. S. (1967). *Transplantation* **5**, 1217–1222.

Kigoshi, S., and Ito, R. (1973). *Experientia* **29**, 1408–1410.

Kigoshi, S., Akiyama, M., and Ito, R. (1976). *Experientia* **32**, 1244–1246.

Krug, U., Krug, F., and Cuatrecasas, P. (1972). *Proc. Natl. Acad. Sci. U.S.A.* **69**, 2604–2608.

Lachmann, P. J. (1971). *Proc. R. Soc. London, Ser. B* **176**, 425–426.

Levey, R. H., and Medawar, P. B. (1966). *Proc. Natl. Acad. Sci. U.S.A.* **56**, 1130–1137.

Lichtenstein, L. M., Gillespie, E., Bourne, H. R., and Henney, C. S. (1972). *Prostaglandins* **2**, 519–528.

Liljeqvist, L. (1973). *Ann. Clin. Res.* **5**, 7–17.

Link, H. (1973). *Ann. Clin. Res.* **5**, 330–336.

Loose, L. D., and diLuzio, N. R. (1973). *J. Reticuloendothel. Soc.* **13**, 70–77.

Love, W. C., Cashell, A., Reynolds, M., and Callaghan, N. (1974). *Br. Med. J.* **3**, 18–21.

Lowry, R. R., and Tinsley, I. J. (1966). *Biochim. Biophys. Acta* **116**, 398–400.

McFarland, W., Heilman, D. H., and Moorhead, J. F. (1966). *J. Exp. Med.* **124**, 851–858.

McHugh, M. I., Wilkinson, R., Elliott, R. W., Field, E. J., Dewar, P., Hall, R. R., Taylor, R. M. R., and Uldall, P. R. (1977). *Transplantation* **24**, 263–267.

Mahler, R. (1975). *In* "Multiple Sclerosis Research" (A. N. Davison *et al.*, eds.), pp. 193–196. Elsevier, Amsterdam.

Markley, K., Evans, G., and Smallman, E. (1967). *Transplantation* **5**, 1535–1537.

Mason, R. J., Stossel, T. P., and Vaughan, M. (1972). *J. Clin. Invest.* **51**, 2399–2407.

Meade, C. J., and Mertin, J. (1976). *Int. Arch. Allergy Appl. Immunol.* **51**, 2–24.

Meade, C. J., Lachmann, P. J., and Brenner, S. (1974). *Immunology* **27**, 227–239.

Meade, C. J., Mertin, J., Sheena, J., and Hunt, R. (1978). *J. Neurol. Sci.* **35**, 291–308.

Melmon, K. L., Bourne, H. R., Weinstein, Y., Shearer, G. M., Kram, J., and Bauminger, S. (1974). *J. Clin. Invest.* **53**, 13–21.

Mertin, J. (1976). *Transplantation* **21**, 1–4.

Mertin, J., and Hughes, D. (1975). *Int. Arch. Allergy Appl. Immunol.* **48**, 203–210.

Mertin, J., and Hunt, R. (1976). *Proc. Natl. Acad. Sci. U.S.A.* **73**, 928–931.

Mertin, J., and Meade, C. J. (1977). *Br. Med. Bull.* **33**, 67–71.

Mertin, J., Hughes, D., Shenton, B. K., and Dickinson, J. P. (1974). *Klin. Wochenschr.* **52**, 248–250.

Mertin, J., Meade, C. J., Hunt, R., and Sheena, J. (1977). *Int. Arch. Allergy Appl. Immunol.* **53**, 469–473.

Miettinen, M., Turpeinen, O., Karvonen, M. J., Elosuo, R., and Paavilainen, E. (1972). *Lancet* **2**, 835–838.

Mihas, A. A., Gibson, R. G., and Hirschowitz, B. I. (1975). *Proc. Soc. Exp. Biol. Med.* **149**, 1026–1028.

Millar, J. H. D., Zilkha, K. J., Langman, M. J. S., Payling Wright, H., Smith, A. D., Belin, J., and Thompson, R. H. S. (1973). *Br. Med. J.* **1**, 765–768.

Morgenstern, E. (1968). *Arzneim.-Forsch.* **18**, 1225–1227.

Morley, J. (1974). *Prostaglandins* **8**, 315–326.

Morrow, S. H., and diLuzio, N. R. (1965). *Proc. Soc. Exp. Biol. Med.* **119**, 647–652.

Munder, P. G., Ferber, E., Modolell, M., and Fischer, H. (1969). *Int. Arch. Allergy Appl. Immunol.* **36**, 117–128.

Nagai, H., Sudo, M., Kuroda, T., and Kurose, T. (1963). *Ann. Paediatr. Jpn.* **9**, 314–319.

Nath, I., Poulter, L. W., and Turk, J. L. (1973). *Clin. Exp. Immunol.* **13**, 455–466.

Nathenson, S. G., and Cullen, S. E. (1974). *Biochim. Biophys. Acta* **344**, 1–25.

Nichaman, M. Z., Sweeley, C. C., and Olson, R. E. (1967). *Am. J. Clin. Nutr.* **20**, 1057–1069.

Nicolau, C., Hildenbrand, K., and Johnson, S. M. (1977). *In* "Virus Transformed Cell Membranes." Academic Press, New York.

Offner, H., and Clausen, J. (1974). *Lancet* **2**, 400–401.

Ohbuchi, S. (1968). *Acta Med. Okayama* **22**, 137–146.

Okada, H., and Cyong, J. (1975). *Jpn. J. Exp. Med.* **45**, 533–534.

Okudaira, H., Kataoka, T., Okada, H., Furuse-Irie, R., Kawachi, S., Nojima, S., and Nishioka, K. (1970). *J. Biochem. (Tokyo)* **68**, 379–394.

Osheroff, P. L., Webb, D. R., and Paulsrud, J. (1975). *Biochem. Biophys. Res. Commun.* **66**, 425–429.

Overath, P., and Träuble, H. (1973). *Biochemistry* **12**, 2625–2634.

Pearce, M. L., and Dayton, S. (1971). *Lancet* **1**, 464–467.

Pelus, L. M., and Strausser, H. R. (1977). *Life Sci.* **20**, 903–914.

Pfizenmaier, K., Starzinski-Powitz, A., Rollinghoff, M., and Wagner, H. (1977). Submitted for publication.

Plescia, O. J., Smith, A. H., Grinwich, K., and Feit, C. (1975a). *In* "Fundamental Aspects of Neoplasia" (A. A. Gottlieb, O. J. Plescia, and D. H. L. Bishop, eds.), pp. 139–151. Springer-Verlag, Berlin and New York.

Plescia, O. J., Smith, A. H., and Grinwich, K. (1975b). *Proc. Natl. Acad. Sci. U.S.A.* **72**, 1848–1851.

Press, M., Hartop, P. J., and Prottey, C. (1974). *Lancet* **1**, 597–598.

Quagliata, F., Lawrence, V. J. W., and Phillips-Quagliata, J. M. (1973). *Cell. Immunol.* **6**, 457–465.

Quastel, M. R., and Kaplan, J. G. (1971). *Exp. Cell Res.* **63**, 230–233.

Rao, G. A., and Abraham, S. (1976). *J. Natl. Cancer Inst.* **56**, 431–432.

Ratsimamanga, A. R., and Nigeon-Dureuil, M. (1959). *C. R. Seances Soc. Biol. Ses Fil.* **153**, 1985–1989.

Resch, K., and Ferber, E. (1972). *Eur. J. Biochem.* **27**, 153–161.

Resch, K., and Ferber, E. (1975). *Proc. Leucocyte Cult. Conf.* **9**, 281–312.

Resch, K., Ferber, E., Odenthal, J., and Fischer, H. (1971). *Eur. J. Immunol.* **1**, 162–165.

Ring, J., Seifert, J., Mertin, J., and Brendel, W. (1974). *Lancet* **2**, 1331.

Robak, J., Dembinska-Kiec, A., and Gryglewski, R. (1975). *Biochem. Pharmacol.* **24**, 2057–2060.

Rosenlund, M. L., Kim, H. K., and Kritchevsky, D. (1974). *Nature (London)* **251**, 719.

Sanderson, C. J., and Taylor, G. A. (1975). *Cell. Tissue Kinet.* **8**, 23–32.

Schairer, H. U., and Overath, P. (1969). *J. Mol. Biol.* **44**, 209–214.

Schroit, A. J., Rottem, S., and Gallily, R. (1976). *Biochim. Biophys. Acta* **426**, 499–512.

Selivonchick, D. P., and Johnston, P. V. (1975). *J. Nutr.* **105**, 288–300.

Shivas, A. A., and Fraser, G. P. (1959). *Nature (London)* **184**, 1813.

Sidky, Y. A., and Auerbach, R. (1968). *Proc. Soc. Exp. Biol. Med.* **129**, 122–127.

Sidky, Y. A., and Hayward, J. S. (1972). *Fed. Proc., Fed. Am. Soc. Exp. Biol.* **31**, 800 (abstr.).

Sidky, Y. A., Daggett, L. R., and Auerbach, R. (1969). *Proc. Soc. Exp. Biol. Med.* **132**, 760–763.

Sidky, Y. A., Hayward, J. S., and Ruth, R. F. (1972). *Immunol. Commun.* **1**, 579–595.

Singer, S. J., and Nicolson, G. L. (1972). *Science* **175**, 720–731.

Smith, J. W., Steiner, A. L., Newberry, W. M., Jr., and Parker, C. W. (1971a). *J. Clin. Invest.* **50**, 432–441.

Smith, J. W., Steiner, A. L., and Parker, C. W. (1971b). *J. Clin. Invest.* **50**, 442–448.

Stockman, G. D., and Mumford, D. M. (1974). *Exp. Hematol. (Copenhagen)* **2**, 65–72.

Strom, T. B., Deisseroth, A., Morganroth, J., Carpenter, C. B., and Merrill, J. P. (1974). *In* "Cyclic AMP, Cell Growth and the Immune Response" (W. Braun, L. M. Lichtenstein, and C. W. Parker, eds.), pp. 209–222. Springer-Verlag, Berlin and New York.

Strom, T. B., Carpenter, C. B., Cragoe, E. J., Norris, S., Devlin, R., and Perper, R. J. (1977). *Transplant. Proc.* **9**, 1075–1079.

Stuart, A. E. (1960). *Lancet* **2**, 896–897.

Stuart, A. E. (1962). *Nature (London)* **196**, 78–79.

Stuart, A. E., and Cooper, G. N. (1963). *Exp. Mol. Pathol.* **2**, 215–218.

Stuart, A. E., and Davidson, A. E. (1963). *Br. J. Exp. Pathol.* **44**, 24–30.

Stuart, A. E., and Davidson, A. E. (1964). *J. Pathol. Bacteriol.* **87**, 305–315.

Stuart, A. E., Biozzi, G., Stiffel, C., Halpern, B. N., and Mouton, D. (1960a). *C. R. Hebd. Seances* **250**, 2779–2781.

Stuart, A. E., Biozzi, G., Stiffel, C., Halpern, B. N., and Mouton, D. (1960b). *Br. J. Exp. Pathol.* **41**, 599–604.

Sudo, M. (1962). *Ann. Paediatr. Jpn.* **8**, 316–323.

Swank, R. L. (1970). *Arch. Neurol. (Chicago)* **23**, 460–474.

Swank, R. L., Lerstad, O., Strøm, A., and Backer, J. (1952). *N. Engl. J. Med.* **246**, 721–728.

Taussig, M. J., and Munro, A. J. (1974). *Nature (London)* **251,** 63–65.

Thompson, R. H. S. (1975). *In* "Multiple Sclerosis Research" (A. N. Davison *et al.,* eds.), pp. 184–191. Elsevier, Amsterdam.

Toyoshima, S., and Osawa, T. (1976). *Exp. Cell Res.* **102,** 438–441.

Tsang, W. M., Belin, J., Monro, J. A., Smith, A. D., Thompson, R. H. S., and Zilkha, K. J. (1976). *J. Neurol., Neurosurg. Psychiatry* **39,** 767–771.

Turnell R. W., and Burton, A. F. (1974). *Cancer Res.* **34,** 39–42.

Turnell, R. W., and Burton, A. F. (1975). *Mol. Cell. Biochem.* **9,** 175–189.

Turnell, R. W., Clarke, L. H., and Burton, A. F. (1973). *Cancer Res.* **33,** 203–212.

Uchimara, I., and Shiraki, H. (1957). *J. Neuropathol. Exp. Neurol.* **16,** 139–208.

Vessey, M. P. (1975). *In* "Multiple Sclerosis Research" (A. N. Davison *et al.,* eds.), p. 229. Elsevier, Amsterdam.

Webb, D. R., and Osheroff, P. L. (1976). *Proc. Natl. Acad. Sci. U.S.A.* **73,** 1300–1304.

Weyman, C., Belin, J., Smith, A. D., and Thompson, R. H. S. (1975). *Lancet* **2,** 33.

Weyman, C., Morgan, S. J., Belin, J., and Smith, A. D. (1977). *Biochim. Biophys. Acta* **496,** 155–166.

Whitney, R. B., and Sutherland, R. M. (1972). *Cell. Immunol.* **5,** 137–147.

Williams, L. T., Snyderman, R., and Lefkowitz, R. J. (1976). *J. Clin. Invest.* **57,** 149–155.

Wolfram, G., Doenicke, A., and Zöllner, N. (1974). *Infusionstherapie* **1,** 537–540.

Wooles, W. R., and diLuzio, N. R. (1963). *Science* **142,** 1078–1080.

Zabriskie, J. B. (1975). *In* "Multiple Sclerosis Research" (A. N. Davison *et al.,* eds.), pp. 142–154. Elsevier, Amsterdam.

Zimecki, M., and Webb, D. R. (1976). *J. Immunol.* **117,** 2158–2164.

Zurier, R. B., and Quagliata, F. (1971). *Nature (London)* **234,** 304–305.

Zurier, R. B., Dukor, P., and Weissmann, G. (1971). *Clin. Res.* **19,** 453.

Zurier, R. B., Dore-Duffy, P., and Viola, M. V. (1977). *N. Engl. J. Med.* **296,** 1443–1446.

Marginal Vitamin C Deficiency, Lipid Metabolism, and Atherogenesis

EMIL GINTER

Institute for Human Nutrition Research
Bratislava, Czechoslovakia

I. Introduction

Vitamin C (ascorbic acid, ascorbate) holds a special position among the vitamins, since most vertebrates synthesize it in the glucuronic acid pathway of glucose metabolism and are therefore not dependent on a supply from external sources. In amphibians, reptiles, and phylogenetically older species of birds, ascorbate is synthesized in the kidneys, while in developmentally higher birds and mammals, vitamin C is synthesized in the liver (Chatterjee, 1973). For reasons which are still a mystery, some birds and mammals (guinea pigs, bats, monkeys, man) have lost the ability to synthesize ascorbic acid. The liver microsomes of these species lack the enzyme of the last stage of ascorbate biosynthesis, gulonolactone oxidase (Burns, 1957). This is assumed to be a specific genetic limitation, mutation of the operon responsible for synthesis of this enzyme. For most of these species, this genetic disturbance is not a real danger, as they are herbivores inhabiting tropical or subtropical regions with an abundant supply of vitamin C the whole year round. The species most seriously affected by this mutation is Homo sapiens, who inhabits the whole of the globe, including regions where the supply of food rich in vitamin C is limited for part of the year. Although advances in agriculture, transport and storage techniques have largely abolished the danger of scurvy (acute vitamin C deficiency), there are probably still, even now, in the second half of the 20th century, millions of people who suffer from marginal vitamin C deficiency for at least part of the year. The aim of this review is to sum up data on the effect of vitamin C deficiency on the metabolism of cholesterol, triglycerides, and various components of the blood vessel wall and to draw attention to the fact that latent vitamin C deficiency (hypovitaminosis C) must be regarded as a risk factor in association with atherosclerosis.

II. Disorders of Lipid Metabolism in Acute Scurvy

Practically all studies of the effect of acute scurvy on lipid metabolism have been carried out with guinea pigs and few with monkeys. The guinea pig model of acute scurvy is attractive because of its simplicity, since guinea pig is extremely sensitive to alimentary vitamin C deficiency. The biological half time of ascorbic acid in the guinea pig is substantially shorter than in man, being in the region of 4 days (Burns et al., 1951; Ginter et al., 1971b). If a guinea pig is put on a vitamin C-free diet, distinct signs of deficiency (lack of appetite, a drop in body weight) are observed within 3 weeks and the animal dies in 4 weeks with typical signs of scurvy. This seemingly convenient "express" model of avitaminosis C makes it very hard to interpret the results, however, since acute vitamin C deficiency is a dynamic process, in which the character of the metabolic disorders alters with the development of scurvy. The administration of a vitamin C-free diet to guinea pigs is immediately followed by a drop in tissue ascorbate levels and as avitaminosis develops they steadily fall still further (Fig. 1). As a result, the individual phases of acute avitaminosis often differ completely in respect of even such basal parameters as nitrogen balance, for example (Ginter, 1970b). The terminal phase of acute avitaminosis C is an immensely complicated pathological state, very hard to define metabolically, in which, alongside vitamin C deficiency, a decisive

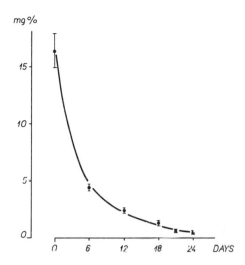

FIG. 1. Drop in vitamin C concentration in guinea pig liver during development of acute scurvy. The vertical bars represent ± the standard error of the mean. The same method of expressing the scatter of the values is used in all the other figures and in the tables.

role is played by many nonspecific factors, such as the abrupt drop in body weight, a negative nitrogen balance, and hemorrhage in various parts of the body.

It is therefore not surprising that the relatively numerous data on disorders of lipid metabolism in acute scurvy are very contradictory. Some authors (Murray and Morgan, 1946; Banerjee and Ghosh, 1960) claim that tissue lipid levels fall in scurvy, while others (Tomlinson, 1942; Baldwin *et al.*, 1944) found no changes and others again (Bessey *et al.*, 1934; Sheppard and McHenry, 1939) described an increase in the concentration of lipid substances in the tissues of scorbutic animals. There is likewise a lack of unanimity on the question of the effect of acute vitamin C deficiency on the plasma-cholesterol levels. Some authors (Mouriquand and Leulier, 1925; Banerjee and Singh, 1958; Banerjee and Bandyopadhyay, 1963; Naydu and Nath, 1968) found no significant changes in scorbutic guinea pigs, while others (Bolker *et al.*, 1956; Banerjee and Ghosh, 1960) described hypercholesterolemia in vitamin C-deficient guinea pigs. In vitamin C-deficient monkeys and humans, a tendency for the serum-cholesterol level to fall was observed (Banerjee and Bal, 1959; Bronte-Stewart *et al.*, 1963; Hodges *et al.*, 1969; Kotzé *et al.*, 1974b). Most authors found a significant drop in the cholesterol concentration in the adrenals of severely scorbutic guinea pigs and monkeys (Mouriquand and Leulier, 1925; Banerjee and Deb, 1951; Belavady and Banerjee,

1954; Banerjee and Singh, 1958; Banerjee and Kawishwar, 1964). Baldwin *et al.* (1944), on the other hand, found no changes in the adrenal-
cholesterol level in scorbutic guinea pigs and Oesterling and Long (1951)
actually described an increase in the adrenal cholesterol concentration in
guinea pigs with mild vitamin C deficiency. Study of the dynamics of
cholesterol levels in guinea pigs adrenals in different phases of avitaminosis
C (Ginter *et al.*, 1965) showed that the discrepancies in these results are
only apparent. In the first stage of avitaminosis C, very pronounced accumulation of esterified (and hence of total) cholesterol occurs in guinea
pig adrenals. As scurvy develops, the cholesterol level returns to normal
and it is not until the terminal stages, when body weight falls, that the
adrenal-cholesterol concentration drops below the control values (Fig. 2).

Acute scurvy interferes markedly with metabolism of the acetate pool.
In avitaminosis C, the function of the tricarboxylic acid cycle is impaired
(Takeda and Hara, 1955; Guchhait and Ganguli, 1961; Banerjee and
Kawishwar, 1964), resulting in slower oxidation of acetate to CO_2. The
incorporation of [1-^{14}C]acetate into the liver glycogen (Kumar and Venkitasubramanian, 1964) and adipose tissue fatty acids of scorbutic guinea
pigs (Kumar and Venkitasubramanian, 1963; Guchhait *et al.*, 1964) is
also slower. On the other hand, significantly more [1-^{14}C]acetate is incorporated into the liver and (especially) the adrenal cholesterol of severely
scorbutic guinea pigs (King *et al.*, 1953), although in mild vitamin C
deficiency the amount of labeled acetate incorporated into the cholesterol in the liver, adrenals, aorta, and epididymal adipose tissue is the

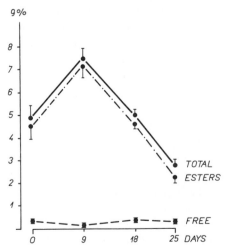

FIG. 2.   Free, esterified, and total cholesterol concentration in guinea pig adrenals
in different phases of acute scurvy. From Ginter (1970b).

same as in the controls (Becker *et al.,* 1953; Bolker *et al.,* 1956; Kumar and Venkitasubramanian, 1963). Some authors attribute elevated cholesterol accumulation in the body of scorbutic guinea pigs to raised utilization of the acetate pool for cholesterol synthesis or to reduced transformation of cholesterol to bile acids in their liver (Banerjee and Ghosh, 1960; Guchhait *et al.,* 1963). The availability of acetate does not seem to be rate limiting in cholesterol synthesis, however (Gould and Swyryd, 1966). The extremely intricate situation in lipid metabolism is complicated still further by the fact that hypoinsulinism develops in guinea pigs with acute scurvy (Banerjee and Ghosh, 1947).

Last but not least, objections to the preceding model of acute scurvy are based on the fact that it does not give a realistic picture of the nutritional situation in modern man. Acute scurvy is rare in civilized human societies, whereas latent vitamin C deficiency is very common. Since acute scurvy and latent vitamin C deficiency are two metabolically very different states, we felt the need for the elaboration of a new model of chronic ascorbic acid deficiency which would have none of the shortcomings of the acute scurvy model and would be closer to the situation in human nutrition.

III. Model of Chronic Latent Vitamin C Deficiency

After a series of preliminary experiments, a standardized technique for inducing chronic latent vitamin C deficiency was evolved (Ginter *et al.,* 1968b). For 14 days, guinea pigs are fed on a modified form of Lund's scorbutogenic diet (Ginter, 1975b), without adding ascorbic acid. In this period the body pool of vitamin C abruptly diminishes, but no discernible sequelae of ascorbate deficiency can yet be detected. After 2 weeks the peroral administration of ascorbic acid is started, in doses of 0.5 mg/animal/day. The controls are fed on the same diet, but their peroral doses of ascorbic acid are much larger (usually 10 mg/animal/day). Body weight, appearance, behavior, and food consumption in guinea pigs with latent vitamin C deficiency follow the same course as in the controls. In this way, guinea pigs can be kept in a state of marginal vitamin C deficiency for a very long time, e.g., 1 year.

Figure 3 shows changes in ascorbate concentration in the spleen during the development of latent vitamin C deficiency. In the 2 weeks when an ascorbate-free diet is given, the vitamin C concentration falls abruptly. In the next phase, when a maintaining dose of ascorbic acid is administered, the ascorbate level remains at approximately the same low value, irrespective of the duration of marginal vitamin C deficiency. The given model

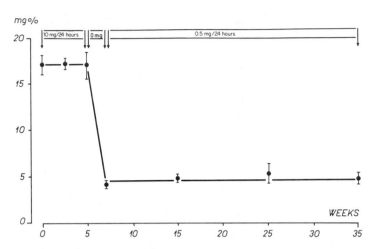

FIG. 3. Vitamin C concentration in the spleen during development of chronic latent vitamin C deficiency in guinea pigs. The ascorbic acid dosage is shown at the top of the figure.

thus creates a situation of equilibrium characterized by a stable low tissue ascorbate level close to the concentrations found in guinea pigs with incipient scurvy. On the other hand, the continuous administration of maintaining doses of ascorbic acid prevents the development of acute scurvy, so that this state, like subclinical vitamin C deficiency, can be described as hypovitaminosis C. An important feature in this model is that when evaluating the effect of hypovitaminosis C, the only variable that has to be taken into account is the substantial depletion of body pool in vitamin C while various secondary phenomena (e.g., loss of body weight) are here immaterial. If any biochemical disturbance is found in deficient animals, the decrease in vitamin C concentration in blood and tissues can be unequivocally denoted as the causal factor. In long-term experiments, during which the experimental animals' body weight increases severalfold, the doses of ascorbic acid can be modified on a body weight basis. So far, however, we still do not know the optimum dose of vitamin C either for man or for guinea pigs.

IV. Model of Alimentary Hypercholesterolemia and Atherosclerosis in Guinea Pig

In most earlier studies investigating the influence of vitamin C on cholesterolemia and atherosclerosis, the experimental animal was the rabbit (Flexner *et al.,* 1941; Chakravarti *et al.,* 1957; Myasnikov, 1958; Zaitsev *et al.,* 1964; Sokoloff *et al.,* 1967; Pool *et al.,* 1971), i.e., the species in which atherosclerosis was first successfully induced (Anitschkow, 1912). Unlike man, the rabbit synthesizes ascorbate, however, and actually reacts to a supply of exogenous cholesterol by an increase in vitamin C synthesis (Ginter, 1970a; Novitskii, 1971). One of the causes of the different results of different teams investigating the possibility of influencing cholesterolemia and atherosclerosis with vitamin C was the choice of species synthesizing ascorbate, such as the rat, rabbit, chicken, and pig (Flexner *et al.,* 1941; Myasnikov, 1958; Fernandéz-Gimeno *et al.,* 1960; Chang, 1965; Cajola, 1968; Hutagalung *et al.,* 1970; Cromwell *et al.,* 1970; Rolek and Dale, 1972). Homeostasis of ascorbate levels in the blood and tissues is exceptionally highly developed in the rat, so that neither the addition of 1% ascorbic acid to a balanced diet, nor its omission from the diet, affects the ascorbate levels in the organs except the kidneys (Ginter, 1975b). Under these conditions, serum- and tissue-cholesterol concentrations are naturally likewise unaffected.

The effect of the addition of 0.2% ascorbic acid to the diet on the turnover of [4-^{14}C]cholesterol was studied in rabbits with cholesterol atherosclerosis (Ginter, 1974). The results of a kinetic analysis of the die-away curves of plasma cholesterol specific activity, in terms of the two-pool model (Goodman and Noble, 1968, Nestel *et al.,* 1969), are given in Table I. Experimental atherosclerosis induced significant enlargement of both cholesterol pools and led to an increased cholesterol turnover rate, irrespective of whether no ascorbic acid or large doses had been administered. The pool and kinetic parameters in rabbits with a zero and a high ascorbic acid intake were found to be practically identical. The course of hypercholesterolemia and cholesterol accumulation in the liver, adrenals, and thoracic aorta in the two groups likewise followed a similar pattern. Owing to endogenous ascorbate synthesis, the vitamin C level in several organs was also the same in the two groups. In keeping with these biochemical findings the degree of atheromatous changes in the aorta and coronary arteries in the two groups corresponded.

For studying the influence of vitamin C deficiency on hypercholesterolemia and atherosclerosis, it is thus obviously necessary to use animals dependent, like man, on exogenous vitamin C. The best would be nonhuman primates, but experiments on large series of monkeys are very exacting. Although Anitschkow (1922) long ago drew attention to the possibility of inducing atherosclerosis in guinea pigs and other authors (Altschul, 1950; Bernick *et al.,* 1962) confirmed it, the guinea pigs were not used for a long time for studying atherogenesis, because a high cholesterol (1–2%) diet induces hemolytic anemia in them (Okey and Greaves, 1939; Ostwald and Shannon, 1964) and the lesions in the blood vessels

Table I

SIZE OF POOLS AND KINETIC PARAMETERS OF CHOLESTEROL TURNOVER IN RABBITS WITH ALIMENTARY ATHEROSCLEROSIS ON ZERO AND HIGH INTAKE OF ASCORBIC ACID

Parameter	Control	Experimental atherosclerosis	
		Vitamin C: 0	Vitamin C: 0.2% in diet
$t_{1/2}\,\alpha$: half-life of first exponential (days)	1.6 ± 0.1 [a]	2.1 ± 0.2	2.0 ± 0.2
$t_{1/2}\,\beta$: half-life of second exponential (days)	19.0 ± 1.2	26.8 ± 3.2	27.8 ± 3.1
M_A: size of pool A (mg/animal)	$1{,}113 \pm 90$	$4{,}174 \pm 451$	$3{,}900 \pm 406$
M_{Bmin}: minimum size of pool B (mg/animal)	$1{,}635 \pm 40$	$4{,}392 \pm 688$	$4{,}569 \pm 715$
PR_A: production rate in pool A = turnover rate (mg/animal/day)	124 ± 7	254 ± 27	247 ± 32
k_A: rate constant for irreversible excretion from pool A (day^{-1})	0.116 ± 0.012	0.061 ± 0.001	0.063 ± 0.004

[a] Mean ± SEM.

are not very marked (Cook and McCullagh, 1939). Guinea pigs fed on a high cholesterol diet were used with success to study questions associated with familial lecithin-cholesterol acyl transferase deficiency (Glomset and Norum, 1973).

By modifying their diet, we succeeded in demonstrating that guinea pigs can be used as suitable model animals for producing alimentary hypercholesterolemia and atherosclerosis (Babala and Ginter, 1968; Ginter *et al.,* 1968a, 1970a). For inducing atheromatous lesions, three factors are important: the cholesterol level in the diet, the fatty acid composition of the diet, and the length of time for which the atherogenic diet is administered. Not more than 0.3% cholesterol should be added to the diet, as larger doses cause serious anemia and high mortality. The diet should have a high content of saturated fatty acids and a low ascorbate and polyunsaturated fatty acid content (milk lipids proved to be a suitable source of fats in the diet). If the guinea pigs were fed on this diet for a sufficient length of time (about 4 months), marked atheromatous lesions developed in their vascular system, mainly in the coronary arteries (Fig. 4).

In guinea pigs, the atheromatous lesions displayed certain morphological differences which depended on the anatomical structure of the individual

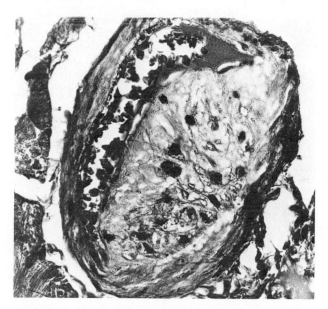

FIG. 4. Endothelized atheromatous material pervaded with histiocytic elements in branch of coronary artery of hypovitaminous guinea pig fed 202 days on cholesterol diet. Hematoxylin and eosin; ×400.

vessels and particularly on the proportion of muscular and elastic components. In vessels with a rather small muscular and elastic component, the vascular wall, in the early phases, displayed edema throughout its entire extent, either in the form of foci or, less frequently, round the whole of the periphery. Focal injury and destruction of endothelial cells were observed and at such sites there was parietal adhesion of masses of the character of coagulated lipemic plasma with disintegrated thrombocytes. These parietal thrombotic masses were successively covered with endothelium and cholesterol later crystallized inside them. In larger vessels of the muscular or elastic type, the process remained limited to the intima, which was separated from the internal elastic membrane; here agglomeration of lipophages or monocytes with minutely vacuolated and

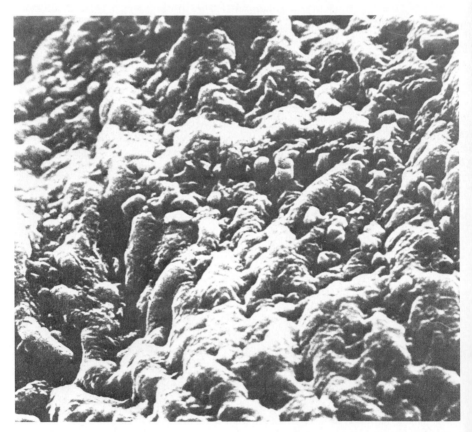

Fig. 5. Intimal surface of aorta of guinea pig fed 4 months on cholesterol diet. Erythrocytes and platelets are scattered over the amorphous covering or are incorporated into it. ×1000. From Weber and Tosi (1971).

finely granular cytoplasm was found. The lipids present in the lesions were mainly of the hydrophobic type (cholesterol and its esters). Of the hydrophylic lipids, sphingomyelin and a variable amount of lecithin could be demonstrated. The mucosubstances demonstrated were mainly neutral; the amount of acid mucosubstances was very small. Oxidoreductase activities very very low. Lysosomal enzyme activities, which are greatly enhanced during the formation of plaques in other animals, showed a less marked increase in the guinea pig (Horáková *et al.*, 1973). Scanning electron microscope studies showed that two phases could be distinguished in the development of cholesterol atherosclerosis in the guinea pigs (Weber and Tosi, 1971). In the first phase, an amorphous substance, diffusely covering the intimal surface of the aorta, was deposited. In the second phase (after about 4 months of cholesterol feeding), erythrocytes and platelets were scattered over this amorphous covering (Fig. 5) and intimal plaques became recognizable. Coronary lipohyalinosis was described in guinea pigs given large doses of cholesterol (Manning *et al.*, 1974).

Cholesterol atherosclerosis in guinea pigs, as distinct from rabbits, develops in the presence of relatively low plasma-cholesterol levels (about 300 mg%) reminiscent of human hypercholesterolemia. There is also a parallel with the pathogenesis of human atherosclerosis in the slow development of atherosclerotic lesions in guinea pigs. On the other hand, the lipoprotein metabolism of guinea pigs is very different from that of man since normal guinea pig plasma contains no detectable high-density lipoproteins and no lipoproteins with alpha mobility (Puppione *et al.*, 1971). It will thus manifestly be more satisfactory to use monkeys for studying the influence of vitamin C on lipoprotein metabolism.

V. Vitamin C in Regulation of Cholesterol Turnover

On using our model of latent ascorbic acid deficiency (a diet containing 10% butter, without additional cholesterol), short-term hypovitaminosis C did not have a marked effect on cholesterol levels in guinea pig blood and tissues. If latent vitamin C deficiency lasted longer than 3 months, however, cholesterol always accumulated in the guinea pig liver and hypercholesterolemia developed (Ginter *et al.*, 1965, 1969c, 1971a, 1973b) (Table II). The hypercholesterolemic action of vitamin C deficiency depends on the lipid composition of the diet. A vitamin C-free diet containing 12.5% cottonseed oil leads to hypercholesterolemia in guinea pigs in only 2 weeks, while the addition of 5% coconut oil potentiates the hypercholesterolemic effect of ascorbate deficiency still further (Fujinami *et al.*, 1971). If a diet containing 4% groundnut oil is given, the hyper-

Table II

Influence of Chronic Latent Vitamin C Deficiency on Total Cholesterol Concentration In Blood Plasma and Liver of Male Guinea Pigs [a]

Blood plasma			Liver		
Duration of deficiency (weeks)	Control	Deficiency	Duration of deficiency (weeks)	Control	Deficiency
16–20	118 ± 14 [b]	171 ± 18	15	368 ± 29 [c]	659 ± 40
22	99 ± 6	132 ± 6	16–20	456 ± 56	627 ± 65
23	95 ± 7	140 ± 8	17–21	395 ± 35	616 ± 70
24	94 ± 7	140 ± 7	20–22	411 ± 33	592 ± 77
26	88 ± 7	139 ± 8	28	325 ± 14	586 ± 106
28	110 ± 6	135 ± 5	31	357 ± 22	661 ± 96

[a] Data from Ginter (1975a).
[b] Milligrams per 100 ml plasma ± SEM.
[c] Milligrams per 100 g wet tissue ± SEM.

cholesterolemic effect of latent vitamin C deficiency is still not manifested after 4 months, but the administration of a diet containing 15% coconut oil and 0.3% cholesterol, under the same conditions, results in significant elevation of the serum cholesterol level in vitamin C-deficient guinea pigs compared with groups given large doses of ascorbic acid (Nambisan and Kurup, 1975). The cholesterol concentration in the other organs of vitamin-deficient guinea pigs remains unchanged, except for an increase in the amount of Liebermann-Burchardt-positive sterols in the skin (Ginter *et al.,* 1973b). If 0.3% cholesterol is added to the diet, however, hypovitaminosis C causes cholesterol to accumulate in various organs, including the thoracic aorta (Ginter *et al.,* 1969a,b) (Table III). In some tissues, cholesterol levels are graduated in correlation to the dose of ascorbic acid, and in some tissues there is a significant negative correlation between the cholesterol concentration and the ascorbate level, i.e., the higher the ascorbate level, the lower the cholesterol concentration, and vice versa (Ginter *et al.,* 1969b). Similar results were reported by Nambisan and Kurup (1975).

A. LOCALIZATION OF INTERFERENCE OF VITAMIN C DEFICIENCY WITH CHOLESTEROL METABOLISM

Serum and tissue cholesterol concentrations are the outcome of a great number of processes mutually bound by feedback mechanisms, such as cholesterol distribution between blood and tissues, endogenous cholesterol synthesis, the absorption of exogenous cholesterol, cholesterol excretion, and the transformation of cholesterol to bile acids.

We followed the passage of labeled cholesterol from the blood plasma to 14 different guinea pig tissues forming the major part of cholesterol pools in the body (liver, kidney, adrenal, small intestine, large intestine, stomach, lung, myocardium, brain, testis, epididymal fat, skeletal muscle, thoracic aorta, and skin). The results obtained from the controls and the vitamin-deficient animals did not differ significantly. Since the total amount of cholesterol in these tissues in the two groups is the same (excepting the liver and the skin), the accumulation of cholesterol in liver and plasma of vitamin C-deficient animals cannot be accounted for by lower cholesterol deposition in other parts of the body.

1. *Vitamin C and Endogenous Cholesterol Synthesis*

Study of cholesterol biosynthesis in the liver of hypovitaminous guinea pigs at different intervals after the administration of [1-^{14}C]acetate did not yield completely conclusive results, but indicated that marginal

Table III

Total Cholesterol Concentrations in the Tissues of Cholesterol-Fed Guinea Pigs Given Various Doses of Ascorbic Acid [a]

Duration of experiment (weeks)	Tissue	Doses of ascorbic acid (mg/animal/day)			
		0.5 (deficiency)	5.0	50.0	
12	Liver	4,017 ± 485 [b]	3,652 ± 310	3,404 ± 42	
	Adrenal	10,774 ± 1,621	10,646 ± 1,047	8,651 ± 527	
	Small intestine	387 ± 19	345 ± 35	272 ± 32	
	Thoracic aorta	548 ± 48	545 ± 96	409 ± 29	
20	Liver	6,622 ± 548	5,611 ± 416	3,509 ± 350	
	Adrenal	7,942 ± 890	7,782 ± 671	5,186 ± 840	
	Small intestine	364 ± 23	317 ± 17	282 ± 20	

[a] Data from Ginter (1975a).
[b] Milligrams of total cholesterol per 100 g of wet tissue.

vitamin C deficiency did not markedly affect endogenous cholesterol synthesis in the liver (Ginter *et al.,* 1965; Ginter and Nemec, 1969). In guinea pigs, the rate of endogenous cholesterol synthesis in the ileum is much higher than in the liver (Swann *et al.,* 1975; Turley *et al.,* 1975, 1976). We found in an *in vivo* experiment (Fig. 6) that the incorporation of [1-¹⁴C]acetate into [¹⁴C]digitonides was at least one order higher in the guinea pig ileum than in the other tissues studied and that latent vitamin C deficiency did not influence this process in the ileum. In the other tissues, we observed a tendency to higher values in the vitamin-deficient group, but it is questionable whether these differences could markedly influence total cholesterol biogenesis. The incorporation of labeled acetate and mevalonate into cholesterol was lower in liver homogenates prepared from vitamin C-deficient baboons (Weight *et al.,* 1974). *In vivo* experiments were rather indicative of elevated cholesterol synthesis in ascorbate-deficient baboons, however (Kotzé *et al.,* 1974b). In animals which synthesize ascorbate (the rat, the rabbit), vitamin C, in

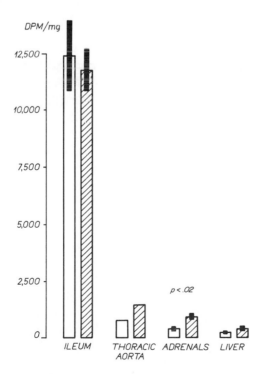

FIG. 6. Specific activity of [¹⁴C]digitonides isolated from different guinea pig tissues 20 min after i.p. injection of [1-¹⁴C]acetate. Control: white columns, hypovitaminosis C: shaded columns.

given circumstances, can stimulate cholesterol synthesis (Popják *et al.,* 1958; Novitskii, 1969; Misra and Srivastava, 1974), while in hamsters fed on a lithogenic diet, even large doses of ascorbic acid do not markedly affect cholesterol biosynthesis (Section V,C). Although the influence of ascorbic acid on endogenous cholesterol synthesis has not been completely elucidated, it is unlikely that the accumulation of cholesterol in the body of hypovitaminous guinea pigs could be due to raised synthesis of endogenous cholesterol.

2. *Ascorbic Acid and Absorption and Excretion of Cholesterol*

Following an intragastric application of [4-^{14}C]cholesterol, hypovitaminous guinea pigs had a significantly higher ^{14}C activity in the gastrointestinal tract and stool and, on the other hand, a substantially lower activity in the blood and tissues (Ginter, 1970b). Raised accumulation of cholesterol in the blood and liver of vitamin C-deficient guinea pigs thus cannot be ascribed to raised absorption of exogenous cholesterol. Marginal vitamin C deficiency tends rather to inhibit this process. Similar results were obtained in humans with acute vitamin C deficiency (Bronte-Stewart *et al.,* 1963).

Myasnikov (1958) drew attention to the possibility that the hypocholesterolemic effect of ascorbic acid might be associated with stimulated secretion of cholesterol from the liver into the bile. The results obtained in studies of the influence of vitamin C on cholesterol levels in rabbit bile are contradictory, however (Kolmakov, 1957; Novitskii, 1969). Some interesting effects of ascorbic acid-2-sulfate on cholesterol excretion have been reported. Verlangieri and Mumma (1973) found sulfation of cholesterol by ascorbic acid-2-sulfate *in vivo;* the resultant product, cholesterol sulfate, was excreted in the stools. Hayashi *et al.* (1974, 1976) reported that sodium ascorbic acid-2-sulfate had a hypocholesterolemic effect on hyperlipemic rats, rabbits, and guinea pigs. On the other hand, Hornig, *et al.* (1974) observed no stimulation of the fecal excretion of cholesterol or cholesterol sulfate by ascorbic acid-2-sulfate in rats. According to our results, marginal ascorbate deficiency does not markedly influence cholesterol excretion in the form of neutral sterols. Guinea pigs were given an intraperitoneal injection of [4-^{14}C]cholesterol and the excretion of [^{14}C]-neutral sterols and [^{14}C]bile acids in their stools was measured for 20 days (Ginter *et al.,* 1971a). The excretion of [^{14}C]sterols by the controls and vitamin-deficient animals was found to be practically the same, so that this factor likewise failed to explain cholesterol accumulation in the blood and liver of hypovitaminous guinea pigs. This experiment was instrumental in discovery of the key to the problem, however; the excretion of [^{14}C]bile acids in the stools was smaller in vitamin-deficient guinea pigs. This result indicated that the rate of cholesterol transformation to its principal catabolic product, bile acids, is slowed down in marginal vitamin C deficiency.

B. THE ROLE OF VITAMIN C IN CHOLESTEROL TRANSFORMATION TO BILE ACIDS

The transformation of cholesterol to bile acids can be studied by two isotope methods. If cholesterol labeled with ^{14}C in position 4 of the cyclic structure is administered, the activity that occurs in the bile acid fraction is the criterion of the rate of the process, as mammals do not possess an enzymatic system capable of splitting the cholesterol nucleus (Chaikoff *et al.*, 1952). If cholesterol labeled in position 26 on the side chain is given, the isopropyl fragment is split off from the side-chain during cholesterol catabolism and ^{14}C is released in the form of carbon dioxide. The rate of cholesterol catabolism is measured from the amount of ^{14}C in the expired CO_2. The bile acids isolated from the liver and gallbladder bile three days after injection of [4-^{14}C]cholesterol were labeled to a lesser extent in hypovitaminous guinea pigs (Table IV). When [26-^{14}C]cholesterol was injected, the amount of $^{14}CO_2$ recovered in 10 days was significantly smaller in guinea pigs with marginal vitamin C deficiency than in the control group (Ginter *et al.*, 1971a). Furthermore, the resaturation of vitamin C-deficient guinea pigs with large doses of ascorbic acid significantly stepped up the rate of [26-^{14}C]cholesterol oxidation to $^{14}CO_2$ (Ginter *et al.*, 1972) (Fig. 7).

Table IV

INFLUENCE OF CHRONIC HYPOVITAMINOSIS C ON THE DISTRIBUTION OF ^{14}C IN NEUTRAL STEROLS AND BILE ACIDS 3 DAYS AFTER INTRAPERITONEAL INJECTION OF [4-^{14}C]CHOLESTEROL [a]

Sample	Fraction	Control	Hypovitaminosis C
Liver (dpm/g wet tissue)	Neutral sterols	23,970 ± 2,292	26,505 ± 2,353
	Bile acids	3,397 ± 635	2,017 ± 173
	Bile acids/ neutral sterols	0.157 ± 0.030	0.080 ± 0.007
Gallbladder bile (dpm/g bile)	Neutral sterols	1,273	1,367
	Bile acids	132,307	108,755
	Bile acids/ neutral sterols	103.9	79.6

[a] Data from Ginter *et al.* (1971a).

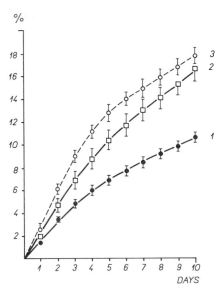

FIG. 7. Oxidation of [26-^{14}C]cholesterol to $^{14}CO_2$ as percentage of dose administered to vitamin C-deficient (1), resaturated pair-fed (2), and resaturated *ad libitum*-fed (3) guinea pigs. From Ginter *et al.* (1972).

Simultaneous determination of the amount of expired $^{14}CO_2$ and of the specific activity of liver or serum cholesterol after the administration of [26-^{14}C]cholesterol allows quantification of the rate of cholesterol transformation to bile acids (Myant and Lewis, 1966; Ginter *et al.*, 1973a). Application of this technique indicated that chronic latent ascorbate deficiency significantly reduced the rate of cholesterol transformation to bile acids in guinea pigs (controls: 11.8 ± 0.6; hypovitaminosis C: 8.3 ± 0.4 mg cholesterol/24 hours/500 g body weight) (Ginter, 1973). Cholesterol is transformed to bile acids in the liver and the rate of this process very probably depends on the ascorbate concentration in the liver cells, since there is a relatively close linear correlation between the rate of bile acid synthesis and the ascorbic acid concentration in the liver (Fig. 8). In guinea pigs given small doses of ascorbic acid, reduced bile acid biosynthesis leads to a decrease in the size of the body pool of bile acids (Hornig and Weiser, 1976). There is a significant direct correlation in guinea pigs between the amount of ascorbate in the liver and the size of the bile acid pool (Fig. 9), which is reminiscent of the correlation between the liver-ascorbate level and the rate of bile acid biosynthesis (Fig. 8).

Cholesterol transformation to bile acids is a multistage process taking place successively in the liver cell microsomes, supernatant fraction, and mitochondria. It involves hydroxylation, dehydrogenation, saturation of a

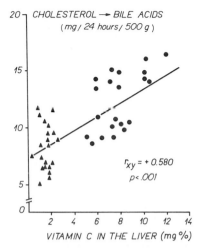

FIG. 8. Linear correlation between liver ascorbic acid concentration and the rate of cholesterol transformation to bile acids in control guinea pigs (●) and guinea pigs with chronic latent vitamin C deficiency (▲). From Ginter *et al.* (1973b).

double bond in the nucleus, 3-ketone reduction, and ω- and β-oxidation of the cholesterol side chain. The transformation of cholesterol to the principal bile acid of guinea pigs, chenodeoxycholic acid, entails two hydroxylations: at position 7α in the cholesterol nucleus and at position 26 on its side chain (Fig. 10). In contrast to ovarian and adrenal tissue (Sulimovici and Boyd, 1968; Shimizu, 1970), ascorbate does not seem

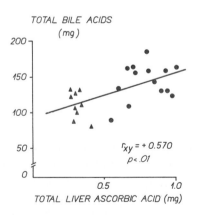

FIG. 9. Linear correlation between amount of ascorbic acid in liver and size of bile acid pool (liver + gallbladder + small intestine) in guinea pigs with a low (0.75 mg twice daily, ▲) and a higher (5 mg twice daily, ●) Na ascorbate intake. The graph was constructed on the basis of data given by Hornig and Weiser (1976).

CHOLESTEROL

7α - HYDROXYLATION ———————➤
(MICROSOMAL)

HO⟍   ''OH

OXYGEN
NADPH
CYTOCHROME
P - 450
ASCORBIC ACID

INTERMEDIATES

26 - HYDROXYLATION ———————➤
(MITOCHONDRIAL)   OH

HO⟍   ''OH

CHENODEOXYCHOLIC ACID

FIG. 10. Scheme of hydroxylation reactions during cholesterol conversion to chenodeoxycholic acid. Ascorbic acid participates in the first reaction, i.e., 7α-hydroxylation of cholesterol to cholest-5-ene-3β,7α-diol and does not participate in 26-hydroxylation (synthesis of 5-β-cholestane-3α,7α-26-triol).

to affect oxidation of the side chain (i.e., 26-hydroxylation) of cholesterol in liver mitochondria (Kritchevsky *et al.*, 1973).

The first step in cholesterol transformation to C_{24} bile acids is the production of 7α-hydroxycholesterol and this reaction is rate limiting for cholesterol catabolism. If the interference of ascorbate deficiency with the biosynthesis of bile acids is localized solely at 7α-hydroxylation level, then 7α-hydroxycholesterol catabolism, as distinct from cholesterol catabolism, ought not to be affected by latent vitamin C deficiency:

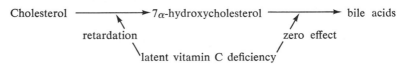

This assumption was verified by synthesizing [26-^{14}C]-7α-hydroxycholesterol [26-^{14}C]cholest-5-ene-3β,7α-diol) and following its oxidation to [14]CO$_2$ *in vivo* (Ginter, 1975a). The results (Fig. 11) show that, unlike the significantly retarded oxidation of [26-^{14}C]cholesterol, the oxidation of [26-^{14}C]-7α-hydroxycholesterol is not significantly affected by latent vitamin C deficiency. In *in vitro* experiments, Kritchevsky *et al.* (1973) did not find statistically significant increase in 7α-hydroxylation of [1,2-^{3}H]-cholesterol in the liver microsomes of normal guinea pigs after the addition of ascorbic acid, but a relatively close correlation was found between the amount of added ascorbate and the rate of 7α-hydroxylation ($r_{xy} = +$

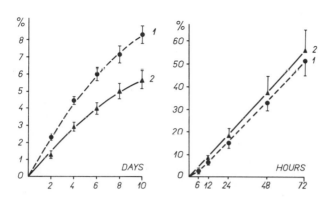

Fig. 11. Oxidation of [26-14C]cholesterol and [26-14C]-7α-hydroxycholesterol to 14CO₂ as percentage of dose administered to control (1) and vitamin C-deficient (2) guinea pigs. Latent vitamin C deficiency significantly reduced the oxidation of [26-14C]cholesterol, while the oxidation of [26-14C]-7α-hydroxycholesterol was not significantly affected. From Ginter (1975a).

0.899). Recently Björkhem and Kallner (1976) reported that the extent of conversion of endogenous cholesterol into 7α-hydroxycholesterol, as determined by mass fragmentography, was more than 10 times lower in incubations with microsomal fraction from vitamin C-deficient guinea pigs than in those from guinea pigs treated with ascorbate. On the other side, 25- and 26-hydroxylation of 5β-cholestane-3α,7α-diol was not significantly affected by the ascorbate status of animals (Fig. 12). It seems therefore highly probable that marginal vitamin C deficiency interferes with the biosynthesis of bile acids solely at the stage of 7α-hydroxylation of the cholesterol nucleus.

Cholesterol-7α-hydroxylase is localized in the microsomal fraction of the liver cell and requires NADPH and oxygen for maximum activity. The cholesterol 7α-hydroxylating system consists of cytochrome P-450 and NADPH cytochrome P-450 reductase (Wada *et al.*, 1968; Scholan and Boyd, 1968). The cytochrome P-450 concentration in guinea pig liver microsomes falls within 24 hours after discontinuing the supply of ascorbic acid (Degkwitz *et al.*, 1972, 1975). After administration of ascorbic acid to vitamin C-deficient guinea pigs, the cytochrome P-450 level in the liver microsomes (Leber *et al.*, 1970) rises parallel with [26-14C]-cholesterol oxidation to 14CO₂ (Ginter and Nemec, 1972) (Fig. 13). It seems feasible that the stimulant effect of ascorbate on the 7α-hydroxylation of cholesterol is mediated through its action on the cytochrome P-450

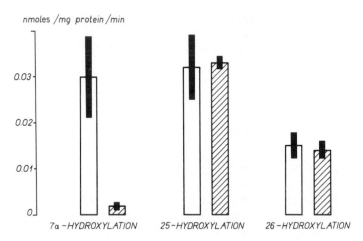

FIG. 12. 7α-hydroxylation of endogenous microsomal cholesterol and 25- and 26-hydroxylation of 5β-cholestane-$3\alpha,7\alpha$-diol by microsomal fraction of liver homogenate from control (unshaded columns) and vitamin C-deficient (shaded columns) guinea pigs. The figure was constructed from the data of Björkhem and Kallner (1976).

level in the liver microsomes. Degkwitz and Kim (1973) assumed that ascorbate played a role in biosynthesis of the heme part of the cytochrome P-450. Partially purified cytochrome P-450 from hepatal microsomes of vitamin C-deficient guinea pig in the presence of excess NADPH-cyto-

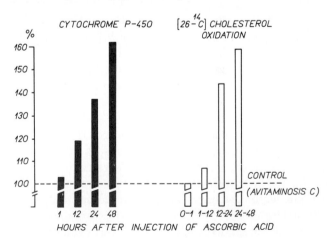

FIG. 13.   Parallel increase in [26-^{14}C]cholesterol oxidation and the cytochrome P-450 level in the liver microsomes of vitamin C-deficient guinea pigs after the administration of ascorbic acid (values in vitamin C-deficient animals = 100%). The left part of the figure was constructed from the data of Leber et al. (1970). From Ginter and Nemec (1972).

chrome P-450 reductase had a much lower capacity to 7α-hydroxylate cholesterol than a corresponding system containing cytochrome P-450 from liver of normal guinea pig (Björkhem and Kallner, 1976). These authors suggested that vitamin C deficiency lowered the specific type of cytochrome P-450 involved in 7α-hydroxylation of cholesterol. It is also possible that the ascorbic-monodehydroascorbic-dehydroascorbic acid redox system is linked up in the transport of electrons from NADPH to oxidized cytochrome P-450. In this association, the finding of elevated catabolism of [1-^{14}C]ascorbic acid to $^{14}CO_2$, and [^{14}C]oxalate in cholesterol-fed guinea pigs (Ginter, 1975b), i.e., under conditions where a continuous supply of large amounts of exogenous cholesterol raises requirements for the reduction of oxidized cytochrome P-450, is interesting. In cholesterol-fed guinea pigs, vitamin C requirements rise at the same time (Ginter and Zloch, 1972). It is probable, however, that the effect of ascorbate on the 7α-hydroxylation of cholesterol is not an effect on the enzyme activity *per se* since addition of ascorbate to the microsomal fraction had no effect on the rate of 7α-hydroxylation (Kritchevsky *et al.*, 1973; Björkhem and Kallner, 1976).

The strong influence of vitamin C on the liver is manifested not only in the transformation of cholesterol to bile acids, but also in detoxication of a variety of pharmacological agents and environmental chemicals (Zannoni and Sato, 1975; Street and Chadwick, 1975), in which microsomal cytochrome P-450 plays a role, as in 7α-hydroxylation of cholesterol. Chronic latent ascorbate deficiency is associated with morphological, as well as functional, changes in the liver cell, the chief one being marked reduction and replacement of the granular endoplasmic reticulum (Sulkin and Sulkin, 1975) (Fig. 14). In protracted marginal vitamin C deficiency, guinea pig liver displays centrolobular fatty degeneration, moderate hyperplasia of the bile ducts and occasionally discrete signs of fibroplasia (Fig. 15). Fatty cirrhosis, with bile duct proliferation, was even observed in the liver of hypovitaminous guinea pigs fed on a diet containing 0.3% cholesterol (Fig. 16). The pathological changes in animals given the same cholesterol diet, plus 100 mg ascorbic acid/animal/day, were less striking (Ginter, 1975b).

C. Vitamin C and Cholesterol Turnover

Chronic marginal vitamin C deficiency is associated with a sharp decline in the liver ascorbate concentration, with a consequent decrease in the rate of cholesterol transformation to bile acids. Lowered bile acid synthesis is associated with lowered absorption of exogenous cholesterol from gastrointestinal tract, but this homeostatic mechanism is not suffi-

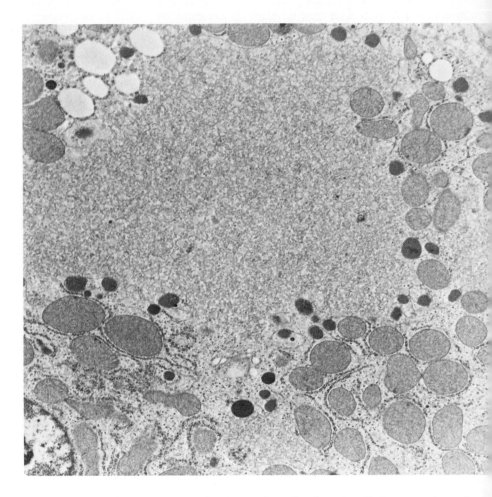

Fɪɢ. 14.   Electron micrograph of a section of a hepatic cell from a guinea pig
that had been on a marginally vitamin C-deficient diet for a period of 104 days. Note
the reduction of the granular endoplasmic reticulum and the encirclement of these
organelles around the mitochondria when they are present. The sharp proliferation
of smooth endoplasmic reticulum to the extent of displacing other organelles is of
special significance. From Sulkin and Sulkin (1975).

ciently effective to be able to compensate slower cholesterol catabolism
in full. This creates a state of imbalance, in which the supply of cholesterol to the system exceeds the rate of its removal, resulting in the
accumulation of cholesterol in the liver and plasma. If marginal vitamin C
deficiency is protracted (5–6 months), the guinea pig liver-cholesterol

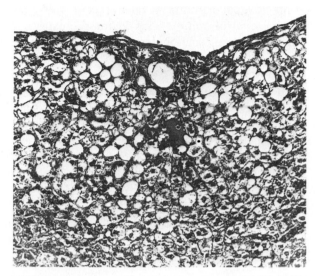

Fig. 15. Fatty degeneration and subcapsular peribiliary fibroplasia causing retraction of surface of liver of guinea pig kept 11 months in a state of latent vitamin C deficiency. Hematoxylin and eosin; ×160.

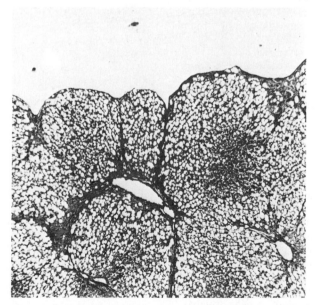

Fig. 16. Fatty cirrhosis of liver of vitamin C-deficient guinea pig fed 6 months on cholesterol diet. Hematoxylin and eosin; ×32.

level rises by 50–70% and plasma level by about 40% (Table II, Section V) above the control values. This increase creates a new state of equilibrium, in which the plasma-cholesterol level of deficient guinea pigs does not undergo any more marked changes, but the kinetic parameters of cholesterol turnover, determined by the two-pool analysis (Nestel *et al.,* 1969), are greatly altered (Table V). The half time of the linear part of the hyperbolic curve in hypovitaminous guinea pigs was significantly prolonged, while the values of the rate constant for irreversible cholesterol excretion and total cholesterol turnover rate were significantly lowered (Ginter, 1974). In golden hamsters, which are normally independent of exogenous vitamin C, relative ascorbate deficiency was induced by ad-

Table V

KINETIC PARAMETERS OF CHOLESTEROL TURNOVER IN GUINEA PIGS AND GOLDEN HAMSTERS FED DIFFERENT DOSES OF VITAMIN C

	Guinea pigs	
Parameter	Control (10 mg ascorbate/day)	Hypovitaminosis C (0.5 mg ascorbate/day)
Half time of first exponential (days)	8.0	7.1
Half time of second exponential (days)	24.0	30.1
Turnover rate: production rate in pool A (mg/animal/day)	37.8	31.8
Fractional turnover rate (% of pool A renewed in 24 hours)	3.6	3.1
Cholesterol transformation to bile acids (mg/24 hours/500 g body weight)	11.8	8.3

	Golden hamsters	
	Ascorbic acid intake	
Parameter	0.5% in diet	Zero
Half-life of plasma cholesterol (days)	15.7	21.5
Half-life of liver cholesterol (days)	16.3	21.5
Size of total cholesterol miscible pool (mg/animal)	128	162
Turnover rate (mg/animal/day)	5.6	5.2
Fractional turnover rate (% of pool renewed in 24 hours)	4.4	3.2
Cholesterol transformation to bile acids (mg/24 hours/100 g body weight)	2.53	2.16

ministering a physiologically unbalanced fat-free, ascorbate-free, high-glucose diet (Ginter *et al.*, 1976). In these animals, just as in vitamin C-deficient guinea pigs, the plasma and liver cholesterol concentration rose compared with the group given the same diet plus 0.5% ascorbic acid, the half-life of plasma and liver cholesterol was prolonged, the size of the body pool of miscible cholesterol increased, the fractional turnover rate fell and the rate of cholesterol transformation to bile acids diminished (Table V, lower part). Total turnover (which equals endogenous choles-terol synthesis on administering a cholesterol-free diet) was not greatly affected.

Latent vitamin C deficiency thus produced in guinea pigs and hamsters changes similar to those produced by alimentary hypercholesterolemia and atherosclerosis in rabbits (Table I, Section IV). All these changes (an increased number of cholesterol molecules per plasma volume unit, prolongation of the mean length of time for which the cholesterol mole-cules persist in the circulating blood, the overall slowing down of choles-terol turnover) speak for the probability of cholesterol being accumulated in the blood vessel walls of vitamin C-deficient animals. Figure 17 fur-nishes evidence of the negative correlation between the amount of [^{14}C]-cholesterol which accumulates in the thoracic aorta and the cholesterol turnover rate, i.e., a decrease in the turnover rate leads to a significant increase in the accumulation of labeled cholesterol in the guinea pig aorta.

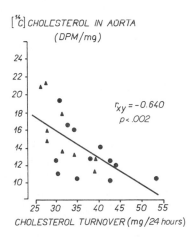

Fig. 17. Negative correlation between cholesterol turnover rate and amount of labeled cholesterol deposited in guinea pig thoracic aorta 42 days after i.p. adminis-tration of [4-^{14}C]cholesterol. (●) Control animals; (▲) guinea pigs kept 27 weeks in state of latent vitamin C deficiency. From Ginter (1975b).

VI. Further Effects of Vitamin C on Lipid Metabolism

A. VITAMIN C AND TRIGLYCERIDE METABOLISM

Fujinami *et al.* (1971) found that the serum triglyceride concentration in guinea pigs rises slightly after only 2 weeks' administration of a vitamin C-free diet. If guinea pigs are given a diet to which 0.3% cholesterol is added, marginal vitamin C deficiency leads in 4 months to marked hypertriglyceridemia and to the accumulation of triglycerides in the liver and the aorta (Nambisan and Kurup, 1975). If latent ascorbic acid deficiency is prolonged still further, the blood triglyceride level rises by 50%, even when the guinea pigs are given a diet with no additional cholesterol (Ginter *et al.*, 1976) (Table VI). A raised vitamin C intake causes triglyceride levels to fall not only in guinea pigs (Nambisan and Kurup, 1975) but also in weanling rats (Nambisan and Kurup, 1974), cholesterol-fed rabbits and rats (Sokoloff *et al.*, 1967), and baboons (Kotzé *et al.*, 1975). Marked hypertriglyceridemia can be induced in golden hamsters by administering an ascorbate-free, fat-free, high-glucose diet (Ginter *et al.*, 1976); the addition of 0.5% ascorbic acid to this diet restores the situation to practically normal (Table VI). The hypotriglyceridemic action of vitamin C in humans will be discussed in Section VIII.

The mechanism of the hypotriglyceridemic action of ascorbic acid is not altogether clear, but it is very probably associated with the effect of ascorbic acid on lypolytic enzyme activities. Normalization of hypertriglyceridemia in cholesterol-fed rabbits and rats was associated with an increase in lipoprotein lipase activity in the blood (Sokoloff *et al.*, 1967). Large doses of ascorbate similarly reduced the blood triglyceride level in guinea pigs and simultaneously raised the lipoprotein lipase activity of the plasma (Fujinami *et al.*, 1971). The effect of large doses of vitamin C on lipoprotein lipase in the heart muscle of baboons (Kotzé *et al.*, 1974a) and in the liver and heart of guinea pigs (Nambisan and Kurup, 1975) is just the reverse, i.e., lipoprotein lipase activity in animals given large doses of ascorbate was much lower than in vitamin C-deficient animals. Ascorbic acid affects myocardial and adipose tissue lipoprotein lipase differently: higher serum ascorbate levels (over 0.35 mg%) appear to inhibit the heart muscle enzyme and to stimulate the adipose tissue enzyme (Kotzé, 1975). Heart and adipose tissue lipoprotein lipase also react to experimental hypertriglyceridemia in the same different manner (Shafrir and Biale, 1970; Vrána *et al.*, 1974). In insulin deficiency, lipoprotein lipase activity decreases in adipose tissue and increases in the heart (Kessler, 1963). In this association it is interesting to note that vitamin C deficiency which leads to hypoinsulinism (Banerjee and Ghosh, 1947) also stimulates

Table VI

INFLUENCE OF VITAMIN C ON BLOOD PLASMA TRIGLYCERIDES IN GOLDEN HAMSTERS AND GUINEA PIGS

Kind of experimental animal	Control	High-glucose fat-free diet	
		Vitamin C: 0	Vitamin C: 0.5% in diet
Golden hamsters	207 ± 11 [a]	690 ± 137	251 ± 13
Guinea pigs		Hypovitaminosis C	
Duration of experiment: 6.5 months	67 ± 7	105 ± 11	
Duration of experiment: 11 months	105 ± 10	159 ± 10	

[a] Milligrams per 100 ml plasma $\pm$ SEM.

lipoprotein lipase activity in the heart (Kotzé *et al.,* 1974a; Nambisan and Kurup, 1975).

The finding that ascorbate had a marked inhibitory effect on hormone-sensitive lipase from adipose tissue (Tsai *et al.,* 1973) led to consideration (Anonymous, 1974) that large doses of vitamin C might inhibit the mobilization of nonesterified fatty acids from depot tissues and in this way lead to obesity. *In vivo* experiments, however, showed that, on the contrary, the mobilization of nonesterified fatty acids is inhibited by vitamin C deficiency (Mueller and Cardon, 1961). Scorbutic guinea pigs do not even respond to the injection of adrenaline by mobilization of nonesterified fatty acids (Mueller, 1962); ascorbic acid, on the contrary, stimulates this process (Mathur *et al.,* 1974). The stimulating action of vitamin C on hormone-induced lipolysis is localized somewhere before the activation of lipase by adenosine 3′,5′-cyclic monophosphate. One possible mechanism is the inhibition of phosphodiesterase activity in adipose tissue (Hynie *et al.,* 1970). In baboons ascorbic acid significantly raised the plasma adenosine 3′,5′-cyclic monophosphate level, but reduced guanosine 3′,5′-cyclic monophosphate levels (Van Wyk and Kotzé, 1975). The preincubation of guinea pig lung fragments with ascorbic acid significantly raised prostaglandin $F_{2\alpha}$ production (Hitchcock, 1975). Although the hypotriglyceridemic effect of vitamin C is unquestionable, the mechanism by which ascorbic acid deficiency interferes with triglyceride metabolism is evidently complex and requires further research.

B. Vitamin C and Gallstone Formation

The initial phase of gallstone formation is a disorder of liver cell metabolism, the production of bile supersaturated with cholesterol (Admirand and Small, 1968). Bile acids and lecithin are the major solubilizing agents for biliary cholesterol. In subjects with cholesterol gallstones, the size of the bile acid pool decreases (Vlahcevic *et al.,* 1970). The reduction of bile acid pool size could lead to a decrease in the proportion of bile acids in relation to cholesterol and this could result in the precipitation of cholesterol and the aggregation of cholesterol crystals into gallstones. A similar metabolic situation develops in guinea pigs with marginal vitamin C deficiency: the rate of cholesterol transformation to bile acids is lowered and so is the [^{14}C]bile acid content of the gallbladder bile of hypovitaminous guinea pigs injected with [4-^{14}C]cholesterol (Table IV, Section V,B). In guinea pigs given small doses of ascorbate, the size of the bile acid pool is also reduced (Hornig and Weiser, 1976). In agreement with these data, a frequent incidence of gallstones was observed in guinea pigs with acute scurvy (Pavel *et al.,* 1969; Bellmann *et al.,* 1974). These findings indicate

that chronic marginal vitamin C deficiency could play a role in the pathogenesis of cholelithiasis and that the intake of large doses of ascorbate
could play a positive role in preventing gallstone formation.

In recently completed experiments we studied the effect of the addition
of 0.5% ascorbic acid to a lithogenic diet (Dam, 1964) on the metabolism
of [26-^{14}C]cholesterol and on gallstone formation in golden hamsters.
Vitamin C markedly accelerated cholesterol turnover (Table V, Section V,
C) and significantly reduced both the incidence and the extent of experimental cholelithiasis and the accumulation of [^{14}C]cholesterol in the gallstones (Table VII). We also succeeded, using the same diet, in inducing
gallstone formation in guinea pigs (Fig. 18). When we administered mount-
ing doses of vitamin C which raised liver ascorbate levels, the number of
guinea pigs free from gallstones rose significantly (Table VII, lower part).

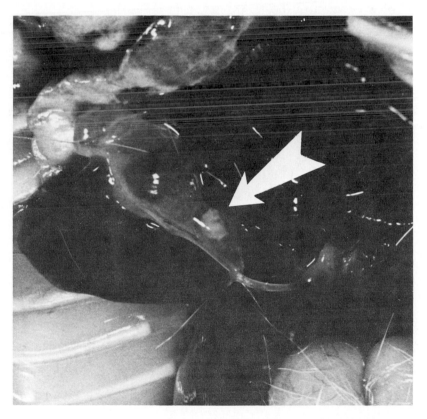

Fig. 18.   Gallstone in gallbladder of vitamin C-deficient guinea pig fed 4 weeks
on lithogenic diet.

Table VII

EFFECT OF VITAMIN C ON THE INCIDENCE OF GALLSTONES AND VITAMIN C CONCENTRATION IN THE LIVER OF GOLDEN HAMSTERS AND GUINEA PIGS FED A FAT-FREE HIGH-GLUCOSE DIET

Kind of experimental animal	Ascorbic acid supplementation				
	Zero	*0.05% in diet*	*0.5% in diet*	*1% in diet*	*1% in diet + 0.5% in water*
Golden hamsters					
Animals free of gallstones (%)	32		56		
Animals with incipient cholelithiasis (%)	26		20		
Animals with advanced cholelithiasis (%)	42		24		
¹⁴C activity in gallstones (dpm/total gallstones)	768		356		
Vitamin C in the liver (mg/100 g wet tissue)	14.7		26.8		
Guinea pigs					
Animals free of gallstones (%)		29		50	63
Vitamin C in the liver (mg/100 g wet tissue)		4.4		15.0	43.8

Whether the incidence of human cholelithiasis can be reduced by preventing latent vitamin C deficiency is still an open question. Large doses of vitamin C did not markedly alter the chemical composition of the bile in human subjects (Pedersen, 1975), but in these experiments ascorbic acid was unfortunately administered only over a very short period (7–15 days).

VII. Vitamin C, Metabolism of Blood Vessel Wall, and Experimental Atherosclerosis

Chronic marginal vitamin C deficiency induces hypercholesterolemia and hypertriglyceridemia in experimental animals. In addition to these two factors promoting atheromatous reconstruction of the vascular system, there is a third important factor, changes in the walls of the blood vessels of vitamin C-deficient animals.

A. Metabolic and Structural Changes in Blood Vessel Wall in Vitamin C Deficiency

1. *Collagen*

The role of vitamin C in collagen synthesis is the longest-known biochemical function of ascorbic acid and it has been elaborated in very great detail. Vitamin C participates in the synthesis of collagen hydroxyproline and hydroxylysine, both of which are formed by the hydroxylation of prolyl and lysyl residues previously incorporated into peptide linkage during the process of ribosomal collagen protein synthesis (Barnes, 1975). Intensive investigations are being carried out to elucidate the precise mode of action of ascorbate in these hydroxylations (Hurych *et al.*, 1973; Rokosova and Chvapil, 1974; Alfano *et al.*, 1975; Barnes, 1975; Cardinale *et al.*, 1975; Levene and Bates, 1975); unfortunately, the interest of these teams is not centered on the connective tissue of the blood vessel wall.

In earlier morphological studies, we already find descriptions of atrophy of collagen in vessel walls (Hojer, 1924), breakdown of collagen fibrils adjacent to capillaries (Wolbach and Bessey, 1942), weakening of collagen bundles in atonic dilated venules (Lee and Lee, 1947), and degeneration of the connective tissue within the vessel walls and perivascular areas (Stolman *et al.*, 1961) in vitamin C-deficient guinea pigs. Electron microscopy revealed depletion of aortic subendothelial collagen (Gore *et al.*, 1965b). Except for just one study (Banerjee and Ghosh, 1961), a decrease in collagen measured as hydroxyproline was also observed in the aorta of scorbutic guinea pigs (Gore *et al.*, 1965a; Kishikawa, *et al.*, 1971); it was particularly pronounced in protracted marginal ascorbate deficiency

(Higuchi *et al.*, 1975). Vitamin C deficiency thus probably slows down collagen synthesis in the blood vessel wall also, resulting in collagen depletion in the blood vessels in the presence of chronic ascorbate deficiency.

2. *Glycosaminoglycans*

Vitamin C deficiency interferes with yet another important component of the connective tissue of the blood vessel wall, i.e., the glycosaminoglycans of the ground substance. The extreme heterogeneity in origin, structure, and turnover of the various glycosaminoglycans makes problems of the influence of ascorbic acid on mucopolysaccharide metabolism tremendously complicated. They have been solved mainly in tissue cultures and in tendonectomized or otherwise injured guinea pigs (Bates and Levene, 1969), but the results are often at variance.

Histochemical and chemical methods showed an increase in total mucopolysaccharides in the aorta of scorbutic guinea pigs (Weber, 1955; Banerjee and Ghosh, 1961), which was caused mainly by an increase in the hyaluronic acid level (Gore *et al.*, 1965a; Kishikawa *et al.*, 1971). The chondroitin sulfate B (in the latest terminology, dermatan sulfate) level in the aorta of guinea pigs with acute scurvy fell, however (Gore *et al.*, 1965a; Kishikawa *et al.*, 1971). When hyperlipemia was induced by coconut oil feeding, the total glycosaminoglycan level in the aorta of guinea pigs kept in a state of latent ascorbate deficiency for 8 weeks fell, owing to a drop in hyaluronic acid, heparan sulfate, and chondroitin-6-sulfate levels (Higuchi *et al.*, 1975). Similar changes were described by Nambisan and Kurup (1975) in the aorta of guinea pigs kept in a state of marginal ascorbate deficiency for 4 months; when a diet with added cholesterol was given, these changes were even more pronounced (Table VIII).

We observed an increase in β-glycosidase activities in the thoracic aorta of guinea pigs kept for an exceptionally long time (11 months) in a state of marginal vitamin C deficiency (Table IX). A significant increase in β-glucuronidase activity was also described in the aorta of guinea pigs kept in a state of latent ascorbic acid deficiency for a shorter length of time (Fujinami *et al.*, 1975; Nambisan and Kurup, 1975). This enzyme degrades polysaccharide fragments split off from acid mucopolysaccharides by hyaluronidase. The cause of the decrease in the glycosaminoglycan content of the aorta of vitamin-deficient guinea pigs could thus be an increase in β-glucuronidase and other hydrolytic enzyme activities (hyaluronidase and β-hexosaminidase) in the aorta of deficient animals (Nambisan and Kurup, 1975). β-Glucuronidase activity in the blood vessels increases with age and rises markedly in lipoid plaques (Kirk, 1969; Lojda, 1974). The finding of raised β-glucuronidase activity in the aorta of vitamin

Table VIII

GLYCOSAMINOGLYCAN LEVELS IN THE AORTA OF GUINEA PIGS FED VARIOUS DOSES OF ASCORBIC ACID [a]

Group	Hyaluronic acid	Heparan sulfate	Chondroitin 4-sulfate	Chrondroitin 6-sulfate	Dermatan sulfate	Heparin
			Basal diet			
Marginal deficiency (0.1 mg ascorbate/100 g b.w.)	1,287 ± 26 [b]	1,280 ± 26	1,050 ± 21	1,459 ± 29	833 ± 17	788 ± 15
Adequate dose of vitamin C (1 mg ascorbate/100 g b.w.)	1,450 ± 28	1,321 ± 27	1,110 ± 22	1,562 ± 30	930 ± 19	926 ± 19
High dose of vitamin C (25 mg ascorbate/100 g b.w.)	1,491 ± 29	1,476 ± 29	1,388 ± 27	1,610 ± 32	956 ± 19	986 ± 20
			Atherogenic cholesterol diet			
Marginal deficiency (0.1 mg ascorbate/100 g b.w.)	1,001 ± 25	990 ± 20	595 ± 15	1,036 ± 26	520 ± 12	610 ± 13
Adequate dose of vitamin C (1 mg ascorbate/100 g b.w.)	965 ± 21	1,100 ± 22	380 ± 18	1,180 ± 31	600 ± 14	730 ± 15
High dose of vitamin C (25 mg ascorbate/100 g b.w.)	989 ± 22	1,124 ± 22	956 ± 20	1,260 ± 31	675 ± 14	824 ± 17

[a] Data from Nambisan and Kurup (1975).

[b] Micrograms uronic acid per gram dry defatted tissue ± SEM.

Table IX

INFLUENCE OF CHRONIC MARGINAL VITAMIN C DEFICIENCY ON ENZYME ACTIVITY
IN THORACIC AORTA OF GUINEA PIGS

Enzyme	Control	Hypovitaminosis C
β-Galactosidase (EC 3.2.1.2.3)	0.046 ± 0.008 [a]	0.070 ± 0.008
β-N-Acetylglucosaminidase (EC 3.2.1.30)	1.75 ± 0.20	2.00 ± 0.21
β-Glucuronidase (EC 3.2.1.31)	0.98 ± 0.12	1.30 ± 0.09
Carboxylic esterases (EC 3.1.1)	6.0 ± 0.4	5.2 ± 0.8
Alkaline phosphatase (EC 3.1.3.1)	0.10 ± 0.01	0.09 ± 0.01
Acid phosphatase (EC 3.1.3.2)	1.40 ± 0.02	1.12 ± 0.09
Succinic dehydrogenase (EC 1.3.99.1)	23.0 ± 1.4	32.0 ± 2.7
Malic dehydrogenase (EC 1.1.1.37)	102 ± 5	100 ± 4

[a] Micromoles per gram wet tissue per 60 minutes $\pm$ SEM.

C-deficient guinea pigs may thus be a sign of the presence of presclerotic changes.

Conversely, large doses of ascorbic acid raise the total glycosaminoglycan level in the guinea pig and rat aorta (Nambisan and Kurup, 1974, 1975). The increase in sulfated glycosaminoglycans (heparan sulfate, chondroitin-4- and 6-sulfate, and dermatan sulfate) is especially marked (Table VIII). At the same time, large doses of ascorbate raise the activity of enzymes concerned with biological sulfation in guinea pig liver (Nambisan and Kurup, 1975). Whether ascorbic acid-2-sulfate plays a role in activation of these processes (Hatanaka et al., 1974; Hornig, 1975; Shapiro and Poon, 1975) is still an open question.

Metabolic disorders and changes in the composition of the intima very probably play an important role in the pathogenesis of atherosclerosis (Robinson et al., 1975). Plasma β-lipoproteins are bound to different mucopolysaccharides to varying degrees. Hyaluronic acid influences the selective permeability of the intima, while heparan sulfates have an anti-lipemic and antithrombotic action. Alteration of these functions can favor atherogenesis through different pathogenetic mechanisms.

B. VITAMIN C AND EXPERIMENTAL ATHEROSCLEROSIS

Menten and King observed diffuse hyperplastic arteriosclerosis in the lungs, liver, spleen, and kidneys of vitamin C-deficient guinea pigs injected with diphtheria toxin as early as 1935. Willis (1953) found subendothelial lipid deposits in the aorta of scorbutic guinea pigs. The administration of ascorbic acid to scorbutic guinea pigs led to rapid resorption of early atherosclerotic lesions (Willis, 1957). Fujinami et al. (1971), in guinea pigs fed on a diet to which coconut oil was added, described atheromatous lesions after only 2 weeks of a scorbutogenic regimen. Other authors (Gore *et al.*, 1965a,b; Ginter *et al.*, 1969a) failed to find explicit atherosclerotic lesions in guinea pigs with acute vitamin C deficiency, but described in them reduced silver stainability of the cement lines and increased incidence of nuclear abnormalities in the aortic endothelium. Electron microscopy revealed separation of the endothelial cells and reduction of the cytoplasmic organelles in the aortic endothelium of scorbutic guinea pigs (Gore *et al.*, 1965b; Kishikawa *et al.*, 1971). The mast cell count fell in the *tunica adventitia* of the aortic wall in scorbutic guinea pigs (Pettersson, 1959). In ovalbumin-sensitized subscorbutic guinea pigs, the administration of cholesterol caused an increase in aortic endothelial turnover and destruction of cells (Wright *et al.*, 1975).

The administration of a 0.3% cholesterol diet to guinea pigs with latent vitamin C deficiency produced marked atheromatous changes in the coronary arteries in a few months (Fig. 4, Section IV). Large doses of ascorbic acid (50–100 mg/animal/day) slowed down atheromatous reconstruction of the vascular system but did not prevent fully the formation of atheromatous lesions in the coronary arteries (Ginter *et al.*, 1969b, Ginter, 1975b). The accumulation of cholesterol in the thoracic aorta of hypovitaminous guinea pigs fed on a cholesterol diet was greater than in animals given a 100-fold larger dose of ascorbate, but not even this dose of vitamin C prevented an increase in the cholesterol concentration in the aorta compared with the low cholesterol diet controls (Ginter *et al.*, 1969b) (Fig. 19). Similar results were obtained by Nambisan and Kurup (1975).

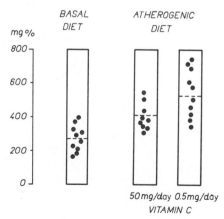

Fig. 19. Total cholesterol concentration in thoracic aorta of control guinea pigs and animals fed 12 weeks on cholesterol diet. The difference between cholesterol-fed animals given 50 or 0.5 mg ascorbic acid daily is statistically significant. From Ginter (1975b).

The continued long-term intake of large amounts of exogenous cholesterol may mask the protective effect of essential fatty acids as well as of vitamin C. Discrepancies between the results of different authors who studied the influence of ascorbic acid on cholesterol atherosclerosis (Section IV) are evidently due partly to this factor. In given circumstances, e.g., in copper deficiency, ascorbic acid actually potentiates an angiopathy (Simpson *et al.*, 1971). On the other hand, in animals synthesizing ascorbate, vitamin C can be shown to have a positive effect if the animals are put in a situation which raises the ascorbate requirements. Vitamin C was shown to have a hypocholesterolemic and/or antiatherosclerotic effect in weanling rats (Nambisan and Kurup, 1974), in hypothyroid rats (Scholz, 1973), in rats with experimental cholestasis and aminonucleoside nephrosis (Froese *et al.*, 1975), in rats with experimental fatty degeneration of the liver (Cajola, 1968), in starved rabbits (Kolmakov, 1957), in rabbits with epinephrine-induced atherosclerosis (Davis and Oester, 1952), and in golden hamsters fed on a fat-free, ascorbate-free, high-glucose diet (Section V,C).

The most important experiments for comprehending the potential role of ascorbic acid deficiency in the pathogenesis of human atherosclerosis, however, are those in which the influence of chronic latent vitamin C deficiency on atherogenesis was studied under conditions of a nutritionally balanced,

FIG. 20. Lipophage layer in intima of thoracic aorta of guinea pig fed on diet with no added cholesterol and kept over 6 months in state of latent vitamin C deficiency. Hematoxylin and eosin; ×400.

low-cholesterol diet. In guinea pigs kept in a state of marginal vitamin C deficiency for over 6 months, we found (Ginter, 1974, 1975b) that edema of the vessel wall, vacuolization of the endothelial cells and parietal adhesion of blood plasma occurred in their aorta even when they were given a diet to which no cholesterol was added. In some deficient animals, the formation of lipophages (Figs. 20 and 21) and even of fresh homogenous atheromatous material was found in the intima of the aorta and the coronary arteries and their branches. It should be emphasized that these findings were made in seemingly healthy animals fed on a standard diet without additional cholesterol, so that the only cause of these changes must have been chronic latent vitamin C deficiency.

After 8 weeks of latent vitamin C deficiency, Fujinami *et al.* (1975) found white patchy plaques in the arch and proximal part of the aorta of two-thirds of their guinea pigs fed on a diet without added cholesterol. The lesions consisted of fibrous thickening of the intima, with lipid accumulation and degenerative changes in the media accompanied by mucopolysaccharide, lipid and calcium deposits. The most marked accumulation of cholesterol and triglycerides was found in the arch of the aorta of deficient animals. In this part of the aorta there was also a significant increase in esterase and lipase activity (Fig. 22). In guinea pigs fed on a diet without

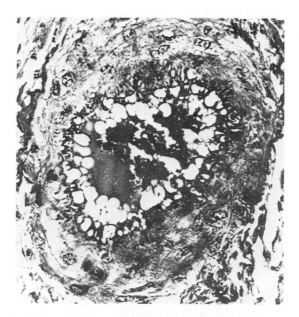

FIG. 21. Intimal foam cells in edematous branch of coronary artery of guinea pig fed on diet with no addition of cholesterol and kept over 6 months in state of latent vitamin C deficiency. Hematoxylin and eosin; ×400.

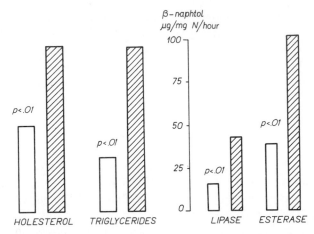

FIG. 22. Significant increase in cholesterol and triglyceride concentration and in lipase and esterase activity in arch of aorta of vitamin C-deficient guinea pigs fed on diet with no added cholesterol: (unshaded columns) controls; (shaded columns) vitamin C deficiency. The figure was constructed from the data of Fujinami *et al.* (1975).

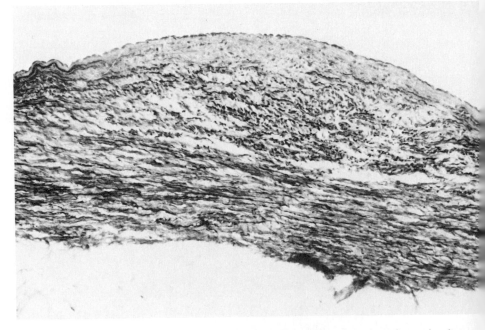

FIG. 23. A section of an aortic arteriosclerotic plaque from a guinea pig that had been on a marginal vitamin C-deficient diet with no added cholesterol for a period of 109 days. Stained with Van-Gieson-Verhoff stain to demonstrate the fibrotic nature of the lesion. From Sulkin and Sulkin (1975).

added cholesterol and kept 100–150 days in a state of marginal vitamin C deficiency, Sulkin and Sulkin (1975) found numerous alterations in the aortic wall; these were large intimal plaques (Fig. 23), which appeared to be of a musculofibrotic type, marked endothelial proliferation, a high degree of metachromasia in the ground substance, and the presence of a fibrous, amorphous material of varying thickness underlying the endothelium (Fig. 24).

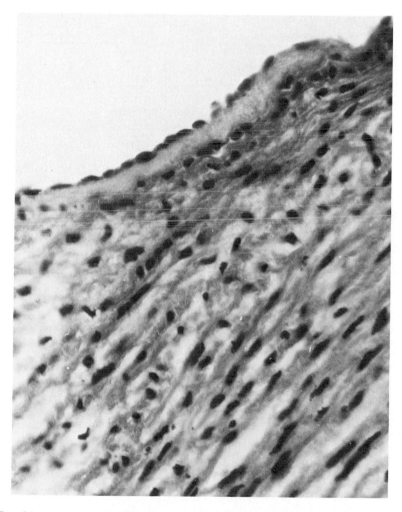

Fig. 24. A section of the aorta of a guinea pig that had been on a marginal vitamin C-deficient diet with no added cholesterol for 105 days. Note the thick band of amorphous substance underlying the epithelium. From Sulkin and Sulkin (1975).

These results demonstrate that chronic latent ascorbic acid deficiency is *per se* capable of producing atheromatous changes in the guinea pig vascular system. The mechanism of this phenomenon is complex and, as shown by the scheme below, it is based on interference with the integrity of the blood vessel wall (impaired collagen and glycosaminoglycan metabolism), on slower catabolism of cholesterol in the liver and resultant hypercholesterolemia and on the development of still incompletely studied disorders of triglyceride metabolism leading to hypertriglyceridemia:

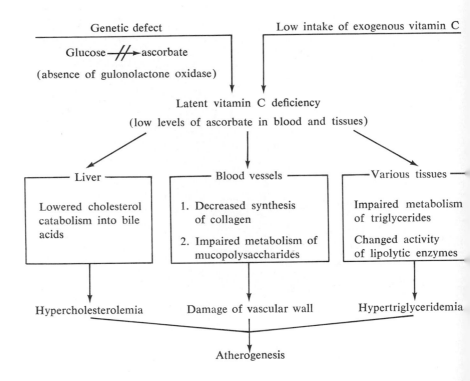

VIII. Vitamin C, Hyperlipemia, and Atherosclerosis in Man

The literature on the effect of ascorbic acid on the blood lipids and on atherosclerosis in man is very extensive and very contradictory. The majority of clinical studies on these problems are less exact than animal experiments. Basic information is often missing, e.g., on the experimental subjects' vitamin C status at the time of starting the experiment and on changes in the composition of their diet during the experiment. Most authors (Bukovskaya, 1957; Anderson *et al.,* 1958, 1972; Hrubá and

Mašek, 1962; Bronte-Stewart *et al.,* 1963; Crawford *et al.,* 1975), though
not all (Spittle, 1971; Hanck, 1973), found that ascorbic acid had no
effect in subjects with initial low cholesterol levels. Many authors (Myasnikova, 1947; Sedov, 1956; Bukovskaya, 1957; Myasnikov, 1960; Fedorova,
1960; Sokoloff *et al.,* 1967; Kishikawa *et al.,* 1971) stated that vitamin C
led to diminution of hypercholesterolemia and hypertriglyceridemia, to a
decrease in the β-lipoprotein level, and to improvement of the state of
health of at least some of their subjects with hyperlipemia and atherosclerosis. It should be stressed that, in most of these studies, a hypocholesterolemic effect was achieved in conjunction with other factors, e.g., a
therapeutic diet. According to other authors (Krivoruchenko, 1963; Samuel
and Salchi, 1964; Peterson *et al.,* 1975), vitamin C did not affect the
plasma-cholesterol level in hypercholesterolemic subjects, or actually raised
it (Spittle, 1971).

A number of authors described seasonal variations of the blood-cholesterol level in man (Tochowicz *et al.,* 1962; Fyfe *et al.,* 1968). The highest
level was usually observed at the time of minimum vitamin C consumption,
but whether there is a causal relationship is still an open question. The
correlation of ascorbate and cholesterol levels in a single blood sample
(Ziffer *et al.,* 1967; Elwood *et al.,* 1970; Bradley *et al.,* 1973) is likewise
not very helpful, since the actual vitamin C concentration in the blood does
not furnish exact information on the subject's nutritional history. A few
authors (Mašek, 1960; Kajaba and Bučko, 1968; Cheraskin and Ringsdorf, 1968) nevertheless found a negative correlation between the vitamin
C supply and the blood-cholesterol level, i.e., the lower the former, the
higher the latter. On the other hand, in nomadic tribes in Kenya known
to have a very low cholesterolemia, raised plasma- or leucocyte-ascorbate
concentrations were associated with higher cholesterol levels (Gatenby
Davies and Newson, 1974).

Cardiomegaly and pronounced electrocardiographic abnormalities, which
returned to normal after ascorbate therapy, have been described in patients
with scurvy (Shafar, 1967; Singh and Chan, 1974). Hume *et al.* (1972),
a few hours after acute myocardial infarction, found an abrupt decrease in
the ascorbate concentration in the leucocytes in association with the
migration of ascorbate-rich leucocytes to the site of the lesions; ascorbic
acid may stimulate protein synthesis in myocardium (Gudbjarnason *et al.,*
1966). In an arteriographic study, Willis *et al.* (1954) found that atherosclerotic changes receded in some of their patients given vitamin C.
Spittle (1973) described the therapeutic use of ascorbic acid for vascular
thrombosis and concluded that vitamin C mobilized the cholesterol localized in the wall of blood vessels, so that it was released into the blood
stream (Spittle, 1971). Lewin (1974) assumed that high serum ascorbate

concentrations would tend to redissolve the arterial deposits, partly through reduction of the surface tension of the serum and partly through the formation of soluble ascorbate anion complexes with calcium localized in the blood vessel wall. These hypotheses have not yet been verified experimentally.

Although we cannot underestimate the therapeutic value of ascorbic acid for diseases of the vascular system, the question of how to prevent hyperlipemia and atherogenesis in man is far more important. The results obtained in experimental animals rank chronic latent ascorbate deficiency among the risk factors in the pathogenesis of atherosclerosis. A widespread incidence of marginal vitamin C deficiency among humans was demonstrated by an analysis of human tissues (Yavorsky *et al.,* 1934) and human arteries (Willis and Fishman, 1955). Permanent chronic vitamin C deficiency is especially frequent among the aged (Hejda, 1969; Wilson and Nolan, 1970; Booth and Todd, 1972; Silink *et al.,* 1972; Burr *et al.,* 1974), but seasonal vitamin C deficiency occurs in all age categories. As far as results obtained in experimental animals can be applied to the human organism, it is probable that chronic latent vitamin C deficiency also slows down the transformation of cholesterol to bile acids in the human liver, with resultant hypercholesterolemia and slower removal of cholesterol from the blood stream. The administration of large doses of ascorbic acid to such subjects ought to stimulate cholesterol catabolism and lead, in time, to diminution of hypercholesterolemia. A daily intake of 300 mg of ascorbic acid during the period of seasonal vitamin C deficiency did, in fact, produce a mild, but statistically significant, decrease in the blood serum-cholesterol level in 7 weeks (Ginter *et al.,* 1970b). In subjects who had an initial plasma-cholesterol and plasma-triglyceride level of over 230 mg% and 200 mg%, respectively, and to whom the administration of two daily doses of 500 mg of ascorbic acid was started during the period of seasonal vitamin C deficiency, a significant decrease was found in the blood-cholesterol level and an exceptionally pronounced decrease in the plasma-triglyceride level (Ginter *et al.,* 1976, 1977). On keeping up the same dose of ascorbic acid, the distinct hypolipemic effect of vitamin C persisted for a whole year (Table X).

The organism of patients with disorders of the cardiovascular system has repeatedly been found to have a poor vitamin C supply (Kishikawa *et al.,* 1971; Samsonov *et al.,* 1972). Knox (1973) carried out a correlation analysis between the standardized mortality ratios for ischemic heart disease and cerebrovascular disease in different parts of England and dietary intakes of a number of nutrients. Vitamin C intakes showed a strong negative correlation, i.e., mortality from cerebrovascular disease was high in regions with low vitamin C intakes, and vice versa (Fig. 25). The

Table X

INFLUENCE OF ASCORBIC ACID ON BLOOD PLASMA LIPIDS IN HYPERLIPIDEMIC PERSONS WITH SEASONAL VITAMIN C DEFICIENCY

Parameter	Number of persons observed	Before treatment	Intake of 1000 mg ascorbic acid daily			
			3 months	6 months	9 months	12 months
Plasma cholesterol (mg/100 ml)	19	263 ± 6	237 ± 8	218 ± 9	238 ± 8	229 ± 8
Plasma triglycerides (mg/100 ml)	24	331 ± 22	205 ± 19	173 ± 19	195 ± 9	188 ± 10
Vitamin C in whole blood (mg/100 ml)	19	0.61 ± 0.08	1.67 ± 0.10	1.39 ± 0.10	1.40 ± 0.12	1.42 ± 0.11

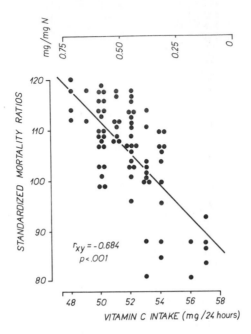

Fig. 25. Negative correlation between vitamin C intakes and cerebrovascular disease standardized mortality ratios in different regions of Great Britain. The figure was constructed from the data of Knox (1973).

relationship between vitamin C intakes and mortality from ischemic heart disease was not so close, but it was likewise statistically highly significant. This type of statistical research does not definitely answer the question of whether vitamin C helps to prevent atherosclerosis from developing in humans. The only way to obtain a full answer to this question would be to conduct an extensive field investigation among a large number of subjects given ascorbic acid over a long period, carrying out a longitudinal study of their blood lipid levels, signs of atherosclerosis and total mortality, which is a more meaningful end point when assessing the health of a whole community (West and Redgrave, 1975). The need for such a study is made all the more urgent by the complete failure of clofibrate and niacin in the secondary prevention of ischemic heart disease (Coronary Drug Project Research Group, 1975).

One obstacle to this study is that we still do not know the optimum dose of vitamin C for the human organism. Pauling (1970) and Stone (1972) regard a daily intake up to two orders higher than the officially recommended dietary allowances for vitamin C in different countries as the optimum. If they were proved to be right, then the dose of 30 mg/adult/day recommended by the FAO/WHO would amount to marginal vitamin

C deficiency. A whole series of laboratories are at present studying the problems of the optimum dose of ascorbic acid (Veen-Baigent *et al.,* 1975; Chatterjee *et al.,* 1975; Yew, 1975; Harper, 1975). Although some authors consider the intake of megadoses of vitamin C to be unnecessary or even harmful (Mašek and Hrubá, 1974; Barness, 1975; Norkus and Rosso, 1975; Schrauzer *et al.,* 1975), well-defined animal experiments indicate that ascorbate requirements are higher than was originally supposed (De Klerk *et al.,* 1973; Rokosova and Chvapil, 1974; Thaete and Grim, 1974; Zannoni and Sato, 1975; Ginter, 1975a; Street and Chadwick, 1975; Kamm *et al.,* 1975; Rivers and Devine, 1975). This applies in a specific manner to different stress situations (pregnancy, the intake of a physiologically unbalanced diet with high sugar and animal fat content, smoking, an excess intake of alcohol and various drugs, the influence of environmental chemical and probably even mental stress) characteristic of our modern civilization, whose future influence can be expected to be still greater.

IX. Conclusions

Use of the model of chronic marginal vitamin C deficiency, which resembles seasonal latent ascorbic acid deficiency in man, made it possible to study, in experimental animals, the consequences of prolonged ascorbate deficiency for lipid metabolism and for the metabolism of the connective tissue of the blood vessel wall. In guinea pigs with latent ascorbic acid deficiency, the rate of the key reaction of the transformation of cholesterol to bile acids in the liver, i.e., microsomal 7α-hydroxylation of the cholesterol nucleus, is slowed down. The slowing down of cholesterol catabolism leads, in hypovitaminous guinea pigs, to hypercholesterolemia, accumulation of cholesterol in the liver, prolongation of the biological half time of plasma cholesterol, slower total cholesterol turnover, and a decrease in the bile acid pool. Conversely, large doses of ascorbic acid stimulate cholesterol catabolism and total turnover. The plasma-triglyceride concentration rises in vitamin C-deficient guinea pigs. The mechanism of this phenomenon is not altogether clear, but it is probably associated with changes in lipolytic enzyme activities in the blood and tissues of vitamin C-deficient animals. Large doses of ascorbate reduce the plasma triglyceride levels in different laboratory animals. In guinea pigs with marginal vitamin C deficiency, the metabolism of the blood vessel wall is impaired: collagen synthesis is disturbed, changes occur in the mucopolysaccharide composition of the ground substance of the connective tissue in the wall of the aorta.

Vitamin C deficiency in guinea pigs is accompanied by elevated accumulation of cholesterol and triglycerides in the arch of the aorta, by a raised incidence of nuclear abnormalities in the aortic endothelium, by separation of the endothelial cells, by marked endothelial proliferation, by foam cell formation, by the appearance of large intimal plaques of musculofibrotic type, and lastly, by atheromatous reconstruction of the vascular system. The pathogenetic mechanism of these changes is probably complex and is based on impairment of the metabolism of cholesterol, triglycerides, and various components of the blood vessel wall. These changes are induced by latent vitamin C deficiency *per se,* even without the addition of cholesterol to the diet, but the simultaneous intake of cholesterol potentiates them still further.

In most human subjects with elevated plasma-cholesterol and plasma-triglyceride levels and latent vitamin C deficiency, resaturation of their tissues with ascorbic acid can significantly lower their blood plasma-cholesterol and triglyceride levels. The prevention of latent vitamin C deficiency means, for at least part of the population, the hope of physiological control of hyperlipemia. Since chronic latent vitamin C deficiency is probably one of the risk factors in the pathogenesis of human atherosclerosis, it would be both useful and necessary to carry out long-term field investigations with the aim of verifying the possibility of utilizing ascorbic acid in the prevention of vascular diseases.

Acknowledgments

I wish to express my sincere thanks to Prof. Zdeněk Lojda (Charles University, Prague) and to Dr. Jozef Babala (Comenius University, Bratislava) for their excellent cooperation in the histological, histochemical, and enzymological studies and to Ing. Rudolf Nemec, Mr. Lubomír Ozdín, and Mr. Ladislav Mikuš (Institute for Human Nutrition Research, Bratislava) for their collaboration in the radioisotope studies and for the computer computations. I should further like to thank Mrs. Anna Javorská and Miss Lydia Marková for their invaluable assistance in the preparation of this manuscript.

I am deeply indebted to Prof. Eva Degkwitz (University of Giessen), Mrs. Dorothy F. Sulkin (Wake Forest University, North Carolina), Dr. Ingemar Björkhem and Dr. Anders Kallner (Karolinska Institutet, Stockholm), Dr. Takao Fujinami (Nagoya City University Medical School), Dr. Dietrich Hornig (Hoffmann-La Roche Ltd., Basel), Prof. E. G. Knox (University of Birmingham), Dr. David Kritchevsky (Wistar Institute of Anatomy and Biology, Philadelphia), and Prof. Giorgio Weber (University of Siena) for kindly having allowed me to use the results of their research in this study.

I express my sincere thanks to the Cambridge University Press, ASP Biological and Medical Press (Elsevier Division), Springer-Verlag, New York Academy of Sciences, *American Journal of Clinical Nutrition, Lipids, Physiologia Bohemoslovaca,* and to Slovak Academy of Sciences for granting us permission to reproduce tabulated data and illustrations.

References

Admirand, W. H., and Small, D. M. (1968). *J. Clin. Invest.* **47**, 1043.
Alfano, M. C., Miller, S. A., and Drummond, J. F. (1975). *Ann. N.Y. Acad. Sci.* **258**, 253.
Altschul, R. (1950). *Am. Heart J.* **40**, 401.
Anderson, J., Grande, F., and Keys, A. (1958). *Fed. Proc., Fed. Am. Soc. Exp. Biol.* **17**, 468.
Anderson, T. W., Reid, D. B. W., and Beaton, G. H. (1972). *Lancet* **2**, 876.
Anitschkow, N. N. (1912). *Proc. Med. Soc. Petersburg* **80**, 1.
Anitschkow, N. N. (1922). *Beitr. Pathol. Anat. Allg. Pathol.* **70**, 265.
Anonymous. (1974). *Nutr. Rev.* **32**, 53.
Babala, J., and Ginter, F. (1968). *Nutr. Dieta* **10**, 133.
Baldwin, A. R., Longenecker, H. E., and King, C. G. (1944). *Arch. Biochem.* **5**, 137.
Banerjee, S., and Bal, H. (1959). *Indian J. Med. Res.* **47**, 663.
Banerjee, S., and Bandyopadhyay, A. (1963). *Proc. Soc. Exp. Biol. Med.* **112**, 372.
Banerjee, S., and Deb, C. (1951). *J. Biol. Chem.* **190**, 177.
Banerjee, S., and Ghosh, N. C. (1947). *J. Biol. Chem.* **168**, 207.
Banerjee, S., and Ghosh, P. K. (1960). *Am. J. Physiol.* **199**, 1064.
Banerjee, S., and Ghosh, P. K. (1961). *Proc. Soc. Exp. Biol. Med.* **107**, 275.
Banerjee, S., and Kawishwar, W. K. (1964). *Indian J. Biochem.* **1**, 136.
Banerjee, S., and Singh, H. D. (1958). *J. Biol. Chem.* **233**, 336.
Barnes, M. J. (1975). *Ann. N.Y. Acad. Sci.* **258**, 264.
Barness, L. A. (1975). *Ann. N.Y. Acad. Sci.* **258**, 523.
Bates, C. J., and Levene, C. I. (1969). *Bibl. "Nutr. Dieta"* **13**, 131.
Becker, R. R., Burch, H. B., Salomon, L. L., Venkitasubramanian, T. A., and King, C. G. (1953). *J. Amer. Chem. Soc.* **75**, 2020.
Belavady, B., and Banerjee, S. (1954). *J. Biol. Chem.* **209**, 641.
Bellmann, H., Rauchfuss, E., Wohlgemuth, B., Schubert, S., Fuchs, K. F., Geissler, F., Haupt, R., Conradi, G., Schönlebe, W., Daniel, E., and Günther, O. (1974). *Z. Gesamte Inn. Med. Ihre Grenzeb.* **29**, 997.
Bernick, S., Patek, P. R., Wells, A. F., and Ershoff, B. H. (1962). *Fed. Proc., Fed. Amer. Soc. Exp. Biol.* **21**, 101.
Bessey, O. A., Menten, M. L., and King, C. G. (1934). *Proc. Soc. Exp. Biol. Med.* **31**, 455.
Björkheim, I., and Kallner, A. (1976). *J. Lipid Res.* **17**, 360.
Bolker, H. I., Fishman, S., Heard, R. D. H., O'Donnel, V. J., Webb, J. L., and Willis, G. C. (1956). *J. Exp. Med.* **103**, 199.
Booth, J. B., and Todd, G. B. (1972). *Geriatrics* **27**, 130.
Bradley, D. W., Maynard, J. E., and Emery, G. E. (1973). *Lancet* **2**, 201.
Bronte-Stewart, B., Roberts, B., and Wells, V. M. (1963). *Br. J. Nutr.* **17**, 61.
Bukovskaya, A. V. (1957). *Sov. Med.* **21**, No. 1, 77.
Burns, J. J. (1957). *Nature (London)* **180**, 553.
Burns, J. J., Burch, H. B., and King, C. G. (1951). *J. Biol. Chem.* **191**, 501.
Burr, M. I., Elwood, P. C., Hole, D. J., Hurley, R. J., and Hughes, R. E. (1974). *Am. J. Clin. Nutr.* **27**, 144.
Cajola, G. (1968). *Boll. Soc. Ital. Biol. Sper.* **44**, 1848.
Cardinale, G. J., Stassen, F. L. H., Kuttan, R., and Udenfriend, S. (1975). *Ann. N.Y. Acad. Sci.* **258**, 278.
Chaikoff, I. L., Siperstein, M. D., Dauben, W. G., Bradlow, H. L., Eastham, J. F.,

Tomkins, G. M., Meier, J. R., Chen, R. W., Hotta, S., and Srere, P. A. (1952). *J. Biol. Chem.* **194**, 413.

Chakravarti, R. N., De, U. N., and Mukerji, B. (1957). *Indian J. Med. Res.* **45**, 315.

Chang, S. C. (1965). *New Med. J.* **8**, 79.

Chatterjee, G. C., Majumder, P. K., Banerjee, S. K., Roy, R. K., Ray, B., and Rudrapal, D. (1975). *Ann. N.Y. Acad. Sci.* **258**, 382.

Chatterjee, I. B. (1973). *Science* **182**, 1271.

Cheraskin, E., and Ringsdorf, W. M. (1968). *Int. J. Vitam. Res.* **38**, 415.

Cook, R. P., and McCullagh, G. P. (1939). *Q. J. Exp. Physiol. Cogn. Med. Sci.* **29**, 283.

Coronary Drug Project Research Group. (1975). *J. Am. Med. Assoc.* **231**, 360.

Crawford, G. P. M., Warlow, C. P., Bennett, B., Dawson, A. A., Douglas, A. S., Kerridge, D. F., and Ogston, D. (1975). *Atherosclerosis* **21**, 451.

Cromwell, G. L., Hays, V. W., and Overfield, I. R. (1970). *J. Anim. Sci.* **31**, 63.

Dam, H. (1964). *Proc. Int. Congr. Nutr., 6th, 1963* p. 6.

Davis, O., and Oester, Y. T. (1952). *Proc. Soc. Exp. Biol. Med.* **81**, 284.

Degkwitz, E., and Kim, K. S. (1973). *Hoppe-Seyler's Z. Physiol. Chem.* **354**, 555.

Degkwitz, E., Höchli-Kaufmann, L., Luft, D., and Staudinger, H. (1972). *Hoppe-Seyler's Z. Physiol. Chem.* **353**, 1023.

Degkwitz, E., Walsch, S., Dubberstein, M., and Winter, J. (1975). *Ann. N.Y. Acad. Sci.* **258**, 201.

DeKlerk, W. A., Kotzé, J. P., Weight, M. J., Menne, I. V., Matthews, M. J. A., and McDonald, T. (1973). *S. Afr. Med. J.* **47**, 1503.

Elwood, P. C., Hughes, R. E., and Hurley, R. J. (1970). *Lancet* **2**, 1197.

Fedorova, E. P. (1960). *Sov. Med.* **21**, No. 11, 56.

Fernandéz-Gimeno, M. A., Lacuara, J. L., Gimeno, A. L., Lema, B., and Malinow, M. R. (1960). *Acta Physiol. Lat. Am.* **10**, 168.

Flexner, J., Bruger, M., and Wright, I. S. (1941). *Arch. Pathol.* **31**, 82.

Froese, P., Leipnitz, W., and Scholz, A. (1975). *Res. Exp. Med.* **165**, 135.

Fujinami, T., Okado, K., Senda, K., Sugimura, M., and Kishikawa, M. (1971). *Jpn. Circ. J.* **35**, 1559.

Fujinami, T., Okado, K., Senda, K., Nakano, S., Higuchi, R., Nakayama, K., Hayashi, K., and Sakuma, N. (1975). *Jpn. J. Atheroscler.* **3**, 117.

Fyfe, T., Dunningan, M. G., Hamilton, E., and Rae, R. J. (1968). *J. Atheroscler. Res.* **8**, 591.

Gatenby Davies, J. D., and Newson, J. (1974). *Am. J. Clin. Nutr.* **27**, 1039.

Ginter, E. (1970a). *Acta Med. Acad. Sci. Hung.* **27**, 23.

Ginter, E. (1970b). "The Role of Ascorbic Acid in Cholesterol Metabolism." Veda, Slovak Acad. Sci., Bratislava.

Ginter, E. (1973). *Science* **179**, 702.

Ginter, E. (1974). *In* "Vitamin C. Recent Aspects of its Physiological and Technological Importance" (G. G. Birch and K. Parker, eds.), p. 179. Applied Science Publishers, London.

Ginter, E. (1975a). *Ann. N.Y. Acad. Sci.* **258**, 410.

Ginter, E. (1975b). "The Role of Vitamin C in Cholesterol Catabolism and Atherogenesis." Veda, Slov. Acad. Sci., Bratislava.

Ginter, E., and Nemec, R. (1969). *J. Atheroscler. Res.* **10**, 273.

Ginter, E., and Nemec, R. (1972). *Physiol. Bohemoslov.* **21**, 539.

Ginter, E., and Zloch, Z. (1972). *Int. J. Vitam. Nutr. Res.* **42**, 72.

Ginter, E., Bilisics, L., and Červeň, J. (1965). *Physiol. Bohemoslov.* **14,** 466.
Ginter, E., Babala, J., Bobek, P., and Ďumbalová, Z. (1968a). *Cor Vasa* **10,** 126.
Ginter, E., Bobek, P., and Ovečka, M. (1968b). *Int. J. Vitam. Res.* **38,** 104.
Ginter, E., Bobek, P., Babala, J., and Barbieriková, E. (1969a). *Cor Vasa* **11,** 65.
Ginter, E., Babala, J., and Červeň, J. (1969b). *J. Atheroscler. Res.* **10,** 341.
Ginter, E., Ondreička, R., Bobek, P., and Šimko, V. (1969c). *J. Nutr.* **99,** 261.
Ginter, E., Babala, J., Ovečka, M., Zloch, Z., and Ondreička, R. (1970a). *Cor Vasa* **12,** 291.
Ginter, E., Kajaba, I., and Nizner, O. (1970b). *Nutr. Metab.* **12,** 76.
Ginter, E., Červeň, J., Nemec, R., and Mikuš, L. (1971a). *Am. J. Clin. Nutr.* **24,** 1238.
Ginter, E., Zloch, Z., Červeň, J., Nemec, R., and Babala, J. (1971b). *J. Nutr.* **101,** 197.
Ginter, E., Nemec, R., and Bobek, P. (1972). *Br. J. Nutr.* **28,** 205.
Ginter, E., Nemec, R., Červeň, J., Bobek, P., Mikuš, L., and Jankela, J. (1973a). *Physiol. Bohemoslov.* **22,** 287.
Ginter, E., Nemec, R., Červeň, J., and Mikuš, L. (1973b). *Lipids* **8,** 135.
Ginter, E., Černá, O., Ondreička, R., Roch, V., and Baláž, V. (1976). *Food Chem.* **1,** 23.
Ginter, E., Černá, O., Budlovský, J., Baláž, V., Hrubá, F., Roch, V., and Šaško, E. (1977). *Int. J. Vitam. Nutr. Res.* **47,** 123.
Glomset, J. A., and Norum, K. R. (1973). *Adv. Lipid Res.* **11,** 1.
Goodman, De W. S., and Noble, R. P. (1968). *J. Clin. Invest.* **47,** 231.
Gore, I., Tanaka, Y., Fujinami, T., and Goodman, M. L. (1965a). *J. Nutr.* **87,** 311.
Gore, I., Fujinami, T., and Shirahama, T. (1965b). *Arch. Pathol.* **80,** 371.
Gould, R. G., and Swyryd, E. A. (1966). *J. Lipid Res.* **7,** 698.
Guchhait, R., and Ganguli, N. C. (1961). *Biochim. Biophys. Acta* **51,** 607.
Guchhait, R., Guha, B. C., and Ganguli, N. C. (1963). *Biochem. J.* **86,** 193.
Guchhait, R., Guha, B. C., and Ganguli, N. C. (1964). *Z Ernaehrungswiss.* **5,** 21.
Gudbjarnason, S., Fenton, J. C., Wolf, P. L., and Bing, R. J. (1966). *Arch. Intern. Med.* **118,** 33.
Hanck, A. B. (1973). *Ernaehrungswissenschaft* **2,** 152.
Harper, A. E. (1975). *Ann. N.Y. Acad. Sci.* **258,** 491.
Hatanaka, H., Yamagata, T., and Egami, F. (1974). *Proc. Jpn. Acad.* **50,** 747.
Hayashi, E., Yamada, J., Kunitomo, M., and Terada, M. (1974). *Jpn. J. Pharmacol.* **24,** Suppl., 117.
Hayashi, E., Yamada, J., Kunitomo, M., Terada, M., Tomita, T., and Kinoshita, T. (1976). *J. Nutr. Sci. Vitaminol.* **22,** 201.
Hejda, S. (1969). *Rev. Czech. Med.* **15,** 145.
Higuchi, R., Fujinami, T., Nakano, S., Nakayama, K., Hayashi, K., Sakuma, N., and Takada, K. (1975). *Jpn. J. Atheroscler.* **3,** 303.
Hitchcock, M. (1975). *Fed. Proc., Fed. Am. Soc. Exp. Biol.* **34,** 798.
Hodges, R. E., Baker, E. M., Hood, J., Sauberlich, H. E., and March, S. C. (1969). *Am. J. Clin. Nutr.* **22,** 535.
Hojer, J. A. (1924). *Acta Paediatr.* **3,** Suppl., 8.
Horáková, J., Lojda, Z., Ginter, E., and Babala, J. (1973). *Cesk. Patol.* **9,** 175.
Hornig, D. (1975). *Ann. N.Y. Acad. Sci.* **258,** 103.
Hornig, D., and Weiser, H. (1976). *Experientia* **32,** 687.
Hornig, D., Weber, F., and Wiss, O. (1974). *Z. Klin. Chem. Klin. Biochem.* **12,** 62.

Hrubá, F., and Mašek, J. (1962). *Nahrung* **6,** 507.

Hume, R., Weyers, E., Rowan, T., Reid, D. S., and Hillis, W. S. (1972). *Br. Heart J.* **34,** 238.

Hurych, J., Hobza, P., Rencova, J., and Zahradnik, R. (1973). "Biology of Fibroblast" (E. Kulonen and J. Pikkarainen, eds.), p. 365. Academic Press, New York.

Hutagalung, R. I., Cromwell, G. L., Hays, V. W., and Chaney, C. H., (1969). *J. Anim. Sci.* **29,** 700.

Hynie, S., Černohorský, M., and Čepelík, J. (1970). *Eur. J. Pharmacol.* **10,** 111.

Kajaba, I., and Bučko, A. (1968). *Rev. Czech. Med.* **14,** 180.

Kamm, J. J., Dashman, T., Conney, A. H., and Burns, J. J. (1975). *Ann. N.Y. Acad. Sci.* **258,** 169.

Kessler, J. I. (1963). *J. Clin. Invest.* **42,** 362.

King, C. G., Burch, H. B., Becker, R. R., and Salomon, L. (1953). *Fed. Proc., Fed. Am. Soc. Exp. Biol* **12,** 470.

Kirk, J. E. (1969). "Enzymes of the Arterial Wall." Academic Press, New York.

Kishikawa, M., Fujinami, T., Sugimura, M., Okado, K., and Senda, K. (1971). *Jpn. J. Med.* **10,** 59.

Knox, E. G. (1973). *Lancet* **1,** 1465.

Kolmakov, V. N. (1957). *Vopr. Med. Chim.* **3,** 414.

Kotzé, J. P. (1975). *S. Afr. Med. J.* **49,** 1651.

Kotzé, J. P., Matthews, M. J. A., and De Klerk, W. A. (1974a). *S. Afr. Med. J.* **48,** 511.

Kotzé, J. P., Weight, M. J., De Klerk, W. A., Menne, I. V., and Weight, M. J. A. (1974b). *S. Afr. Med. J.* **48,** 1182.

Kotzé, J. P., Menne, I. V., Spies, J. H., and De Klerk, W. A. (1975). *S. Afr. Med. J.* **49,** 906.

Kritchevsky, D., Tepper, S. A., and Story, J. A. (1973). *Lipids* **8,** 482.

Krivoruchenko, I. V. (1963). *Ter. Arkh.* **35,** No. 4, 48.

Kumar, M., and Venkitasubramanian, T. A. (1963). *Indian J. Exp. Biol.* **1,** 227.

Kumar, M., and Venkitasubramanian, T. A. (1964). *Naturwissenschaften* **51,** 40.

Leber, H. W., Degkwitz, E., and Staudinger, H. (1970). *Hoppe-Seyler's Z. Physiol. Chem.* **351,** 995.

Lee, R. E., and Lee, N. Z. (1947). *Am. J. Physiol.* **149,** 465.

Levene, C. I., and Bates, C. J. (1975). *Ann. N.Y. Acad. Sci.* **258,** 288.

Lewin, S. (1974). *In* "Vitamin C. Recent Aspects of its Physiological and Technological Importance" (G. G. Birch and K. Parker, eds.), p. 221. Applied Science Publishers, London.

Lojda, Z. (1974). *Cesk. Patol.* **10,** 1.

Manning, P. J., Lee, S. S., and Yamanaka, W. K. (1974). *Atherosclerosis* **20,** 437.

Mašek, J. (1960). *Nutr. Dieta* **2,** 193.

Mašek, J., and Hrubá, F. (1974). *Vnitr. Lek.* **20,** 670.

Mathur, A. K., Ramanathan, R., and Misra, U. K. (1974). *Int. J. Vitam. Nutr. Res.* **44,** 19.

Menten, M. L., and King, C. G. (1935). *J. Nutr.* **10,** 141.

Misra, U. K., and Srivastava, N. (1974). *Int. J. Vitam. Nutr. Res.* **44,** 230.

Mouriquand, G., and Leulier, A. (1925). *C. R. Seances Soc. Biol. Ses Fil.* **93,** 1314.

Mueller, P. S. (1962). *J. Lipid Res.* **3,** 92.

Mueller, P. S., and Cardon, P. V., Jr. (1961). *J. Lipid Res.* **2,** 83.

Murray, H. C., and Morgan, A. F. (1946). *J. Biol. Chem.* **163,** 401.

Myant, N. B., and Lewis, B. (1966). *Clin. Sci.* **30,** 117.

Myasnikov, A. L. (1958). *Circulation* **17,** 99.

Myasnikov, A. L. (1960). "Atherosclerosis." Medgiz, Moscow.

Myasnikova, I. A. (1947). *Tr. Voenno-Morsk. Med. Akad. (Leningrad)* **8,** 140.

Nambisan, B., and Kurup, P. A. (1974). *Atherosclerosis* **19,** 191.

Nambisan, B., and Kurup, P. A. (1975). *Atherosclerosis* **22,** 447.

Naydu, S. G., and Nath, M. C. (1968). *J. Nutr. Diet.* **5,** 203.

Nestel, P. J., Whyte, H. M., and Goodman, De W. S. (1969). *J. Clin, Invest.* **48,** 982.

Norkus, E. P., and Rosso, P. (1975). *Ann. N.Y. Acad. Sci.* **258,** 401.

Novitskii, A. A. (1969). *Cor Vasa* **11,** 302.

Novitskii, A. A. (1971). *Cor Vasa* **13,** 280.

Oesterling, M. J., and Long, C. N. H. (1951). *Science* **113,** 241.

Okey, R., and Greaves, V. (1939). *J. Biol. Chem.* **129,** 111.

Ostwald, R., and Shannon, A. (1964). *Biochem. J.* **91,** 146.

Pauling, L. (1970). *Proc. Natl. Acad. Sci. U.S.A.* **67,** 1643.

Pavel, I., Chisiu, N., and Sdrobici, D. (1969). *Nutr. Dieta* **11,** 60.

Pedersen, L. (1975). *Scand. J. Gastroenterol.* **10,** 311.

Peterson, V. E., Crapo, P. A., Weininger, J., Ginsberg, H., and Olefsky, J. (1975). *Am. J. Clin. Nutr.* **28,** 584.

Pettersson, T. (1959). *Acta Pathol. Microbiol. Scand.* **46,** 11.

Pool, W. R., Newmark, H. L., Dalton, C., Banziger, R. F., and Howard, A. N. (1971). *Atherosclerosis* **14,** 131.

Popják, G., Gosselin, L., Gore, I. Y., and Gould, R. G. (1958). *Biochem. J.* **69,** 238.

Puppione, D. L., Sardet, C., Yamanaka, W., Ostwald R., and Nichols, A. V. (1971). *Biochim. Biophys. Acta* **231,** 295.

Rivers, J. M., and Devine, M. M. (1975). *Ann. N.Y. Acad. Sci.* **258,** 465.

Robinson, R. W., Likar, I. N., and Likar, L. J. (1975). "Glycosaminoglycans and Arterial Disease." Karger, Basel.

Rokosova, B., and Chvapil, M. (1974). *Connect. Tissue Res.* **2,** 215.

Rolek, D. F., and Dale, H. E. (1972). *Atherosclerosis* **15,** 185.

Samsonov, M. A., Paramonova, E. G., Tchunakova, E. P., and Sytcheva, A. N. (1972). *Vopr. Pitan.* **31,** No. 3, 51.

Samuel, P., and Salchi, O. B. (1964). *Circulation* **29,** 24.

Scholan, N. A., and Boyd, G. S. (1968). *Hoppe-Seyler's Z. Physiol. Chem.* **349,** 1628.

Scholz, A. (1973). *Klin. Wochenschr.* **51,** 518.

Schrauzer, G. N., Ishmael, D., and Kiefer, G. W. (1975). *Ann. N.Y. Acad. Sci.* **258,** 377.

Sedov, K. R. (1956). *Ter. Arkh.* **28,** No. 2, 58.

Shafar, J. (1967). *Lancet* **2,** 176.

Shafrir, E., and Biale, Y. (1970). *Eur. J. Clin. Invest.* **1,** 19.

Shapiro, S. S., and Poon, J. P. (1975). *Biochim. Biophys. Acta* **385,** 221.

Sheppard, M., and McHenry, E. W. (1939). *Biochem. J.* **33,** 655.

Shimizu, K. (1970). *Biochim. Biophys. Acta* **210,** 333.

Silink, S. J., Nobile, S., and Woodhill, J. M. (1972). *J. Geriatr.* **10,** 27.

Simpson, C. F., Robbins, R. C., and Harms, R. H. (1971). *J. Nutr.* **101,** 1359.

Singh, D., and Chan, W. (1974). *Singapore Med. J.* **15,** 60.

Sokoloff, B., Hori, M., Saelhof, C., McConnell, B., and Imai, T. (1967). *J. Nutr.* **91,** 107.

Spittle, C. R. (1971). *Lancet* **2,** 1280.

Spittle, C. R. (1973). *Lancet* **2,** 199.

Stolman, J. M., Goldman, H. M., and Gould, B. S. (1961). *Arch. Pathol.* **72,** 535.

Stone, I. (1972). "The Healing Factor." Grosset, New York.

Street, J. C., and Chadwick, R. W. (1975). *Ann. N.Y. Acad. Sci.* **258,** 132.

Sulimovici, S., and Boyd, G. S. (1968). *Steroids* **12,** 127.

Sulkin, N. M., and Sulkin, D. F. (1975). *Ann. N.Y. Acad. Sci.* **258,** 317.

Swann, A., Wiley, M. H., and Siperstein, M. D. (1975). *J. Lipid Res.* **16,** 360.

Takeda, Y., and Hara, M. (1955). *J. Biol. Chem.* **214,** 657.

Thaete, L. G., and Grim, J. N. (1974). *Am. J. Clin. Nutr.* **27,** 719.

Tochowicz, L., Ciba, T., Kocemba, J., and Szopińska-Ciba, L. (1962). *Pol. Tyg. Lek.* **17,** 587.

Tomlinson, T. H. (1942). *Public Health Rep.* **57,** 978.

Tsai, S., Fales, H. M., and Vaughan, M. (1973). *J. Biol. Chem.* **248,** 5278.

Turley, S. D., Horton, B. J., and West, C. E. (1975). *Proc. Aust. Biochem. Soc.* **8,** 46.

Turley, S. D., West, C. E., and Horton, B. J. (1976). *Atherosclerosis* **24,** 1.

Van Wyk, C. P., and Kotzé, J. P. (1975). *S. Afr. J. Sci.* **71,** 28.

Veen-Baigent, M. J., Ten Cate, A. R., Bright-See, E., and Rao, A. V. (1975). *Ann. N.Y. Acad. Sci.* **258,** 339.

Verlangieri, A. J., and Mumma, R. O. (1973). *Atherosclerosis* **17,** 37.

Vlahcevic, Z. R., Bell, C. C., Buhag, I., Farrar, J. T., and Swell, L. (1970). *Gastroenterology* **59,** 165.

Vrána, A., Fábry, P., and Kazdová, L. (1974). *Nutr. Metab.* **17,** 282.

Wada, F., Hirata, K., Nakao, K., and Sakamoto, Y. (1968). *J. Biochem. (Tokyo)* **64,** 415.

Weber, G. (1955). *Arch. "De Vecchi" Anat. Patol. Med. Clin.* **23,** 339.

Weber, G., and Tosi, P. (1971). *Virchows Arch. A* **353,** 325.

Weight, M. J., Kotzé, J. P., De Klerk, W. A., and Weight, N. (1974). *Int. J. Biochem.* **5,** 287.

West, C. E., and Redgrave, T. G. (1975). *Am. Lab.* **7,** 23.

Willis, G. C. (1953). *Can. Med. Assoc. J.* **69,** 17.

Willis, G. C. (1957). *Can. Med. Assoc. J.* **77,** 106.

Willis, G. C., and Fishman, S. (1955). *Can. Med. Assoc. J.* **72,** 500.

Willis, G. C., Light, A. W., and Gow, W. S. (1954). *Can. Med. Assoc. J.* **71,** 526.

Wilson, C. W. M., and Nolan, C. (1970). *Ir. J. Med. Sci.* **3,** 345.

Wolbach, S. B., and Bessey, O. A. (1942). *Physiol. Rev.* **22,** 233.

Wright, H. P., Evans, M., and Green, R. P. (1975). *Atherosclerosis* **21,** 105.

Yavorsky, M., Almaden, P., and King, C. G. (1934). *J. Biol. Chem.* **106,** 525.

Yew, M. S. (1975). *Ann. N.Y. Acad. Sci.* **258,** 451.

Zaitsev, V. F., Myasnikov, L. A., Kasatkina, L. V., Lobova, N. M., and Sukasova, T. I. (1964). *Cor Vasa* **6,** 19.

Zannoni, V. G., and Sato, P. H. (1975). *Ann. N.Y. Acad. Sci.* **258,** 119.

Ziffer, H., Frank, O., Christakis, G., Talkington, L., and Baker, H. (1967). *Am. J. Clin. Nutr.* **20,** 858.

Arterial Enzymes of Cholesteryl Ester Metabolism

DAVID KRITCHEVSKY AND H. V. KOTHARI [1]

The Wistar Institute of Anatomy,
University of Pennsylvania,
Philadelphia, Pennsylvania

I. Introduction

The atherosclerotic plaque is characterized by lipid accumulation and a variable connective-tissue reaction. The important feature of atheroma lipids apparently is the predominance of cholesterol, particularly in its esterified form (Weinhouse and Hirsch, 1940; Böttcher *et al.,* 1960; Böttcher, 1964; Smith, 1965; Kritchevsky, 1967, 1972b). In time, the arteries of humans and animals accumulate free and ester cholesterol even when they do not seem to change morphologically. These moieties increase dramatically during the induction of atherosclerosis in experimental animals. The principal increase is in esterified cholesterol. Early experiments relating the lipid spectra of arterial atheromata and plasma showed that

[1] Present address: CIBA-Geigy Corporation, Ardsley, New York.

the two were parallel, which led to the conclusion that accumulated arterial lipid was derived wholly from the blood (Weinhouse and Hirsch, 1940; Page, 1941; Mead and Gouze, 1961). However, the fatty acid spectra of the cholesteryl esters of serum and plaques differ, which suggests a metabolic process beyond that of simple filtration (Tuna and Mangold, 1963).

The distribution of cholesterol in all mammalian tissues and the high levels of cholesterol in atherosclerotic tissue have been well documented (Kritchevsky, 1958; Cook, 1958). Except in a few tissues such as the blood plasma, adrenals, and gonads, nearly all body cholesterol exists in the free form. It appears to serve a crucial role in membranes of mammalian cells and to be present in a rather constant relationship with the other major category of compounds in the membranes, the phospholipids. However, cholesteryl esters have not been shown to be essential to any tissue or function. One can assume that cholesteryl esters do not serve an indispensable structural role in arterial tissue since fetal and infant arteries have very low concentrations (Portman and Alexander, 1966; Scott et al., 1966).

The origin and mechanism of the deposition of free and ester cholesterol in arterial wall and the effects of local metabolism have become favorite objects for research on atherosclerosis. Many investigations have indicated that most atheroma lipids derive from blood plasma. Perhaps the most important cause of free cholesterol deposition in the arterial wall is that the sterol cannot be significantly metabolized therein, apart from esterification or possibly slight degradation (Brooks et al., 1966; Adams, 1973). The origin of cholesteryl esters is not restricted to plasma. A significant amount of cholesterol is locally esterified (St. Clair et al., 1969; Day et al., 1970; Dayton and Hashimoto, 1970). With respect to metabolism, much evidence indicated that normal, as well as atherosclerotic, tissues are capable of hydrolysis and synthesis of cholesteryl esters. Moreover, pronounced changes in esterifying enzyme activities take place during experimentally induced atherosclerosis in various species. Again, since normal arteries have very little or no cholesteryl esters, they would seem to have a well-regulated ester metabolism which is subject to environmental influences. Thus, one may recognize the significance of the role played by these enzymes in atherosclerosis. Their identity, their interplay and competition for substrate, as well as the manner in which their activities are controlled within the tissue are matters of great interest.

This review is concerned primarily with arterial enzymes involved in synthesis and hydrolysis of cholesteryl esters. It is not intended to review fully all aspects of cholesteryl ester accumulation in the arterial wall; the treatment of the subject matter will be subordinated to characterizing various arterial enzymes of cholesteryl ester metabolism.

II. Origin and Mechanism of Accumulation of Arterial Cholesteryl Esters

It has been demonstrated that the arterial wall can synthesize the principal types of lipids (Stein and Stein, 1962), and that cholesterol feeding stimulates phospholipid synthesis in the arteries of experimental animals (Zilversmit *et al.,* 1961; Cox *et al.,* 1963). However, it is generally conceded that most of the lipid that accumulates in arterial walls is not generated locally, but comes from the blood. Since Hirsch and Weinhouse (1943) summarized the early evidence pointing to the remarkable similarity between lipids of human plasma and plaques, the case for the hematogenous origin has been greatly strengthened by further important work. Biggs and Kritchevsky (1951) demonstrated that labeled cholesterol, fed to animals, moved from the blood into arterial walls. Similar entry from blood into the arterial wall has been shown for fatty acids in rabbits (Zilversmit *et al.,* 1961), and for phospholipids in chickens (Christensen, 1962). Although sterols are synthesized by the arterial wall, this metabolic route seems to make a negligible contribution to the cholesterol deposited in atherosclerotic lesions (Zilversmit, 1968; Bell *et al.,* 1970). Page (1954) advanced the filtration hypothesis by suggesting that plasma β-(low density) lipoprotein enters the arterial wall and, because it is unstable, sheds its load of free and esterified cholesterol. The presence of such lipoprotein is normal and atherosclerotic intima has been demonstrated by ultracentrifugation (Hanig *et al.,* 1956), by immunoflorescence methods (Kao and Wissler, 1965; Walton and Williamson, 1968; Scott and Hurley, 1970; Shimamoto and Numano, 1974), and by immunoelectrophoresis (Tracy *et al.,* 1965), as well as by radioisotope and histochemical techniques (Adams *et al.,* 1968, 1970; Klimov *et al.,* 1974).

In spite of this evidence that lipoproteins directly leak from the lumen and penetrate the arterial intima, another line of investigation has shown that the respective entry rates of free and esterified cholesterol are disproportionate to their contributions in plasma. Newman and Zilversmit (1962, 1964) studied the rates of accumulation of cholesterol and cholesteryl esters during the development of atherosclerosis in the rabbit. Table I (Newman and Zilversmit, 1964) shows the increase of free and ester cholesterol in the aorta during 120 days of cholesterol feeding. The data are plotted on semilogarithmic paper. Both moieties increase logarithmically, the ester increasing from a negligible value to one greater than that for free cholesterol. It is evident that free and ester cholesterol did not increase proportionately. In this experiment, the ratio of free cholesterol to ester cholesterol is 20:1 at zero time and changes to 0.89:1 after 90 days of cholesterol feeding. The experiment of Newman and Zilversmit

Table I

INCREASE OF FREE AND ESTER CHOLESTEROL IN RABBIT THORACIC AORTA
DURING THE 120 DAYS OF CHOLESTEROL FEEDING [a]

Days on cholesterol diet	Free-cholesterol (F) (mg)	Ester cholesterol (E) (mg)	F/E
0	0.40	0.20	20.0
15	0.62 ± 0.12	0.47 ± 0.23	1.32
30	0.87 ± 0.22	1.99 ± 0.61	0.41
60	6.31 ± 2.33	10.45 ± 3.26	0.60
90	9.84 ± 2.42	11.00 ± 3.14	0.89
120	11.94 ± 2.74	11.55 ± 2.89	1.03

[a] Adapted from Newman and Zilversmit (1964).

(1964), together with other studies (Adams and Morgan, 1966; Adams et al., 1968), suggests that in normal arteries and in the early lesion, penetration of the aorta wall by intact lipoproteins is probably not the main, and certainly not the only, mechanism of lipid uptake. Different rates of uptake and disappearance of lipid constituents of lipoproteins could be interpreted, however, as the result of differences in the metabolism of lipoprotein constituents within the arterial wall (Day, 1967).

The preceding interpretation was supported, in part, by measurements of levels or types of cholesteryl esters in arterial tissue. The results from various laboratories have shown that the composition of cholesteryl esters in atheroma is significantly different from that of cholesteryl esters present in plasma (Tuna et al., 1958; Swell et al., 1960; Mead and Gouze, 1961). Oleic acid (18:1) and linoleic acid (18:2) esters together amount to about 80% of total cholesteryl esters and tend to be most variable components. Cholesteryl esters in atheroma contain less linoleic acid and more oleic acid than do plasma cholesteryl esters. Figure 1 (taken from Portman, 1970) shows oleic acid/linoleic acid ratios in cholesteryl esters of aorta and of plasma from normal and atherosclerotic squirrel monkeys. Similar results were obtained in studies with rabbits (Zilversmit et al., 1961) and with humans (Dayton et al., 1965).

It is evident that the mechanism for accumulation of cholesteryl esters by the arterial wall is undoubtedly complex and may be the result of many processes. The quantitative significance of uptake of intact lipoprotein and transfer of cholesteryl ester to endothelial cells thus remains a subject for continuing investigation.

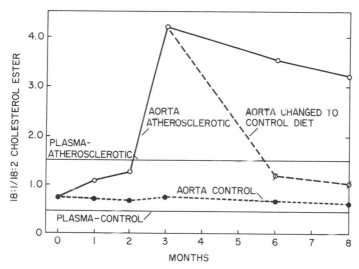

FIG. 1. A comparison of the cholesteryl ester composition of aorta and plasma for a group of normocholesterolemic and a group of hypercholesterolemic squirrel monkeys: (●——●) control group; (O——O) atherogenic diet group From Portman (1970).

III. Cholesteryl Ester Metabolism in Arteries

Cholesteryl ester synthesizing and hydrolyzing enzyme activities have been described in the aortas of various species. These activities are shown to modify in atherosclerosis: the synthesizing activities are greatly increased, while the hydrolytic activities are generally decreased or remain unchanged. The impressive variety of enzymes in cholesteryl ester metabolism of normal and atherosclerotic arteries, as well as the diversity of the assay methods used, reflect the lack of an experimental model founded on well-characterized enzyme systems. This implies that the knowledge of the arterial cholesteryl ester metabolism is still rather fragmentary and qualitative in nature.

The study of cholesteryl ester metabolism has been performed at different levels of tissue organization. They include investigations of intact tissue under various conditions, tissue cultures of arterial cells as well as crude preparations such as homogenates, and also of enzymes of various degrees of purity. When one considers in addition the variations due to species, presence or absence of atherosclerosis, and methods of tissue sampling, it is easy to understand the difficulty in reconciling the observations that have been made.

A. INTACT ARTERIAL TISSUE *in Vitro*

The use of intact tissue has the advantage of a structured system suitable for reactions involving a multistage sequence, such as fatty acyl synthesis, activation, and esterification. The main limitation is that the identity and quantity of all components remain obscure. Nevertheless, this approach has provided valuable information regarding arterial metabolism.

As early as 1962, Stein and Stein reported the hydrolysis as well as synthesis of cholesteryl esters by aorta slices. The aortas of various species (rabbit, rat, dog, and baboon) were shown to utilize free fatty acids to esterify cholesterol. Day and Gould-Hurst (1966) studied the cholesteryl esterase activity of normal and atherosclerotic rabbit aorta. Tissue segments were incubated with labeled cholesteryl oleate in Kreb-Ringer phosphate, pH 7.4, medium. Both normal and atherosclerotic aorta showed the ability to hydrolyze the cholesterol oleate. The activities of normal and atherosclerotic arteries were similar. No esterification activity for free cholesterol was determined. Similarly, the presence of cholesterol-esterifying enzymes was disputed (Newman and Zilversmit, 1966) when cholesterol was used as the labeled precursor. However, it later became apparent that the inability to demonstrate esterification in that system must have been due to the choice of cholesterol as precursor, which apparently did not easily reach the site of enzyme activity (Newman *et al.*, 1968). On the other hand, Felt and Benes (1969) have demonstrated that a small piece of rat aorta caused the esterification of labeled cholesterol. This ATP and CoA-dependent system in the arterial wall preferentially forms saturated esters. They also indicated that rat aorta hydrolyzed cholesteryl palmitate at a rate 15 times the rate of cholesterol esterification.

Parallel and subsequent work revealed that arterial wall metabolism in atherosclerosis is deviated towards the production of the oleate ester. Hence, St. Clair *et al.* (1968) have shown that radioacetate is incorporated much more extensively into fatty acids of perfused pigeon aortas which were atherosclerotic than into fatty acids of normal aortas. The most striking change resulting from induced atherosclerosis was an increase in the synthesis of oleate and in the quantity of radiooleate esterified with cholesterol. Similar observations were made in a later study on the influence of atherosclerosis on the composition, synthesis and esterification of lipids in the aortas of squirrel monkeys (St. Clair *et al.*, 1969).

Again, Day and Wahlquist (1968) have shown with combined biochemical and radioautographic techniques that radiooleate was specifically taken up by intimal foam cells when it was incubated with strips of rabbit aorta. Five times more oleate was taken up by atherosclerotic than by normal aorta, and 10 times more oleate was esterified with cholesterol.

This group made a similar study of the oleate metabolism of human arteries (Wahlquist *et al.,* 1969). Although the oleate radioactivity was concentrated over foam cells, relatively little oleate was esterified with cholesterol compared to that incorporated into lecithin, and atherosclerosis did not influence this process as markedly as it did in the rabbit.

Bowyer *et al.* (1968) observed that cholesteryl esters are taken up by the perfused normal rat aortas. The resistance of cholesteryl oleate to hydrolysis, as compared to cholesteryl linoleate and stearate, was particularly marked. This fairly selective hydrolysis could certainly contribute to determining the composition of the esters in athcroma. Day *et al.* (1970) have studied the question in a different way by incubating whole atherosclerotic aorta *in vitro* with labeled free fatty acids (palmitic, oleic, linoleic), and so labeling the endogenous cholesteryl esters present in the intima. The removal of these labeled cholesteryl esters could then be followed in a subsequent incubation period. The data from these experiments lend no support to the concept that cholesteryl esters are hydrolyzed and removed at different rates in the arterial intima.

On the basis of the previously mentioned *in vitro* experiments and several other *in vivo* studies, it became evident that arterial walls are active in esterifying as well as hydrolyzing cholesteryl ester, and that these activities are changed during atherosclerosis (Dayton and Hashimoto, 1970; Zilversmit and Hughes, 1973; Stein and Stein, 1973; Bell *et al.,* 1975).

B. ESTERIFICATION OF CHOLESTEROL BY FOAM CELLS

The foam cells have been considered active in the accumulation of arterial lipids. Geer and Guidry (1964) found that the atherosclerotic plaques contain the highest proportion of *oleic acid* foam cells and have suggested this as evidence for the esterification of cholesterol in the foam cells of the lesion. Indeed, Day and Wilkinson (1967) showed that acetate was incorporated into fatty acids and that the fatty acids were further esterified with cholesterol by foam cells. In regression studies with pigeons, an increase in cholesterol esterification parallels the appearance of a fat-filled cell within the arterial wall. When cholesterol is removed from the diet of these birds, the foam cells gradually disappear (Wagner and Clarkson, 1973) along with a rapid decline in cholesteral esterification (St. Clair *et al.,* 1972). These findings strongly suggest the conclusions that Smith *et al.* (1967) and Geer and Guidry (1964) made from histological and chemical correlations, i.e., that the foam cell has special capabilities to form cholesteryl esters. Day and Tume (1969) investigated the cholesterol esterase activity of rabbit peritoneal macrophages, a cell type presumed to be metabolically similar to arterial foam cells. The hydrolysis of cholesteryl ester was facilitated, while the esterification of cholesterol was inhibited by the presence of lecithin. Also observed was an ester synthetase with a pH optimum at 6.3 in a cell-free preparation. This esterifying activity did not require ATP or CoA.

It is generally conceded that foam cells have a smooth muscle cell origin. The vacuoles arising in smooth muscle cells are filled with lipids which almost exclusively consist of cholesterol, mostly in esterified form. Peters *et al.* (1973) and Peters and DeDuve (1974) have shown that in rabbit after cholesterol feeding, the aortic smooth muscle cell transformed progressively into a foam cell. The cholesterol content of the cell increased up to 16 times over the control. The distribution of cholesterol was altered from a plasma membrane type in normal smooth muscle cells to one resembling that of lysosomal enzymes in foam cells. Cholesterol storage was held responsible for the increased stability and decreased lysosome density. Compared to the control, atheromatous cells show a striking increase in lysosomal enzymes, paralleled to their marked increase in cholesterol content. However, a smaller increase in cholesteryl esterase activity was indicated. Subsequently, this acid cholesteryl esterase was characterized as having a pH optimum at 4.2 and a strong substrate preference for esters of unsaturated fatty acids (Takano *et al.,* 1974). More recently this technique has been applied to human aorta research and has revealed the presence of cholesterol ester synthesizing and hydrolyzing enzyme activities.

C. Tissue Culture Cells and Organ Culture of Aorta

The potential value of cell, tissue and organ culture techniques for the study of the vascular wall and the role of that tissue in atherosclerosis is receiving attention. With the exception of some limited evidence, the first studies of cholesteryl ester metabolism in tissue culture cells were those of Rothblat *et al.* (1966, 1967). In their studies with tissue culture cells, cholesteryl ester synthesizing activity was low but the hydrolyzing activity was substantial. One cell line (5178Y) that was unique in its having a particularly high cholesteryl ester content was shown to differ from L cells (which have lower cholesteryl ester content) by having a reduced cholesteryl ester hydrolyzing activity (Rothblat *et al.,* 1967). Recently, St. Clair (1974) and St. Clair and Harpold (1975) have used organ culture of aorta to study the esterification of cholesterol. The technique provides a suitable model for studying the interaction of arterial wall with selected blood components, such as lipoproteins or other exogenous factors. Normal and atherosclerotic squirrel monkey aortas were cultured in a medium that contained bovine albumin and monkey serum LDL, with either radioactive cholesterol or oleic acid as a substrate. There was a positive and significant correlation of stimulation of cholesterol esterification to the extent of atherosclerosis, as measured by the cholesterol content of the arterial tissue.

In another study, cholesterol esterification was stimulated completely *in vitro* in previously normal pigeon aorta maintained in a culture medium containing normocholesterolemic (NCS) or hypercholesterolemic (HCS) pigeon serum. Under these conditions, esterification of oleic acid-1-^{14}C to cholesterol was stimulated as much as sevenfold, and was independent of both the concentration of oleic acid in the culture medium and the uptake of oleic acid-1-^{14}C into the arterial segments. Stimulation of esterification to cholesterol was seen as early as one day after culture with HCS. When different concentrations of NCS or HCS were added to the culture medium, the stimulation of cholesterol esterification was proportional to the concentration of cholesterol in the culture medium up to a concentration of 2–4 mg/ml. However, it was impossible to determine the nature and mode of enzyme activation responsible for increased cholesterol esterification. In agreement with the interpretation of Hashimoto *et al.* (1974), the possibility could not be excluded that this stimulation may have been due to changes in the size of the free cholesterol pool available to the enzyme.

D. Cell-Free Enzyme Systems

Aortas of various species contain a number of enzymes capable of forming and/or hydrolyzing cholesteryl esters in cell-free preparations. Tissue homogenates and subfractions thereof, as well as extracts of acetone-dried tissue, have been employed for the preparation of enzymes.

Initial indirect evidence for cholesteryl ester hydrolyzing enzyme in a cell-free preparation was obtained by Zemplenyl *et al.* (1963), who demonstrated (but did not identify as such) a nonspecific esterolytic activity using aqueous extracts from acetone powders of the aorta. Howard and Portman (1966) reported the hydrolysis of cholesteryl linoleate by 100,000 *g* supernatant fractions from rat and squirrel monkey aortas. However, parallel efforts to detect synthetic activity in cell-free systems were without success. Stein *et al.* (1963) failed to detect significant incorporation of linoleic acid into cholesteryl ester by homogenates of normal dog or rabbit aortas. Parker *et al.* (1966, 1974) had similar results using linoleic and palmitic acid in cell-free preparations of normal and atherosclerotic rabbit aorta. Preparations from normal or atherosclerotic squirrel monkey aortas also failed to catalyze the utilization of palmitic or linoleic acid or of the corresponding acyl CoA for cholesterol esterifications (Portman, 1967; Portman and Alexander, 1969). Abdulla *et al.* (1968), under special assay conditions, showed a high level of lecithin cholesterol fatty acyltransferase (LCAT) activity in homogenates of human and rabbit aorta, and a pronounced increase in this activity with atherosclerosis. These workers used linoleate ^{14}C-labeled lecithin as a substrate in a two-phase system (water-isopropyl ether) in which exogenous cholesterol was required. Taurocholate as well as Ca^{2+} ion were inhibitory. However, LCAT activity was not detected in squirrel monkey aorta (Portman, 1969), nor in rat aorta (Eisenberg et al., 1969). In fact, the observations of Abdulla et al. (1968) remained unsubstantiated for a long time but have been confirmed recently (Patelski et al., 1975).

Systematic investigations on arterial cholesteryl ester hydrolyzing enzymes began with the work of Patelski et al. (1967), who provided evidence of a cholesteryl esterase in the acetone powders of pig aorta. Activity was measured using glycerol-water extracts of dry tissue and cholesteryl oleate as a substrate at pH 8.6. Reduced glutathione and taurocholate stimulated the activity. Subsequently, Patelski et al. (1968) studied this enzyme in atherosclerotic rat and rabbit aortas. Compared to controls, the enzyme activities were greatly reduced with atherosclerosis in both species. More recently, however, changes in cholesteryl ester hydrolyzing activity in atherosclerotic baboon aorta were not observed (Howard et al., 1971).

Miller et al. (1968a,b) reported the presence of cholesteryl ester synthesizing, as well as hydrolyzing, activities in homogenates and lysosome-like fractions of normal human aorta. Approximately 16% of the total activity was found in particulate matter referred to as lysosome-like particles. The enzyme activity could be released by Triton X-100 treatment. In the human aorta, optimal hydrolysis was found at pH 6.6 or 7.4, depending on the nature of substrate dispersion (Kothari et al., 1970); the enzyme activity was partially inhibited by heavy metal ions and by p-CMB (1 mM). Taurocholate protected the enzyme from inactivation during incubation of the homogenate. Similar enzyme was described in the acetone powders of rat and rabbit aortas (Kothari et al., 1973). Cholesterol feeding exerted a significant enhancing effect on aortic S/H ratio in rabbits (Kritchevsky et al., 1974). When compared in species resistant and susceptible to atherosclerosis, consistently higher hydrolyzing activities were found in resistant species (Kritchevsky and Kothari, 1974). It is interesting to note that the lysosome-like nature of the human enzyme was described also by studies on a different species using quite different techniques. Patelski and Tipton (1971) determined the subcellular localization of cholesteryl esterase in pig aorta. Their results corresponded to localization in human aorta where 84% of the enzyme activity was found in the 10,000 g supernatant and 16% in the lysosomal fraction.

Peters *et al.* (1973) have reported an acid cholesteryl ester hydrolase in the lysosomes of isolated smooth muscle cells from normal and athero-sclerotic rabbit aortas. In their studies, accumulation of cholesteryl esters in lysosomes was inversely related to cholesteryl esterase activity. The suggestion was made, therefore, that the storage of the esters may be the consequence of a relative enzyme deficiency. Takano *et al.* (1974) have reported on the kinetics and properties of this enzyme, along with a critical evaluation of its identity and characteristics. The enzyme, besides being a lysosomal hydrolase, is shown to have a pH optimum of 4.25, with strong preference for esters of unsaturated fatty acids as substrate.

Comparable to the preceding findings, Smith *et al.* (1974a,b) have reported the presence of cholesteryl esterase in normal pig and grossly normal human aortas. The hydrolysis of cholesteryl oleate by acetone-butanol extracts proceeded most rapidly between pH 4.2 and 4.5. Sodium taurocholate led to enhanced hydrolysis with an optimum concentration of 3–4 mM, and also afforded protection of the enzyme against the effect of preincubation with N-ethylmaleimide or iodoacetic acid. Within the group studied, however, cholesteryl esters of saturated fatty acids were hydrolyzed faster than those of unsaturated fatty acids.

On the other hand, Brecher *et al.* (1973), using high-speed supernatant of rat and monkey aortas, found that cholesteryl oleate and linoleate were hydrolyzed to a greater extent than cholesteryl palmitate and stearate. Hydrolysis of a variety of labeled cholesteryl esters added as an acetone solution was demonstrated in both microsomal and high-speed supernatant fractions. The total enzyme activity was similar in both fractions. A broad pH optimum for the enzyme activity was observed and activity was neg-ligible below pH 5.5 or above 9.5. Preincubation of the enzyme solution or addition of bile salt did not afford protection to hydrolytic activity. Experiments in rhesus monkey did not demonstrate any significant change in the enzyme activity with atherosclerosis. No conclusions were drawn concerning the effect of atherosclerosis on the enzyme activity because of the unknown extent to which equilibration of substrate with preexisting substrate pools had occurred.

Similar uncertainties were reported by St. Clair *et al.* (1970), who measured cholesteryl ester hydrolysis in a 1000 *g* aortic supernatant frac-tion obtained from White Carneau pigeons with various degrees of athero-sclerosis. More recently Patelski *et al.* (1975) reinvestigated the question of differences in rates of hydrolysis of various cholesteryl esters using pig aorta acetone-butanol powder extracts. The rates of reaction for unsatu-rated acid esters were considerably higher than those for esters of satu-rated fatty acids. The values obtained were in the numerical order: linoleate > linolenate > palmitate > oleate > stearate.

It is evident that arterial walls of both resistant and susceptible species contain enzymes capable of hydrolyzing cholesteryl esters. Their capacity to metabolize cholesteryl esters *in vitro* remains unchanged with atherosclerosis. Inasmuch as most enzyme preparations from atherosclerotic arteries are contaminated with endogenous esters, *in vitro* determination of enzyme activity would tend to underestimate hydrolytic capacity. Rather than viewing the accumulation of the cholesteryl esters in atherosclerotic arteries as a consequence of an enzyme deficiency at the cellular or molecular level, therefore, such an accumulation would appear to be the result of hyperactive or overabundant enzyme or enzymes responsible for the ester synthesis.

At least four different esterifying mechanisms in arterial tissue have been reported (Abdulla *et al.*, 1968; Kothari *et al.*, 1970; St. Clair *et al.*, 1970; Proudlock and Day, 1972). Although the relative contribution of cholesterol esterification to the total accumulation of cholesteryl esters in atherosclerotic arteries is not known, the stimulation in cholesterol esterification has been shown to correlate well with the progression (St. Clair *et al.*, 1970; Kritchevsky *et al.*, 1974; Day and Proudlock, 1974) and regression (St. Clair *et al.*, 1972) of atherosclerotic lesions. The unequivocal demonstration of stimulation of these activities is perhaps the least important evidence regarding local synthesis of esters.

Abdulla *et al.* (1968) have reported the presence of LCAT in arterial tissue from man and rabbit. Evidence from several other laboratories, however, suggests that, if present, this enzyme is in low concentration in arterial wall tissue. Recently, Patelski and Piorunska (1975) reported evidence for the presence of cholesteryl ester-lysolecithin acyltransferase activity in normal pig aorta and designated it as $(-)$-LCAT. A mechanism may exist which is phospholipid dependent for degradation of the esters.

Several workers have shown the presence of fatty acyl CoA-cholesterol acyltransfease in arterial wall (Felt and Benes, 1969; St. Clair *et al.*, 1970; Hashimoto and Dayton, 1971; Hashimoto *et al.*, 1974; Proudlock and Day, 1972; Brecher *et al.*, 1973; Morin *et al.*, 1974). This enzyme requires ATP and CoA, has a pH optimum at 7.0 to 7.5 and is localized primarily in microsomes. This system esterifies endogenous cholesterol; however, little or no esterification occurs with exogenous cholesterol. With atherosclerosis the enzyme activity is greatly stimulated, and increases of more than 50-fold have been reported in rabbit (St. Clair *et al.*, 1970; Hashimoto *et al.*, 1974), pigeon (St. Clair *et al.*, 1972) and monkey (Brecher *et al.*, 1973).

Aortic cholesterol ester hydrolase has been studied by Kothari *et al.*, (1973) and by Kothari and Kritchevsky (1975) using acetone dry powders of aorta. The enzyme appears to be similar to that of pancreatic tissue (Vahouny *et al.,* 1964; Hyun *et al.,* 1969; Murthy and Ganguly, 1962) in its pH optimum, bile salt requirement and other molecular properties. The enzyme was distributed in all subcellular fractions including lysosomes. In rabbits, after 7 days on atherogenic regimen, the enzyme's activity was stimulated by 29.5% (Kritchevsky *et al.,* 1974).

Another enzyme has been reported in arteries from several species, including normal and atherosclerotic rabbit (Proudlock and Day, 1972; Brecher and Chobanian, 1974), normal and atherosclerotic monkey (Brecher and Chobanian, 1974), and normal swine (Morin *et al.,* 1974) aortas. The enzyme was found in high speed supernatant and mitochondria (swine) fractions and did not require cofactors. The properties of this enzyme were reminiscent of pancreatic cholesteryl esterase (reported as lipase) described by Schramm and Wolff (1940). The identity of this enzyme with cholesteryl ester hydrolase of aorta (Kothari *et al.,* 1970) and pancreas (Vahouny *et al.,* 1964) cannot be ruled out at present.

Stimulation of cholesterol esterification is the earliest change in lipid metabolism of the arterial wall, and it is associated with the development of atherosclerosis. Whether all or only certain enzymes are increased in atherosclerotic lesions of different morphological types, from different animal species, or under different sets of experimental conditions is unknown, as is the relative contribution of each enzyme to the total newly synthesized cholesteryl ester.

IV. Enzymes of Cholesteryl Ester Metabolism

Enzymes which hydrolyze long-chain fatty acid esters of cholesterol are found in many mammalian tissues. They have been given the name of sterol-ester hydrolases (EC 3.1.1.13) by the Enzyme Commission; however, since cholesterol esters are their natural, if not only, substrates, it seems preferable to use the name cholesterol-ester hydrolase or cholesterol esterase.

Cholesterol esterases catalyze not only the hydrolysis of cholesterol esters, but also the synthesis of these esters from cholesterol and free fatty acids. The assumption that both activities exist in the same protein (Hyun *et al.,* 1969) is essentially true for pancreatic enzyme, and that enzyme is correctly named according to this criterion; about the intracellular "cholesterol esterase," we can be less certain. It is possible that many enzymes are identical with "lipases" or lysophospholipases or similar carboxyl esterases (Brockerhoff and Jensen, 1974). Even for the pancreatic enzyme Borgström and his coworkers (Morgan *et al.,* 1968;

Erlanson and Borgström, 1970; Filipek-Wender and Borgström, 1971) have concluded that the cholesteryl esterase and monoglyceride hydrolase are identical.

A characteristic feature of cholesterol ester hydrolase as a synthesizing enzyme is its independence from energy donors, in particular from ATP. This sets it apart from the acyl CoA-cholesterol O-acyltransferase (EC 2.3.1.—) which also has been found in mammalian tissues. A third pathway to cholesterol esters involves the transfer of fatty acids from position sn-2 of phosphatidylcholine by the enzyme lecithin: cholesterol O-acyltransferase (EC 2.3.1.—). An excellent review by Vahouny and Treadwell (1968) discusses all three enzymes and is especially valuable for its detailed description of many assay procedures.

V. Arterial Enzymes in Synthesis and Hydrolysis of Cholesteryl Esters

A list of aortic enzymes of cholesteryl ester metabolism is given in Tables II and III. The major emphasis in the tables has been the source of the enzyme and optimal pH of the assay system. They also provide a comparison of methods for studying the enzymes in various species. A comparison of specific activities was omitted because determinations from different laboratories using different methodology vary widely. The observed flexibility in optimum conditions for these enzymes suggests that they are different enzymes or that they exist in multiple forms: a "soluble," a microsomal, and a lysosomal cholesteryl ester hydrolase have been described. This subcellular distribution is common to both synthesizing and hydrolyzing activity. In the following section only those studies will be discussed which presently allow a distinction of activities.

A. Acyl CoA: Cholesterol O-Acyltransferase (ACAT)

Activity of this enzyme has been characterized in liver (Goodman *et al.,* 1964) and adrenal gland (Longcope and Williams, 1963); it is believed to be responsible for the intracellular formation of cholesteryl esters by these tissues. The presence of ACAT in other tissues also has been reported (Vahouny and Treadwell, 1968).

ACAT has been studied in the arteries of several species using the assay described by Goodman *et al.* (1964). Synthesis of cholesteryl esters by ACAT occurs along a well-organized pathway probably regulated by membrane structure. Attempts to study the enzyme in isolation, therefore, have been unsuccessful. There appears to be general agreement that normal arteries have a low level of ACAT, and that its activity is greatly increased during atherosclerosis. The increased enzyme activity in arterial tissue has provided a means for studying the properties of the enzyme. Most of the current information on arterial ACAT has been obtained through such studies.

1. Preparation of the Enzyme

Because this is a microsomal enzyme, isolated microsomes provide a most efficient enzyme preparation. Intima media or only intima of aortas are usually homogenized in a suitably buffered solution (pH 7.4), or in a 0.25 M sucrose solution. The whole homogenate is fractionated and the low-speed supernatant (900–10,000 g), or high-speed ($> 100,000$ g) residue and supernatant are used for enzyme determination. Recently, Patelski *et al.* (1975) have observed ACAT activity in extracts of acetone-butanol powders of pig aortas. This method, if confirmed, may prove valuable as a much sought after method for purifying the enzyme.

2. Substrate and Assay

Generally, preparation of substrate and assay conditions are similar to those first described by Goodman *et al.* (1964), and later modified by Suzue and Marcel (1972). The incubation medium contains a suitably buffered solution (pH 7.4) and labeled fatty acyl CoA or a mix of labeled fatty acid, CoA, ATP, Mg^{2+} with the enzyme preparation. Cholesterol is derived from an endogenous source. With particulate microsomal preparation, little or no exogenous cholesterol is esterified. In contrast, microsomes from liver and adrenal glands esterify both exogenous fatty acid and cholesterol. Proudlock and Day (1972) have shown that particulate microsomes of aorta preparation do esterify exogenous cholesterol. Patelski *et al.* (1975) have determined the enzyme activity at pH 6.5 using both exogenous fatty acid and cholesterol.

3. Activators and Inhibitors

The enzyme activity is greatly enhanced by the inclusion of the sulfydryl protecting agent, dithiothreitol, in the incubation system (Proudlock and Day, 1972). No definitive information is available regarding the inhibitors of the enzyme. As would be expected, sodium taurocholate and sodium dodecyl sulfate, at concentrations between 10^{-5} and 10^{-4}, inhibited 50% of normal activity (Morin *et al.*, 1974). The reported effects of some pharmacologically active agents are discussed later.

4. Cofactors

As shown in Table IV (from Hashimoto *et al.*, 1973), the incorporation of labeled palmitate into cholesteryl ester by normal microsomes was

Table II

CHOLESTERYL ESTER SYNTHESIZING ENZYMES IN ARTERIAL TISSUE

Enzyme	Species	Enzyme preparation	pH optima	Activity in atherosclerosis	Reference
Lecithin: cholesterol O-acetyltransferase (LCAT) (EC 2.3.1.–)	Rabbit	Extracts from wet tissue	7.0	Increased	Abdulla et al., 1968
	Human	Extracts from wet tissue	7.0	Increased	Abdulla et al., 1968
	Pig	Extracts from AcBu powder	7.0	Not determined	Patelski and Torlinska, 1973
Acyl CoA: O-acetyltransferase (ACAT) (EC 2.3.1.–)	Rat	Tissue slices	7.4	Not determined	Felt and Benes, 1969
	Rat	High-speed supernatant; microsomes	7.4	Not determined	Hashimoto and Dayton, 1974
	Rabbit	Subcellular fractions	7.5	Increased	St. Clair et al., 1970
	Rabbit	High-speed supernatant; microsomes, mitochondria	7.4	Increased	Hashimoto et al., 1973
	Rabbit	High-speed supernatant; microsomes	7.5	Increased	Proudlock and Day, 1972
	Rabbit	Microsomes	7.4	Increased	Brecher and Chobanian, 1974
	Pigeon	Subcellular fractions	7.5	Increased	St. Clair et al., 1970

Enzyme	Species	Preparation	pH	Activity	Reference
	Squirrel monkey	Perfused arterial segments	7.0	Increased	St. Clair et al., 1959
	Rhesus monkey	Microsomes	7.4	Increased	Brecher and Chobanian, 1974
	Dog	Cell-free preparation	7.4	Not determined	Hashimoto and Dayton, 1974
	Cockerel	Cell-free preparation	7.4	Not determined	Hashimoto and Dayton, 1974
	Human	Homogenates	7.4	Increased	Chobanian and Manzur, 1972
	Swine	Subcellular fractions	7.5	Not determined	Morin et al., 1974
Cholesterol ester hydrolase (EC 3.1.13)	Human	Subcellular fractions	6.1	Increased	Kothari et al., 1970
	Rabbit	Acetone ether	6.1	Increased	Kritchevsky et al., 1974
	Rabbit	High-speed supernatant	5.2	Increased	Brecher and Chobanian, 1974
	Rabbit	High-speed supernatant	5.0	Increased	Proudlock and Day, 1972
	Swine	Subcellular fractions	5.6	Not determined	Morin et al., 1974
	Rat	Acetone-ether powder extracts	6.1	Not determined	Kothari et al., 1973
	Dog	Acetone-ether extracts	6.1	Not determined	Kritchevsky and Kothari, 1974
	Pigeon	Acetone-ether extracts	6.1	Not determined	Kritchevsky and Kothari, 1974
	Baboon	Acetone-ether extracts	6.1	Not determined	Kritchevsky and Kothari, 1974
	Mouse	Acetone-ether extracts	6.1	Not determined	Kritchevsky and Kothari, 1974

Table III

CHOLESTERYL ESTER HYDROLYZING ENZYMES IN ARTERIAL TISSUE

Enzyme	Species	Enzyme preparation	pH optima	Activity in atherosclerosis	Reference
Cholesterol esterase	Rat	Subcellular fractions	7.4	Not determined	Howard and Portman, 1966
	Rat	Extracts from AcBu powders	8.6	Decreased	Patelski et al., 1968
	Rat	Tissue slices	7.4	Not determined	Felt and Benes, 1969
	Rat	Extracts from acetone-ether powders	6.6	Not determined	Kothari et al., 1973
	Rat	High-speed supernatant; microsomes	7–8.5	Unchanged	Brecher and Chobanian, 1974
	Pig	Extracts from AcBu powders	8.6	Not determined	Patelski et al., 1967
	Pig	Subcellular fractions; lysosomes	8.6	Not determined	Patelski and Tipton, 1971
	Pig	Extracts from AcBu powders	4.2–4.5	Not determined	Smith et al., 1974a,b
	Rabbit	Extracts from AcBu powders	8.6	Decreased	Patelski et al., 1968
	Rabbit	Extracts from AcBu powders	6.6 7.4	Unchanged	Kritchevsky et al., 1974

Species	Preparation	pH	Effect	Reference
Rabbit	Subcellular fractions; lysosomes	4.2	Increased	Peters *et al.*, 1973
Squirrel monkey	Subcellular fractions	7.4	Not determined	Howard and Portman, 1966
Rhesus monkey	High-speed supernatant; microsomes	7–8.5	Unchanged	Brecher and Chobanian, 1974
Pigeon	Subcellular fractions	7.4	Uncertain	St. Clair *et al.*, 1970
Pigeon	Extracts from acetone-ether powders	6.6	Not determined	Kritchevsky *et al.*, 1974
Baboon	Extracts from AcBu powders	3.6	Unchanged	Howard *et al.*, 1971
Baboon	Extracts from acetone-ether powders	6.6	Not determined	Kritchevsky *et al.*, 1974
Dog	Extracts from acetone-ether powders	6.6	Not determined	Kritchevsky *et al.*, 1974
Mouse	Extracts from acetone-ether powders	6.6	Not determined	Kritchevsky *et al.*, 1974
Human	Subcellular fractions; lysosomes	6.6, 7.5	Not determined	Kothari *et al.*, 1970
Human	Extracts from AcBu powders	4.2–4.5	Not determined	Smith *et al.*, 1974a,b

Table IV

COFACTOR REQUIREMENTS FOR CHOLESTEROL ESTERIFICATION
BY NORMAL MICROSOMES [a,e]

Substrate and cofactors	Cholesterol esterification (cpm/mg protein)			
	(1)[b]	(2)	(3)	(4)
Palmitate	0.03	0	0	0
Palmitate + CoA	0	0.12	0	0
Palmitate + ATP	0	0.13	0	0
Palmitate + ATP + CoA [c,d]	1.00	1.00	1.00	1.00
Palmityl CoA [c]	3.91	4.27	22.43	4.54

[a] After Hashimoto et al. (1973).

[b] Experiment number.

[c] $p < 0.025$, comparison of palmityl CoA and palmitate + ATP + CoA values.

[d] Set equal to 1.00 (average of four experiments = 284 ± 50).

[e] Incubation medium consisted of 0.1 ml cell-free homogenate and 0.5 ml 0.1 M phosphate buffer containing 0.5 mg defatted bovine albumin and 0.4 μCi [1-14C]palmityl CoA. The reaction mixture was incubated for 2 hours under air at 37°C.

completely dependent on the presence of ATP and CoA. However, the enzyme was much more active when preformed palmityl CoA was used as the substrate. Similar cofactor dependence was observed with microsomes derived from atherosclerotic rabbit aorta, suggesting that formation of acyl CoA intermediate is a rate-limiting step in the esterification of cholesterol by the enzyme.

5. Effect of pH

The pH for optimum activity is 7.4, as reported by Hashimoto et al. (1974), Proudlock and Day (1972), and Morin et al. (1974). The pH characteristics of the aorta enzyme resemble those of the liver microsomal enzyme but differ from an adrenal enzyme, which is sharp and optimum at 6.6. Figure 2 gives a pH-activity relationship of ACAT from microsomes of normal and atherosclerotic rabbit aortas. In this case the substrate was [1-14C]palmityl CoA; when, however, [1-14C]oleic acid was used as a substrate, the pH optimum was the same but the profile changes and activity were lower (Fig. 3). The lower incorporation of free fatty acid into cholesteryl ester at optimum pH is consistent with results given in Table IV. Esterification of free fatty acid with cholesterol in the presence or absence of cofactors, at lower pH, indicates the presence of a cofactor-independent enzyme similar to pancreatic cholesterol ester hydrolase.

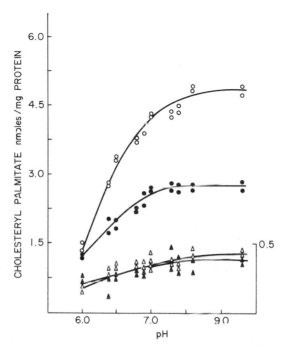

FIG. 2. Incorporation of palmityl group of [1-14C]palmityl CoA into cholesteryl ester derived from normal and atherosclerotic microsomes as a function of pH. The expanded ordinate scale at the right applies to the data for normal microsomes. Incubation time was 16 min. Circles indicate atherosclerotic microsomes and triangles indicate normal microsomes. Overall difference in the values between atherosclerotic and normal microsomes was significant at the 0.05% level as assessed by the analysis of variance. From Hashimoto *et al.* (1974).

6. Acyl CoA: Cholesterol Acyltransferase in Atherosclerosis

Fatty ACAT has been shown to be stimulated several fold in atherosclerotic aortas from pigeons (St. Clair *et al.*, 1970), rabbits (Hashimoto *et al.*, 1973, 1974; Brecher and Chobanian, 1974) and monkeys (Brecher and Chobanian, 1974). As shown in Table V, incorporation of fatty acid radioactivity into cholesteryl ester is greater with cell-free homogenates derived from rabbit atherosclerotic aortas than with those derived from normal aortas. Further studies in rabbits (Hashimoto *et al.*, 1974) have concluded that the stimulation of the activity is due to induction of the enzyme. Neither an activator of the enzyme in the soluble fraction of the atherosclerotic aortic homogenate, nor an inhibitor in the soluble fraction of the normal aortic homogenate could be demonstrated. The optimum within the pH range covered for esterification and the apparent K_m values were approximately the same in normal and atherosclerotic microsomes,

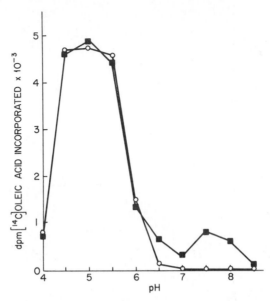

<small>Fig. 3. Effect of pH on incorporation of free fatty acid into cholesteryl ester by whole intimal homogenate of atherosclerotic rabbit aorta with or without cofactors: (■) cofactors added; (○) without cofactors. From Proudlock and Day (1972).</small>

suggesting that the enzymes were probably the same. The concentration of unesterified cholesterol and the cholesterol-esterifying activity of the microsomes were examined. The free cholesterol concentrations of atherosclerotic microsomes were two- to threefold greater than those of normal microsomes, whereas the increase in the cholesterol-esterifying activity of the same atherosclerotic microsomes was 25-fold that of normal microsomes. The possibility that a small increase in the concentrations of free cholesterol in the atherosclerotic microsomes could produce a large increase in cholesterol esterification seems unlikely but cannot be ruled out. It is known from experience with several enzymes that small increases in substrate concentration may promote allosteric control and greatly capacitate the enzyme. Brecher and Chobanian (1974) suggested also that the reason for the increased ACAT activity is the presence of more enzyme in the atherosclerotic preparations. Parker *et al.* (1966) have observed a proliferation of endoplasmic reticulum in aortic smooth muscle cells as a result of cholesterol feeding. Portman and Alexander (1972) have reported that the microsomal fraction from nonatherosclerotic aortic tissue largely contains plasma membrane fragments, which proliferate as a result of aging or hyperlipemia. If the fatty ACAT is localized in endoplasmic

Table V
Esterification of Cholesterol with [1-14C]Palmityl CoA
with Time of Incubation [a,c]

Hours	Cholesterol esterification (cpm/mg protein)				
	1	2	4	8	16
Aortic homogenates	1930 [b]	4472	8684	14558	21485
Normal	31	101	199	354	626

[a] After Hashimoto *et al.* (1973).

[b] Values represent average of three incubations with duplicate aliquots from the pooled homogenate of three aortas.

[c] Incubation medium consisted of 0.1 ml cell-free homogenate and 0.5 ml 0.1 M phosphate buffer containing 0.5 mg defatted bovine albumin and 0.4 μCi [1-14C]palmityl CoA. The mixture was incubated at 37°C in air. Difference between atherosclerotic and normal values is significant ($p < 0.0005$) as assessed by the analysis of variance.

reticulum, one might expect more enzyme in atherosclerotic tissues than in normal aorta.

B. Cholesterol Ester Hydrolases

Several enzymes catalyzing synthesis and/or hydrolysis of cholesteryl esters (referred to as cholesterol ester hydrolases) have been found in arterial tissue preparations. Cholesteryl ester synthesizing activities that are independent of cofactors and require little energy have been studied in aorta by several groups; the presence of the enzyme in aortas of various species resistant or susceptible to atherosclerosis has been reported (Kothari *et al.*, 1970; Kritchevsky and Kothari, 1974). Activities were determined with extracts of acetone-ether powders of aorta and substrates made of exogenous cholesterol and exogenous free fatty acid. The enzyme had a pH optimum at 6.1 and was dependent on bile salts for activity. Evidence has been obtained indicating that the enzyme reversibly catalyzes synthesis as well as hydrolysis of cholesteryl esters. Proudlock and Day (1972) have found a very active enzyme with a pH maximum of 5.0 in homogenates of atherosclerotic rabbit intima. The activity was distributed in the high-speed (104,000 g) supernatant, in the pellets, and in the floating lipid layer (lipid skin). All fractions were found to incorporate either [1-14C]oleic acid or [4-14C]cholesterol into cholesteryl esters. Brecher and Chobanian (1974) have found a similar enzyme activity in high-speed

(161,000 g) supernatant fractions of normal and atherosclerotic rabbit and monkey aortas. The incorporation of [1-^{14}C]oleic acid into cholesteryl ester was maximum at pH 5.2, and higher in atherosclerotic aorta than in normal aorta. Morin *et al.* (1974) have observed esterification of [4-^{14}C]cholesterol or [1-^{14}C]palmitate during long periods of incubation (18 hours) with crude microsomes, mitochondria, and supernatant fractions of normal swine aorta. The activity was found over a rather broad pH range between 4.5 and 6.5, with the optimum occurring near 5.6.

It is reasonable to assume that the above mentioned synthesizing activities properly derive from the same enzyme. The reason for the difference in pH optima is not apparent. Methodological differences in preparation of enzyme and substrates could explain the discrepancies in optimum pH values. In order to arrive at this conclusion, experimental evidence in support must be obtained by characterizing the enzymes. All these enzymes, if not the same, are similar to those found in peritoneal macrophages (Day and Tume, 1969), alveolar macrophages (Tume and Day, 1970), and the pancreatic tissue and juice (Hernandez and Chaikoff, 1957; Vahouny *et al.*, 1964).

Characterization of cholesterol ester hydrolase has been performed using acetone-ether powders of normal male rat and rabbit aortas. The details of the preparation of enzyme and substrates have been published (Kothari *et al.*, 1973). Synthetic activity was determined using an emulsion that contained 2.05 μmoles [4-^{14}C]cholesterol, 6.22 μmoles oleic acid, and 4.10 μmoles sodium taurocholate in 0.2 ml of 0.1 M phosphate buffer, pH 6.1. The final volumes of the incubation mixture were made up to 1.0 ml. The hydrolytic activity was routinely assayed with micellar substrate containing 1.30/μmoles [4-^{14}C]cholesteryl oleate, 2.58/μmoles sodium taurocholate and 1.5 mg lecithin in phosphate buffer (pH 6.6), in a total volume of 1.0 ml. Both activities were affected by the physical form of the substrates. Synthesis of cholesteryl oleate was most effective when the reactants were present as an emulsion. In the absence of bile salt or when a micellar dispersion of cholesterol and oleic acid was used, little esterification took place. The rate of hydrolysis was three times greater with micellar substrate than with emulsified substrate.

1. Effects of Cofactors and Bile Salts

As shown in Table VI, the addition of CoA or ATP singly or together did not affect ester formation. Sodium taurocholate was essential for synthesis but was found inhibitory at higher concentrations. Sodium taurocholate, at a concentration of 2 μmoles, stimulated hydrolysis when added to either micellar or albumin-dispersed substrate; however, it inhibited

Table VI
Effect of Cofactors on the Synthesis of Cholesterol Oleate
by Rat and Rabbit Aorta Enzyme [a,b]

Incubation system	Cholesterol esterified (nmoles)	
	Rat	Rabbit
Control	52	24
Control plus 2 μmoles CoA	55	21
Control plus 10 μmoles ATP	52	22
Control plus (2 μmoles CoA and 10 μmoles ATP)	56	22

[a] From Kothari *et al.* (1973).

[b] Esterification was measured using emulsified substrate with or without the indicated amounts of CoA and ATP. The table is a composite of two experiments.

hydrolysis at a concentration of 5.5 μmoles/ml. Replacement of bile salt by Tween 20 reduced the extent of hydrolysis.

2. Effect of pH

The pH-activity relationship for synthesis and hydrolysis of cholesteryl oleate by rat and rabbit enzyme is shown in Fig. 4 (a and b). Enzymatic synthesis of ester occurred over a narrow pH range (maximum at 6.0 to 6.1). The pH optimum at which hydrolysis occurred was a function of the physical state of the substrate. With micellar substrate, maximum hydrolysis was observed at pH 6.6, while albumin-dispersed substrate was hydrolyzed over a wide pH range (6.5 to 8.8), with a peak occurring from pH 7.0 to 8.0. In a subsequent study on the purification of enzyme, evidence was obtained showing that the enzyme hydrolyzing the albumin-dispersed substrate at an alkaline pH was distinctly different from that acting on the micellar substrate (Kothari and Kritchevsky, 1975).

3. Purification

The details of purification have been published (Kothari and Kritchevsky, 1975). Both hydrolysis and synthesis are partially concentrated by adjusting the pH to 5.7, followed by acetone fractionation, DEAE-cellulose chromatography, and Sephadex G-100 filtration. The results of a typical purification sequence are given in Table VII. The specific activities of the final product were between 100 and 140 times greater than those of the original material. During purification, the source of both activities was fractionated, eluted, and filtered through columns in a similar manner. Both activities were concentrated to the same extent.

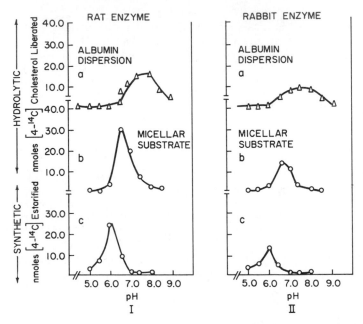

FIG. 4. The pH-activity relationship for synthesis and hydrolysis of cholesteryl ester by rat (a) and rabbit (b) enzymes. For synthesis, usual emulsified substrate was used: phosphate buffer for pH 4.5 to 5.5 and phosphate buffer for pH 5.5 to 8.0. For hydrolysis, the micellar substrate was prepared at pH 6.6; variations in pH were made by adding either 0.2 *M* HCl or 0.2 *m* NaOH. The albumin-dispersed substrate for hydrolysis was prepared in phosphate buffer at pH 7.4. pH was adjusted by adding either 0.2 *m* HCL or 0.2 *M* NaOH. From Kothari *et al.* (1973).

DEAE-cellulose column chromatography of the whole extracts gave elution profiles of protein and the enzymes (Fig. 5). Protein was eluted as five major peaks with a recovery of 80 to 90%. Cholesteryl ester-synthesizing and -hydrolyzing activities were eluted simultaneously at NaCl concentrations between 0.14 and 0.175 *M*. Under peak IV, about 15% of the total protein was eluted with 80 to 85% recovery of the enzyme activities. In these experiments, lipase was eluted at NaCl concentrations between 0.09 and 0.14 *M* (peak III), and nonspecific esterase was eluted between 0.03 and 0.08 *M* NaCl concentrations (peak II). The protein of peak II was found to catalyze the hydrolysis of *O*-nitrophenyl acetate and albumin-dispersed cholesteryl oleate at pH 7.4; however, it was inactive toward the micellar cholesteryl oleate at pH 6.6. On the other hand, the protein of peak IV was most active in hydrolyzing cholesteryl oleate at pH 6.6 and did not hydrolyze *O*-nitrophenyl acetate. The results suggested that the enzyme that acted on micellar substrate was different from the enzyme that hydrolyzed albumin-dispersed substrate. The enzyme eluted under peak II

Table VII

Purification of Cholesteryl Ester Synthesizing and Hydrolyzing Activities from Acetone-Dried Powder of Rat and Rabbit Aortas [a]

Purification sequence	Total protein (mg)	Synthetic activity			Hydrolytic activity		
		Total units	Specific activity	Purification	Total units	Specific activity	Purification
Rat enzyme							
Whole extract	128.0	664.0	5.2	1.0	960.0	7.5	1.0
pH 5.7 supernatant	72.5	723.9	10.1	1.9	889.4	12.5	1.6
40% acetone precipitate	9.8	616.2	63.0	12.1	699.4	71.4	9.5
DEAE-cellulose chromatography [b]	2.6	478.5	191.3	36.0	548.7	219.3	29.0
Sephadex G-100 chromatography	0.66	411.0	632.2	120.0	475.5	731.1	98.6
Rabbit enzyme							
Whole extract	140.5	478.1	3.4	1.0	434.0	3.1	1.0
pH 5.7 supernatant	86.2	559.9	6.5	1.6	391.2	4.6	1.5
40% acetone precipitate	8.5	461.5	59.8	17.6	317.8	38.5	12.4
DEAE-cellulose chromatography	2.8	401.5	146.8	52.4	285.7	106.6	41.4
Sephadex G-100 chromatography	0.74	361.4	487.2	143.2	240.8	324.8	104.7

[a] From Kothari and Kritchevsky (1975).
[b] DEAE = O-(diethylaminoethyl).

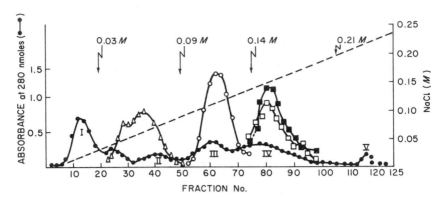

FIG. 5. *O*-(Diethylaminoethyl)(DEAE)-cellulose column chromatography of the whole extract from acetone-dried powder of rabbit aorta. The DEAE-cellulose column was equilibrated with 0.001 *M* NaCl solution. The whole extract (56.0 mg protein) was applied. The column was eluted with a linear gradient (0.005–0.250 *M*) of NaCl. Fractions, each containing 5 ml, were collected at a flow rate of 30 ml/hour. The elution of the protein was followed by measuring absorbance at 280 nmoles, and the elution of the enzymes was determined by the usual assay procedure. Cholesteryl ester synthesizing and hydrolyzing were eluted with peak IV, and the recovery was 89%: (●——●) protein E_{280}; (▲——▲) nonspecific esterase; (O——O) lipase; (■——■) cholesteryl ester synthesizing activity; and (□——□) cholesteryl ester hydrolyzing activity. From Kothari and Kritchevsky (1975).

seemed to be nonspecific and hydrolyzed cholesteryl oleate. The requirements for optimum activity were comparable to the assay conditions for aortic cholesteryl ester hydrolase reported by other laboratories (Patelski *et al.,* 1968; Brecher and Chobanian, 1974). Under these conditions of emulsified substrate at alkaline pH, and with crude enzyme preparation, what one essentially measures is nonspecific esterase activity. However, the nonspecific esterase does hydrolyze cholesteryl esters; its contribution to arterial cholesteryl ester metabolism may be significant, therefore, and deserves further consideration.

4. *Substrate Specificity*

The enzyme showed little specificity with regard to the sterol as well as fatty acid. All six of the β(OH) sterols tested were able to serve as substrates for the synthetic activity, although they differed in their relative activity. The results of esterification of a number of sterols with [1-^{14}C]oleic acid are given in Fig. 6. Esterification of [4-^{41}C]cholesterol with various fatty acids was measured. As may be seen in Table VIIIa, oleic acid was most effective in the esterification of cholesterol; with increasing saturation,

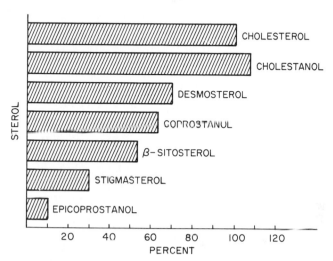

FIG. 6. Esterification of [1-¹⁴C]oleic acid with different sterols using rat aorta acetone powder (cholesterol = 100). From Kritchevsky and Kothari (1974).

Table VIII

RATE OF ESTERIFICATION OF [4-¹⁴C]CHOLESTEROL
(nmoles/mg protein/hour) WITH VARIOUS FATTY ACIDS
BY RAT AND RABBIT AORTA ENZYMES [a]

Fatty acid	Rate	
	Rat	Rabbit
Oleic (18:1)	49.0	37.8
Linoleic (18:2)	41.5	29.5
Linolenic (18:3)	27.5	24.7
Arachidonic (20:4)	22.6	19.0
Palmitic (16:0)	19.6	13.6
Stearic (18:0)	13.8	7.6
Butyric (4:0)	0.0	0.0

[a] All assay mixtures contained 2.05 μmoles [4-¹⁴C]cholesterol, 6.22 μmoles free fatty acids, 4.10 μmoles sodium taurochlorate, and 0.05 M phosphate buffer, pH 6.1. Partially purified enzyme (1 mg protein) was used for all determinations. Incubations were at 37°C, and the amount of esterified [4-¹⁴C]cholesterol was determined initially and at intervals of 1, 2, and 3 hours. The values given are the mean of duplicate experiments.

progressively less esterification was observed. The saturated fatty acids were even less effective. Palmitic acid was about 40% as effective as oleic acid, stearic acid esterified cholesterol poorly, and butyric acid had no effect at all. The relative rates of hydrolysis of various esters, as determined with albumin-dispersed substrates (pH 6.6) are given in Table IX.

Although maximum esterification was observed with oleic acid, and maximum hydrolysis occurred with cholesteryl linoleate, the enzyme seems to be fairly nonspecific; it is synthetically active with several long-chain fatty acids, and can hydrolyze cholesteryl esters that differ in fatty acid moiety. The observed differences in reaction rates, therefore, are not due to enzyme specificity as it is normally understood (i.e., substrate-enzyme recognition at specific binding sites), but to the physicochemical properties of the fatty acid dispersion.

5. Identity of the Enzyme

The enzymes of rat and rabbit were found to have similar stability, solubility and ionic properties. In addition, the comparison of K_m values of the enzymes from the two species suggested that the same enzyme was being investigated in the two species (Kothari et al., 1973). Several lines

Table IX

RATE OF HYDROLYSIS OF VARIOUS CHOLESTERYL ESTERS BY RAT AND RABBIT AORTA ENZYMES [a]

Cholesteryl ester	Cholesterol liberated (nmoles/mg protein/hour)	
	Rat	Rabbit
Oleate	16.2	13.0
Linoleate	20.7	14.4
Linolenate	14.0	9.6
Palmitate	13.5	9.5
Stearate	12.5	8.8
Laurate	10.0	8.0
Acetate	12.2	10.2

[a] The assay mixture contained 1.30 μmoles cholesteryl ester, 2.58 μmoles sodium taurocholate, 0.5 mg bovine serum albumin, and 0.075 M phosphate buffer, pH 6.6. Partially purified enzyme (40% acetone precipitate) was used for all determinations. Incubations were carried out at 37°C, and the activity was measured by determining free and esterified cholesterol at 2, 4, and 6 hours of incubations. The values expressed are the mean of duplicate experiments.

of evidence indicated that the enzyme of aorta is similar to the enzymes of pancreas and intestine. The similarity is suggested because of the specificity of the enzymes, as well as the similarity of the conditions required for optimum activity (such as pH, physical form of substrates, and the requirement for bile salts). Further support is provided by the molecular weight of aorta enzyme, which was estimated to be 140,000 daltons (Kothari and Kritchevsky, 1975). The estimated molecular weight of pancreas enzyme is 65,000 (Hyun *et al.*, 1972), and this enzyme forms a dimer (mol. wt. 135,000) on treatment with acetone. The estimated molecular weight of aorta enzyme extracted from acetone-powders is close to that reported for the dimer of pancreatic enzyme.

6. Acid Cholesteryl Ester Hydrolases

Apart from some morphological studies, the involvement of lysomes in atherosclerotic processes was first investigated by Miller *et al.* (1966, 1968b), Kothari *et al.* (1970), and Bonner *et al.* (1972). The presence of a cholesteryl esterase was reported in lysosome-like fractions of grossly normal human aorta, and it was postulated that the activity of this enzyme may be inadequate for preventing cholesteryl ester accumulation during the onset and progression of atherosclerosis. This postulate was given credence by the finding (Peters *et al.*, 1973) of low density lysosomes in the smooth muscle cells from aortic fatty streaks in rabbits that had a high concentration of cholesterol, but a cholesteryl ester hydrolase activity relatively lower than that found in high density lysosomes. More recently a lysosomal acid cholesteryl ester hydrolase has been investigated in pig and human aortas (Smith *et al.*, 1974a) and also in rabbit aortic smooth muscle cells (Takano *et al.*, 1974).

Smith *et al.* (1974b) have studied the enzyme using extracts of acetone-butanol powders of aortas. Activity was determined by adding the ester dissolved in a small volume of acetone to the enzyme preparation; incubation was at 37°C for 3–4 hours. The optimum pH for hydrolysis was 4.3 for the pig enzyme and 4.5 for a similar human enzyme preparation. The activity of both human and pig aorta enzymes was strongly dependent on the sodium taurocholate concentration. Maximum hydrolysis of cholesteryl oleate occurred with between 3 and 4 mM of the bile salt; higher concentrations were inhibitory. Sodium taurocholate afforded protection of the enzyme against the effects of preincubation with N-ethylmaleimide or iodoacetic acid. The activity could be increased or decreased by various sterols or steroids. The hydrolysis of cholesterol palmitate was enhanced by additions of (0.26 μmole) cholesterol, cholestanol, stigmasterol, and sitosterol. In contrast, 5α-cholestane and cholest-4-en-3-one were inhibitory. With pig aorta enzyme the hydrolysis of cholesteryl esters of saturated fatty acids from C_{12} to C_{22} was greatest with cholesteryl myristate. Esters of unsaturated acids were hydrolyzed more slowly than corresponding saturated esters.

An enzyme activity having a similar pH optimum for cholesterol ester hydrolysis has been characterized in homogenates and subfractions of rabbit aorta smooth muscle cells (Takano *et al.*, 1974). Activities were determined using mixed micelles of 5 μmoles [4-^{14}C]cholesteryl oleate, 0.4 mM egg yolk lecithin, 0.3 mM sodium taurocholate, 25 μg bovine serum albumin per ml, and 0.05 M acetate buffer, pH 4.25. Under the assay conditions, the highest rate of cholesteryl oleate hydrolysis was observed at pH 4.25, and there was no measurable activity around neutrality in higher phosphate of tris buffer.

The presence of sodium taurocholate was essential for the enzyme assay. With a lower concentration of bile salt, the rate of reaction was lower but linear; at a higher concentration the extent of hydrolysis was greater. Most surprisingly, the reaction was dependent on the presence of lecithin in the incubation medium (Fig. 7). The function of lecithin in the system seems to be more than that of forming mixed micelles with cholesteryl ester and bile salt. It is tempting to suggest that the hydrolysis of the ester in this system is probably carried out in two steps: first, the hydrolysis of lecithin to lysolecithin by lysosomal phospholipase (pH 4–5); and

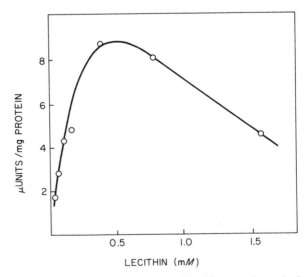

FIG. 7. Effect of lecithin concentration on cholesteryl oleate hydrolysis. Graph shows enzyme activity as a function of final lecithin concentration in assay mixture. Standard assay conditions, except for lecithin concentration. Postnuclear supernatant, 6.2 μg protein per assay, 60-min incubation. From Takano *et al.* (1974).

second, the phospholipid-dependent degradation of the ester. Cholesterol ester lysolecithin acyltransferase, has recently been reported in a pig aorta preparation by Patelski and Piorunska (1975). In this postulated two-step mechanism, the concentrations of lysolecithin in microenvironments at any given time during linear reaction are probably very low and would not inhibit the overall reaction as the high concentration of lysolecithin did.

Returning to the hydrolytic activity, the enzyme was slightly activated by 10 mM $CaCl_2$, whereas $CuCl_2$ was inhibitory at this concentration. EDTA and eserine had no effect on enzyme activity. Among the sulfhydryl group inhibitors p-chloromercuribenzoate was strongly inhibitory at a 0.1 mM concentration, while N-ethylmaleimide had little effect on enzyme activity, and iodoacetamide became inhibitory only at 10 mM concentrations.

The substrate specificity of the enzyme was different than that described for acid cholesterol ester hydrolase from pig aorta. Hydrolytic activity was much greater against the unsaturated than against the corresponding saturated fatty acid esters.

The subcellular localization of the enzyme was studied in isolated aortic smooth muscle cells from normal rabbit aorta with the "inner-layering" technique described by Peters *et al.* (1972). The distribution of cholesteryl esterase resembled most closely that of the lysosomal marker N-acetyl-β-glucosaminidase, indicating lysosomal localization of the enzyme.

In addition to these aortic enzymes, the presence of a lysosomal cholesterol esterase in rat liver has been reported by Stoffel and Greten (1967), and an energy-independent cholesterol esterifying activity has been found in rat liver homogenates and lysosomal fractions (Stokke, 1972a; Nilsson *et al.,* 1973). The lysosomal enzyme of human liver has been studied by Stokke (1972b). Hydrolytic activity was maximum at pH 5, synthetic activity at pH 3.8. A deficiency of the lysosomal cholesterol esterase of human liver has been found in a case of cholesterol storage disease and the related Wolman disease (Burke and Schubert, 1972; Sloan and Fredrickson, 1972a,b). There are certain parallels between the pathophysiology of the lipid storage diseases and atherosclerosis and, therefore, the study of the lysosomal cholesterol ester hydrolase in arteries is important.

VI. Arterial Enzymes in Age and Atherosclerosis

A. Influence of Age on Aortic Cholesteryl Ester Hydrolase

A recent review (Kritchevsky, 1972a) of lipid metabolism in aging has summarized data which suggest that as an organism ages there is an increasing inability to metabolize lipids. Thus sterol synthesis, degradation, and turnover are all reduced in aging rats. Fatty acid synthesis and oxidation and triglyceride synthesis are reduced in the epididymal fat of old rats, but lipolysis in this tissue is unaffected by age (Benjamin *et al.,* 1961). Lipolytic activity in rat aorta seems to increase with age, being significantly lower in aortas of 2- to 3-month-old rats than in those of older (7 to 24 months) animals (Zemplenyi and Grafnetter, 1959; Dury, 1961).

Influence of age on aortic cholesteryl ester hydrolase was determined in rat (Table X). The rate of both synthesis and hydrolysis of cholesteryl oleate increases as the age of aortas increases. However, while the rate of synthesis only increased by 79% between the ages of 2 and 24 months, hydrolytic capacity increased by 1160%. Thus, the synthesis/hydrolysis ratio went from 1.95:1 in 2-month-old rats to 0.80:1 in 12-month-old rats and to 0.31:1 in 24-month-old rats.

These results parallel the findings of Zemplenyi and Grafnetter (1959), who reported that lipolysis in rat aorta increased 81% in animals of ages between 2 and 7 months ($p < 0.001$), 36% in animals of ages between 3 and 12 months, and 24% in animals of ages between 2 and 24 months. Dury (1961) compared lipolysis in aortas of rats aged 3 to 4 months and 15 to 18 months, and found that lipolysis was 54 to 95% higher in older aortas.

The rat is resistant to cholesterol-induced atherosclerosis, and the ability of the aorta to hydrolyze ester cholesterol may be a part of its protective mechanism. The results of Kritchevsky *et al.* (1974), taken with those of Zemplenyi and Grafnetter (1959) and Dury (1961), suggest that the activity of all lipolytic enzymes is increased in older rats. The influence of age on the lipolytic activity of aortas of other species should be studied to determine whether increasing activity is a generalized phenomenon peculiar to the rat or common in other atherosclerosis-resistant species.

Table X
INFLUENCE OF AGE ON SYNTHESIS AND HYDROLYSIS OF CHOLESTEROL OLEATE
BY RAT AORTA PREPARATIONS [a]

Age (months)	Number of pools	Average protein (mg/ml)	Synthesis (S)[b]	Hydrolysis (H)[b]	S/H
2	4	2.04	$3.9 \pm 0.17_a$[c]	$2.0 \pm 0.62_a$	1.95
12	3	1.49	5.5 ± 1.62	$6.9 \pm 2.36_b$	0.80
24	4	0.90	$7.0 \pm 0.41_a^\alpha$	$23.2 \pm 2.46_{ab}$	0.31

[a] From Kritchevsky *et al.* (1973).
[b] Nanomoles per milligram protein per hour.
[c] Standard error; values with same subscript are significantly different.

B. ARTERIAL ENZYMES IN ATHEROSCLEROSIS

As outlined in the introduction, the increase in the cholesteryl ester content of arterial tissue is a hallmark of atherosclerosis in man and virtually in all experimental animals. By analogy with cholesteryl ester storage disease and Wolman's disease (Sloan and Fredrickson, 1972a,b), an enzyme deficiency would lead to cholesteryl ester accumulation. Measurements of arterial cholesteryl ester-hydrolyzing activities do not, however, support such obvious conclusions. Most studies have indicated that cholesteryl ester hydrolyzing activities of atherosclerotic aortas are not significantly different from those of normal aortas (Brecher *et al.*, 1973; Howard *et al.*, 1971; Kritchevsky *et al.*, 1974). Peters *et al.* (1973) have found a moderate increase in acid cholesterol ester hydrolase in atherosclerotic rabbit aorta. More recently, using improved methods of assay and enzyme preparation, a substantial increase of hydrolytic activity in atherosclerotic rabbit aortas has been observed (H. V. Kothari, I. D. Cargill, and R. J. Ryan, unpublished observations)

Another line of investigation has shown that animals resistant to experimentally induced atherosclerosis (e.g., rats) have higher levels of these enzymes than animals that are particularly susceptible, such as the rabbit (Patelski *et al.*, 1968; Bonner *et al.*, 1972). It is suggested that the higher levels of the enzymes may be a part of a protective mechanism in resistant species. It is becoming increasingly clear that a major part of hydrolyzing activity is lysosomal and that the activity increases together with the activities of other lysosomal enzymes during fatty streak formation (Kothari *et al.*, 1970; Bonner *et al.*, 1972; Peters *et al.*, 1973). Nevertheless, the lysosomal activity may be inadequate for preventing cholesteryl ester accumulation in the cell, especially in susceptible species which have a relatively low activity of the enzyme. An even more important consideration, however, concerns the reversible functions of cholesteryl ester hydrolase in physiological conditions. The influences on the directions of reaction *in vivo* are unknown. In resistant species and in normal susceptible species, the reaction may be thought to be controlled as the enzyme irreversibly catalyzes hydrolysis of esters. A cellular event such as increased free cholesterol may lead to the release of this control of the enzyme, rendering it reversible or even irreversible in the opposite direction.

On the other hand, it has been established that, in atherosclerotic aortas, the esterification of cholesterol is markedly stimulated. The cholesteryl ester synthesizing capacity of atherosclerotic aorta is increased, regardless of whether the atherosclerosis is induced by cholesterol feeding or by a semisynthetic, cholesterol-free atherogenic diet. St. Clair *et al.* (1970) have reported stimulation of esterification shortly after the institution of an atherogenic diet. The activity of 900 g supernatant fractions from White Carneau pigeon aortas increased 10-fold after only 2 weeks of cholesterol feeding, a time when no visible lesion was present. Similarly, Hashimoto *et al.* (1974) observed approximately 16- to 50-fold stimulation of ACAT in atherosclerotic aorta preparations. A recent report by Day and Proudlock (1974) described an increased oleic acid incorporation into cholesteryl ester in intact arterial segments from a rabbit that had been fed a cholesterol diet for only three days. We have observed a similar phenomenon in rabbits (Kritchevsky *et al.*, 1974). The synthetic activity was increased by 295% on day 7, and the hydrolytic activity was increased by only 58%. A sharp increase in synthetic-hydrolytic (S/H) ratio was seen after 7 days of atherogenic regimen. No atheromata were visible. Thus, the natural propensity towards an increased aortic S/H level is increased by the administration of an atherogenic regimen.

Most evidence suggests that the stimulation of cholesterol esterification is one of the earliest changes in atherogenesis. The reasons for increased esterification remain unknown, however; increased enzyme(s) synthesis or increased enzyme(s) capacities or both may contribute to the observed high esterifying activity. The precise relationship between the esterifying and hydrolyzing activities and their role singly and together in the atherosclerotic process remains to be clarified.

VII. Enzymes in Species Resistant or Susceptible to Atherosclerosis

Susceptibility to atherosclerosis varies widely among different species, and while within a given species susceptibility varies from one anatomical site to another. The reasons for these differences are largely unexplained, but any metabolic or structural feature which displays a high correlation with susceptibility would provide an important clue to understanding critical mechanisms of atherosclerosis. Resistance to atherosclerosis has been attributed to a high ratio of α- to β-lipoproteins in plasma (Olson, 1958), to high lipolytic activity in the arterial wall (Zemplenyi, 1968), to homeostatic mechanisms which resist the development of hypercholesterolemia (Mancini *et al.*, 1965), and to high levels of lysosomal enzymes in the arterial wall (Bonner *et al.*, 1972). Although all are probably valid, these reasons fail to explain many known specific and anatomical differences in propensity to atherogenesis (Hashimoto and Dayton, 1974).

The possibility has been suggested that resistant species have high levels of cholesteryl ester hydrolyzing enzymes, which provide them with a protective mechanism for resisting accumulation of cholesteryl esters. In susceptible species, the propensity of arterial tissue to develop atherosclerosis

Table XI

CHOLESTEROL ESTER SYNTHESIZING (S) AND HYDROLYZING (H) ACTIVITIES
OF ACETONE DRY-POWDER PREPARATIONS OF AORTAS OF VARIOUS SPECIES [a,b]

Species	Experiment 1			Experiment 2		
	S	H	S/H	S	H	S/H
Susceptible						
Human	6.5	8.3	0.78	6.6	6.9	0.96
Baboon	6.2	7.5	0.83	5.4	6.2	0.87
Swine	5.5	4.8	1.15	6.7	7.0	0.96
Rabbit	6.5	7.0	0.93	5.8	6.0	0.97
Chicken	8.0	8.1	0.99	6.3	6.5	0.97
Resistant						
Rat	10.0	16.0	0.63	10.6	19.6	0.54
Mouse	9.2	14.0	0.66	7.3	12.7	0.57
Dog	4.0	14.5	0.28	6.5	18.0	0.36

[a] Synthesis and hydrolysis of cholesterol ester is described as nanomoles of substrate converted per milligram of protein per hour.
[b] From Kritchevky and Kothari (1974).

was related to the innate capacity of the tissue to esterify cholesterol. As given in Tables XI and XII both resistant and susceptible species can synthesize and hydrolyze cholesteryl esters. In a given species, the separate capacities to synthesize and to hydrolyze cholesteryl esters may not bear a relationship to specific susceptibility or resistance to atherosclerosis; if, however, these capacities are examined in relation to each other, such as in a ratio of S/H, they become more meaningful.

Species differences in aortic cholesteryl ester metabolism were examined for their correlations with known susceptibilities to atherosclerosis (Kritchevsky and Kothari, 1974). When compared, the synthetic activity alone

Table XII

CHOLESTEROL ESTER SYNTHETASE (S) AND HYDROLASE (H) ACTIVITY IN PROXIMAL
AND DISTAL PORTIONS OF AORTAS OF WHITE CARNEAU AND SHOW RACER PIGEONS [a]

Aorta portion	Number of pools	S/H ratio $\pm$ S.E.M.	
		White Carneau	Show Racer
Proximal	5	0.65 ± 0.08 [b]	0.48 ± 0.03 [c]
Distal	5	0.95 ± 0.10	0.52 ± 0.05 [c]

[a] From Kritchevsky and Kothari (1973).
[b] Versus WC distal, $p < 0.05$.
[c] Versus WC distal, $p < 0.01$.

indicated no significant correlation to various susceptible and resistant species. Hydrolytic activities were two to three times higher in all resistant species than in susceptible animals (Table X). Determinations of S/H ratios indicated that resistant species have a lower S/H ratio (about 0.51) than do susceptible species (about 0.94). Experiments to determine possible intraspecific differences were performed using aortas from White Carneau (susceptible) and Show Racer (resistant) pigeons (Lofland and Clarkson, 1959). The ratio of aortic cholesterol ester S/H activity was 1.21 in the White Carneau pigeon and 0.73 for the Show Racer (Kritchevsky and Kothari, 1973). Since the spontaneous atherosclerosis which occurs in White Carneau pigeons was found almost exclusively in the distal portion of the artery (Clarkson et al., 1959), the S/H ratios in the proximal and distal portions of the arteries from White Carneau and Show Racer pigeons

Table XIII

CHOLESTEROL ESTERIFICATION BY THORACIC AND ABDOMINAL AORTIC MICROSOMES DERIVED FROM MALES OF SEVERAL SPECIES [a,b]

| | Incorporation of the palmityl group of palmityl CoA into cholesterol esters (pmoles/mg protein) | | |
	4 min	8 min	16 min
Rat aorta			
Thoracic (T)	34.2 ± 9.2 [c]	57.7 ± 15.9	90.8 ± 25.8
Abdominal (A)	10.7 ± 4.0	18.4 ± 6.8	30.7 ± 6.8
T vs A, $p < 0.01$			
Dog aorta			
Thoracic (T)	11.2 ± 1.5	17.6 ± 2.9	21.2 ± 2.9
Abdominal (A)	7.5 ± 1.4	12.8 ± 2.4	24.8 ± 8.6
T vs A, NS			
Rabbit aorta			
Thoracic (T)	10.6 ± 2.0	16.7 ± 2.5	24.2 ± 0.7
Abdominal (A)	7.4 ± 0.5	12.8 ± 1.0	18.5 ± 1.3
T vs A, $p < 0.01$			
Cockerel aorta			
Thoracic (T)	5.6 ± 0.5	0.3 ± 1.7	13.3 ± 2.5
Abdominal (A)	9.3 ± 2.1	15.1 ± 2.2	24.3 ± 4.9
T vs A, $p < 0.01$			

[a] From Hashimoto and Dayton (1974).

[b] Incubation medium consisted of 0.1 M phosphate buffer (pH 7.4) containing 1% albumin, 0.4 μCi[1-^{14}C]palmityl-CoA (sp. act., 58 μCi/μmole) and 0.3–0.5 mg microsome. Reaction mixture was shaken at 37°C under air. Significance of the difference between the values obtained with thoracic and abdominal aortas was assessed by the analysis of variance.

[c] Mean ± standard deviation of three experiments.

were determined. The results (Table XI) suggest that an aberration in cholesterol ester metabolism may be among the elements of aortic metabolism which predispose to atherosclerosis.

Hashimoto and Dayton (1974) studied the esterification of cholesterol by aortic microsomes that had been derived from several species. The substrate used was [1-^{14}C]palmityl CoA. As shown in Table XIII cholesterol-esterifying activity of microsomes from thoracic aortas varied with species. ACAT activity was highest in rat, followed by dog, rabbit, and cockerel, in that order. Such results confirm that the comparison of esterifying activities alone cannot indicate a correlation between enzyme activity and susceptibility of the species. Similarly, in a separate experiment, no significant difference was found in the esterifying activities between Show Racer and White Carneau pigeons.

VIII. Effect of Pharmacologically Active Agents on the Enzymes

With only circumstantial evidence available, attempts at the chemotherapy of atherosclerosis have been empirical and confined largely to controlling individual plasma lipids, mainly cholesterol. Effective agents are few and questionable because of the marked side effects they produce. Control of enzymatic mechanisms regulating the formation of lipoprotein and their components offer promise as a possible means of controlling lipids, homeostasis, and atherosclerosis. In part, this approach has been followed successfully for cholesterol, and its application to other important lipid classes can be anticipated, particularly to cholesteryl esters, the biosynthesis of which depends on esterification processes.

Of three main possible ways of lowering levels of arterial cholesteryl esters, the stimulation of hydrolysis seems most promising. Other possibilities appear less feasible (i.e., efflux or resorption of arterial cholesteryl esters back to plasma, and interference with cholesteryl ester synthesis in arterial tissue). Since the major part (80%) of accumulated cholesteryl esters is derived from plasma (Dayton, 1974) controlling local synthesis may not be especially useful in this area; however, it may be important in other respects. Enzymes of cholesteryl ester metabolism in various tissues are similar, and therefore, inhibition of ester biosynthesis in liver, arteries and other extrahepatic sites of ester formations will lower not only ester levels but also levels of lipoproteins as a whole. The above considerations have recently inspired searches for agents capable of influencing these enzymes *in vitro* as well as *in vivo*.

Preliminary experiments have been done which relate to the influence of hypolipidemic drugs on aortic cholesteryl esterase activity in cholesterol-fed rabbits (Kritchevsky *et al.,* 1975). Rabbits were fed an atherogenic diet alone or augmented with either nicotinic acid, D-thyroxine, Atromid-S (ethyl *p*-chlorophenoxylisobutyrate), or β-sitosterol. The four compounds tested had been shown to inhibit experimentally induced atherosclerosis in rabbits. The rabbits were fed the diets for 10 days, and then the aortic cholesteryl ester synthesizing (S) or hydrolyzing (H) activities were determined. The addition of cholesterol to the basal diet increased the S/H ratio by 177%. Compared to the atherogenic regimen, the hypolipidemic drugs all reduced the S/H ratios. The reductions were nicotinic acid, 66%; D-thyroxine, 33%; Atromid-S, 16%; and β-sitosterol, 43%. The mechanism of action of these compounds has been attributed to their hypolipidemic properties. However, the shift of S/H values to lower levels by drug treatment indicated a direct action on the aortic metabolism that could not be explained solely on the basis of cholesterol levels.

Brecher and Chobanian (1974) have tested *in vitro* other hypolipidemic agents, ethyl *p*-chlorophenoxylisobutyrate (CPIB) and 2-methyl-2[*p*-(1,-2,3,4-tetrahydro-1-naphthyl)-phenoxy] propionic acid (TPIA), for their effects on cholesterol-esterifying activities of rabbit and monkey aortas. Both compounds were found to inhibit microsomal ACAT as well as cholesteryl ester hydrolase of supernatant fractions. The addition of either CPIB or TPIA to the microsomal system reduced both the rate and the extent of oleic acid incorporation into cholesteryl ester in a concentration-dependent manner. TPIA was the more potent inhibitor; it reduced incorporation 50% at 0.5 mM, while 5.0 mM CPIB was required to achieve a similar level of inhibition. The addition of these compounds to aortic high-speed supernatant fractions had similar effects. These compounds have been shown to inhibit several microsomal enzymes involved in lipid metabolism (Maragoudakis, 1971; Lamb *et al.,* 1973); however, the mechanisms of these hypolipidemic drugs are still not completely understood.

Several pharmacologically active agents with amphipathic chemical properties such as SKF 525-A (diethylamino diphenylvalerate HCl) and SQ 10,591 (2,2″-[1-methyl-4,4-diphenylbutylidene)bis-(*p*-phenyleneowy)]-bis-triethylamine oxalate), by *in vitro* preparation of ovarian mitochondria and microsomes (Morin *et al.,* 1974), have been shown to inhibit cholesterol esterification. SQ 10,591 seems to selectively inhibit the formation of cholesteryl ester also by rat liver after *in vivo* administration (Lerner *et al.,* 1970). Recently, Morin *et al.* (1974) have shown *in vitro* inhibition of aortic ACAT activity to occur because of these compounds. SKF 525-A and SQ 10,591 at 5×10^{-5} M concentrations inhibited esterification of palmityl CoA by microsomes of swine aorta down to 56% and 44% of control values. Similar inhibitory effects of the anionic amphipathic compounds (such as sodium dodecylsulfate and sodium taurocholate) and of anionic polymeric compounds (such as polyphlorethin phosphate, dextran sulfate, and heparin) were observed. It has been suggested that the mechanism of the inhibitory effects of SKF 525-A and SQ 10,591 was via an alteration of the microsomal membranes so as to limit diffusion of the palmitate and palmityl CoA substrates to the sites of esterification.

IX. Conclusions

It is evident that our knowledge of arterial cholesteryl ester metabolism in health and in disease is still fragmentary. None of the enzymes has been isolated; exact measurements of important intermediates and coenzymes are lacking; and while some observations are contradictory, others suggest factors and interactions which have not been considered so far. Even the fragments give a fairly rounded view, however, and pinpointing of the unsolved problems at least has become possible.

In the area of identification and characterization of the enzymes much remains to be done. The use of conventional methods of homogenization and subcellular preparation is greatly hindered by the toughness of the arterial tissue. Methods of subfractionation of the tissue are making only limited progress. Low levels of enzymes coupled with a lack of sufficiently sensitive assay methods have greatly hindered investigations of enzyme properties. These factors often conspire to make present techniques too unsophisticated to satisfy the precise requirements of, for example, kinetic experiments. The identification of the enzymes is based, in most cases, only on pH-optimum characteristics. Identification by one or two parameters may often be ambiguous when the enzymes of one species are compared with those of another, unless the species are closely related, and unless the comparisons are made by precise and identical procedures. Characterization by pH-activity relationship deserves further consideration. For a number of enzymes the presence of anionic amphipathic or anionic polymeric molecules has been shown to shift pH optima by 1 or even 2 units on either side. The apparent difference in pH optimum for a given enzyme may result from the presence of such molecules in crude enzyme preparations. Similarly, the requirements for bile salts and substrate specificity of the enzyme are the two areas of contention in the present literature. Most of the available information requires reconfirmation. Only by understanding the characteristics of these enzymes, however, can their precise roles in atherosclerosis be elucidated.

Of the many quantitative changes that have been described, the most striking and consistent is the increased esterifying activity in atherosclerosis. This may be either a primary change, or secondary to an increase in lipids, particularly cholesterol. Although increase in enzyme synthesis has often been suggested, the possibility of potentiation of the esterifying enzymes by changed environment cannot be ruled out. As indicated earlier, arterial tissue has all three known pathways for the esterification of cholesterol, and the activities of all increase during atherosclerosis. This is rather puzzling because they probably have quite different molecular structures, because their mechanisms are not similar, and because they probably have different functions. However, one common factor is that in atherosclerosis they all display an increase in their substrate concentration. Even a small increase in substrate concentration, at least in the case of ACAT, may release the allosteric control and greatly capacitate the enzyme. Stimulation of the activity in only three days of cholesterol feeding to the rabbit, when no proliferation of the endoplasmic reticulum is seen, provides support for the above concept of allosteric regulation of the enzyme. The *in vitro* activation of the enzyme in an organ culture of normal pigeon aorta also points to molecular regulation of the enzyme. Similar experiments with organ culture in the presence of a protein synthesis inhibitor, such as puromycine, may provide clues to the mechanism of increase of ACAT activity.

The precise role of the lysosomal cholesterol ester hydrolase remains to be clarified. A correlation between relatively low enzyme activity and the accumulation of esters has been suggested. Such a correlation is questionable; however, regression studies have shown a quick disappearance of cholesteryl esters, indicative of their active metabolism. Whether this enzyme reversibly catalyzes the esterification of cholesterol or not is an open question. Normally, a reversal of hydrolase function of a lysosomal enzyme would be theoretically impossible. However, in very special conditions like atherosclerosis, the spontaneous reversal of hydrolysis reaction does seem a possibility.

The role of the arterial enzymes in cholesteryl ester metabolism is one about which we know even less than we know about atherosclerosis. Future progress in understanding the pathogenesis of atherosclerosis, however, will largely depend upon advances in our knowledge of these enzymes.

References

Abdulla, Y. H., Orton, C. C., and Adams, C. W. M. (1968). *J. Atheroscler. Res.* **8,** 967.

Adams, C. W. M. (1973). "Atherosclerosis: Initiating Factors." Associated Scientific Publishers, Amsterdam.

Adams, C. W. M., and Morgan, R. S. (1966). *Nature (London)* **210,** 175.

Adams, C. W. M., Virag, S., Morgan, R. S., and Orton, C. C. (1968). *J. Atheroscler. Res.* **8,** 679.

Adams, C. W. M., Morgan, R. S., and Bayliss, O. B. (1970). *Atherosclerosis* **11,** 119.

Bell, F. P., Day, A. J., Gent, M., and Schwartz, C. J. (1975). *Exp. Mol. Pathol.* **22**, 366.
Biggs, M. W., and Kritchevsky, D. (1951). *Circulation* **4**, 34.
Bonner, M. J., Miller, B. F., and Kothari, H. V. (1972). *Proc. Soc. Exp. Biol. Med.* **139**, 1359.
Böttcher, C. J. F. (1964). *Proc. R. Soc. Med.* **57**, 792.
Böttcher, C. J. F., Boelsme-Van Houte, E., ter Haar Romeny-Wachter, C. C., Woodford, F. P., and Van Gent, C. M. (1960). *Lancet* **2**, 116?
Bowyer, D. E,, Howard, A. N., Gresham, G. A., Bates, D., and Palmer, B. V. (1968). *Prog. Biochem. Pharmacol.* **4**, 235.
Brecher, P. I., and Chobanian, A. V. (1974). *Circ. Res.* **35**, 692.
Brecher, P. I., Kessler, M., Clifford, C., and Chobanian, A. V. (1973). *Biochim. Biophys. Acta* **316**, 386.
Brockerhoff, H., and Jensen, R. G. (1974). "Lipolytic Enzymes." Academic Press, New York.
Brooks, C. J. W., Harland, W. A., and Steel, Q. (1966). *Biochim. Biophys. Acta* **125**, 620.
Burke, J. A., and Schubert, W. K. (1972). *Science* **176**, 309.
Chobanian, A. V., and Manzur, F. (1972). *J. Lipid Res.* **13**, 201.
Christensen, S. (1962). *J. Atheroscler. Res.* **2**, 131.
Clarkson, T. B., Prichard, R. W., Netsky, M. G., and Lofland, H. B. (1959). *AMA Arch. Pathol.* **68**, 143.
Cook, R. P. (1958). "Cholesterol: Chemistry, Biochemistry, and Pathology." Academic Press, New York.
Cox, G. E., Trueheart, R. E., Kaplan, J., and Taylon, C. B. (1963), *Arch. Pathol.* **76**, 166.
Day, A. J. (1967). *Adv. Lipid Res.* **5**, 185.
Day, A. J., and Gould-Hurst, P. R. S. (1966). *Biochim. Biophys. Acta* **116**, 169.
Day, A. J., and Proudlock, J. W. (1974). *Atherosclerosis* **19**, 253.
Day, A. J., and Tume, R. K. (1969). *Biochim. Biophys. Acta* **176**, 367.
Day, A. J., and Wahlquist, M. L. (1968). *Circ. Res.* **23**, 779.
Day, A. J., and Wilkinson, G. K. (1967). *Circ. Res.* **21**, 593.
Day, A. J., Wahlquist, M. L., and Tume, R. K. (1970). *Atherosclerosis* **12**, 253.
Dayton, S. (1974). *Proc. Int. Symp. Atheroscler., 3rd, 1973* p. 21.
Dayton, S., and Hashimoto, S. (1970). *Atherosclerosis* **12**, 371.
Dayton, S., Hashimoto, S., and Pearce, M. L. (1965). *Circulation* **32**, 911.
Dury, A. (1961). *J. Gerontol.* **16**, 114.
Eisenberg, S., Stein, Y., and Stein, O. (1969). *Biochim. Biophys. Acta* **176**, 557.
Erlanson, C., and Borgström, B. (1970). *Scand. J. Gastroenterol.* **5**, 395.
Felt, V., and Benes, P. (1969). *Biochim. Biophys. Acta* **176**, 435.
Filipek-Wender, H., and Borgström, B. (1971). *Acta Biochim. Pol.* **18**, 1.
Geer, J. C., and Guidry, M. A. (1964). *Exp. Mol. Pathol.* **3**, 485.
Goodman, D. S., Dykin, D., and Shiratori, T. (1964). *J. Biol. Chem.* **239**, 1335.
Hanig, M., Shainoff, J. R., and Lowry, A. D., Jr. (1956). *Science* **124**, 176.
Hashimoto, S., and Dayton, S. (1971). *Proc. Soc. Exp. Biol. Med.* **137**, 1186.
Hashimoto, S., and Dayton, S. (1974). *Proc. Soc. Exp. Biol. Med.* **145**, 89.
Hashimoto, S., Dayton, S., and Alfin-Slater, R. B. (1973). *Life Sci.* **12**, 1.
Hashimoto, S., Dayton, S., Alfin-Slater, R. B., Bui, P. T., Baker, N., and Wilson, L. (1974). *Circ. Res.* **34**, 176.
Hernandez, H. H., and Chaikoff, I. L. (1957). *J. Biol. Chem.* **228**, 447.

Hirsch, E. F., and Weinhouse, S. (1943). *Physiol. Rev.* **23,** 185.

Howard, A. N., Patelski, J., Bowyer, D. E., and Gresham, G. A. (1971). *Atherosclerosis* **17,** 29.

Howard, C. F., Jr., and Portman, O. W. (1966). *Biochim. Biophys. Acta* **125,** 623.

Hyun, J., Kothari, H. V., Herm, E., Mortenson, J., Treadwell, C. R., and Vahouny, G. V. (1969). *J. Biol. Chem.* **244,** 1937.

Hyun, J., Treadwell, C. R., and Vahouny, G. V. (1972). *Arch. Biochim. Biophys.* **152,** 233.

Kao, V. C. Y., and Wissler, R. W. (1965). *Exp. Mol. Pathol.* **4,** 465.

Klimov, A. N., Doviagina, T. N., Popov, A. V., and Bankovskaya, E. B. (1974). *Proc. Int. Symp. Atheroscler., 3rd, 1973* p. 85.

Kothari, H. V., and Kritchevsky, D. (1975). *Lipids* **10,** 322.

Kothari, H. V., Bonner, M. J., and Miller, B. F. (1970). *Biochim. Biophys. Acta* **202,** 325.

Kothari, H. V., Miller, B. F., and Kritchevsky, D. (1973). *Biochim. Biophys. Acta* **296,** 446.

Kritchevsky, D. (1958). "Cholesterol." Wiley, New York.

Kritchevsky, D. (1967). In "Atherosclerotic Vascular Disease" (A. N. Brest and J. H. Moyer, eds.), p. 1. Appleton, New York.

Kritchevsky, D. (1972a). *Mech. Ageing Dev.* **1,** 275.

Kritchevsky, D. (1972b). *Lipids* **7,** 305.

Kritchevsky, D., and Kothari, H. V. (1973). *Biochim. Biophys. Acta* **326,** 489.

Kritchevsky, D., and Kothari, H. V. (1974). *Steroids Lipids Res.* **5,** 23.

Kritchevsky, D., Genzano, J. C., and Kothari, H. V. (1973). *Mech. Ageing Dev.* **2,** 345.

Kritchevsky, D., Tepper, S. A., Genzano, J. C., and Kothari, H. V. (1974). *Atherosclerosis* **19,** 459.

Kritchevsky, D., Tepper, S. A., and Kothari, H. V. (1975). *Artery* **1,** 437.

Lamb, R. G., Hill, P. M., and Fallon, H. J. (1973). *J. Lipid Res.* **14,** 459.

Lerner, L. J., Harris, D. N., Yiacas, E., Hilf, R., and Michel, I. (1970). *Am. J. Clin. Nutr.* **23,** 1241.

Lofland, H. B., and Clarkson, T. B. (1959). *Circ. Res.* **7,** 234.

Longcope, C., and Williams, R. H. (1963). *Endocrinology* **72,** 735.

Mancini, M., Rossi, G. B., Oriente, P., and Cali, A. (1965). *Nature (London)* **207,** 1206.

Maragoudakis, M. E. (1971). *J. Biol. Chem.* **246,** 348.

Mead, J. F., and Gouze, M. L. (1961). *Proc. Soc. Exp. Biol. Med.* **106,** 4.

Miller, B. F., Aiba, T., Keyes, F. P., Curreri, P. W., and Branwood, A. W. (1966). *J. Atheroscler. Res.* **6,** 352.

Miller, B. F., Bonner, M. J., and Kothari, H. V. (1968a). *Fed. Proc., Fed. Am. Soc. Exp. Biol.* **27,** 440.

Miller, B. F., Bonner, M. J., and Kothari, H. V. (1968b). *Circulation* **38,** 4.

Morgan, R. G. H., Barrowman, J., Filipek-Wender, H., and Borgström, B. (1968). *Biochim. Biophys. Acta* **167,** 355.

Morin, C. R., Edralin, G. G., and Woo, J. M. (1974). *Atherosclerosis* **20,** 27.

Murthy, S. K., and Ganguly, J. (1962). *J. Biol. Chem.* **83,** 460.

Newman, H. A. I., and Zilversmit, D. B. (1962). *J. Biol. Chem.* **237,** 2078.

Newman, H. A. I., and Zilversmit, D. B. (1964). *J. Atheroscler. Res.* **4,** 261.

Newman, H. A. I., and Zilversmit, D. B. (1966). *Circ. Res.* **18,** 293.

Newman, H. A. I., Gray, G. W., and Zilversmit, D. B. (1968). *J. Atheroscler. Res.* **8**, 745.

Nilsson, A., Norden, H., and Wilhelmsson, L. (1973). *Biochim. Biophys. Acta* **296**, 593.

Olson, R. E. (1958). *Perspect. Biol. Med.* **2**, 84.

Page, I. H. (1941). *Ann. Intern. Med.* **14**, 1741.

Page, I. H. (1954). *Circulation* **10**, 1.

Parker, F., Ormsly, J. W., Peterson, N. F., Odland, G. F., and Williams, R. II. (1966). *Circ. Res.* **19**, 700

Parker, F., Schimmelbusch, W., and Williams, R. H. (1974). *Diabetes* **13**, 182.

Patelski, J. (1977). *Adv. Exp. Med. Biol.* **82**, 882.

Patelski, J., and Tipton, K. F. (1971). *Atherosclerosis* **15**, 288.

Patelski, J., and Torlinska, T. (1973). *Proc. Int. Symp. Phospholipids, 1972* p. 91.

Patelski, J., Waligora, Z., and Szule, S. (1967). *J. Atheroscler. Res.* **7**, 453.

Patelski, J., Bowyer, D. E., Howard, A. N., and Gresham, G. A. (1968). *J. Atheroscler. Res.* **8**, 221.

Patelski, J., Pniewska, M., Piorunska, M., and Obrebska, C. (1975). *Atherosclerosis* **22**, 287.

Peters, T. J., and DeDuve, C. (1974). *J. Exp. Mol. Pathol.* **20**, 228.

Peters, T. J., Muller, M., and DeDuve, C. (1972). *Gastroenterology* **57**, 542.

Peters, T. J., Takano, T., and DeDuve, C. (1973). *Atherogenesis: Initiating Factors, Ciba Found. Symp., 1972* p. 197.

Portman, O. W. (1967). *J. Atheroscler. Res.* **7**, 617.

Portman, O. W. (1969). *Ann. N.Y. Acad. Sci.* **162**, 120.

Portman, O. W. (1970). *Adv. Lipid Res.* **8**, 41.

Portman, O. W., and Alexander, M (1966). *Arch. Biochem. Biophys.* **117**, 357.

Portman, O. W., and Alexander, M. (1972). *Biochim. Biophys. Acta* **260**, 460.

Proudlock, J. W., and Day, A. J. (1972). *Biochim. Biophys. Acta* **260**, 716.

Rothblat, G. H., Hartzell, R. W., Jr., Mialhe, H., and Kritchevsky, D. (1966). *Biochim. Biophys. Acta* **116**, 133.

Rothblat, G. H., Hartzell, R. W., Jr., Mialhe, H., and Kritchevsky, D. (1967). *Wistar Inst. Symp. Monogr.* **6**, 129.

St. Clair, R. W. (1974). *Proc. Int. Symp. Atheroscler., 3rd, 1973* p. 64.

St. Clair, R. W., and Harpold, G. J. (1975). *Exp. Mol. Pathol.* **22**, 1975.

St. Clair, R. W., Lofland, H. B., Jr., and Clarkson, T. B. (1968). *J. Lipid Res.* **9**, 739.

St. Clair, R. W., Lofland, H. B., Jr., and Clarkson, T. B. (1969). *J. Atheroscler. Res.* **10**, 193.

St. Clair, R. W., Lofland, H. B., Jr., and Clarkson, T. B. (1970). *Circ. Res.* **27**, 213.

St. Clair, R. W., Clarkson, T. B., and Lofland, H. B. (1972). *Circ. Res.* **31**, 664.

Schramm, G., and Wolff, A. (1940). *Hoppe-Seyler's Z. Physiol. Chem.* **263**, 73.

Scott, P. J., and Hurley, P. J. (1970). *Atherosclerosis* **11**, 77.

Scott, R. F., Florentin, R. A., Daoud, A. S., Morrison, E. S., Jones, R. M., and Hutt, M. S. R. (1966). *Exp. Mol. Pathol.* **5**, 12.

Shimamoto, T., and Numano, F. (1974). *Proc. Int. Symp. Atheroscler., 3rd, 1973* p. 87.

Sloan, H. R., and Fredrickson, D. S. (1972a). *In* "The Metabolic Basis of Inherited Diseases" (J. B. Stanbury, J. B. Wyngaarden, and D. S. Fredrickson, eds.), 3rd ed., p. 808. McGraw-Hill, New York.

Sloan, H. R., and Fredrickson, D. S. (1972b). *J. Clin. Invest.* **51**, 1923.

Smith, A. G., Brooks, C. J. W., and Harland, W. A. (1974a). *Steroids Lipids Res.* **5**, 150.

Smith, A. G., Harland, W. A., and Brooks, C. J. W. (1974b). *Biochem. Soc. Trans.* **2**, 488.

Smith, E. B. (1965). *J. Atheroscler. Res.* **5**, 224.

Smith, E. B., Evans, P. H., and Dowhan, M. D. (1967). *J. Atheroscler. Res.* **7**, 131.

Somer, J. B., Bell, F. P., and Schwartz, C. J. (1974). *Atherosclerosis* **20**, 11.

Stein, Y., and Stein, O. (1962). *J. Atheroscler. Res.* **2**, 400.

Stein, Y., and Stein, O. (1973). *Atherogenesis: Initiating Factors, Ciba Found. Symp., 1972* p. 165.

Stein, Y., Stein, O., and Shapiro, B. (1963). *Biochim. Biophys. Acta* **70**, 33.

Stoffel, W., and Greten, H. (1967). *Hoppe-Seyler's Z. Physiol. Chem.* **348**, 1145.

Stokke, K. T. (1972a). *Biochim. Biophys. Acta* **270**, 156.

Stokke, K. T. (1972b). *Biochim. Biophys. Acta* **280**, 329.

Suzue, G., and Marcel, Y. L. (1972). *Biochemistry* **11**, 1704.

Swell, L., Field, H., Jr., Schools, P. E., Jr., and Treadwell, C. R. (1960). *Proc. Soc. Exp. Biol. Med.* **105**, 662.

Takano, T., Black, W. J., Peters, T. J., and DeDuve, C. (1974). *J. Biol. Chem.* **249**, 6732.

Tracy, R. E., Dzoga, K. R., and Wissler, R. W. (1965). *Proc. Soc. Exp. Biol. Med.* **118**, 1095.

Tume, R. K., and Day, A. J. (1970). *J. Reticuloendothel. Soc.* **7**, 338.

Tuna, N., and Mangold, H. K. (1963). *In* "Evolution of the Atherosclerotic Plaque" (R. J. Jones, ed.), p. 85. Univ. of Chicago Press, Chicago, Illinois.

Tuna, N., Reckers, L., and Frantz, I. D., Jr. (1958). *J. Clin. Invest.* **37**, 1153.

Vahouny, G. V., and Treadwell, C. R. (1968) *Methods Biochem. Anal.* **16**, 219.

Wagner, W. D., and Clarkson, T. B. (1973). *Proc. Soc. Exp. Biol. Med.* **143**, 804.

Wahlquist, M. L., Day, A. J., and Tume, R. K. (1969). *Circ. Res.* **24**, 123.

Walton, K. W., and Williamson, N. (1968). *J. Atheroscler. Res.* **8**, 599.

Weinhouse, S., and Hirsch, E. F. (1940). *Arch. Pathol.* **29**, 31.

Zemplenyi, T. (1968). *In* "Enzyme Biochemistry of the Arterial Wall," p. 214. Lloyd-Luke, London.

Zemplenyi, T., and Grafnetter, D. (1959). *Gerontologia* **3**, 55.

Zemplenyi, T., Lojda, Z., and Mrhova, O. (1963). *In* "Atherosclerosis and Its Origin" (M. Sandler and G. H. Bourne, eds.), p. 459. Academic Press, New York.

Zilversmit, D. B. (1968). *Ann. N.Y. Acad. Sci.* **149**, 710.

Zilversmit, D. B., and Hughes, L. B. (1973). *Atherosclerosis* **18**, 141.

Zilversmit, D. B., Sweeley, C. C., and Newman, H. A. I. (1961). *Circ. Res.* **9**, 235.

Phospholipase D

MICHAEL HELLER

Department of Biochemistry, The Hebrew University, Hadassah Medical School, Jerusalem, Israel

I. Introduction

Three decades have passed since the first description by Hanahan and Chaikoff (1947a, 1948) of an enzyme in carrot roots and cabbage leaves, catalyzing the degradation of phosphatidylcholine to phosphatidic acid plus choline. The existence of such an enzyme was predicted 15 years earlier by Contrardi and Ercoli (1933).

The mode of action of hydrolytic enzymes acting upon lipid substrates has attracted considerable attention in recent years. In many cases it was reported that such enzymes act preferentially on substrates which form aggregates in aqueous media, i.e., micelles, liposomes, or other forms of particles. There are numerous cases in which a substrate is hardly recognized by the enzyme when present as monomers, but was readily cleaved upon transformation into interfaces of oil and water or air and water. There are also several examples of such hydrolases which were able to act on monomeric forms of lipids, e.g., below their critical micellar concentrations (CMC).[1]

Phospholipase D belongs to such a class of enzymes which function in a heterogeneous system, cleaving water insoluble substrates. In several studies, the adsorption of the enzyme at the interface of lipid and water or oil and water was shown to be a crucial step for the performance of the catalytic reaction. If the reaction rates are proportional to the interfacial areas, an increase in such surface area should lead to more efficient reactions.

There have been numerous attempts to identify an enzyme catalyzing reaction in organisms other than plants, and only recently has additional information been gathered to indicate that such activity is present in microorganisms as well as in mammalia. Thus the major and more detailed studies were done with the enzymes from the plant kingdom, and therefore their relative contribution is larger.

[1] Key to abbreviations in chapter: Asolectin, soybean phospholipid mixture; CM, carboxymethyl; CMC; critical micellar concentration; CPC, cetylpyridinium chloride; CTAB, cetyltrimethylammonium bromide; DEAE, diethylaminoethyl; DFP, diisopropylfluorophosphate; DOC, deoxycholate; DTT, dithiothreitol; EDTA, ethylenediaminotetraacetate; K_m, Michaelis constant; PC, phosphatidylcholine (lecithin); p-CMB, p-chloromercury benzoate; p-CMPS, p-chloromercuriophenyl sulfonate; PE, phosphatidylethanolamine; PLD, phospholipase D; PS, phosphatidyl serine; SDS, sodium dodecylsulfate.

The plant and microbial enzymes exist in both particulate and soluble forms, whereas the hitherto described mammalian enzymes were obtained only in a particulate form. Nonetheless, the different forms catalyze the following general reaction:

$$\text{Phosphatidyl—O—R}' + \text{R}''\text{—O—H} \xrightleftharpoons{\text{Ca}^{2+}} \text{phosphatidyl—O—R}'' + \text{R}'\text{—O—H} \quad (1)$$

A specific example is illustrated:

$$\text{Phosphatidyl choline} + \text{H}_2\text{O} \xrightleftharpoons{\text{Ca}^{2+}} \text{phosphatidic acid} + \text{choline} \quad (2)$$

Even today there is considerable uncertainty about the physiological role for phospholipase D in cellular metabolism. This has been emphasized in a recent study on a transfer reaction to methanol, by certain phospholipids from leaves, either *in situ* or *in vitro*. The results led the investigators, Roughan and Slack (1976) to doubt the existence of an enzyme having phospholipase D activity *in vivo*. They postulated that in the plant, a membrane-bound protein expresses certain catalytic activity only under "nonphysiological" conditions and only after being released from the tissue; hence it will only act *in vitro*. Since we do not share the same "enthusiasm," we present in this review several aspects related to phospholipase D and its catalytic properties. This subject has not been treated, to my knowledge, as a separate topic; it is often included as a short section in chapters of treatises, books, monographs, or review articles dealing with general or specific phospholipid metabolism or phospholipases (for pertinent examples please refer to the following list: Kates, 1970; Hill and Lands, 1970; Hitchcock and Nichols, 1971; Van Den Bosch *et al.*, 1972; Dawson, 1973; Galliard, 1973, 1975; Brockerhoff and Jensen, 1974). One exception is a recent review devoted exclusively to phospholipase D and was published in German by Nolte and Acker (1975b).

II. General Description of the Reaction

Reaction (1) implies that the reaction catalyzed by phospholipase D is a reversible transfer of the phosphatidyl moiety between two nucleophilic compounds containing a primary hydroxylic group (polar head group). With water as acceptor, this reaction will become a hydrolysis and the products will be phosphatidic acid and a water soluble nucleophile containing a hydroxyl such as choline [cf. reaction (2)]. Aqueous solutions of primary alcohols act as excellent nucleophilic acceptors for the phosphatidyl moiety. The exclusive formation of a phosphatidyl alcohol, or in a mixture with phosphatidic acid, depends on the properties of the alcoholic acceptor, its reactivity and concentrations. The transfer reaction has been demonstrated with phospholipase D from various sources and, therefore, in this respect, seems to be unique among phospholipases. Its broad substrate specificity, coupled to its ability to catalyze the transfer of a phosphatidyl moiety, makes it a valuable tool for a variety of purposes:

1. Preparation of phospholipids having different polar head groups, but retaining the original fatty acid composition.

2. Similarly, the enzyme may assist in modifying the polar head groups of phospholipids bound to biological membranes while retaining the original lipid backbone.

3. The susceptibility of the polar head groups of the membrane-bound phospholipids to the action of phospholipase D may aid in the determination of the asymmetry of the membranes and the location of the phospholipids.

4. Entrapment of phospholipase D in liposomes or other vehicles made of "inert" lipids (e.g., sphingomyelin plus cholesterol) for biochemical-pharmacological studies of either enzyme repair or, alternatively, intracellular modifications of phospholipids.

III. Methods of Determining Phospholipase D Activity

The enzyme catalyzes both hydrolysis and transfer reactions; therefore the choice of the appropriate method has to consider the type of the reaction, the type of substrate, the form of its dispersion, and the type of activator and nucleophilic acceptor.

Rates of the reaction can be measured by determining the rates of substrate disappearance or, alternatively, product formation.

Precautions have to be taken, in the case of impure or partially purified enzyme preparations, to ensure lack of interference by other enzymes which might act on either the substrate or products or both and affect the interpretation (see below).

Phospholipase D catalyzes reactions involving phospholipids of different forms. This includes a variety of naturally occurring phospholipids containing a mixture of saturated and unsaturated fatty acids which may be presented to the enzyme in a "pure" form or as "soluble" or membrane-bound lipoproteins. Furthermore, the enzyme also catalyzes the hydrolysis of lyso compounds [e.g., monoacylglycerophosphorylcholine (Davidson and Long, 1958; Long *et al.*, 1967a; Strauss *et al.*, 1976)], or of phosphatidylcholine having short-chain fatty acids (M. Wells, personal communication). This implies that the enzyme is capable of acting on different forms of substrates, most probably at different rates. No systematic study has been published to indicate the efficiency of the catalytic reaction with well-defined substrate systems in which the actual form and concentration of the substrate and/or enzyme have been examined. Except for a few instances, most of the published values should be considered as apparent, although they may well be reproducible.

Many studies have employed phosphatidylcholine, mainly as "purified egg yolk lecithin." Simple, mechanical dispersion of this compound in water forms coarse liposomes, which are hardly affected by the enzyme. Ultrasonic irradiation, organic solvents (i.e., diethyl ether, methanol, ethanol, etc.) or detergents are required, as well as Ca^{2+} ions to make it a suitable substrate for phospholipase D (Kates, 1960; Kates and Sastry, 1969; Yang, 1969; Galliard, 1973; Heller *et al.*, 1975). Calcium ions are obligatory, but each of the activators already mentioned will yield different rates of hydrolysis. With phospholipase D from peanut or cabbage and with egg yolk lecithin as substrate, the most effective activator is sodium dodecyl-sulfate (SDS), at a molar ratio of approximately PC-SDS 2:1 (Dawson and Hemington, 1967; Chen and Barton, 1971; Heller *et al.*, 1968, 1974, 1975, 1976). Measurements of rates, using a method which follows the change continuously, have been done either by acidimetry (Grossman *et al.*, 1974) or by measuring a change in surface properties using a monolayer technique (Quarles and Dawson, 1969c). Most of the published data are based on rates obtained by fixed-time incubations using one of the following methods: physical, acidimetric, spectrophotometric, or radiochemical. Except for the methods measuring continuous changes, the products had to be separated from the substrate. Water-soluble products were separated from lipids by either (a) acidification at the end of reaction with trichloro-acetic acid or perchloric acid followed by extraction with ether or (b) addition of chloroform and methanol according to Folch *et al.* (1957) or Bligh and Dyer (1959) to form a biphasic system. Both procedures terminate the reaction and allow separation between water- and lipid-soluble products. Identification of the products was done by thin-layer chromatography and chemical analysis.

The most sensitive and probably most specific procedure for determining phospholipase D activity and rates of reaction utilizes labeled substrates. They may be prepared biochemically (Stoffel, 1975) or biologically including isolation of the labeled phospholipid from BSC_1 kidney cells from monkey grown in tissue culture in the presence of $[^3H]CH_3$-choline (Ascher *et al.*, 1969) or *Escherichia coli*, yeast, or rainbow trout grown in the presence of $[^{14}C]CH_3$-choline (Quarles and Dawson, 1969c; Bilinski *et al.,* 1968) or chlorella, yeast, or *Hemophilus parainfluenza* grown in the presence of ^{32}P (Yang *et al.,* 1967; Hauser and Dawson, 1967; Ono and White, 1970a). The commercially available, uniformly labeled [^{14}C]phosphatidylcholine is also obtained by growing algae in the presence of $^{14}CO_2$. Substrate in which either the lipid- or the water-soluble moieties is specifically labeled may serve for either assay, but a uniformly labeled [^{14}C]phosphatidylcholine offers the advantages of identifying both lipid- and water-soluble products. Futhermore, it also allows a certain control for the presence of other enzymes in the preparations acting on either the substrate, products, or both. For example, partially purified preparations of phospholipase D from cabbage have been shown to contain a phosphodiesterase (Davidson and Long, 1958) and from peanuts, to contain a lysophospholipase A in addition to the phosphodiesterase (Strauss *et al.,* 1976).

Apart from these procedures which measure changes in the H^+ concentration or in the surface properties of the substrate, the alternative methods are less sensitive and even less specific. For example, the amounts (or concentrations) of the polar head groups released by phospholipase D action can be measured spectrophotometrically. These include the determination of choline by triiodide or ammonium reineckate methods, the periodide or ninhydrin methods for ethanolamine, or the periodate oxidation-chromotropic acid reagent or glycerokinase + glycerol-3-phosphate dehydrogenase for glycerol determinations (cf. Grossman *et al.,* 1974). These procedures also require a simultaneous separation and quantitative determination of the other products, whether phosphatidic acid or phosphatidyl alcohol, to ensure a measurement of the phospholipase D-catalyzed reaction alone.

The acidimetric procedure has been used only with short-chain phosphatidylcholine as substrate and below their critical micellar concentrations (CMC) (M. Wells, personal communication). However, this pH-metric method is not applicable above the CMC for these compounds or with liposomes of phosphatidylcholines containing long-chain fatty acids. Changes in H^+ concentration released by the cleavage of the ester bond can be followed either by a pH-stat or spectrophotometrically with a colored indicator. A choline-specific electrode, developed at Corning by Baum *et al.* (1973), was tested with egg yolk phosphatidylcholine but, unfortunately, substrate coating of the polymeric membrane prevented its applications (H. Cohen and M. Heller, unpublished).

The use of monolayer technique for measuring phospholipase D activity was introduced by Quarles and Dawson (1969c). The measurements of surface properties such as pressure, potential, or radioactivity offer a sensitive, reproducible, and continuous procedure for determining rates or activities when radioactive substrates are used, and all three parameters can be measured simultaneously, but nonlabeled substrates enable only two of them (cf. Dawson, 1969). It should be emphasized, however, that this method has one principal disadvantage—namely, it requires sophisticated instrumentation that is not commercially available. Moreover, for the analysis of the data and interpretation of the results one must be aware of the distinct and unique two-dimensional state of the substrate involved. This has led to a modified definition of substrate concentrations: "the number of molecules per unit surface" (Verger and de Haas, 1976; Verger *et al.*, 1973). Substrate concentrations or actual amounts of enzyme molecules involved in the catalysis are also uncertain. A kinetic analysis based on assumptions pertinent to the specific situations has been put forward by Verger and de Haas (1976; Verger *et al.*, 1973) for phospholipase A-catalyzed reactions and can be successfully applied for phospholipase D, with some minor modifications.

Practically, it is possible to label phospholipids with a radioactive isotope whether alone, in a pure form, or in a complex, as part of a membrane, for instance. Therefore, the method employing radioactivity seems to be the method of choice. Some assay systems most commonly practiced are given in the following sections.

A. HYDROLYSIS

1. *The Ether System*

Although it has been considered as a "bulk phase" assay system, it is in fact a good example of a reaction occurring at a water–ether interphase. This has been demonstrated indirectly by Heller and Arad (1970) and confirmed by Chen and Barton (1971). The reaction mixture contains 15–100 mM buffer at pH values ranging from 5.4 to 5.8, and occasionally 6.5 or higher; $CaCl_2$ (40–100 mM); phosphatidylcholine (*ex ovo* alone or mixed with labeled substrate) from 1 to 7 mM; and enzyme. Ether is added in 0.1 to 1 vol of the aqueous phase, to form a biphasic system. Shaking is essential during incubations which are carried out at 25–30°C for 10 to 60 min (Yang *et al.*, 1967; Dawson and Hemington, 1967; Kates and Sastry, 1969; Grossman *et al.*, 1974; Heller *et al.*, 1975). The reaction is terminated with acid ($HClO_4$ or Cl_3CCOOH), and the aqueous phase extracted with ether. If the substrate was uniformly labeled with [14]C (Grossman *et al.*, 1974), both products could be identified and measured. If only choline is labeled, its amounts can be determined only in the aqueous phase.

2. The Detergent System

One of the most powerful activators is sodium dodecylsulfate (SDS), which is added to the reaction mixture in amounts that will give phosphatidylcholine: SDS molar ratios ranging from 1 to 3 (Dawson and Hemington, 1967; Heller *et al.,* 1968, 1975; Heller and Arad, 1970; Tzur and Shapiro, 1972). The activity may be measured by preparing the reaction mixture in one of the following ways:

1. Mixing aqueous solutions of phosphatidylcholine and SDS with buffer and Ca^{+2}. The enzyme, always added last, initiates the reaction (Dawson and Hemington, 1967; Heller *et al.,* 1975; Tzur and Shapiro, 1972).

2. Same as in (1) except that the phosphatidylcholine "solution" is ultrasonically irradiated prior to the addition of the SDS solution, or preferably after the addition of the SDS solution and the rest of the reagents, but before adding the enzyme (Dawson and Hemington, 1967).

3. Same as in (1) except that the enzyme was added only after a period in which the system reached "organizational equilibrium" without ultrasonic irradiation by preincubating it for extended periods of time (explanations will be discussed later, cf. Section X,B) (Heller *et al.,* 1977).

4. Mixing solutions of phosphatidylcholine and of SDS in chloroform and methanol, in appropriate molar proportions, removing the organic solvents completely (by N_2 and freeze drying), and then adding the buffer, Ca^{2+}, and enzyme, in that order (Heller *et al.,* 1977).

The concentrations of the various solutions and the conditions of the reaction are similar to those described for the ether system. The concentration of the SDS is either equal (Dawson and Hemington, 1967; Rakhimov *et al.,* 1976a) or one-half that of phosphatidylcholine (Heller *et al.,* 1968, 1975, 1977; Heller and Arad, 1970; Tzur and Shapiro, 1972).

In both systems the formation of phosphatidic acid and, occasionally, estimation of its quantities should accompany the quantitative determination of the water-soluble polar head group (e.g., choline).

3. The Monolayer System

A suitable quantity of phosphatidylcholine ([^{14}C]methylcholine) alone or in a mixture with an appropriate amphipath is spread in petrol-ether (bp 60–80°C)-chloroform (4:1 by vol.) on a clean water surface containing 10 mM $CaCl_2$ and dimethylglutarate buffer (10 mM; pH 6.4). The solvent is allowed to evaporate, a magnetic stirrer is started for 1 min, stopped, and the surface pressure adjusted to a desired value by moving the barrier. The enzyme is then injected through the film, and stirring is started again. The change in radioactivity due to the removal of the [^{14}C]choline from the film in a free, subphase-soluble form, is recorded continuously either alone or in conjunction with alterations in surface pressure. Alternatively, the surface pressure could be maintained constant, by having the barrier move concurrently (Dawson, 1969; Quarles and Dawson, 1969c.)

B. TRANSPHOSPHATIDYLATION (OR BASE-EXCHANGE) SYSTEM

In essence the conditions for this reaction are similar to those described for hydrolysis, except that the appropriate alcohol (nucleophile) which acts as the polar-head-group acceptor [cf. Eq. (1)], for the phosphatidyl moiety is present in appropriate concentrations (Yang *et al.,* 1967; Benson *et al.,* 1965; Dawson, 1967; Heller and Arad, 1970; Kovatchev and Eibl, 1977).

In the case of the mammalian Ca^{2+}-stimulated base exchange, either the brain microsomal-bound phospholipids (phosphatidylcholine, ethanolamine, serine) were prelabeled (Saito *et al.,* 1975; Gaiti *et al.,* 1975, 1976) or else the substrate was asolectin (soya bean phospholipid mixture) (Saito *et al.,* 1974). In the first instance, the brain microsomes containing the enzyme were incubated with unlabeled alcohol base (choline, ethanolamine, or serine), and the release of labeled, water-soluble product was followed. In the second system, the brain microsomes were incubated with unlabeled phospholipid (from exogenous source) and with the appropriate labeled alcohol base, and the labeled phospholipid isolated and quantitated (Saito *et al.,* 1974, 1975).

IV. Purification Procedures

During the last decade several laboratories have reported the partial or complete purification of phospholipase D from a variety of sources. A brief description of the procedures is outlined below.

A. HIGHER PLANTS

The predominant occurrence of this enzyme in the plant kingdom directed most of the early attempts toward the isolation of phospholipase D from these sources.

1. *Particulate*

The enzyme present in plastides prepared either from sugar beets, spinach or cabbage leaves, or from carrot root chromoplasts has never been purified. The specific activities of the enzyme in these organelles range from 30 to 70 milliunits/mg dry weight for carrots and sugar beets (Kates and Sastry, 1969; Galliard, 1973). These preparations were shown to contain other enzymatic activities, which also affected phospholipids, i.e., phosphatidic acid phosphatase and phospholipase C (Kates and Sastry, 1969). It has also been isolated from the particulate fraction of immature peanut seeds (mithochondria and microsomes) with a specific activity of 1.5 milliunits/mg protein (Heller *et al.,* 1968). It is worth mentioning that in the red alga (*Porphyridium cruentum* Nägeli) (which is a lower plant), the enzyme is particle bound and resisted attempts of solubilization and purification (Anita *et al.,* 1970).

2. *Soluble*

Much more progress has been achieved with nonparticulate fractions of plant tissue extracts. It is noteworthy to point out that during the process of extensive purification, losses of enzymatic activity were encountered, particularly at the final stages.

a. *Cabbage*

1. Initial attempts were made by Davidson and Long (1958) from the 4×10^5-*g* $\times$ min supernatant of the homogenate of the inner light-green leaves of Savoy cabbage. After heat coagulation and acetone precipitation, followed by a calcium phosphate gel step, the enzyme was reprecipitated by acetone. A 46-fold purification to a specific activity of 15 units/mg protein with an overall yield of 51% was reported. It was claimed that the calcium phosphate gel step resulted in an unstable enzyme (Davidson and Long, 1958).

2. Yang *et al.* (1967) modified the above procedure by changing the pH to 6.5 prior to the step of heat coagulation and added another final step of DEAE-cellulose chromatography. The specific activity was brought to only 11 units/mg protein and the yield was lower, i.e., 21% with a 110-fold purification. The product was also unstable, but neither the degree of purity nor the accompanying enzymatic activities were specified. The possibility of the removal of a natural inhibitor during the course of the purification, the presence of which was first suggested by Kates (1954), was also raised here.

3. Another modification of Davidson and Long's procedure was reported by Dawson and Hemington (1967), who repeated it up to the first acetone precipitation (a stable enzyme preparation having a specific activity of 2 units/mg protein) and introduced a glycerol density gradient electrophoresis step at pH 5. An unstable enzyme peak, representing 80 to 90% of the applied activity but with unspecified amounts of protein was obtained, which had to be stabilized by serum albumin to prevent inactivation. In this case too, neither specific activity nor the presence of contaminating proteins was reported.

b. Cottonseeds

1. The enzyme was originally purified to some extent by Tookey and Balls (1956) from defatted cottonseed meal by extracting, then precipitating by NaCl, and finally a second extraction was followed by a calcium phosphate gel step. An 86-fold purification to a specific activity of 27 or 57 milliunits/mg protein was obtained. Since the yields were higher than 100% a removal of an inhibitor was proposed. The partially purified enzyme was not very stable.

2. A more detailed and thorough procedure was recently introduced by Mady'arov (1976) and Rakhimov *et al.* (1976a) using acetone powders of cottonseed meal. The meal was extracted at pH 8 and chromatographed in succession through DEAE-cellulose I, Sephadex G-100 (or G-200), DEAE-cellulose II, and again Sephadex G-200. Although acidification to pH 6.0 plus incubation at 50°C increased the activity at a very early stage, the enzyme was more stable at pH 8.0 at the more advanced stage of the purification. Two forms of the enzyme were eluted either from the ion exchanger or molecular sieve. The final product had a specific activity of 7 units/mg protein, which represents a 175-fold purification, but the yield was very low (1%). The possibility of a size transformation leading to the formation of enzyme molecules devoid of catalytic activity was suggested to explain both the lability and low recoveries of the activity. This possibility is very attractive, especially in view of the fact that this enzyme has been brought very close to homogeneity.

c. Peanut Seeds. A homogeneous phospholipase D was purified from the cytosol of dry or germinating peanut seeds by a sequence which included $(NH_4)_2SO_4$ precipitation, DEAE-cellulose, and gel filtration either through Sephadex G-200 (Tzur and Shapiro, 1972) or through Sepharose 6B, followed by preparative disc gel electrophoresis on polyacrylamid (Heller *et al.,* 1974, 1975). The Tzur-Shapiro procedure concentrated the enzyme 1170-fold to a specific activity of 234 units/mg protein with a 36% yield. At this stage the enzyme was 20% pure. By the alternative procedure, the phospholipase D was separated completely from the other proteins and was thus brought to homogeneity. Due to molecular size transformation and lability of the active enzyme in dilute solutions, considerable losses were encountered, and a reproducible specific activity was not reported.

B.   MICROORGANISMS

The phospholipase D from a microbial source *(Corynebacterium ovis)* degrades sphingomyelin and lyso lecithin (Souček *et al.,* 1971). Using a combination of $(NH_4)_2SO_4$ and methanol precipitation followed by CM-Sephadex chromatography, the enzyme, which is secreted by the microorganism into the cultivation medium, was concentrated 176-fold to a specific activity of 2.65 units/mg protein with a yield of 37.5%. The enzyme also seems to be unstable. However, the degree of purity or the presence of foreign enzymes were not reported.

C.   MAMMALIA

Only particulate enzymes have been hitherto described from animal sources.

1.   *Human Eosinophils*

An extract, obtained from human leukocyte fraction enriched with eosinophils, following freezing, thawing, and ultrasonic irradiation, was chromatographed on DEAE-cellulose, Sephadex G-100 and CM-cellulose. A 162-fold concentration with a specific activity of about 3 units/mg protein, with a 40% overall yield was obtained. Isoelectric focusing revealed one band with phospholipase D activity and four bands of other proteins (Kater *et al.,* 1976).

2.   *Rat Brain Microsomes*

The procedure was developed for the enzyme catalyzing the Ca^{2+}-stimulated base exchange: 22- to 29-day-old rat brain microsomes were solubilized by a mixture of two ionic detergents (0.8% Miranol H2M and 0.5% sodium cholate), then fractionated with $(NH_4)_2SO_4$, chromatographed on Sepharose 4B and DEAE-cellulose. A 159-fold purified enzyme, having a specific activity of 0.84 milliunits/mg protein, was obtained. The enzyme required the presence of glycerol for stabilization (T. Taki and J. N. Kanfer, personal communication).

V. Characteristics of the Catalytic Protein

Meaningful information regarding the specific features of phospholipase D could not be obtained until a complete purification of the enzyme to homogeneity had been achieved. With only a few examples available, some data have been accumulated.

A. MOLECULAR WEIGHT

1. A molecular weight of 71,000 ± 3,000 for the soluble cottonseed enzyme was established by gel filtration on Sephadex G-200 or by disc gel electrophoresis. Bands from the gel retained their catalytic activity. During the purification process, the enzyme molecules of this size aggregated to heavier forms, but still retained enzymatic activity. The disc gel electrophoresis was carried out without detergents or reducing agents, thus no final evidence for a minimal molecular weight is available (Mady'arov, 1976).

2. A molecular weight of 200,000 ± 10,000 of fresh solutions of the native, soluble, and catalytically active phospholipase D from peanut seeds was determined by gel filtration on Sepharose 6B. A minimal weight of 22,000 ± 3,000 was obtained by sedimentation equilibrium ultracentrifugation at either acidic, neutral, or alkaline conditions. Longer runs on the ultracentrifuge reduced the molecular size. Similar values were also attained by sedimentation velocity ultracentrifugation studies. Disc gel electrophoresis using SDS polyacrylamide or analytical ultracentrifugation in the presence of 8 M urea yielded two sets of molecular weights: one in the range of 46,000 to 50,000 and the other at about 98,000. The identification of several molecular sizes suggested a possible oligomer formation having a molecular weight of 200,000 and being composed of monomers of 20,000 to 25,000 daltons (Heller *et al.,* 1974, 1977).

3. The partially purified enzyme from human eosinophils displayed a molecular weight value of approximately 60,000 based on Sephadex G-100 gel filtration studies. However, the enzyme was still in an impure state, and molecular sieving was the only method used (Kater *et al.,* 1976).

4. The bacterial enzyme obtained from filtrate of *Corynebacterium pseudotuberculosis (ovis)* was partially purified, and from gel filtration data using Sephadex G-200, the authors calculated a molecular weight of around 90,000 (Souček *et al.,* 1971).

B.   Enzyme Composition

Fragmentary evidence has been accumulating on the amino acid composition, N-terminal amino acid, lipid content, and other details.

1. The pure cottonseed enzyme has glutamic acid at its amino acid -NH$_2$ terminus. Since it was the only one, it was concluded that only one type of polypeptide chain exists (Mady'arov, 1976).

2. Total hydrolysis of the pure peanut enzyme revealed the amino acid composition (Table I). The distribution of the amino acids was as follows: 30% acidic, 30–40% hydrophobic, and 10% basic. Only traces of tryptophan and no measureable SH groups were detected. Glycine was the only acid at the N-terminus and therefore, only one type of peptide is suspected. A partial molar volume of 0.7 cm^3/g was calculated from the amino acid composition. The enzyme does not seem to have bound lipids (Heller *et al.*, 1974).

C.   Stability

1. The relative thermostability of the soluble enzyme from cabbage leaves was employed to denature other proteins during the process of purification by warming to 55°C for 5 min. At the highest stage of purity, the enzyme was highly unstable, even when stored at −15°C (Davidson and

Table I

Amino Acid Composition of Purified
Phospholipase D from Peanut Seeds

Amino acid	moles/100 moles [a]
Glutamic acid	16.02
Aspartic acid	12.44
Glycine	9.49
Alanine	9.49
Leucine	8.08
Valine	7.07
Lysine	5.65
Isoleucine	5.14
Proline	4.93
Arginine	4.73
Phenylalanine	4.37
Threonine	4.16
Serine	3.52
Tyrosine	2.67
Histidine	2.22

[a] Results of analysis after hydrolysis for 24 hours at 110°C (from Heller *et al.*, 1974).

Long, 1958) or when kept at 0–4°C for 1 week, during which time it lost about 50% of its activity (Yang *et al.,* 1967). It was found most stable at pH values between 6.5 and 7.0 (Yang *et al.,* 1967). In Dawson and Hemington hands the most purified enzyme adsorbed irreversibly to glass surfaces. Serum albumin prevented this adsorption and also protected it from loss of activity over a period of several months at −15°C (Dawson and Hemington, 1967).

2. The decrease in the activity of the cottonseed phospholipase D during purification was explained by Mady'arov (1976) as a consequence of an equilibrium process in which the catalytically active protein oligomer is undergoing changes in its molecular size, devoid of enzymatic activity, and therefore escapes detection. Differences in thermal stability were encountered between the soluble and the silica-gel-immobilized phospholipase D. The soluble enzyme lost activity gradually at 50°C until a plateau at 40% of initial value was reached after 60 min. The immobilized enzyme was more sensitive and lost activity completely within 45 min. Also, the soluble enzymes' maximal activity was at 45°C (pH 5.6) whereas the immobilized enzymes' maximal activity was at 30°C (pH 5.6 or 7.5) (Rakhimov *et al.,* 1976a).

3. Concentrated solutions of the peanut enzyme are stable at 4°C and pH > 7.4. Addition of 0.5 M glycerol or 3–4 M $(NH_4)_2SO_4$ can also stabilize the enzyme. Dry powders could be stored for long periods at either 4°C or −20°C. The enzyme is extremely sensitive to acidic pH values and loses activity rapidly even at or close to its catalytic optimum at pH 5.6.

Under these conditions it undergoes rapid and irreversible inactivation which cannot be prevented by raising the pH or by adding ultrasonically irradiated suspensions of lecithin either with or without Ca^{2+} ions (Heller *et al.,* 1974, 1975). The instability also seems to be associated with transformations in the molecular size of the catalytic protein from an active form of about 200,000 daltons to smaller aggregates (Heller *et al.,* 1974, 1975, 1976, 1977). The enzyme is not particularly thermostable; although it withstood warming to 45°C for 10 min, it was inactivated at 55°C or higher (Heller *et al.,* 1975). It is very sensitive to surfactants, and incubation of the partially purified enzyme with serum albumin caused its inactivation (Tzur and Shapiro, 1972), and with β lipoproteins caused strong inhibition (Heller and Arad, 1970).

4. The enzyme from *C. ovis* is stable both in the crude stage, when present in the extracellular supernatant or even in the partially purified state, when stored at 4°C. Losses of activity occurred only when the purification passed beyond the step of CM-Sephadex chromatography (it could be stabilized by albumin or neopepton) (Souček *et al.,* 1971). The enzymatic activity of the cardiolipin specific phospholipase D from *H. parainfluenza* decreased by 98% at 60°C for 60 min, but the crude enzyme could

be stored at $-20°C$ for several months without loss of activity (Ono and White, 1970b).

D. ISOELECTRIC POINT

The pure enzyme from peanut seeds had a pI of 4.65 which was determined either by isoelectric focusing or by elution from a DEAE-cellulose column (Heller *et al.,* 1974). The pI of a crude extract from human eosinophiles was 4.8 to 5.0, but on further purification, a higher value of 5.8 to 6.2 was obtained (Kater *et al.,* 1976).

E. KINETIC DATA

Determinations of parameters related to concentrations or changes in concentrations of the substrate, in a range in which most of these substrates do not form true solutions, has to be considered with some reservations. Thus the true meaning of the K_m values shown in Table II may be different from the classical definitions. The reader is referred to the excellent critical discussions by Brockerhoff (1974), Brockerhoff and Jensen (1974) and to that of Verger and de Haas (1976).

VI. Occurrence, Distribution, and Some Developmental Aspects

Contrardi and Ercoli (1933) speculated on the existence of an enzyme having phospholipase D activity, although its occurrence was demonstrated unknowingly and indirectly several years earlier when Chibnall and Channon isolated phosphatidic acid from cabbage leaves (1927). Actual enzymatic activity was shown by Hanahan and Chaikoff (1947a,b, 1948) who repeated earlier studies more systematically and suggested that the original observations on the existence of phosphatidic acid in cabbage leaves were based on artifacts resulting from a hydrolytic process degrading phospholipids during the extraction of these leaves.

The enzyme was detected in two forms, depending on the source, developmental stage, and method of isolation: (a) a particulate enzyme, bound to subcellular organelles of plant tissues, and (b) a soluble form, nonsedimentable from homogenates following high-speed centrifugation. The "solubility" of the enzyme does not exclude its association with intracellular, labile organelles which might or do undergo disruption during homogenization, and release components into the solution. Such a possibility was raised by Galliard (1973) and was based on an observation in which a high specific activity of phospholipase D in a particulate fraction was isolated by density gradient centrifugation from floret tissues of cauliflower. These fractions banded at areas with densities equivalent to those of microsomes and lysosomes, with a relatively higher specific activity in the latter. Supporting data for such distribution however, were not reported (Clermont, 1972).

A. PLANTS

Kates (1954) has separated homogenates of carrot roots or sugar beets and spinach or cabbage leaves into particulate plastid fraction and soluble cytoplasm by high-speed centrifugation and found the phospholipase D in association with the particulate fractions only. The cytoplasmic fractions were virtually inactive and were also inhibitory. On the other hand, Davidson and Long (1958) reported that the enzyme was present in both soluble and particle-bound forms in homogenates of cabbage leaves. Quarles and Dawson (1969a), in their survey on the distribution of phospholipase D in plants, claim that they were unable to detect activity in the chloroplast fraction or any other particulate matter. The cabbage leaves were either ground with sand or homogenized in a Waring Blendor. Acker *et al.* (1952) were unable to detect the enzymatic activity under similar conditions in press juices of spinach leaves, and in the case of carrot roots it was very much dependent on the variety. The discrepancy was explained by the differences in the developmental stages of the plants, in addition to the selection of the species. Attempts to solubilize the plant particulate enzyme, not to mention purification, have been unsuccessful. The particle-bound enzyme from mammalian origin, on the other hand, has been solubilized by detergents and was partially purified (T. Taki and J. N. Kanfer, personal communication).

The soluble form of phospholipase D was found initially by Tookey and Balls (1956) in latex serum of *Hevea brasiliensis* (Smith, 1954), and in cottonseeds or cabbage leaves. In the latter experiments, the solubility was defined as a material that does not sediment at $26,360 \times g$ for 20 min. Higher activities of phospholipase D were reported by Acker and Bücking (1956) in extracts of barley malt, using an assay system in which activity was measured by the release of free choline. This system is an excellent example of selection of an assay system without checking it, because the formation of choline was misleading, having resulted from the combined action of a highly active, soluble phospholipase B and a soluble phosphodiesterase. The first enzyme removed both fatty acids forming glycerophosphorylcholine which was subsequently degraded by the phosphodiesterase.

Table II

APPARENT K_m VALUES AND THE CONDITIONS OF THEIR DETERMINATION

Source of enzyme [a]	Substrate and reaction [b]	Activators	pH	Temperature (°C)	K_m (M) [c]	Reference
Spinach leaves (P)	Phosphatidylcholine (egg yolk) (H)	Ether	4.7	25	1.30×10^{-2}	Kates, 1954
Carrot roots (S)	Phospholipids (soybeans) (H)	Ether; Ca^{2+}	5.5	30	1.00×10^{-2}	Einset and Clark, 1958
Cabbage leaves (S)	Phospholipid (mixture) (H)	NaCl	5.9	25	2.10×10^{-2}	Tookey and Balls, 1956
Savoy cabbage leaves (S)	1-Monoacylphosphatidylcholine (H)	Ca^{2+}	5.8	38	1.50×10^{-4}	Long et al., 1967a
Cabbage leaves (S)	Phosphatidylcholine (H)	Ether; Ca^{2+}	5.6	37	1.50×10^{-3}	Saito et al., 1974
Cabbage leaves (S)	Phosphatidylcholine-ethanolamine (T)	Ether; Ca^{2+}	9.0	37	1.25×10^{-3}	Saito et al., 1974
Cabbage leaves (S)	Phosphatidylcholine-choline (T)	Ether; Ca^{2+}	9.0	37	2.50×10^{-3}	Saito et al., 1974
Peanut seeds (P)	Phosphatidylcholine (H)	Ether; Ca^{2+}	5.7	25	6.30×10^{-4}	Heller et al., 1968
Peanut seeds (S)	Phosphatidylcholine (H)	Ether; Ca^{2+}	5.7	25	1.25×10^{-2}	Heller et al., 1968
Peanut seeds (S)	Phosphatidylcholine (H)	Ultrasonics; Ca^{2+}	5.7	25	3.38×10^{-3}	Heller et al., 1968
Rat brain microsomes (S*)	Phosphatidylcholine (H)	Ca^{2+}	6.0	37	8.33×10^{-4}	Saito and Kanfer, 1975
Rat brain microsomes (S*)	Phosphatidylcholine-ethanolamine (T)	Ca^{2+}	7.2	37	1.33×10^{-5}	Saito et al., 1975
Rat brain microsomes (S*)	Phosphatidylcholine-serine (T)	Ca^{2+}	7.2	37	4.33×10^{-5}	Saito et al., 1975
Rat brain microsomes (S*)	Phosphatidylcholine-choline (T)	Ca^{2+}	7.2	37	6.75×10^{-4}	Saito et al., 1975

			pH	°C	K_m	Reference
Rat brain microsomes (P)	Phosphatidylcholine-choline (T)	Ca^{2+}	7.2	37	1.69×10^{-4}	Saito *et al.*, 1975
Corynebacterium ovis (S)	1-Monoacylphosphatidylcholine (H)	Ca^{2+}	8.0	37	8.30×10^{-3}	Souček *et al.*, 1971
Corynebacterium ovis (S)	Sphingomyelin (H)	Ultrasonics	8.0	37	6.20×10^{-3}	Souček *et al.*, 1971
Red alga (*Porphyridium cruentum*) (Son)	Phosphatidylcholine (H)	Ca^{2+}	7.0	35	6.60×10^{-4}	Antia *et al.*, 1970
Hemophilus parainfluenza (Son)	Diphosphatidyl glycerol (cardiolipin) (H)	Triton X-100; Mg^{2+}	7.5–8.0	37	2.4×10^{-4}	Ono and White, 1970b

[a] P = particulate; S = soluble; S* = solubilized by detergents; Son = ultrasonics.
[b] H = hydrolysis; T = transfer.
[c] K_m values are only apparent.

$$
\begin{array}{l}
H_2C-O-\overset{\overset{O}{\|}}{C}-(CH_2)_n-R \\[2pt]
R-(CH)_n-\overset{\overset{O}{\|}}{C}-O-\overset{|}{C}-H \\[2pt]
H_2C-O-\overset{\overset{O}{\|}}{\underset{\underset{O_-}{|}}{P}}-O-CH_2CH_2\overset{+}{N}(CH_3)_3
\end{array}
\xrightarrow{\text{phospholipase B}}
$$

$$
\begin{array}{l}
H_2C-OH \\[2pt]
HO-\overset{|}{C}-H \\[2pt]
H_2C-O-\overset{\overset{O}{\|}}{\underset{\underset{O^-}{|}}{P}}-O-CH_2CH_2\overset{+}{N}(CH_3)_3
\end{array}
\quad + \; 2R(CH_2)_nCOO^-
$$

(3)

$$
\begin{array}{l}
H_2C-OH \\[2pt]
HO-\overset{|}{C}-H \\[2pt]
H_2C-O-\overset{\overset{O}{\|}}{\underset{\underset{O_-}{|}}{P}}-O-CH_2CH_2\overset{+}{N}(CH_3)_3
\end{array}
\xrightarrow{\text{phosphodiesterase}}
$$

(4)

$$
\begin{array}{l}
H_2C-OH \\[2pt]
HO-\overset{|}{C}-H \\[2pt]
H_2C-\overset{\overset{O}{\|}}{\underset{\underset{O_-}{|}}{P}}-OH \; + \; HOCH_2CH_2\overset{+}{N}(CH_3)_3
\end{array}
$$

The apparent result mimicked the action of a phospholipase D. Further examinations by Acker and his associates showed that the extracts contained low activities of phospholipase D and most of the enzyme was actually particulate. The extent of the differences in the activities of both phospholipases varies with the developmental stages of the barley. The mature, dormant barley corn content of phospholipase D was high and that of phospholipase B, low. Furthermore, homogenization has brought up the fact that the barley corn phospholipase D was in fact particle bound (Acker and Ernst, 1954; Acker and Bücking, 1956; Acker and Müller, 1965; Nolte and Acker, 1975a).

A superficial survey of 10 common vegetables showed that their filtered homogenates contained a Ca^{2+}-dependent phospholipase D with rutabaga, carrot, and beet taking the lead (Einset and Clark, 1958). A more thorough survey on the distribution of phospholipase D was done in 11 plants. Both the presence and the actual activity were determined using only a limited portion of the plant (either the leaves, the roots or the bulbs, or the seeds or the globes only). The conclusion drawn from this survey was that leaves of savoy cabbages or brussels sprouts had the highest, whereas the onion bulbs the lowest activities (42 milliunits/mg dry weight and 0.3 milliunits/mg dry weight, respectively). Intermediate values between these two extremes were quoted for leaves of turnip, lettuce, potato, and parsley; roots of carrots, globes of beet roots, and seeds of peas (Davidson and Long, 1958).

More systematic and comprehensive studies were undertaken by Quarles and Dawson (1969a) who have compared the distribution and quantitative content of the enzyme in 24 plants, exploring the activity in subcellular fractions from individual tissues of the same species, and also the changes occurring during development. Highest activities were recorded for various swollen storage tissues such as the central stalk of the cabbage, leaf stalk of the celery, stem of Kohl-rabi, flower of cauliflower, carrot roots, and the seeds of peas or marrows. Other rich sources discovered or rediscovered were the seeds of peanuts (Heller *et al.,* 1968) and cotton (Mady'arov, 1976). However, the generalization about the swollen storage tissues should be taken with some reservation, because many such tissues, including fruits and seeds as well as potato tubers, exhibited either very low enzymatic activity or none at all (Quarles and Dawson, 1969a).

A major extension of the preceding survey was carried out by a Russian group on extracts of some 206 species belonging to 49 families of Far Eastern plants (Vaskovsky *et al.,* 1972). The huge enterprise examined the extracts of leaves, stalks, and roots, using standard assay conditions which included deoxycholate as an activator. They have not reported on the situation in other plant tissues (e.g., seeds), neither have they looked into changes occurring during growth or other developmental stages. Most of the data was presented as qualitative or semiquantitative results, with the exception of 10 families, covering 15 species, which was presented in a form of activities and specific activities.

Unlike most of the hydrolytic or transfer enzymes in seeds, phospholipase D in pea cotyledons decreased during germination and growth (Quarles and Dawson, 1969a). An opposing observation was made in peanut seeds in which subcellular location and pattern of phospholipase D activities during germination and growth appeared to be "normal" (Heller *et al.,* 1968). Homogenates of immature peanut seeds contained only 5% activity of the dry seeds, most of which appeared to be associated with particles (mitochondria and microsomes). Upon maturation, the seed loses water, its metabolic activities decrease, and its phospholipase D localization shifts almost exclusively to the soluble portion, with a tremendous increase

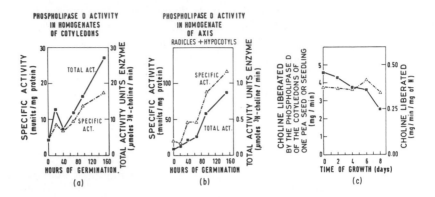

FIG. 1.   Phospholipase D activity during developmental changes. Activity in (a) homogenates of cotyledons and (b) axial tissue of germinating peanut seeds (from Heller *et al.*, 1968). (c) Loss of phospholipase D from cotyledons during growth of the pea plant (■: total activity/seed or seedling; △: activity/mg N in cotyledons). From Quarles and Dawson (1969a).

in the activity. Furthermore, upon imbibition, followed by germination, and growth in the dark, the activity of the enzyme in both the cotyledons and axial tissues rise rapidly (Heller *et al.*, 1968). (Fig. 1).

B.   MICROORGANISMS

Although phospholipase D was first detected in higher plants, and for many years has been considered to be unique there, recent studies have demonstrated phospholipase D activities in other types of plants and in other organisms. Fossum and Höyem (1963) and Souček *et al.* (1967, 1971) have shown that the toxin of *C. ovis* is capable of hydrolyzing sphingomyelin and lysolecithin, but not lecithin, through a phospholipase D-like enzyme. Similarly, Ono and White (1970a,b), Rampini (1975), Cole *et al.* (1974), and Audet *et al.* (1975) have described a phospholipase D, highly specific for cardiolipin (diphosphatidylglycerol), in *H. parainfluenza* and *E. coli,* respectively. Extracts of red algae (*Porphyridium cruentum* Nägeli) exhibited phospholipase D activity resembling that of higher plants (Antia *et al.,* 1970). In baker yeast cells, a mitochondrial-bound phospholipase D was described, the synthesis of which is regulated by glucose repression, and thence in mitochondrial turnover (Grossman *et al.,* 1973). This enzyme has been detected by Comes and Kleining (1973) and by Yamaguchi *et al.* (1973) on examination of a large number of various fungi and showed that the species *Streptomyces hachijoensis* is capable of producing the enzyme.

C. Mammalia

The occurrence of mammalian phospholipase D was proposed some years ago by Dils and Hübscher (1961) as an explanation of their observations on the base exchange reactions, or choline incorporation into rat liver microsomal phospholipids which were stimulated by Ca^{2+}, and did not require energy. The hydrolytic activity of this enzyme has only recently been shown unequivocally when phospholipase D was solubilized and partially purified by Saito and Kanfer (1975; T. Taki and J. N. Kanfer, private communication) from rat brain microsomes. Similarly, a phospholipase D, which was not stimulated by Ca^{2+} but by Mg^{2+}, acting on alkyl and alk-1-enyl phospholipids was also described in rat brain microsomes (Wykle and Schremmer, 1974).

VII. Substrate Specificity

Phospholipase D from certain sources catalyzes the hydrolysis of a wide range of phospholipids. It has been observed that the action of a crude enzyme preparation may, under one set of conditions, be limited to a small number of phospholipids, but the specificity becomes broader if the experimental conditions are altered. In order to find out the true specificity, whether narrow (for one substrate) or broad (multiple substrates), it is mandatory to present the substrate in as many ways as possible, by varying the pH, temperature, etc. In certain cases, the enzyme has been capable of carrying out the degradation when phospholipids were added either as mixtures (i.e., Asolectin, a crude soybean phospholipid mixture) or bound to protein (e.g., serum lipoproteins or membrane bound). Thus one of the factors governing substrate specificity is its physical state. The other possibility exists that a phospholipase D preparation will have a strict specificity for only one substrate or at most two. Such is the case notably with the bacterial enzymes.

A. Plants

The basic data concerning the specificity of the enzyme toward certain substrates have been obtained with either crude, partially purified, or highly purified enzyme preparations, although not the entire spectrum of substrates has yet been examined with the most highly purified enzyme (Kates, 1956; Davidson *et al.,* 1956; Davidson and Long, 1958; Chen and Barton, 1971). Furthermore, several reports have appeared only on the extent of hydrolysis as measured by the formation of water-soluble choline, ethanolamine, or serine. In other cases, although phosphatidic acid formation was determined, the presence of phosphatidic acid phosphatase was clearly ascertained with a release of water-soluble inorganic phosphate (Kates, 1956). Also, the activities of phosphomono- and diphosphoesterases were reported in preparations of soluble cabbage enzymes (Davidson *et al.,* 1956; Davidson and Long, 1958). All these factors should be borne in mind when evaluating the specificity of phospholipase D in quantitative terms.

The insoluble enzyme from the chloroplasts of leaves or roots and the soluble enzyme from cabbage leaves were capable of hydrolyzing naturally occurring as well as synthetic phospholipids as is shown in Table III. In addition, *o*-lysine or *o*-alanine derivatives of phosphatidylglycerol (Bonsen *et al.,* 1965, 1966) were also hydrolyzed. Cardiolipin (diphosphatidylglycerol) resisted the cabbage enzyme as did phosphatidylglycerophosphate (de Haas *et al.,* 1966). This is an example of a substrate which was examined only under one set of conditions (i.e., Ca^{2+} plus ether) but not reexamined under other experimental conditions.

The plastid enzyme from cabbage required ether but not Ca^{2+}, although a crude mixture of soybean phospholipids (asolectin) was degraded even without ether (Kates, 1956). The soluble cabbage enzyme requires both ether at Ca^{2+} or ether-chloroform, ethanol-chloroform, or sodium dodecylsulfate (Davidson *et al.,* 1956; Davidson and Long, 1958; Chen and Barton, 1971; Dawson and Hemington, 1967). In addition to diacylglycerophospholipids, the monoacylglycerophosphorylcholine (lysolecithin), the 1-alkenyl-2-acylglycerophospholipids (plasmalogens) as well as the dialkyl derivatives of glycerophospholipids [1,2-ditetradecyl,-1,2-dihexadecyl-,1,2-dioctadecyl-*sn*-glycero-3-phosphorylcholines] were degraded by the soluble cabbage enzyme (Davidson *et al.,* 1956; Davidson and Long, 1958; Chen and Barton, 1971). Phospholipase D from cabbage and carrots hydrolyzed various synthetic 1-alkyl-2-acyl- and 1-alkenyl-2-acyl-*sn*-glycero-3-phosphorylcholines at rates one-tenth to one-third that of the 1,2-diacylphosphatidylcholines (Waku and Nakazawa, 1972). The hydrolysis of phosphatidyl inositol has not been demonstrated with phospholipase D (cf. Galliard, 1973, 1975). The soluble PLD, prepared according to Yang *et al.* (1967) from cabbage and incubated with rat liver microsomes resulted in the hydrolysis of PC, PS, and PE, and the phosphatidic acid formed remained bound to the microsomal membrane (Kapoor *et al.,* 1974).

The soluble enzyme from peanut seeds has also a broad specificity. Aqueous dispersions of various phospholipids in the presence of the appropriate activators, or else as constituents of certain lipoproteins (e.g., red cell membranes), were degraded by the enzyme: phosphatidylcholine, ethanolamine, serine, glycerol, or diphosphatidylglycerol-cardiolipin (the last one only in the absence of ether or in the presence of deoxycholate).

Hydrolysis of pure sphingomyelin by peanut seeds enzyme either in the presence of Triton X-100 or SDS was not detected. However, it has occurred by cabbage enzyme (Negishi *et al.,* 1971). A quantitative examination of sphingomyelin disappearance from rat liver microsomes incubated with the enzyme did not confirm earlier qualitative observations, and the lipid remained intact (Heller *et al.,* 1968, 1974, 1975, 1976; Heller and Arad, 1970; Roelofsen and van Deenen, 1973; Tzur and Shapiro, 1972). 1-Monoacylglycerophosphorylcholine (1-lysolecithin) was slowly degraded by the partially purified peanut enzyme (Strauss *et al.,* 1976).

The possibility of having more than one phospholipase D with a stringent requirement for substrate was initially raised by Lands and Hart (1965) who reported that phospholipids containing alkenyl, acyl derivatives of glycerophosphorylcholine or glycerophosphorylethanolamine (choline or ethanolamine plasmalogens) from beef heart treated with the soluble cabbage enzyme were degraded with the exception of the choline plasmalogen (cf. also Hill and Lands, 1970). In contrast, freshly prepared chloroplast phospholipase D from the same source hydrolyzed the choline plasmalogen but not the ethanolamine plasmalogen in a natural mixture obtained from different heart tissues (Hack and Ferrans, 1959). Similarly, freshly prepared, soluble cabbage leaf enzyme degraded synthetic choline plasmalogens to the extent of about 40% in 20 hours (Slotboom *et al.,* 1967). These results might partially satisfy Lands' proposal for the existence of "isophospholipase D" in cabbage leaves, which, however, might be due to differences in the species or variants.

B. Microorganisms

The discovery of phospholipase D activities in certain microorganisms with the ability to catalyze the cleavage of only one or mostly two phospholipids might be the answer to Lands' hypothesis. Thus, the enzyme in the endotoxin of *C. ovis* was the first phospholipase D described to remove choline from sphingomyelin either in the pure form or bound to serum lipoproteins or erythrocyte membranes. Although it also acted upon 1-acylglycerophosphorylcholine (1-lysolecithin), it did not degrade any other glycerophospholipid whether in a pure form or protein bound, and neither Ca^{2+} nor an activator (e.g., ether) was necessary for its action. This observation rules out the possibility that the peanut enzyme did not hydrolyze sphingomyelin because of its physical properties in an aqueous environment (Souček *et al.,* 1967, 1971).

Another phospholipid-specific phospholipase D was obtained from ultrasonically irradiated cells of *H. parainfluenza,* with a remarkable specificity for diphosphatidylglycerol (cardiolipin). The Mg^{2+}-activated enzyme did

Table III

Substrate Specificity and Comparative Rates by Cabbage Phospholipase D

Preparation	Activators	Substrate	Hydrolysis rate	Reference
			Relative [a]	
I. Soluble, partially purified	Ether; Ca^{2+}	Phosphatidylcholine (egg yolk)	Fast	Davidson and Long, 1958
	Ether; Ca^{2+}	Phosphatidylcholine (egg yolk, hydrogenated)	Moderate	Davidson and Long, 1958
	Ether; Ca^{2+}	Phosphatidylcholine, di-C$_{14}$, L-α	Fast	Davidson and Long, 1958
	Ether; Ca^{2+}	Phosphatidylcholine, di-C$_{16}$, DL-α	Fast	Davidson and Long, 1958
	Ether; Ca^{2+}	Phosphatidylcholine, di-C$_{18}$, DL-α	Moderate	Davidson and Long, 1958
	Ether; Ca^{2+}	Phosphatidylcholine, di-C$_{18}$, β	Slow	Davidson and Long, 1958
	Ether; Ca^{2+}	1-Monacylphosphatidylcholine	Moderate	Davidson and Long, 1958
	Ether; Ca^{2+}	Phosphatidylethanolamine (ox brain)	Moderate	Davidson and Long, 1958
	Ether; Ca^{2+}	Phosphatidylethanolamine (egg yolk)	Slow	Davidson and Long, 1958
	Ether; Ca^{2+}	Phosphatidylethanolamine, di-C$_{14}$, DL-α	Slow	Davidson and Long, 1958
	Ether; Ca^{2+}	Phosphatidylethanolamine, di-C$_{14}$, β	Slow	Davidson and Long, 1958
	Ether; Ca^{2+}	Sphingomyelin	Slow	Davidson and Long, 1958
	Ether; Ca^{2+}	Phosphatidylglycerol (spinach leaves)	Moderate	Haverkate and van Deenen, 1964
	Ether; Ca^{2+}	Choline plasmalogen (beef heart)	Zero	Lands and Hart, 1965
	Ether; Ca^{2+}	Choline plasmalogen, 1-C$_{16}$, 2-C$_{18:1}$	Slow	Slotboom et al., 1967
			μmoles/min	
II. Chloroplasts, crude	Ether [b]	Phosphatidylcholine (egg yolk)	1.00	Kates, 1956
	Ether [b]	Phosphatidylcholine (egg yolk)	1.40	Kates, 1956
	Ether	Phosphatidylcholine (egg yolk, hydrogenated)	0.50	Kates, 1956
	Ether	Phosphatidylcholine (yeast)	1.00	Kates, 1956
	Ether	Phosphatidylcholine (yeast, hydrogenated)	1.05	Kates, 1956
	Ether	Phosphatidylcholine, di-C$_{14}$, L-α	1.18	Kates, 1956
	Ether	Phosphatidylcholine, di-C$_{16}$, L-α	1.48	Kates, 1956
	Ether	Phosphatidylcholine, di-C$_{16:1}$, L-α	0.64	Kates, 1956
	Ether		0.17	Kates, 1956

		Rate	Reference
Ether	Phosphatidylcholine, di-C$_{18:1}$, L-α	1.15	Kates, 1956
Ether	1-Monoacylphosphatidylcholine (egg)	0.26	Kates, 1956
Ether	1-Monoacylphosphatidylcholine, mono-C$_{18}$	0	Kates, 1956
Ether	1-Monoacylphosphatidylcholine, mono-C$_{18:1}$	0	Kates, 1956
Ether	Phosphatidylethanolamine, di-C$_{14}$, L-α	0.12	Kates, 1956
Ether	Phosphatidylserine, di-C$_{14}$, L-α	0.04	Kates, 1956
Ether	Phospholipid mixture (soybean)[c]		
	Phosphatidylcholine	0.19	Kates, 1956
Ether	Phosphatidylethanolamine	0.11	Kates, 1956
Ether	Phosphatidylserine	0.02	Kates, 1956
—	Phosphatidylcholine	0.12	Kates, 1956
—	Phosphatidylserine	0.003	Kates, 1956
Ether	Choline plasmalogen (beef heart)	Moderate	Hack and Ferrans, 1959
Ether	Ethanolamine plasmalogen (beef heart)	Zero	Hack and Ferrans, 1959
III. Soluble, partially purified			
Ether:chloroform (10:1); Ca^{2+}	Phosphatidylcholine (egg)	0.92	Chen and Barton, 1971
Ether:chloroform (10:1); Ca^{2+}	Phosphatidylcholine (egg, hydrogenated)	0.145	Chen and Barton, 1971
Ether:chloroform (10:1); Ca^{2+}	Dialkylphosphatidylcholine, C$_{14}$, L-α	0.055	Chen and Barton, 1971
Ether:chloroform (10:1); Ca^{2+}	Dialkylphosphatidylcholine, C$_{16}$, L-α	0.034	Chen and Barton, 1971
Ether:chloroform (10:1); Ca^{2+}	Dialkylphosphatidylcholine, C$_{18}$, L-α	0.024	Chen and Barton, 1971
SDS; Ca^{2+}	Dialkylphosphatidylcholine, C$_{14}$, L-α	0.117	Chen and Barton, 1971
SDS; Ca^{2+}	Dialkylphosphatidylcholine, C$_{16}$, L-α	0.03	Chen and Barton, 1971
SDS; Ca^{2+}	Dialkylphosphatidylcholine, C$_{18}$, L-α	0.023	Chen and Barton, 1971
IV. Soluble, purified			
SDS; Ca^{2+}	Phosphatidylcholine (egg)	0.083	Dawson and Hemington, 1967
SDS; Ca^{2+}	Phosphatidylethanolamine (egg)	0.02	Dawson and Hemington, 1967

[a] Fast: ≥ 6 μmoles/hour; moderate: ≥ 3 μmoles/hour; slow: < 3 μmoles/hour.
[b] No Ca^{2+} was added; virtually no activity without ether.
[c] A commercial product containing a mixture of choline, ethanolamine, and serine phospholipids at a molar ratio of 9.3:9.8:1.

not degrade phosphatidylethanolamine, glycerol, serine; or a mixture of phosphatidylcholine, di- and monomethylethanolamine; nor ceramidephosphorylglycerol or glycerophosphate; nor ceramide phosphorylethanolamine (Ono and White, 1970a,b).

A very similar enzyme was described in two strains of *E. coli*. In the cell free extracts of *E. coli* B, a cardiolipin-specific phospholipase D was obtained which required both Mg^{2+} and ATP for activity, but did not hydrolyze phosphatidylethanolamine or phosphatidylglycerol (Cole *et al.,* 1974). In *E. coli* K-12, a similar enzymatic activity was indirectly invoked when the organism was transferred from a deficient medium to a normal medium (Rampini, 1975).

C. MAMMALIA

In mammals, a rat brain microsomal Mg^{2+}-dependent lysophospholipase was found which hydrolyzes ethanolamine and choline from the respective 1-alkyl- or alkenylglycerophosphorylethanolamine or choline (Wykle and Schremmer, 1974). The very same tissue revealed an interesting observation which supports the assumption of the existence of isophospholipase D. Saito and Kanfer (1975), Saito *et al.,* (1975), and Miura and Kanfer (1976) in their studies on the Ca^{2+}-activated base exchange were able to solubilize with the aid of detergents, three separate activities, each catalyzing the exchange of a different base, viz., choline, ethanolamine, and serine. The exchange enzymatic activity has been shown by the same group to be intimately related to the hydrolytic activity (e.g., phospholipase D activity); hence, it is reasonable to assume the existence of separate enzymes, each specific for the appropriate class of phospholipids.

D. STRUCTURAL CONSIDERATIONS AND STEREOSPECIFICITY

Most of the naturally occurring phospholipids have the L-α configuration (or the *sn*-glycerol-3-phosphoryl-). Phospholipase D preparations from plants have been shown to be nonspecific. The cabbage phospholipase D has been employed in the elucidation of the structures of both the naturally occurring and the synthetic phosphatidyl glycerols, as well as their respective aminoacyl esters, i.e., *o*-lysyl or *o*-alanyl phosphatidylglycerols (Haverkate and van Deenen, 1964). It was also applied for the product formed *de novo* by sheep brain mitochondria from L-α-glycerophosphate (*sn*-glycero-3-phosphate) and CDP-D-diglyceride (Davidson and Stanacev, 1970).

The cardiolipin-specific phospholipase D from *H. parainfluenza* enabled the determination of the specific locus on the cardiolipin molecule which is cleaved by the enzyme (Astrachan, 1973).

1. Phosphatidylglycerol

Phosphatidylglycerol was discovered in chloroplasts by Benson and Maruo (1958), although it was later found also in bacteria and animal tissues (cf. Strickland, 1973). It contains two asymmetric centers, and can therefore exist in any of four stereoisomeric forms.

The action of phospholipase D yielded water-soluble and lipid-soluble products, identified as glycerol and phosphatidic acid, respectively. The latter compound, subjected to alkaline hydrolysis (1 N KOH, 20 min, 55°C) which was shown neither to cause phosphate migration nor racemization (Kates, 1955, 1956; Long and Maguire, 1954), yielded a water-soluble product, identified as L-α-glycerophosphate, as determined quantitatively by its specific dehydrogenase.

Applying phospholipase C to the intact phospholipid also releases a glycerophosphate, which was inert to the action of the specific dehydrogenase. It was thus concluded that the diglyceride portion of phosphatidylglycerol has the L-α configuration whereas the glycerol moiety is D. Therefore, the molecule of phosphatidyl glycerol should be L-α phosphatidyl-D-glyccrol or 1,2-diacyl-*sn*-glycero-3-phosphoryl-1'-*sn*-glycerol (Haverkate and van Deenen, 1964; Davidson and Stanacev, 1970).

Phosphatidyl glycerol   Phosphatidic acid   (5)

L-α-Glycerophosphate

[The asterisk (*) represents an asymmetrical carbon.]

2. *Diphosphatidylglycerol (Cardiolipin)*

The site of action of the cardiolipin-specific phospholipase D prepared by the method of Ono and White (1970a) on a ^{32}P-labeled cardiolipin extracted from *E. coli* B has been studied. The hydroylsis products were identified as phosphatidic acid and phosphatidyl glycerol, each of which were further characterized as described in the following sequence (Astrachan, 1973):

$$
\begin{array}{l}
\text{(1)}H_2C\!-\!O\!-\!\overset{O}{\overset{\|}{C}}\!-\!R_1 \\
\text{(2)}R_2\overset{O}{\overset{\|}{C}}\!-\!O\!-\!\overset{|}{C}\!-\!H \\
\text{(3)}H_2C\!-\!O\!-\!\overset{|}{P}\!-\!O\!-\!CH_2 \\
\qquad\qquad OH
\end{array}
$$

(1')$H_2C\!-\!O\!-\!\overset{O}{\overset{\|}{P}}\!-\!O\!-\!CH_2$(3'')Cardiolipin

(2')$HO\!-\!C\!-\!H$ $H\!-\!C\!-\!O\!-\!\overset{O}{\overset{\|}{C}}\!-\!R_3$(2'')[Bis-(1,1'',2,2'' diacyl-

$R_4\!-\!C\!-\!O\!-\!CH_2$(1'')*sn*-glycero-3,3''-

phosphoryl)-1',3'-*sn*-

glycerol]

↓ phospholipase D

$$
\text{3-}sn\text{-Phosphatidyl-1'-}sn\text{-glycerol} \qquad + \qquad \text{3-}sn\text{-Phosphatidic acid} \tag{6}
$$

$R_2\overset{O}{\overset{\|}{C}}\!-\!O\!-\!C\!-\!H$ $H_2C\!-\!O\!-\!\overset{O}{\overset{\|}{C}}\!-\!R_1$ H_2COH $HO\!-\!CH$ $H_2C\!-\!O\!-\!P\!-\!O\!-\!CH_2$ OH

$+ \; R_3\overset{O}{\overset{\|}{C}}\!-\!O\!-\!C\!-\!H$ $H_2C\!-\!O\!-\!\overset{O}{\overset{\|}{C}}\!-\!R_4$ $H_2C\!-\!O\!-\!P\!-\!OH$ OH

phospholipase C ↓   [OH⁻] ↓

1,2-*sn*-Diacylglycerol   *sn*-Glycero-1-phosphate   *sn*-Glycerol-3-phosphate

$R_2\overset{O}{\overset{\|}{C}}\!-\!O\!-\!C\!-\!H$ $CH_2\!-\!O\!-\!\overset{O}{\overset{\|}{C}}\!-\!R_1$ $H_2C\!-\!OH$

$+ \; HO\!-\!C\!-\!H$ $H_2C\!-\!O\!-\!\overset{O}{\overset{\|}{P}}\!-\!OH$ OH $H_2C\!-\!OH$

$H\!-\!C\!-\!OH$ $H_2C\!-\!O\!-\!\overset{O}{\overset{\|}{P}}\!-\!OH$ OH $H_2C\!-\!OH$

VIII. Modifiers of Enzymatic Activity

A. pH

1. *Plants*

A wide range of pH optimum values of pant phospholipase D has been reported, from 6 for the enzyme in the serum of rubber latex (Smith, 1954) to 4.8 for the spinach leaves or sugar beet plastids enzyme (Kates, 1954).

The pH optimum of cabbage leaf enzymes vary as a function of the substrate, the conditions of dispersion or the type of activator employed.

Ultrasonically treated phosphatidylcholine particles were hydrolyzed optimally at a pH of 4.9, but this value shifted to 5.2 when "large" particles of that substrate were activated by ether. It could be shifted, up an additional 1.5 pH units, when long-chain anions were included as activators. Phosphatidic acid, added to large phosphatidylcholine particles, caused the optimum of the reaction to move to pH = 6.5, irrespective of the amounts of activator added. At low concentrations of sodium dodecylsulfate (SDS) (i.e., lecithin: SDS, molar ratio = 5), the optimum was pH 5.4; at higher SDS concentrations (i.e., a molar ratio up to 2) the value increased from 5.6 to 6.8, depending on the amount of hydrolysis. The pH profile curves measured under each set of conditions seemed quite sharp (Dawson and Hemington, 1967; Quarles and Dawson, 1969b). In the monolayer system, two rates of PC hydrolysis were observed: the initial slow reaction which exhibited a broad pH-hydrolysis curve with slightly elevated values at pH 6; and a fast reaction, with a sharp pH activity response and a maximum at pH 6.5 (Quarles and Dawson, 1969c). A shift in pH due to anionic amphipaths was also described using the same enzyme acting on the C_{14}–C_{18} dialkyl analogues of phosphatidylcholine. In the presence of SDS at a 1:1 molar ratio, and in the presence of Ca^{2+}, these substrates were hydrolyzed at a maximal rate when the pH of the reaction mixture was 6.5 to 7.0 (Chen and Barton, 1971).

Ether-activated hydrolysis of phosphatidylcholine by the enzyme from cottonseeds occurred most effectively at pH 5.6. Dodecylsulfate replaced the ether as an activator and at a molar ratio of PC:SDS of 10:3 shifted the optimal pH to 6.4 (Rakhimov *et al.*, 1976a). The immobilized version of the very same enzyme (adsorbed to silica gel) showed practically two pH optima (5.6 and 7.5), although the same enzyme had only one (5.6) prior to adsorption. Since the immobilized enzyme did not require activators for carrying out the catalysis, the presence of unbound enzyme was thus ruled out. However, the existence of two forms of enzyme was postulated (Rakhimov *et al.*, 1976b). The particulate phospholipase D from barley exhibited a pH shift to 6.5 due to the addition of a mixture of ether and SDS (Nolte and Acker, 1975a). In contrast to the higher plants, the phosphohydrolase from red algae, which did not require an activator or other cofactors, hydrolyzed its substrate optimally at pH 7.0 (Antia *et al.*, 1970).

2. Microorganisms

The cardiolipin-specific phospholipase D from *H. parainfluenza,* and the enzyme from *C. ovis* which cleaves sphingomyelin and monoacylphosphatidylcholine catalyzed the reactions optimally at a pH between 7.5 to

9 (Ono and White, 1970b; Souček *et al.*, 1971). The coliform cardiolipin-degrading enzyme had a very sharp pH-activity curve with an optimum at 7.0 (R. Cole and P. Proulx, personal communication).

3. *Mammalia*

Phosphatidylcholine was hydrolyzed by the human eosinophil phospholipase D in the presence of Ca^{2+} and ethanol at pH values ranging from 4.5 to 6.0 (Kater *et al.*, 1976). Similarly, the solubilized enzyme from rat brain microsomes displayed a broad curve between pH 4.5 and 8.0 with a peak at 6.0. The transphosphatidylation reaction to choline, carried out by a protein which is present in the same enzymatic preparation, had a very sharp pH optimum at 7.2, although the particulate microsomal enzyme, prior to solubilization did catalyze the reaction at pH 9.0 (Saito and Kanfer, 1975; Saito *et al.*, 1975).

B. METAL IONS

1. *Plants*

There is a strong dependence on the presence of Ca^{2+} for maximal activity of both the soluble and insoluble forms of phospholipase D, mainly with phosphatidylcholine as substrate (Davidson and Long, 1958; Davidson *et al.*, 1956; Einset and Clark, 1958). This contrasts with earlier observations made on a plastid enzyme, which was found to function well without any added calcium ions (Kates, 1953, 1954); however the discrepancy was explained by the presence of sufficient quantities of "endogenous" ion in the enzyme preparation (Davidson *et al.*, 1956; Davidson and Long, 1958; Kates, 1960). Ca^{2+} is far more effective as an activator than any other ion tested, but it did not appear indispensable. Short-term incubations of 3 minutes showed the superiority of Ca^{2+} with only Ni^{2+} being able to replace it slightly. Incubations for 2 hours revealed that a variety of cations could influence the activity of the enzyme (e.g., $Ca^{2+} > Ni^{2+} > Co^{2+} > Mg^{2+} = Mn^{2+} > Zn^{2+}$, and several monovalent cations to a lesser extent) (Einset and Clark, 1958). The purified enzyme from cabbage leaves had an absolute requirement for Ca^{2+} and displayed maximal activity at a concentration of 0.1 *M,* higher concentrations were inhibitory (Davidson and Long, 1958; Saito and Kanfer, 1975), although the commercial enzyme prepared by the same method was recently found to respond maximally at 28 m*M* or higher. The optimal concentrations of the cation were independent of the amounts of enzyme, but were proportional to the concentration of phosphatidylcholine and the optimum ratio was 15 μmoles of Ca^{2+}/μmole of ovolecithin. In accordance with the carrot enzyme of Einset and Clark (1958), the soluble cabbage enzyme could also be activated by Sr^{2+}, Ba^{2+}, or Zn^{2+} which at an optimal concentration of 0.1 M exhibited only 67%, 34%, and 12% (respectively, the capacity of Ca^{2+} (Davidson and Long, 1958). Further purified cabbage enzyme displayed an absolute dependency on Ca^{2+} with an optimum at 35–50 mM, and this cation could not be replaced by Mg^{2+}, Ba^{2+}, Sr^{2+}, or low concentration of cationic amphipaths (Dawson and Hemington, 1967). Moreover, addition of Mg^{2+} to a medium containing Ca^{2+} caused inhibition. The range of concentration at which Ca^{2+} produced its maximal effect was dependent upon the conditions of the reaction. For instance, the rate of the hydrolysis of ultrasonically irradiated phosphatidylcholine particles was dependent both on the pH and Ca^{2+} (Dawson and Hemington, 1967). Using the monolayer system, only low concentrations of Ca^{2+} (approximately 0.2 mM) were required to produce maximal activation at the pH optimum of 6.4. Here, too, Mg^{2+} was unable to replace Ca^{2+} (Quarles and Dawson, 1969c).

The peanut seed phospholipase D had an absolute requirement for Ca^{2+} and neither Mg^{2+} nor cetyltrimethylammonium bromide (a cationic detergent) could replace it (Heller *et al.*, 1968, 1975).

NaCl was shown to activate the partially purified enzyme from cottonseeds (Tookey and Balls, 1956). However, using purified phospholipase D from the same source, it has recently been shown in fact that divalent cations were essential, and that Sr^{2+} was superior to Ca^{2+} with ether as an activator, although by replacing the solvent with SDS, the reverse was true. Optimal results were obtained with 50 mM of the cations which, in the presence of ether, had the following order of activation: $Sr^{2+} > Ca^{2+} > Ba^{2+} > Mn^{2+} > Zn^{2+}$ (Rakhimov *et al.*, 1976a). Although the soluble enzyme could not perform its catalytic powers in the absence of a divalent cation, the immobilized phospholipase D, adsorbed to silica gel, was able to do so. This suggested that if the enzyme *in vivo* is, in fact, particulate, or somehow adsorbed, it could catalyze the hydrolysis even without any added activator (Rakhimov *et al.*, 1976b).

The red algal enzyme had no requirements for a cation, although 2.5 mM of either Ca^{2+}, Sr^{2+}, or Mg^{2+} could slightly stimulate the rates of substrate hydrolysis (Antia *et al.*, 1970).

2. Microorganisms

The enzymes from this kingdom do not yield consistent results. The *C. ovis* enzyme does not require a metal ion for the degradation of either sphingomyelin or lysophosphatidylcholine (Souček *et al.*, 1971). On the other hand, the cardiolipin-specific phospholipase D either from *H. para-*

influenza or *E. coli* B required Mg^{2+} at a level of 10 mM. When only 1 mM Mg^{2+} was added, other cations could further potentiate the reaction in the following decreasing order of effectivity: $Mg^{2+} > Co^{2+} > Mn^{2+} > Ca^{2+}$ (Ono and White, 1970b; Cole *et al.,* 1974).

3. *Mammalia*

Although the human eosinophil phospholipase D was assayed in the presence of 1 mM Ca^{2+}, no evidence was presented for its actual requirements (Kater *et al.,* 1976). Similarly, although Ca^{2+} was not obligatory for the detergent-solubilized enzyme from rat brain microsomes, it did stimulate at 5 m$M,$ and higher concentrations were inhibitory. Mg^{2+} could be used equally well. Essentially, since EDTA (at 12.5 mM) did not affect the hydrolysis rates, it would seem that unless the preparation contains sufficient amounts of bound Ca^{2+}, there was no need for cations at all (Saito and Kanfer, 1975). The enzyme from a similar source, which hydrolyzed 1-hexadecylglycerophosphorylethanolamine, was stimulated exclusively by 5 mM Mg^{2+}, since Ca^{2+} as well as Zn^{2+} or Mn^{2+} had no effect or were inhibitory (Wykle and Schremmer, 1974).

C. SOLVENTS

Most preparations of phospholipase D respond to the addition of organic solvents, therefore their effects have been studied in some detail. Only information regarding the gross effects will be given here, whereas the analysis of the mode of action will be presented in Section X,A).

1. *Plants*

The activities of the insoluble enzymes from plastids and the soluble forms from cabbage and carrots are stimulated by the addition of organic solvents: particularly, diethyl ether, ketones (*n*-dipropyl, methyl, pentyl), and esters (butyl acetate, ethyl butyrate) (Kates, 1957, 1960; Davidson *et al.,* 1956; Davidson and Long, 1958; Einset and Clark, 1958). Dawson and Hemington (1967) have shown that ether exerted only very limited activating effect on the hydrolysis of large particles of phosphatidylcholine (1-5 μm) by the purified enzyme from cabbage, unless two phases were formed.

Tookey and Balls (1956) were unable to show any effect of ether or other solvents on the activity of their partially purified enzyme from cottonseeds. Recent reexamination using a highly purified enzyme from the same source has, however, revealed that ether does in fact stimulate the hydrolysis of phosphatidylcholine, but in a very irregular manner. At a solvent/medium ratio of 0.1 a maximum was obtained which by increasing the ratio to 0.25 reverted to a minimum and at higher ratios, an increase was again observed. Other organic solvents such as benzene or hexane were equally effective or even better, although acetone was less stimulating (Rakhimov *et al.*, 1976a). Both the particulate and the soluble forms of the peanut seeds enzyme were activated by ether; surprisingly, acetone, which forms miscible mixtures with water, was even more effective and chloroform and petrol ether, which do not mix with water and form separate phases, were without effect (Heller *et al.*, 1968; Heller and Arad, 1970).

Ultrasonically irradiated particles of phosphatidylcholine having diameters smaller than 0.3 μm, could be hydrolyzed by phospholipase D. However, 16% (v/v) ether which formed a separate phase on the aqueous medium, increased the rates of hydrolysis up to twofold or fivefold for the cabbage and peanut seed enzymes, respectively (Dawson and Hemington, 1967; Heller and Arad, 1970).

Solvents did affect the rates of hydrolysis of phospholipids other than phosphatidylcholine. Compounds such as phosphatidyl glycerol were hydrolyzed completely by the commercial cabbage enzyme when ether was present, but it could be degraded even without ether by the peanut enzyme. However, saturating concentrations of ether doubled the rates (Heller and Arad, 1970). The dialkyl ether analogues of phosphatidylcholines are insoluble in diethyl ether and thus they were probably not hydrolyzed by the cabbage enzyme either with or without this solvent. These compounds were, however, soluble in chloroform or in a mixture of ether and chloroform at 10:1 (v/v). This solvent mixture was reported to have better stimulating properties than ether alone (Davidson and Long, 1958) and was also useful in promoting the hydrolysis, albeit at a slow rate, of the dialkyl phospholipids, and even with relatively high concentrations of the enzyme (7 mg/ml = 2.8 IU) (Chen and Barton, 1971).

Certain phospholipids such as monoacylglycerophosphorylcholine or diphosphatidylglycerol (cardiolipin) not only did not require ether or other solvents, but their hydrolysis was prevented by the solvents when either the cabbage or peanut seeds enzyme were employed (Davidson and Long, 1958; Long *et al.*, 1967a; Heller *et al.*, 1968). Similarly, the red algal phospholipase D activity was either unaffected or even slightly depressed by ether (Antia *et al.*, 1970).

2. *Microorganisms and Mammalia*

Phospholipase D from these sources either did not respond to the inclusion of ether (e.g., *C. ovis:* Souček *et al., 1971*), were not at all examined for a solvent effect (*E. coli* B: Cole *et al., 1974;* R. Cole and P. Proulx, personal communication; rat brain microsomes: Wykle and Schremmer, 1974; human eosinophils: Kater *et al., 1976*), or else lost activity following exposure to ether (*H. parainfluenza:* Ono and White, 1970b; rat brain microsomes: Saito and Kanfer, 1975).

D. DETERGENTS, SURFACTANTS, AND AMPHIPATHS

The reaction catalyzed by phospholipase D is also stimulated by anionic, cationic, and nonionic detergents, and frequently in a more vigorous and superior fashion compared to ether or other forms of activation. This is not surprising considering the type of substrates under consideration. The data are not always gathered in a systematic way, although several laboratories have attempted to approach the problem of the effects of surfactants on the reaction by a methodological approach.

1. *Anionic*

Certain amphipaths in this class cause considerable activation of the hydrolysis of phospholipids, especially phosphatidylcholine by the cabbage enzyme. A narrow range of concentrations between 10 and 40 mM of either sodium dodecylsulfate or deoxycholate stimulated the plastid enzyme, and higher concentrations inhibited the plastid enzyme (Kates, 1957, 1960). The most potent and stimulating detergents of the soluble cabbage enzyme were sodium dodecylsulfate, monocetylphosphoric acid, phosphatidic acid, and triphosphoinositide, which produced their maximal effect at a mole% of 50, 35, and 6, respectively, for the first three compounds (mole% = number of moles of the detergent/100 moles of phosphatidyl choline). SDS had a tremendous stimulatory effect on both the "large" and the "small" ultrasonically irradiated particles of phosphatidylcholine having the dimensions of 1–5 μm or 0.3 μm, respectively, and this, of course, in the presence of Ca^{2+}. The ability to activate the hydrolysis was not shared by all anionic surfactants; dicetylphosphoric acid or phosphatidylserine exhibited only a fraction of that achieved by SDS. Others, like cardiolipin, saponin, DOC, taurocholate, phosphatidylserine, or phosphatidyl inositol, had virtually no effect (Dawson and Hemington, 1967). These anionic amphipaths, which accelerated the hydrolysis of phosphatidylcholine particles in the "bulk" phase, also caused a shift of the pH optimum of the reaction, but only when a minimal threshold concentration of the detergent was attained (Quarles and Dawson, 1969a). In a monolayer spread on an aqueous surface, the rate of hydrolysis of pure phosphatidylcholine molecules could be controlled by regulating the surface pressure between 3 and 28 dyn/cm. Addition of anionic amphipaths such as phosphatidic acid at a molar ratio of substrate to activator of 2:1 in the mixed monolayer, allowed the extension of the hydrolysis to higher pressures, beyond 28 dyn/cm, up to the region of collapse pressure of the film. This effect was facilitated only with higher concentrations of Ca^{2+} (e.g., 1–40 mM, compared to 0.2 mM in the restricted range of pressures) and inclusion of certain carboxylic anions as buffers (e.g., propionate up to hexanoate or isobutyrate or isovalerate) in the subphase, together with the amphipath. Less effective than phosphatidic acid were stearoylhydrogensulfate or phosphatidyl inositol (Quarles and Dawson, 1969c). The slow hydrolysis of the dialkyl analogues of phosphatidylcholine containing C_{14}, C_{16}, or C_{18} chains, by the cabbage enzyme, required higher concentrations of SDS than for the diacyl counterparts, to promote optimal stimulation of the reaction (i.e., a molar ratio of 1:1 was required). Addition of the dialkyl analogues to mixtures of diacylphosphatidylcholine and SDS at a molar ratio of 2:1 (substrate: detergent) caused inhibition of the hydrolysis of the phosphatidylcholine (Chen and Barton, 1971).

SDS and taurocholate at phosphatidylcholine/detergent molar ratios of 2:1 and 5:4, respectively, stimulated considerably the hydrolysis of the phospholipid by the peanut seed enzyme. Phosphatidic acid and DOC were also effective (Heller *et al.,* 1968, 1975; Heller and Arad, 1970; Tzur and Shapiro, 1972). A reaction already activated by ether could be further stimulated by calcium salts of phosphatidic acid, phosphatidyl glycerol, or phosphatidyl methanol provided that the activator was present at a mole% of 4 to 8 (Heller and Arad, 1970).

Seven millimolar SDS was more effective than 5% (v/v) ether in activating the reaction catalyzed by the particulate phospholipase D from barley. However, a combination of ether and only 3.5 mM SDS activated more than each alone (Nolte and Acker, 1975a). The hydrolysis catalyzed by the cottonseed enzyme which was applied to a mixture of phosphatidylcholine and SDS at a ratio of 10:3 (on a molar basis) proceeded at three times the rate obtained with ether as activator (Rakhimov *et al.,* 1976a).

In contrast to the phospholipase D from plants which was stimulated by the anionic detergents, responses of bacterial or mammalian enzymes have been inconsistent. The reaction catalyzed by the enzyme from *H. para-*

influenza, routinely assayed in the presence of 0.7% Triton X-100, was slightly activated by 10 mM DOC, but totally inhibited by 1 mM SDS (Ono and White, 1970b). The enzyme from *E. coli* B was completely inhibited by anionic detergents (Audet *et al.,* 1975), but no data are available on the effects of these surfactants on either the mammalian enzyme or that from *C. ovis* (Saito and Kanfer, 1975; Kater *et al.,* 1976; Souček *et al.,* 1971).

2. *Cationic and Nonionic*

Cationic detergents at all concentrations completely inhibited the activity of the plant chloroplast enzymes (Kates, 1957). In general, the cationic amphipaths, such as cetyltrimethylammonium bromide (CTAB), cetylpyridinium chloride (CPC), stearoylamine, or palmitoylamine, were potent inhibitors also for the soluble cabbage enzyme. Under certain circumstances CTAB could, however, reverse the inhibition produced by an excess of anionic detergents (Dawson and Hemington, 1967). In contrast to the cabbage enzyme, the phospholipase D from peanuut seeds was activated by CTAB or by the nonionic Triton X-100, although these detergents could accelerate the rate of the reaction to only one-sixth of optimal concentrations of SDS and required 5–10 mM CTAB and 16 mM Triton X-100 (based on the formula weight). Furthermore, by analogy with the negatively charged detergents, the positively charged CTAB could further stimulate the already activated reaction due to the presence of ether (Heller and Arad, 1970). Both detergents had only a negligible effect on the soluble cottonseed enzyme (Rakhimov *et al.,* 1976a). At a final concentration of 0.1 (w/v), one nonionic detergent (Triton N-101) stimulated the reaction, another nonionic (Tween 20) and a cationic (hexadecylpyridinium chloride) inhibited the hydrolysis of cardiolipin by the enzyme from *H. parainfluenza.* These effects were additive to those of the already present one (e.g., Triton X-100 at 0.07% w/v). It was not clear whether the Triton X-100 is obligatory or the enzyme can also catalyze the degradation of cardiolipin in its absence (Ono and White, 1970b).

E. INHIBITORS

Some of the effectors which cause stimulation of the enzymatic reaction do have a relatively narrow range of concentrations in which their consequences are usually expressed; at other concentrations, these substances may be quite inhibitory. This was the case with charged amphipaths, such as sodium dodecylsulfate (SDS) or cetyltrimethylammonium bromide

(CTAB) (Kates, 1957, 1960; Dawson and Hemington, 1967; Heller *et al.*, 1968; Heller and Arad, 1970; Tzur and Shapiro, 1972; Ono and White, 1970b; Chen and Barton, 1971; Cole *et al.*, 1974), or with solvents (Kates, 1957, 1960).

1. Bases

In some instances, the water-soluble products of the hydrolytic reaction were reported to act as inhibitors. Choline and ethanolamine inhibited the hydrolysis of ultrasonically treated particles of phosphatidylcholine and SDS by the phospholipase D from cabbage at pH 5.4–5.8. This inhibition was not due to the reversibility of the reaction. The concentrations causing maximal inhibition were 30 and 100 mM for ethanolamine and choline, respectively, and the inhibition by ethanolamine could be partially alleviated by increasing the concentrations of Ca^{2+}. This might be explained by a competition for certain negative charges at the site of enzymatic reaction (Dawson and Hemington, 1967).

2. Anions

Fluoride has been shown to inhibit the plastid enzymatic activity, and the inhibition was also reversed by Ca^{2+} ions, which alone had no effect (Kates, 1954, 1960). The hydrolysis of cardiolipin by the enzyme of *H. parainfluenza*, which requires Mg^{2+} for its activity, was unaffected by 10 mM of either NaF or KCN (Ono and White, 1970b). EDTA had a pronounced effect on various enzyme preparations: The plant enzymes, requiring Ca^{2+} for maximal activity, were inhibited by concentrations of EDTA far beyond its capacity to chelate equimolar amounts of Ca^{2+}. Thus, a homogenate of cabbage leaves which was shown to contain 40 mM Ca^{2+} was inhibited by only 10 mM EDTA (Davidson and Long, 1958). The purified enzyme from the same source, requiring 37.5 mM Ca^{2+} for optimal activity, was totally inhibited by only 8.3 mM of EDTA (Dawson and Hemington, 1967). Similarly, the purified enzyme from peanut seeds acted optimally when 50 to 60 mM Ca^{2+} were included; however, the reaction rate could be diminished to a small fraction of its values by only 10 mM EDTA (Heller *et al.*, 1976). The rat brain microsomal phospholipase D is not strictly dependent on Ca^{2+} and thus was not affected at all by EDTA (Saito and Kanfer, 1975). The same source provides another phospholipase D which acts on the 1-hexadecyl glycerophosphorylethanolamine, requires Mg^{2+} ions, and is totally inhibited by equimolar concentrations of EDTA (Wykle and Schremmer, 1974). Other enzymes also requiring Mg^{2+} were the cardiolipin-specific phospholipases D from bacteria, which, as expected, were both inhibited by equimolar concentrations of the chelating agents (Ono and White, 1970b; Cole *et al.,* 1974).

3. *Group-Specific Reagents*

p-Chloromercury benzoate (*p*-CMB) at 10^{-4} *M* abolished almost completely the activity of the partially purified enzyme from cabbage. This effect could be prevented or reversed either partially or totally, by 2 m*M* reduced glutathione. Since this reagent binds to sulfhydryl groups so avidly it was rather surprising that thiol alkylating reagents, such as iodoacetate, iodoacetamide, or *N*-ethylmaleimide, at 1 m*M* concentrations had virtually no depressing effect; on the contrary, they were even slightly stimulatory (Yang *et al.,* 1967). The same reagent, iodoacetamide at relatively high concentrations (10 m*M*) had only a limited effect on the activity of the phospholipase from *H. parainfluenza* (Ono and White, 1970b). Saito and Kanfer (1975), however, found that *p*-chloromercuriophenyl sulfonate (*p*-CHPS), which is another organic mercurial with very high affinity for thiol groups, was a very potent inhibitor, and at 60 μ*M* abolished the activity of the rat brain microsomal phospholipase D. They concluded that this inhibition would indicate the presence of an essential SH group, especially since the effect was reversed by 0.6 m*M* dithiothreitol (DTT) (Saito and Kanfer, 1975).

In an attempt to find out whether the phospholipase D from cabbage has an essential serine, Yang *et al.* (1967) used diisopropylfluorophosphate (DFP), but it had no effect even at 2 m*M*.

4. *Natural and Proteinous Inhibitors*

Several natural, poorly characterized factors, isolated from a variety of sources, have the ability to diminish the hydrolytic reaction of phospholipase D. Such an inhibitor of high molecular weight and heat lability was found in the extracts of certain leaves (Kates, 1954; Davidson and Long, 1958). Another inhibitor, which was isolated from cabbage leaves, was heat labile, but apparently of low molecular weight (was dialyzable); it affected the activity of the enzyme from cabbage only and not that of cottonseeds (Tookey and Balls, 1956). Surveying the distribution of phospholipase D in a variety of plant tissues and using a very sensitive assay system in which both dodecylsulfate and ultrasonically treated substrate were employed instead of ether, Quarles and Dawson (1969a) could not detect any inhibitory substance in the leaf extracts. More recently, however, a very stable factor of high molecular weight ($>$ 100,000 daltons), which was resistant to heat, acid, or alkali, was obtained from saliva of cows, dogs, or men. This factor inhibited the hydrolysis of phosphatidylcholine by soluble phospholipase D in grass leaves or celery stalks (Dawson and Hemington, 1974).

Basic proteins, such as protamine sulfate, are strongly inhibitory to the hydrolysis of ultrasonically treated phosphatidylcholine particles by the cabbage enzyme, regardless of the presence of SDS (Dawson and Hemington 1967).

In variance with the results of Dawson and Hemington (1967), who found that serum albumin protected the cabbage enzyme and prevented its adsorption to charged surfaces such as glass, the purified peanut seeds phospholipase D was inactivated by serum albumin. Furthermore, β-lipoprotein fractions from bovine or rat sera were also extremely inhibitory (Tzur and Shapiro, 1972; Heller and Arad, 1970).

IX. Transphosphatidylation or Base Exchange

A unique and remarkable property of phospholipase D is the reaction in which polar head groups (choline, ethanolamine, or serine) are transferred directly into phospholipids. These reactions have been implicated in the metabolism of phospholipids in animal and plant tissues (Dils and Hübscher, 1959, 1961; Hübscher et al., 1959; Ferrari and Benson, 1961; Sastry and Kates, 1965) and involve transfer of a phosphatidyl moiety from a phosphoglyceride to an alcohol [(Eq. 1)]. Particulars of the reaction, as well as the enzyme(s) involved, will be discussed in detail in this section.

A. Plants

1. *The Enzyme(s)*

The first system to demonstrate a direct transphosphatidylation was described by Benson et al. (1965) who reported on the formation of phosphatidyl ethanol and phosphatidyl methanol during the extraction of certain plant tissues, containing phospholipase D activity, with ethanol or methanol. Similar results were also reported by Douce et al. (1966), confirmed again, and the products analyzed and characterized by Bartles and van Deenen (1966).

A constant ratio of phosphatidylcholine phosphohydrolase activity to an activity of transphosphatidylation to either ethanolamine or methanol was retained by phospholipase D, throughout a procedure yielding a 110-fold or 1000-fold purification from savoy cabbage leaves or Virginia peanut seeds, respectively (Yang *et al.*, 1967; Yang, 1969; Tzur and Shapiro, 1972; Heller *et al.*, 1975). This strongly suggested that both reactions could be associated with the same protein. Further support for this conclusion came from additional lines of evidence (Yang *et al.*, 1967):

1. Both reactions had a range of optimum of pH between 5.5 and 6.0.

2. Both activities were strongly inhibited by 10^{-4} M p-CMB but not by other thiol reagents.

3. Both reactions required Ca^{2+} absolutely, at a concentration of 40 mM.

4. Both activities exhibited a similar rate of inactivation upon storage at 4°C.

This concept has recently been challenged by Saito *et al.* (1974) who used a commercial lyophilized powder prepared from cabbage leaves and brought to a degree of purity equivalent to step 3 in Yang's procedure (1969). Using an assay system which determined the formation of phosphatidic acid from phosphatidylcholine microdispersions as a measure of phosphatidohydrolase, and the incorporation of labeled choline or ethanolamine into phospholipids for the transphosphatidylase (or base exchange) activities, respectively, they were able to demonstrate differences between the two types of reactions as follows:

1. The hydrolase had a pH optimum at 5.6; the transferase at 9.0, with almost no overlapping values.

2. Hemicholinium-3, a biphenylcholine derivative, is a lipid soluble choline analogue (Schueler, 1955) and a reported competitive inhibitor of choline permease in animal tissues, subcellular fractions, and other forms of biological vesicles (Haga and Noda, 1973; Weissbach *et al.*, 1971). This drug had very little effect on the hydrolase activity even at 2.5 mM but was a noncompetitive inhibitor of both ethanolamine and choline incorporation into phospholipids with K_i values of 1.25 $\times$ $10^{-3}M$ and 2.5 $\times$ $10^{-3}M$, respectively.

3. An absolute requirement for Ca^{2+} for both reactions was observed. The hydrolase reached an optimum at 28 mM and leveled off at higher concentrations, whereas the transferase showed maximal activity at 4 mM Ca^{2+}, which decreased at higher concentrations.

These data may be interpreted in terms of either a "two-headed" enzyme exhibiting both activities or else as two separate proteins, each catalyzing a different reaction. A successful separation and purification from plant sources should prove useful in reaching a final decision.

2. The Alcoholic Acceptor

Yang *et al.* (1967) have described a *K* value which was defined as *percent acceptor concentration required to produce equal rates of hydrolysis and transfer* in the presence of Ca^{2+} and ether. The *K* values for ethanolamine, ethanol, glycerol, and serine were 0.31, 0.68, 1.1, and > 10, respectively. Hydroxyl-containing compounds such as inositol, glucose, or DL-glycerol-1-phosphate were inactive as acceptors, although 2-propanol could substitute for ethanol. At high alcohol concentrations, the transphosphatidylation was found to be predominant over the hydrolysis; thus at 4% (v/v) of ethanol, the enzyme was activated significantly, but both ethanolamine and glycerol were inhibitory. Higher concentrations of any alcohol, even ethanol, caused a drop in the enzymatic activity (Yang *et al.*, 1967). Some of these results were also obtained by Dawson (1967) who demonstrated that several mono and diols may be useful as acceptors. Thus, ethanolamine or 1-propanol will accept the phosphatidyl moiety from phosphatidylcholine particles (either ultrasonically irradiated or in the presence of SDS), but serine or 2-propanol will not. Although not every compound containing a hydroxyl function was active, it was concluded as a guideline, that many water soluble compounds having a primary alcohol, acted as acceptors. Many of these substances will indeed stimulate the hydrolysis of phosphatidylcholine but will neither act as acceptors nor promote transfer. This reaction was found very useful in preparing a number of analogues to phosphatidylglycerol, starting from ovolecithin (phosphatidylcholine from egg yolk) and diols such as ethylene glycol, 1,2- or 1,3-propanediol, or 1,4-butandiol. The products served to test the specificity of the lysyl-*t*-RNA phosphatidyl glycerol transferase which catalyzes the incorporation of lysine or other amino acids into *O*-aminoacylphosphatidyl glycerol (Lennarz *et al.*, 1967).

In their systematic survey, Kovatchev and Eibl (1977) have studied the transferring capability of a crude phospholipase D preparation from cabbage in order to apply it as a preparatory method for PC analogues having desired polar head groups. The conversion of at least 30% of the starting amounts of phosphatidyl choline into the appropriate phosphatidyl alcohol, occurred with the following acceptors, in the presence of Ca^{2+} and ether: (1) diols, $HO(CH_2)_nOH$ up to $n = 5$; (2) halogenated alcohols $HO(CH_2)_2 - X$ in which $X = F$, Cl, Br; and (3) $CH_2 = CHCH_2OH$, $C \equiv C-CH_2OH$. Other mono and diols, or all carboxylic alcohols which were examined (e.g., serine or its methyl, isopropyl, or butyl esters, hydroxy lactate, hydroxypropionate or glycolate, phenol, and phenylethanol) were either of low effectivity or inactive as acceptors. Synthetic phosphatidylcholines or analogues which transferred their phosphatidyl moiety to methanol during incubation periods of 1 to 7 hours included di-C_{14}, di-C_{16}, 1,2-cyclopentadecylketone-3, 1-C_{16}, and 3-propandiolphosphorylcholine. All the alcohols mentioned had no effect on the total conversion of phosphatidylcholine by phospholipase D. Dawson (1967) has claimed that the cabbage phospholipase D does not possess the ability to catalyze an exchange between intact phospholipids, an hypothesis which was tested by mixing [^{32}P]phosphatidylcholine with equimolar proportions of phosphatidylethanolamine or phosphatidylinositol. Dawson (1967), Yang et al. (1967), and Jezyk and Hughes (1973) reported that transfer activities require Ca^{2+}. At variance with Dawson's findings, a transphosphatidylation was elegantly demonstrated by Stanacev and Stuhne-Sekalec (1970) and Stanacev et al. (1973b) in which a crude cabbage phospholipase D catalyzed the transfer of a prosphatidyl moiety between two molecules of phosphatidyl glycerol, one acting as donor and the other as acceptor, to form cardiolipin:

$$2 \text{ Phosphatidyl glycerol} \rightleftharpoons \text{diphosphatidyl glycerol (cardiolipin)} + \text{glycerol} \quad (7)$$

The discrepancy between the results lies probably in the following: (a) The choice of phosphatidyl glycerol in Stanacev's studies versus phosphatidylethanolamine or choline in Dawson's. (b) The transfer occurred in the absence of Ca^{2+}, and under these circumstances the hydrolase is much less effective, thus maintaining relative high concentrations of both the donor and acceptor (cf. Yang et al., 1967). The transphosphatidylation was not very efficient, and only 8–10% of the initial amounts of phosphatidyl glycerol were recovered as cardiolipin, the rest as phosphatidic acid or unreacted phosphatidyl glycerol. In view of the recent findings of Saito et al. (1974), it is possible that a separate enzyme, present in the crude cabbage preparation, could be responsible for the transferase activity, but its concentrations were relatively low.

B. MICROORGANISMS

The first indication that such a transferase reaction might be operative in bacteria was the finding of de Siervo and Salton (1971) of the almost quantitative conversion of phosphatidyl glycerol to cardiolipin by a particulate fraction from Micrococcus lysodeikticus. The importance of this pathway in cardiolipin biosynthesis was convincingly demonstrated by Hirschberg and Kennedy (1972), who found that a membranous fraction from E. coli catalyzed the formation of cardiolipin from phosphatidyl glycerol with a concomitant release of equimolar amounts of glycerol. Other experimental results, compatible with this reaction as being a major route for cardiolipin biosynthesis, have been reported but still require verification (see, for instance, Stanacev *et al.,* 1973b; Van Den Bosch, 1974; Kates and Marshal, 1975).

C. MAMMALIA

1. *The Reaction and Its Assay*

A particulate fraction from a variety of tissues in different species catalyzes a non-energy-dependent, calcium-stimulated incorporation of L-serine, ethanolamine, and choline into phospholipids. It has been suggested that a reversal of phospholipase D action is responsible for this base exchange. Since it is not a *de novo* pathway, it merely represents a replacement or replenishment device of a certain fraction of preformed, endogenous phospholipids, by means of exchanging their polar head groups.

In spite of conflicting results by Nagley and Hallinan (1968), Stein and Stein (1969), and Sundler *et al.* (1972) on one hand, and by Treble *et al.* (1970) on the other hand, it may be concluded that the exchange reactions of choline and ethanolamine *in vivo* seem to be of minor metabolic importance. It should, however, be emphasized that the exchange of L-serine with the ethanolamine moiety of phosphatidylethanolamine is still considered the only mechanism apparently available to mammalian tissues for the formation of phosphatidylserine (Borkenhagen *et al.,* 1961; Hübscher, 1962). Despite the uncertainty concerning the physiological role of such reactions, and their quantitative contribution to phospholipid metabolism and turnover, they exist *in vivo* and upon fractionation of nervous tissue, they seem to be confined to membranous structures, such as endoplasmic reticulum (microsomes) either alone or together with plasma membranes (Porcellati *et al.,* 1971, 1977; Kanfer, 1972). Such reactions occur *in situ* at selected domains of the membrane, i.e., limited to small pools of membrane-bound phospholipids which constitute only 3–7% of the total available phospholipid molecules (Porcellati, 1976; Porcellati *et al.,* 1977; Gaiti *et al.,* 1976). It is therefore possible that these reactions might be related to localized and restricted changes in charge densities of the membranes.

The base-exchange activities *in vitro* are incomparably higher, as shown by assay using microsomal preparations whose bound phospholipids were prelabeled *in vitro,* either by a base-exchange reaction, by the CDP-base *de novo* pathways, or by injecting one radioactive base at a time, and isolating the labeled microsomal fraction. The base-exchange activity was then measured by a chase experiment by adding an unlabeled base, e.g., 2 mM of ethanolamine or L-serine or 4.5 mM choline, to a medium containing an addition to the labeled microsomes, 0.1–2.5 mM $CaCl_2$ and a buffer at pH 8.1 (Gaiti *et al.,* 1975, 1976).

Similar conditions for the particulate enzyme were employed by Saito *et al.* (1975) and Miura and Kanfer (1976), but in these experiments the incorporation into the membrane-bound phospholipids, as measured by Millipore filtration, was done with ^{14}C-labeled, 0.03 mM ethanolamine, 0.084 mM L-serine, or 0.38 mM choline. The medium at pH 9.0 contained 0.25–4 mM Ca^{2+}. Following the "solubilization" of the enzyme(s), exogenous phospholipid mixture (i.e., asolectin) had to be supplemented at a range of 0.2 to 0.8 mM (based on phosphorus), and the CaCl$_2$ had to be elevated to 8–24 mM.

A control in which free base was omitted was always added. Substantial hydrolysis occurred, which confirmed earlier findings of Dils and Hübscher (1961) concerning the possible involvement of phospholipase D in the base exchange. They were able to detect a small but definite release of phosphatidic acid from microsomal phospholipids but could not, due to inaccurate or insensitive methods, detect the release of choline. These results were in fact confirmed and extended by Saito *et al.* (1975) and T. Taki and J. N. Kanfer (personal communication), who partially purified the phospholipase D from the solubilized rat brain microsomes (cf. Section IV,C,2).

2. Acceptors and Donors

The activities of the transfer enzymes of intact microsomal preparations involve not only the diacylphospholipids, but also alkyl- and alkenyl-containing, membrane-bound phospholipids (Saito, *et al.,* 1975; Porcellati *et al.,* 1977). In addition to choline, ethanolamine, and L-serine, other hydroxyl containing compounds such as threonine or mono- and dimethylethanolamine acted as acceptors. Using the prelabeled microsomes, unlabeled free ethanolamine, or L-serine exchanged with phosphatidylethanolamine, phosphatidylserine, or phosphatidylcholine, free choline was able to exchange only with phosphatidylethanolamine or phosphatidylcholine. The order of reactivity of the bases was ethanolamine > L-serine > choline. It should be noted that the various methods of prelabeling the microsome-bound phospholipids yielded different rates of exchange, and consequently it was suggested that more than one pool of phosphatidylethanolamine, phosphatidylserine, or phosphatidylcholine exist in rat brain microsomes (Gaiti *et al.,* 1976; Porcellati, 1976; Porcellati *et al.,* 1977).

3. Properties of the Enzyme(s)

The base-exchange enzymes catalyzing the transfer of ethanolamine and serine, but not choline, were solubilized by a mixture of a zwitterionic detergent Miranol H2M (0.8% w/v) and sodium cholate (0.5% w/v) in the presence of 20% glycerol. Separate fractions, each possessing a principal activity for the incorporation of either ethanolamine, serine, or choline, were obtained in good yields (Miura and Kanfer, 1976). Differences between the particulate and solubilized enzymes included: (a) A high pH optimum of 9 for the particulate enzyme compared to 7.2 for the soluble fraction. (b) The base exchange activities of the microsomes resisted heating up to 42.5°C, but lost activity rapidly upon further heating, totally at 55°C. There was gradual decrease in all exchange activities of the soluble enzyme upon heating to 60°C; however even at that temperature, 30–50% of the initial value still remained. (c) High ionic strength affected both forms of enzymes; 0.1 M, 0.14 M, and 0.3 M for LiCl, NaCl, and KCl, respectively, caused 50% inactivation of the particulate enzyme. The reverse order, i.e., 0.085 M, 0.174 M, and 0.33 M for KCl, NaCl, and LiCl, respectively, caused the same inactivation of the soluble enzymes. It was claimed, using a series of monovalent cations, that their destructive effects paralleled their ionic radii. (d) An exogenous phospholipid mixture in the form of asolectin was essentially inhibitory to the exchange enzymes in the intact microsomes which already had their built-in phospholipids, but they were an indispensable requirement for the soluble enzyme(s). (e) Both forms of enzyme preparations showed an absolute requirement for Ca^{2+}; Mg^{2+} could not substitute. The particulate enzyme had optimal activity in the presence of 0.24 mM, 0.8 mM, and 4 mM Ca^{2+} for choline, ethanolamine, and serine, respectively. In the soluble form, more Ca^{2+} was apparently needed, and for the same order of base incorporation, 8 mM, 8 mM, and 24mM cation were necessary. (f) Diethyl ether, tetrahydrofuran, or n-butanol, which have a stimulatory action on the plant enzymes, had a deleterious effect on both forms of the enzyme at low concentrations. (g) The detergents Miranol DM and H2M, both zwitterionic, which stimulated at low concentrations, solubilized the particulate enzyme(s) at higher concentrations and eventually inhibited, in both particulate and soluble forms at higher levels. All other detergents tested, caused 50% inhibition at approximately the same concentration range, below 0.5% (w/v), and included the anionic SDS, DOC, sodium taurocholate, the nonionic Triton X-100 and NCF-54, Tween 20 and 80, cutscum, Brij 58 and 93, and others as well as the cationic CTAB. (h) Group-specific inhibitors such as p-CMPS will inhibit the activities of both forms of the enzyme partially or completely within a narrow range of concentrations, e.g., 2–10 $\times$ 10^{-5} M. DTT will prevent but not reverse an already inhibited enzyme. Hemicholinium-3 interfered with the incorporation of the bases by the particulate enzyme in the following order: choline > ethanolamine > serine. After solubilization of the enzyme this drug behaved as a noncompetitive inhibitor with choline and serine and exhibited a mixed-type inhibition when ethanolamine incorporation was studied. The K_i values of 4.67 $\times$ 10^{-3} M, 2.96 $\times$ 10^{-2} M, and

1.12×10^{-2} M, for the preceding order of bases, respectively, were estimated (Saito and Kanfer, 1975; Saito *et al.*, 1975; Miura and Kanfer, 1976; T. Taki and J. N. Kanfer, personal communication).

The progress in the transphosphatidylation reaction made it clear that although the base-exchange enzymes catalyze a reaction which resembles the reverse of a phospholipase D-like reaction, distinct proteins might exist with different affinities for either the phospholipid under consideration or the specific acceptor, whether an alcohol or water. Cross-reactivity of each preparation should be examined in order to demonstrate its specificity.

4.   *Structural Considerations Related to Transphosphatidylation*

The phospholipid obtained by transphosphatidylation of egg phosphatidylcholine with 4% glycerol catalyzed by cabbage phospholipase D and its deacylation product were analyzed. Determinations of phosphorus, vicinal hydroxyl groups, products of exhaustive hydrolysis by acetic acid, and the stereospecific determination of D-glycerol-1-phosphate led Yang *et al.* (1967) to propose the following formula: 1-phosphatidyl-DL-glycerol or in accordance with I.U.B.: 3-*sn*-phosphatidyl-1' (and 3') -*sn*-glycerol. This conclusion was challenged by Batrakov *et al.* (1975) who used circular dichroism to examine the stereospecificity of the reaction. They compared the product with natural and synthetic phospholipids and decided that it was exclusively, 3-*sn*-phosphatidyl-1'-*sn*-glycerol. Joutti and Renkonen (1976) recently reexamined the problem using a more biological approach. They incubated phospholipase C from *Bacillus cereus* with one of the following: *sn*-3-phosphatidyl-1'-*sn*-glycerol; *sn*-3-phosphatidyl-3'-*sn*-glycerol or the phosphatidylglycerol obtained from the enzymatic reaction of phospholipase D. The analysis of the product (e.g., α-glycerophosphate) showed the formation of only 50% of *sn*-3-glycerol phosphate, indicating unequivocally the lack of stereospecificity of phospholipase D, because if it were producing one or the other isomer then either no *sn*-3-glycerophosphate or 100% of it had to be formed.

X. Possible Mechanism and Mode of Action

This subject should be treated in a general context of phospholipase reactions, relating a particulate enzyme to soluble substrate or soluble enzymes acting on insoluble substrates. Some of the ideas in this section are based on fragmentary evidence assembled from several approaches and mainly concern the action of soluble plant enzyme preparations on insoluble phospholipids.

The basic difficulties lie in the realm of the substrates which form complex structures due to self-aggregation in aqueous media (Gatt and Barenholz, 1973; Cordes and Gitler, 1973). Secondly, there has been only limited progress in the purification of phospholipase D, due mainly to the instability of the enzyme as it approaches homogeneity. Consequently, the interactions between phospholipase D and phospholipids should be classified as enzyme reactions occurring in heterogeneous systems. It is now more recognized that most enzymatic reactions occur at interfaces, and those of phospholipase D are no exception (James and Augenstein, 1966; McLaren and Packer, 1970).

Phospholipase D, like other lipolytic enzymes acts on both natural and synthetic phospholipids, whether in a pure form or, more likely, in complex aggregates with other cellular components present in biological membranes or lipoproteins. For this reason, the conventional approach of an enzyme functioning in dilute aqueous solutions of substrates is meaningless. As a consequence such systems must be treated differently and interfacial enzyme kinetics of lipolysis was introduced (Gatt and Barenholz, 1973; Brockerhoff and Jensen, 1974; Verger and de Haas, 1976).

The development of conceptual approaches to elucidate the mode of action of phospholipase D naturally followed certain paths paved by studies on similar heterogeneous systems.

A. COALESCENCE

The pioneering studies of Kates (1957, 1960) showed that chloroplastbound phospholipase D acted on pure phosphatidylcholine or soybean phospholipids in the presence of water-immiscible organic solvents, stimulated the reaction, and caused the substrate to coalesce with the plastid, as evidenced microscopically. Other water-soluble solvents were nonstimulatory and, consequently, did not cause any visible interaction between enzyme and substrate. Soybean phosphatides did not require a solvent for activation but coalesced with the plastid enzyme due to the presence of a natural component in the mixture which replaced the solvent. The substrate and enzymatic activity were recovered in the complex, and the reaction proceeded in the coalesced form (Kates and Gorham, 1957). The explanation for this phenomenon resides partly in changes in the dielectric constant of the medium by the organic solvent, increasing the attraction between the lipophylic surface of the substrate and the chloroplast. Another possibility, an elaboration of the previous one, is solvent adsorption onto the surface of substrate particles (micelles) and onto the surface of the chloroplast which also contain lipids, rendering both surfaces more lipophilic, causing mutual attraction, and leading finally to coalescence (Kates, 1957, 1960). This explanation is only partially acceptable because it must also answer observations such as the fact that several water-immiscible solvents (i.e., chloroform and hydrocarbons) were nonstimulatory; alternatively, water-soluble solvents such as alcohols, lacked, in Kates' experiments, an activating effect because "they penetrated the surface of the substrate particles, reversed its properties and conferred upon them hydrophilicity." Not only is the insoluble plastid enzyme activated by solvents but also the soluble phospholipase D, and in view of later data which demonstrated pronounced stimulatory action by both types of organic solvents (ethers as well as alcohols), Kates' explanations deserve modification (Davidson and Long, 1958; Yang *et al.*, 1967; Dawson and Hemington, 1967; Dawson, 1967; Heller *et al.*, 1968; Heller and Arad, 1970; Rakhimov *et al.*, 1976a).

B. SURFACE CHARGE DENSITY AND ADSORPTION ON A "SUPERSUBSTRATE"

Another approach, introduced to explain the mode of action of phospholipases, involves the effects of the electrostatic fields at the phospholipid–water interfaces. The contribution of the surface charge alone cannot explain all the experimental results and has to be considered together with other factors. Thus, the activity of phospholipase D, whether particulate or soluble (cf. Section VIII,C), is stimulated or inhibited by charged amphipaths suggesting that both the physical form of the substrate and its surface charge play important roles in controlling the rates of hydrolysis. For example, the enzyme from cabbage is activated by anionic amphipaths but not by cationic detergents. The addition of the charged amphipaths may have dispersive action due to the reduction of interfacial packing. However, this was not evidenced in the case of phospholipase D, most probably due to the large concentration of Ca^{2+} ions required. Therefore, it may be concluded that anionic SDS with a large excess of calcium ions did not support the formation of smaller particles, as was expected, but rather more complex structures.

The surface charge is expressed in terms of zeta potentials, which determine the rates of hydrolysis of charged particles by phospholipase action (Bangham and Dawson, 1959, 1962; Dawson, 1964, 1973; Dawson *et al.*, 1976). In the absence of Ca^{2+}, negatively charged amphipaths produced large changes in the negative zeta potential, but Ca^{2+} reduced or totally abolished this change. So, although the precise mechanism in this case was not understood, it was proposed that Ca^{2+} promoted the adsorption of the enzyme onto the surface of the substrate particles revising, indirectly, the older idea of Kates. In fact, the adsorption of the enzymes in the absence of Ca^{2+} was accompanied by denaturation due to the highly negatively charged surface. With Ca^{2+} present, the decrease in the zeta potential prevented the denaturation but did not prevent adsorption of the enzyme, and was a prerequisite for the formation of an "enzyme-substrate complex." Not unexpected, successful adsorption also occurred on particles of phosphatidylcholine-SDS-Mg^{2+}, which also prevented the denaturation of the enzyme, but could not promote any hydrolysis of the substrate (Dawson and Hemington, 1967; Heller *et al.*, 1976, 1977; Rakhimov *et al.*, 1976a).

Maximal activation by SDS was obtained at a molar ratio of phosphatidylcholine to SDS of 2:1 (cf. Section VIII,D). Proton magnetic resonance (PMR) studies have shown that at this ratio the intensity of the choline head group is only half the value for single bilayered vesicles of PC obtained by ultrasonic irradiation (Seiter and Chan, 1973) (Fig. 2). Moreover, addition of excess Ca^{2+} to the mixture is accompanied by a considerable decrease in the intensities, whereas omission of Ca^{2+} caused an increase in the intensities of PC protons, indicating a higher solubilization of PC by SDS. On the other hand, in the presence of Ca^{2+}, some precipitation of the PC-SDS-Ca^{2+} aggregates occurred accompanied by a decrease in the intensity. It therefore appears that although addition of more SDS causes the solubilization of more PC, it also causes the precipitation of more of the mixed aggregates. Consequently, maximal solubility of these complexes is obtained at an optimal range of PC:SDS molar ratio of 1.6 to 4. The paramagnetic cation Mn^{2+} can affect PMR spectra through its effect on relaxation times. Manganese dodecylsulfate is soluble, therefore the addition of $MnCl_2$ to

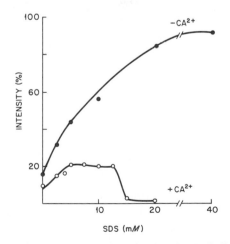

FIG. 2. Dependence of the intensity of PMR signals of choline head group of 20 m*M* phosphatidylcholine on SDS concentrations. One hundred percent intensity is taken as the value of single bilayered PC vesicles obtained by ultrasonic irradiation (●: without $CaCl_2$; ○: with 200 m*M* $CaCl_2$).

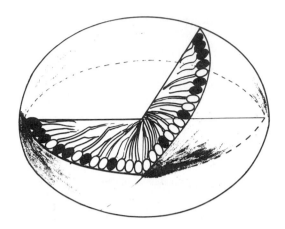

FIG. 3. A proposed model for the micelle of PC-SDS aggregates (●~ : SDS; ○⸂: PC).

PC-SDS or PC-SDS-Ca^{2+} complexes caused broadening or elimination of the PMR signals of those choline groups facing the medium. These results were interpreted as the existence of micellar structures of the complexes in which a higher density of SDS will be expected at the regions of lower curvature of the ellipsoidic micelle as shown in Fig. 3 (Heller et al., 1977).

Complexes of PC-SDS-Ca^{2+} (or Mg^{2+}) adsorb phospholipase D purified either from cabbage leaves (Dawson and Hemington, 1967; Chen and Barton, 1971), peanut seeds (Heller et al., 1974, 1975, 1976, 1977; Heller, 1976), or cottonseeds (Rakhimov et al., 1976a,b). The enzymatic activity was associated with these complexes. If the phosphatidylcholine (egg lecithin) was replaced by di-C_{14} alkyl analogue of phosphatidylcholine, no adsorption to such complex occurs (Chen and Barton, 1971). These substances can be degraded by phospholipase D, but even under favorable conditions, when the ratio of substrate to detergent was 1:1, the rates of hydrolysis were much lower than with phosphatidylcholine. If we consider adsorption as an important factor—and these compounds do not adsorb—then other mechanisms must be operating, and these will be discussed later (Chen and Barton, 1971).

A term *supersubstrate* was coined by Brockerhoff (1974) to describe a surface with certain physicochemical properties; it is for all practical purposes an aggregate of substrate molecules with or without nonsubstrate amphipaths, and it is more available to certain enzymatic reactions than in simpler forms. This description seems to fit the complexes previously discussed.

Purified phospholipase D tends to be highly unstable and certain surfaces, macromolecules or simply storage in more concentrated solutions, prevent inactivation. A subunit structure for phospholipase D was proposed in the cases of peanut seeds and cottonseeds to explain the observed multiplicity of molecular sizes and interconversion in the molecular sizes (Heller *et al.,* 1974, 1976; Mady'arov, 1976; Rakhimov *et al.,* 1976a).

A monomer having a molecular weight of 22,000 ± 3,000 undergoes aggregation to form an oligomer of 200,000 ± 10,000 having catalytic activity (Heller *et al.,* 1974, 1977). A shift of the equilibrium n(monomer) $\rightleftharpoons$ (monomer)$_n$ to the right may be occurring on the surface of the supersubstrate, and could be, for instance, a consequence of an increase in protein concentration (Fig. 4). This would explain the nonlinear upward increase in activity due to the addition of more enzyme molecules. An artificial supersubstrate made of phosphatidylcholine-detergent-cation complex may be substituted by a "natural" one, i.e., a biological membrane, which also causes such a shift of equilibrium producing an active enzyme without any added detergent (Heller and Arad, 1970; Heller *et al.,* 1975). Alternatively, an appropriate molecular size may be fixed by "immobilizing" the soluble cottonseed enzyme following adsorption onto silica gel beads (Rakhimov *et al.,* 1976b). Although this is not a covalent attachment, the fundamental behavior of the enzyme is modified. The enzyme becomes more sensitive to temperature, loses its absolute requirement for Ca^{2+} or activator, and hydrolyzes at a different pH optimuum (7.5) in addition to the old 5.6. This is a very attractive model and provides an excellent oppor-

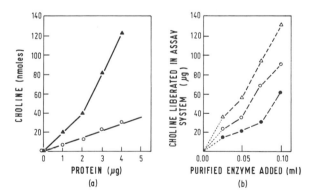

FIG. 4. Effect of enzyme concentrations on the activity of phospholipase D. (a) A representative experiment showing the activity of a partially purified (O) and completely purified (▲) enzyme from peanut seeds (from Heller *et al.,* 1976). (b) A modified presentation showing the effect of enzyme concentrations on its adsorption on PC-SDS-Ca^{2+} mixed aggregates. Mixing at 0°C, centrifugation and assay in sediment (O), supernatant (●), and total recovery of enzymatic activty (△). From Dawson and Hemington (1967).

tunity to study the mode of action of the same enzyme in different forms, provided it is not being washed off the beads during the reaction.

C. Monolayers

The interactions of phospholipase D with its substrates were also followed by the monolayer technique. This method was first introduced for enzymatic reactions by Hughes (1935), who measured the hydrolysis of a film of phosphatidylcholine by phospholipase A and followed the decrease of the surface potential.

Heller and Arad (1970) showed in a simpler way that the peanut enzyme catalyzes the reaction at an interface of water and ether. Most of the substrate (phosphatidylcholine) was soluble in the ether phase, but no enzymatic activity was detected there. It was assumed that the substrate diffuses toward the reaction area (i.e., interface) in which a layer of protein was observed. Increasing the size of the interfacial area or mixing the reaction mixture vigorously, which was accompanied by elevated rates of reaction, supported such an assumption (Heller and Arad, 1970; Rakhimov *et al.,* 1976a). More direct proof was obtained by isolating an interfacial film formed during the reaction, which contained almost all the enzymatic activity but only a small fraction of the total phospholipid (Chen and Barton, 1971). More elaborate studies of the action of phospholipase D at air–water surface films of phosphatidylcholine labeled with [^{14}C]choline were followed by the monolayer radioactivity technique (Quarles and Dawson, 1969c). This technique is extremely sensitive, and requires only small amounts of lipids. It has to be pure or, alternatively, its exact composition must be known since it determines the molecular orientation, the density, and the water structure at the surface. The studies of Quarles and Dawson (1969c) were done with long-chain phospholipids, under uncontrolled surface densities (e.g., random number of phosphatidylcholine molecules/ cm^2). In the course of hydrolysis the radioactive head group is removed from the phospholipid and from the surface, whereas the phosphatidic acid remains in the film. The latter product contributes a negative charge to the film and therefore has a profound influence on the reaction. The action of phospholipase D on films at high surface pressures ceased (i.e., when the "concentration" of the substrate at the air–water interface was high) but resumed only if negatively charged amphipaths, such as phosphatidic acid and, to a lesser extent, stearoyl hydrogen sulfate, were included in the film. The most reasonable explanation for this effect is an enhanced adsorption of the enzyme molecules to, or penetration between, the closely packed substrate molecules, although this was not measured directly (Quarles and Dawson, 1969c). Such a mechanism would fit with that proposed for the bulk phase with the complexes of substrate with SDS and Ca^{2+}.

D. A MODEL OF THE REACTION

The transphosphatidylation reaction, in which there is a transfer of the phosphatidyl electrophil from one alcoholic nucleophil to another, was used to propose a model for the reaction mechanism. Based on exchange reaction between the choline of phosphatidylcholine and free [^{14}C]choline, catalyzed by the partially purified cabbage phospholipase D, Yang *et al.* (1967) suggested that a phosphatidyl-enzyme complex exists. Since the reaction is inhibited by *p*-CMB it was suggested that the enzyme may contain an "essential" SH, as in the following sequence:

$$\text{Phosphatidylcholine} + \text{enzyme-SH} \rightleftharpoons \text{phosphatidyl-S-enzyme} + \text{choline} \quad (8)$$

$$\begin{align} & + H_2O \rightleftharpoons \text{phosphatidic acid} + \text{enzyme-SH} \\ \text{Phosphatidyl-S-enzyme} & \\ & + \text{ROH} \rightleftharpoons \text{phosphatidyl alcohol} + \text{enzyme-SH} \end{align} \quad (9)$$

A similar mechanism was proposed by Stanacev *et al.* (1973b) to explain the formation of diphosphatidyl glycerol (cardiolipin) from two molecules of phosphatidyl glycerol (cf. Section IX,A,2). Since better yields of diphosphatidyl glycerol were obtained in the absence of Ca^{2+}, it is not quite clear which step requires this cation, hence it was omitted from the preceding scheme. Whether the SH group is essential has never been shown directly, and except for *p*-CMB or *p*-CMPS, none of the other thiol-blocking reagents was capable of interfering with the catalysis. Furthermore, direct measurements of SH in the highly purified peanut seed phospholipase D failed to show its presence (Heller *et al.*, 1974).

The premises for Yang's proposal are founded on the identity of the protein catalyzing both hydrolysis and transfer (Yang *et al.*, 1967; Tzur and Shapiro, 1972). The recent finding by Saito and Kanfer (1975) on the possible dissociation between the two activities, cast some doubt on the proposed mechanism. Purification of the two enzymes will, most probably, assist in solving this problem.

E. FLUIDITY OF THE SUBSTRATES

The contribution of the "gel to liquid-crystalline transition" of the substrate is another factor which was not extensively explored in the case of the reactions catalyzed by phospholipase D. This factor alone cannot account for the observed data but can be combined with other factors such as surface charge (Chen and Barton, 1971). The extent of hydrolysis of the dialkyl analogues of phosphatidylcholine (di-C_{14}, di-C_{16}, di-C_{18}) is inversely proportional to their respective T_m values. The T_m is the temperature at which a transition occurs in the phase of a phospholipid, spontaneously swollen in an aqueous medium. When phospholipids are placed in water, they will swell and form liquid crystals (liposomes) only if the temperature exceeds the melting temperature of their hydrocarbon chains (T_m) (Ladbrooke and Chapman, 1969; Chapman, 1973). The addition of negatively charged amphipaths to the dialkylphospholipids tends to decrease their T_m, consequently their internal fluidity increases and they become more susceptible to hydrolysis. Although this was observed, no direct binding of the enzyme to a complex of dialkylphosphatidylcholine (C_{14})-SDS-Ca^{2+} was obtained. It does not exclude some kind of interaction which is apparently weaker and does not persist during centrifugation. This promotes a smaller degree of degradation as compared to the diacylphospholipids (Chen and Barton, 1971).

Acknowledgments

The author is indebted to Dr. E. R. Berman and Dr. H. Cedar for a critical reading of the manuscript and for many helpful suggestions.

References

Acker, L., and Bücking, H. (1956). *Z. Lebensm.-Unters. -Forsch.* **104,** 423–428.

Acker, L., and Ernst, G. (1954). *Biochem. Z.* **325,** 253–257.

Acker, L., and Müller, K. (1965). *Nahrung* **9,** 3–14.

Acker, L., Diemair, W., and Jäger, R. (1952). *Biochem. Z.* **322,** 471–485.

Antia, N. J., Bilinski, E., and Lau, Y. C. (1970). *Can. J. Biochem.* **48,** 643–648.

Ascher, Y., Heller, M., and Becker, Y. (1969). *J. Gen. Virol.* **4,** 65–76.

Astrachan, L. (1973). *Biochim. Biophys. Acta* **296,** 79–88.

Audet, A., Cole, R., and Proulx, P. (1975). *Biochim. Biophys. Acta* **380,** 414–420.

Bangham, A. D., and Dawson, R. M. C. (1959). *Biochem. J.* **72,** 408–492 and 493–496.

Bangham, A. D., and Dawson, R. M. C. (1962). *Biochim. Biophys. Acta* **59,** 103–115.

Bartles, C. T., and van Deenen, L. L. M. (1966). *Biochim. Biophys. Acta* **125,** 395–397.

Batrakov, S. G., Panosayan, A. G. A., Kogan, G. A., and Bergelson, L. D. (1975). *Biochem. Biophys. Res. Commun.* **66,** 755–762.

Baum, G., Lynn, M., and Ward, F. B. (1973). *Anal. Chim. Acta* **65,** 385–391.

Benson, A. A., and Maruo, B. (1958). *Biochim. Biophys. Acta* **27,** 189–195.

Benson, A. A., Freer, S., and Yang, S. F. (1965). *Proc. Int. Conf. Biochem. Lipids, 9th, 1965,* p. 16.

Bilinski, E., Antia, N. J., and Lau, Y. C. (1968). *Biochim. Biophys. Acta* **159,** 496–502.

Bligh, E. G., and Dyer, W. J. (1959). *Can. J. Biochem. Physiol.* **37,** 911–917.
Bonsen, P. P. M., de Haas, G. H., and van Deenen, L. L. M. (1965). *Biochim. Biophys. Acta* **106,** 93–105.
Bonsen, P. P. M., de Haas, G. H., and van Deenen, L. L. M. (1966). *Biochemistry* **6,** 1114–1120.
Borkenhagen, L. F., Kennedy, E. P., and Fielding, L. (1961). *J. Biol. Chem.* **236,** PC28–PC30.
Brockerhoff, H. (1974). *Bioorg. Chem.* **3,** 176–183.
Brockerhoff, H., and Jensen, R. G. (1974). "Lipolytic Enzymes," pp. 282–288. Academic Press, New York.
Chapman, D. (1973). *In* "Form and Function of Phospholipids" (G. B. Ansell, J. N. Hawthorne, and R. M. C. Dawson, eds.), pp. 117–142. Elsevier, Amsterdam.
Chen, S. J., and Barton, P. G. (1971). *Can. J. Biochem.* **49,** 1362–1375.
Chibnall, A. C., and Channon, H. J. (1927). *Biochem. J.* **21,** 233–246.
Clermont, H. (1972). *Physiol. Veg.* **10,** 153–158.
Cole, R., Benns, G., and Proulx, P. (1974). *Biochim. Biophys. Acta* **337,** 325–332.
Comes, P., and Kleining, H. (1973). *Biochim. Biophys. Acta* **316,** 13–18.
Contrardi, A., and Ercoli, A. (1933). *Biochem. Z.* **261,** 275–302.
Cordes, E. H., and Gitler, C. (1973). *Prog. Bioorg. Chem.* **2,** 2 53.
Davidson, F. M., and Long, C. (1958). *Biochem. J.* **69,** 458–466.
Davidson, F. M., Long, C., and Penny, I. F. (1956). *In* "Biochemical Problems of Lipids" (G. Popjak and E. le Breton, eds.), pp. 253–262. Butterworth, London.
Davidson, J. B., and Stanacev, N. Z. (1970). *Can. J. Biochem.* **48,** 633–642.
Dawson, R. M. C. (1964). *In* "Metabolism and Physiological Significance of Lipids" (R. M. C. Dawson and D. N. Rhodes, eds.), p. 179. Wiley, New York.
Dawson, R. M. C. (1967). *Biochem. J.* **102,** 205–210.
Dawson, R. M. C. (1969). *In* "Methods in Enzymology" (J. M. Lowenstein, ed.), Vol. 14, pp. 633–648. Academic Press, New York.
Dawson, R. M. C. (1973). *In* "Form and Function of Phospholipids" (G. B. Ansell, J. N. Hawthorne, and R. M. C. Dawson, eds.), pp. 97–116. Elsevier, Amsterdam.
Dawson, R. M. C., and Hemington, N. (1967). *Biochem. J.* **102,** 76–86.
Dawson, R. M. C., and Hemington, N. (1974). *Biochem. J.* **143,** 427–430.
Dawson, R. M. C., Hemington, N. L., Miller, N. G. A., and Bangham, A. D. (1976). *J. Membr. Biol.* **29,** 179–184.
de Haas, G. H., Bonsen, P. P. M., and van Deenen, L. L. M. (1966). *Biochim. Biophys. Acta* **116,** 114–124.
de Siervo, A. J., and Salton, M. R. J. (1971). *Biochim. Biophys. Acta* **239,** 280–292.
Dils, R. R., and Hübscher, G. (1959). *Biochim. Biophys. Acta* **32,** 293–294.
Dils, R. R., and Hübscher, G. (1961). *Biochim. Biophys. Acta* **46,** 505–513.
Douce, R., Faure, M., and Marechal, J. (1966). *C. R. Hebd. Seances Acad. Sci., Ser. C.* **262,** 1549–1552.
Einset, E., and Clark, W. L. (1958). *J. Biol. Chem.* **231,** 703–715.
Ferrari, R. A., and Benson, A. A. (1961). *Arch. Biochem. Biophys.* **93,** 185–192.
Folch, J., Lees, M., and Sloane-Stanley, G. H. (1957). *J. Biol. Chem.* **226,** 497–509.
Fossum, K., and Höyem, T. (1963). *Acta Pathol. Microbiol. Scand.* **57,** 295–300.
Gaiti, A., Brunetti, M., and Porcellati, G. (1975). *FEBS Lett.* **49,** 361–364.
Gaiti, A., Brunetti, M., Woelk, H., and Porcellati, G. (1976). *Lipids* **11,** 823–829.
Galliard, T. (1973). *In* "Form and Function of Phospholipids" (G. B. Ansell, J. N. Hawthorne, and R. M. C. Dawson, eds.), pp. 272–276. Elsevier, Amsterdam.

Galliard, T. (1975). *In* "Recent Advances in the Chemistry and Biochemistry of Plant Lipids" (T. Galliard and E. I. Mercer, eds.), pp. 133–135, 190, and 328–329. Academic Press, New York.

Gatt, S., and Barenholz, Y. (1973). *Annu. Rev. Biochem.* **42**, 61–90.

Grossman, S., Cobley, J., Hogue, P. K., Kearney, E. B., and Singer, T. P. (1973). *Arch. Biochem. Biophys.* **158**, 744–753.

Grossman, S., Oestreicher, G., and Singer, T. P. (1974). *Methods Biochem. Anal.* **22**, 174–204.

Hack, M. H., and Ferrans, V. J. (1959). *Hoppe-Seyler's Z. Physiol. Chem.* **315**, 157–162.

Haga, T., and Noda, H. (1973). *Biochim. Biophys. Acta* **291**, 564–575.

Hanahan, D. J., and Chaikoff, I. L. (1947a). *J. Biol. Chem.* **168**, 233–240.

Hanahan, D. J., and Chaikoff, I. L. (1947b). *J. Biol. Chem.* **169**, 699–705.

Hanahan, D. J., and Chaikoff, I. L. (1948). *J. Biol. Chem.* **172**, 191–198.

Hauser, H., and Dawson, R. M. C. (1967). *Biochem. J.* **105**, 401–407.

Haverkate, F., and van Deenen, L. L. M. (1964). *Biochim. Biophys. Acta* **84**, 106–108.

Heller, M. (1976). *Proc. Int. Conf. Biochem. Lipids, 19th, 1976,* p. 60.

Heller, M., and Arad, R. (1970). *Biochim. Biophys. Acta* **210**, 276–286.

Heller, M., Aladjem, E., and Shapiro, B. (1968). *Bull. Soc. Chim. Biol.* **50**, 1395–1408.

Heller, M., Mozes, N., Peri, I., and Maes, E. (1974). *Biochim. Biophys. Acta* **369**, 397–410.

Heller, M., Mozes, N., and Maes, E. (1975). *In* "Methods in Enzymology" (J. M. Lowenstein, ed.), Vol. 35, Part B, pp. 226–232. Academic Press, New York.

Heller, M., Mozes, N., and Peri, I. (1976). *Lipids* **11**, 604–609.

Heller, M., Greenzaid, P., and Lichtenberg, D. (1977). *Proc. CNRS Int. Colloq. Enzymes Lipid Metab., 1977,* p. 51.

Hill, E. E., and Lands, W. E. M. (1970). *In* "Lipid Metabolism" (S. J. Wakil, ed.), pp. 231–233. Academic Press, New York.

Hirschberg, C. B., and Kennedy, E. P. (1972). *Proc. Natl. Acad. Sci. U.S.A.* **69**, 648–651.

Hitchcock, C., and Nichols, B. W. (1971). "Plant Lipid Biochemistry," pp. 197–199. Academic Press, New York.

Hübscher, G. (1962). *Biochim. Biophys. Acta* **57**, 555–561.

Hübscher, G., Dils, R. R., and Pover, W. F. R. (1959). *Biochim. Biophys. Acta* **36**, 518–528.

Hughes, A. (1935). *Biochem. J.* **29**, 437–443.

James, L. K., and Augenstein, L. G. (1966). *Adv. Enzymol.* **28**, 1–40.

Jezyk, P. F., and Hughes, H. N. (1973). *Biochim. Biophys. Acta* **296**, 24–33.

Joutti, L. K., and Renkonen, O. (1976). *Chem. Phys. Lipids* **17**, 264–266.

Kanfer, J. N. (1972). *J. Lipid Res.* **13**, 468–476.

Kapoor, C. L., Prasad, R., Shipstone, A. C., and Garg, N. K. (1974). *Indian J. Biochem. Biophys.* **11**, 78–80.

Kater, L. A., Goetzl, E. J., and Austen, K. F. (1976). *J. Clin. Invest.* **57**, 1173–1180.

Kates, M. (1953). *Nature (London)* **172**, 814–815.

Kates, M. (1954). *Can. J. Biochem. Physiol.* **32**, 571–583.

Kates, M. (1955). *Can. J. Biochem. Physiol.* **33**, 575–589.

Kates, M. (1956). *Can. J. Biochem. Physiol.* **34**, 967–980.

Kates, M. (1957). *Can. J. Biochem. Physiol.* **35**, 127–142.

Kates, M. (1960). *In* "Lipide Metabolism" (K. Bloch, ed.), pp. 206–216. Wiley, New York.

Kates, M. (1970). *Adv. Lipid Res.* **8**, 225–265.

Kates, M., and Gorham, P. R. (1957). *Can. J. Biochem. Physiol.* **35**, 119–126.

Kates, M., and Marshall, O. (1975). *In* "Recent Advances in the Chemistry and Biochemistry of Plant Lipids" (T. Galliard and E. I. Mercer, eds.), pp. 134–135. Academic Press, New York.

Kates, M., and Sastry, P. S. (1969). *In* "Methods in Enzymology" (J. M. Lowenstein, ed.), Vol. 14, pp. 197–203. Academic Press, New York.

Kovatchev, S., and Eibl, H. J. (1977). *Proc. CNRS Int. Colloq. Enzymes Lipid Metab. 1977,* p. 52.

Ladbrooke, B. D., and Chapman, D. (1969). *Chem. Phys. Lipids* **3**, 304–356.

Lands, W. E. M., and Hart, P. (1965). *Biochim. Biophys. Acta* **98**, 532–538.

Lennarz, W. J., Bonsen, P. P. M., and van Deenen, L. L. M. (1967). *Biochemistry* **6**, 2307–2312.

Long, C., and Maguire, M. F. (1954). *Biochem. J.* **57**, 223–226.

Long, C., Odavič, R., and Sargent, E. J. (1967a). *Biochem. J.* **102**, 216–220.

Long, C., Odavič, R., and Sargent, E. J. (1967b). *Biochem. J.* **102**, 221–229.

McLaren, A. D., and Packer, L. (1970). *Adv. Enzymol.* **33**, 245–308.

Mady'arov, Sh. R. (1976). *Biokhimiya* **41**, 255–259.

Miura, T., and Kanfer, J. (1976). *Arch. Biochem. Biophys.* **175**, 654–660.

Nagley, P., and Hallinan, T. (1968). *Biochim. Biophys. Acta* **163**, 218–225.

Negishi, T., Fujino, Y., and Ito, S. (1971). *Nippon Nogei Kagaku Kaishi* **45**, 426–428; *Chem. Abstr.* **76**, 11413g (1972).

Nolte, D., and Acker, L. (1975a). *Z. Lebensm.-Unters. -Forsch.* **158**, 149–156.

Nolte, D., and Acker, L. (1975b). *Z. Lebensm.-Unters. Forsch.* **159**, 225–233.

Ono, Y., and White, D. C. (1970a). *J. Bacteriol.* **103**, 111–115.

Ono, Y., and White, D. C. (1970b). *J. Bacteriol.* **104**, 712–718.

Porcellati, G. (1976). *Biochimie* **58**, 981–987.

Porcellati, G., di Jeso, F., and Malcorati, M. (1966). *Life Sci.* **5**, 769–779.

Porcellati, G., Arienti, G., Pirotta, M., and Giorgini, D. (1971). *J. Neurochem.* **18**, 1395–1417.

Porcellati, G., Gaiti, A., Woelk, H., de Medio, G. E., Brunetti, M., and Trovarelli, F. (1977). *Proc. CNRS Int. Colloq. Enzymes Lipid Metab, 1977,* p. 2.

Quarles, R. H., and Dawson, R. M. C. (1969a). *Biochem. J.* **112**, 787–794.

Quarles, R. H., and Dawson, R. M. C. (1969b). *Biochem. J.* **112**, 795–799.

Quarles, R. H., and Dawson, R. M. C. (1969c). *Biochem. J.* **113**, 697–705.

Rakhimov, M. N., Mady'arov, Sh. R., and Abdumalikov, A. Kh. (1976a). *Biokhimiya* **41**, 452–457.

Rakhimov, M. N., Mady'arov, Sh. R., and Abdumalikov, A. Kh. (1976b). *Biokhimiya* **41**, 569–572.

Rampini, C. (1975). *C. R. Hebd. Seances Acad. Sci.* **281**, 1431–1433.

Roelofsen, B., and van Deenen, L. L. M. (1973). *Eur. J. Biochem,* **40**, 245–257.

Roughan, P. G., and Slack, C. R. (1976). *Biochim. Biophys. Acta* **431**, 86–95.

Saito, M., and Kanfer, J. (1975). *Arch. Biochem. Biophys.* **169**, 318–323.

Saito, M., Bourque, E., and Kanfer, J. (1974). *Arch. Biochem. Biophys.* **164**, 420–428.

Saito, M., Bourque, E., and Kanfer, J. (1975). *Arch. Biochem. Biophys.* **169**, 304–317.

Sastry, P. S., and Kates, M. (1965). *Can. J. Biochem.* **43**, 1445–1453.

Schueler, F. W. (1955). *J. Pharmacol. Exp. Ther.* **115**, 127–143.

Seiter, C. H. A., and Chan, S. J. (1973). *J. Am. Chem Soc.* **95**, 7541–7553.

Slotboom, A. J., de Haas, G. H., and van Deenen, L. L. M. (1967). *Chem. Phys. Lipids* **1**, 192–208.

Smith, R. H. (1954). *Biochem. J.* **56**, 240–250.

Souček, A., Michalec, Č., and Součkova, A. (1967). *Biochim. Biophys. Acta* **144**, 180–182.

Souček, A., Michalec, Č., and Součkova, A. (1971). *Biochim. Biophys. Acta* **227**, 116–128.

Stanacev, N. Z., and Stuhne-Sekalec, L. (1970). *Biochim. Biophys. Acta* **210**, 350–352.

Stanacev, N. Z., Davidson, J. B., Stuhne-Sekalec, L., and Domazet, Z. (1973a). *Can. J. Biochem.* **51**, 286–304.

Stanacev, N. Z., Stuhne-Sekalec, L., and Domazet, Z. (1973b). *Can. J. Biochem.* **51**, 747–753.

Stein, Y., and Stein, O. (1969). *J. Cell Biol.* **40**, 461–483.

Stoffel, W. (1975). *In* "Methods in Enzymology" (J. M. Lowenstein, ed.), Vol. 35, Part B, pp. 533–541. Academic Press, New York.

Strauss, H., Leibovitz-Ben Gershon, Z., and Heller, M. (1976). *Lipids* **11**, 442–448.

Strickland, K. P. (1973). *In* "Form and Function of Phospholipids" (G. B. Ansell, J. N. Hawthorne, and R. M. C. Dawson, eds.), pp. 25–26. Elsevier, Amsterdam.

Sundler, R., Arvidson, G., and Åkesson, B. (1972). *Biochim. Biophys. Acta* **280**, 559–568.

Tookey, H. L., and Balls, A. K. (1956). *J. Biol. Chem.* **218**, 213–224.

Treble, D. H., Frumkin, S., Balint, J. A., and Beeler, D. A. (1970). *Biochim. Biophys. Acta* **202**, 163–171.

Tzur, R., and Shapiro, B. (1972). *Biochim. Biophys. Acta* **280**, 290–296.

Van Den Bosch, H. (1974). *Annu. Rev. Biochem.* **43**, 243–277.

Van Den Bosch, H., Van Golde, L. M. G., and van Deenen, L. L. M. (1972). *Ergeb. Physiol., Biol. Chem. Exp. Pharmakol.* **66**, 92–98.

Vaskovsky, V. E., Gorovoi, P. G., and Suppes, Z. S. (1972). *Int. J. Biochem.* **3**, 647–656.

Verger, R., and de Haas, G. H. (1976). *Annu. Rev. Biophys. Bioeng.* **5**, 77–117.

Verger, R., Mieras, M. C. E., and de Haas, G. H. (1973). *J. Biol. Chem.* **248**, 4023–4034.

Waku, K., and Nakazawa, Y. (1972). *J. Biochem. (Tokyo)* **72**, 149–155.

Weissbach, H., Thomas, E., and Kaback, H. R. (1971). *Arch. Biochem. Biophys.* **147**, 249–254.

Wykle, R. L., and Schremmer, J. M. (1974). *J. Biol. Chem.* **249**, 1742–1746.

Yamaguchi, T., Okawa, Y., Sakaguchi, K., and Muto, N. (1973). *Agric. Biol. Chem.* **37**, 1667–1672.

Yang, S. F. (1969). *In* "Methods in Enzymology" (J. M. Lowenstein, ed.), Vol. 14, pp. 208–211. Academic Press, New York.

Yang, S. F., Freer, S., and Benson, A. A. (1967). *J. Biol. Chem.* **242**, 477–484.

Screening for Inhibitors of Prostaglandin and Thromboxane Biosynthesis

RYSZARD J. GRYGLEWSKI

Department of Pharmacology, Copernicus Academy of Medicine in Cracow, Cracow, Poland

I. Introduction

Many *in vitro* methods are employed to predict the anti-inflammatory potency of newly synthesized compounds. These methods are essentially based on the interaction of drugs with enzyme and nonenzymic proteins. Anti-inflammatory drugs are supposed to protect albumin against heat denaturation (Mizushima, 1964), to displace marker compounds from binding sites of albumin (Skidmore and Whitehouse, 1965), to induce fibrinolysis in plasma clots (Gryglewski, 1966), to accelerate disulfide interchange reaction between serum protein and sulfhydryl reagents (Gerber *et al.,* 1967), to stabilize erythrocyte (Brown *et al.,* 1967) and lysosomal (Miller and Smith, 1966) membranes, as well as to inhibit a wide range of enzymes including uncoupling of oxidative phosphorylation (Whitehouse and Haslam, 1962) and inhibition of cyclic AMP phosphodiesterase (Weinryb *et al.,* 1972; Moffat *et al.,* 1972).

None of these methods seems to be satisfactory for a predictive assessment of anti-inflammatory drugs (Glenn *et al.,* 1973). These methods lack specificity, although occasionally a parallelism between *in vitro* and *in vivo* data may occur. In most instances millimolar concentrations of drugs have to be used to induce an effect *in vitro,* whereas only micromolar concentrations are expected to be reached in body fluids *in vivo.* Nor is there convincing evidence that any of the above *in vitro* reactions is essential for the mechanism of anti-inflammatory activity of drugs. In

1971 Vane and his colleagues (Vane, 1971; Smith and Willis, 1971; Ferreira *et al.*, 1971) discovered that the target biomolecule for non-steroidal anti-inflammatory drugs is arachidonic acid cyclooxygenase, a component of the prostaglandin synthetase system.

Vane (1972a,b) has postulated that aspirinlike drugs exert their pharmacological action through inhibition of prostaglandin biosynthesis *in vivo,* and his concept has been supported by evidence from many different laboratories, as reviewed by Flower (1974). Inhibition of prostaglandin biosynthesis *in vitro* is therefore the most promising rational approach for prediction of anti-inflammatory activity of newly synthesized compounds. Unfortunately, it has become evident that there is no direct interrelationship between antiprostaglandin synthetase potency *in vitro* and anti-inflammatory efficiency *in vivo.* Several factors dissociate the concordance of the *in vitro* and *in vivo* data, the most important being pharmacokinetic properties of drugs which cannot be foreseen in a single *in vitro* test. For instance acidic nonsteroidal anti-inflammatory drugs are unequally bound to albumin (Table I). It can be expected that their antiprostaglandin synthetase potency *in vivo* is an exponent of their "plasma-unbound" fraction. Consequently only this fraction will contribute to an acute anti-inflammatory effect. Therefore it is not enough to measure the antienzymic potency of a drug *in vitro*. This has to be supplemented by measuring its avidity to bind to albumin. Combining these two measurements allows one to obtain an approximate *in vitro* index for prediction of anti-inflammatory potencies within a series of prostaglandin synthetase inhibitors (Gryglewski *et al.*, 1976a).

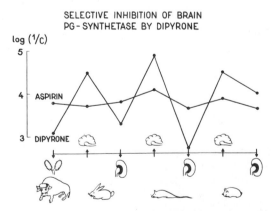

FIG. 1.   Schematic representation of uniform inhibition by aspirin and selective inhibition by dipyrone of microsomal prostaglandin synthetases derived from bovine seminal vesicle microsomes and from rabbit, rat, and guinea pig brains and kidney medullas (Dembinska-Kiec *et al.*, 1976). Ordinate shows log $(1/C)$, where C is molar concentration of either aspirin or dipyrone which results in a 50% inhibition of enzymic activity.

Table I

INHIBITION OF PROSTAGLANDIN BIOSYNTHESIS IN BOVINE SEMINAL VESICLE
MICROSOMES AND DISPLACEMENT OF 8-ANILINO-1-NAPHTHALENE SULFONATE
FROM BOVINE SERUM ALBUMIN BY ANTI-INFLAMMATORY DRUGS

Drugs	Inhibition of PG synthetase IC_{50} (μM)	Binding to albumin IC_{50} (μM)
Acidic nonsteroidal anti-inflammatory drugs		
Indomethacin	0.10	140
Mefenamic acid	0.25	160
Naproxen	13	10000
Niflumic acid	33	160
Ibuprofen	50	630
Fenoprofen	56	500
Phenylbutazone	148	1000
Aspirin	189	5600
Dipyrone	500	10000
Nonacidic nonsteroidal anti-inflammatory drugs		
Flumizole	0.10	Inactive at 10^3
L 8027 [a]	5.90	650
Benzydamine	820	Inactive at 10^4
Amidopyrine	1000	Inactive at 10^4
Anti-inflammatory steroids		
Hydrocortisone	Inactive at 300	Not tested
Dexamethasone	Inactive at 300	Not tested
Fluocinolone	Inactive at 300	Not tested

[a] L 8027 is 1'-(isopropyl-2-indoyl)-3-pyridyl-3-ketone (Deby *et al.*, 1971).

We have recently found (Dembinska-Kiec *et al.*, 1976) that anti-enzymic activity of any prostaglandin synthetase inhibitor is the same in various microsomal preparations, providing that concentrations of the substrate and cofactors are the same. The basic activity of prostaglandin synthetases from brain, seminal vesicles, or kidney medulla microsomal preparations derived from various species—all microsomal enzymes are equally susceptible to the inhibitory action of aspirin (Fig. 1). Most of the acidic anti-inflammatory drugs listed in Table I behave like aspirin, except for dipyrone. Dipyrone is a selective inhibitor of brain synthetase sharing this property with paracetamol (Flower and Vane, 1972).

Uniform susceptibility of microsomal prostaglandin synthetases to most of the anti-inflammatory drugs enables one to use a single microsomal preparation (e.g., bovine seminal vesicle microsomes; see Table I) and to extrapolate the calculated antienzymic potencies of drugs on other tissues.

There is one biological system that does not fit this scheme. In blood platelets, arachidonic acid is converted via prostaglandin endoperoxides to thromboxane A_2 and those labile substances induce release and aggregation of platelets (Hamberg et al., 1975). Nonsteroidal anti-inflammatory drugs inhibit platelet aggregation; however, their antiaggregatory and anti-prostaglandin synthetase potencies may differ from each other (compare Tables I and III). Aspirin, dipyrone (Table III), ditizole (Caprino et al., 1973) and L 8027 (Deby et al., 1971; Gryglewski, 1977) are the most representative examples. One possibility is that certain prostaglandin synthetase inhibitors are also inhibitors of thromboxane A_2 isomerase. Another possibility is that platelet cyclooxygenase has a preferential susceptibility to certain prostaglandin synthetase inhibitors. In any case it is strongly recommended to include the third test for in vitro activity of prostaglandin synthetase inhibitors, namely to investigate their anti-aggregatory properties and their efficacy to inhibit formation of thromboxane A_2 by platelets.

II. Inhibition of Prostaglandin Synthetase

Ram (Samuelsson et al., 1967) and bovine (Takeguchi et al., 1971) seminal vesicle microsomes are the richest sources of arachidonic acid cyclooxygenase, a component of prostaglandin synthetase, which is sensitive to inhibitory action of nonsteroidal anti-inflammatory drugs (see Flower, 1974). The incubation mixture contains microsomal enzyme, arachidonic acid, and usually glutathione and a phenolic compound, e.g., adrenaline or hydroquinone, in a 0.05–0.1 M buffer of pH 8.0–8.3. For studies with inhibitors, Ku and Wasvary (1975) have recommended the use of a low concentration of arachidonic acid (0.2–2.0 μM), low temperature (25°C) and short time (10 min) of incubation. The activity of the enzyme is estimated by measuring the products generated (PGE_2, $PGF_2\alpha$, PGD_2, or malonyldialdehyde). The formed prostaglandins can be quantified by bioassay (Vane, 1971), by radiochemical assay (Tomlinson et al., 1972), by radioimmunoassay (Levine, 1972), or by gas–liquid chromatography-mass spectrometry (Hamberg, 1972). The indirect methods of measuring of enzymic activity include polarographic measuring of oxygen uptake (Lands et al., 1971) and spectrophotometric measuring of transformation of adrenaline to adrenochrome (Takeguchi and Sih, 1972). Other methods for assay of prostaglandin synthetase activity have been reviewed by Sih and Takeguchi (1973).

The concentration of arachidonic acid in the incubation mixture dramatically influences the rate of reaction, the ratio of products formed and the antienzymic potencies of certain inhibitors (Flower *et al.*, 1973; Gryglewski, 1974; Ho and Esterman, 1974; Robak *et al.*, 1975). When arachidonic acid was used at a wide range of concentrations varying from 0.1 to 1000 μM and reported K_m values also varied from 1 to 100 μM (Robak *et al.*, 1975). This may explain that antiprostaglandin synthetase potencies of anti-inflammatory drugs differ considerably from one laboratory to another (Gryglewski, 1974).

In our laboratory prostaglandin synthetase activity is assayed as follows: Homogenate of bovine seminal vesicle glands in 0.25 M sucrose (1:4 w/v) is centrifuged at 10,000 g for 10 min and the resulted supernatant is centrifuged at 100,000 g for 60 min. The precipitate is resuspended in distilled water and lyophilized. The microsomal powder (BSVM) usually contains 60–65% protein. The incubation mixture comprises 3–6 mg of BSVM in 2 ml of 66 mM phosphate buffer pH 8.0, glutathione (166 μM), hydroquinone (45 μM), and a test compound (0.01–1000 μM). After 5 min of preincubation at 37°C sodium arachidonate (10 μM) is added and incubation carried on for 20 min. The reaction is stopped by boiling for 30 sec. The formed prostaglandins are bioassayed in terms of PGE_2 equivalents directly in the boiled and centrifuged (1000 g) incubation mixture. Prostaglandins are assayed using a rat stomach strip (Vane, 1957) which is superfused with Krebs bicarbonate (3 ml/min, 37°C) containing a mixture of combined antagonists (Gilmore *et al.*, 1968) and indomethacin (1 μg/ml). An average enzymic activity is 1360 ± 84 ng PGE_2 equivalents per 1 mg of BSVM protein (mean ± S.E., $n = 100$). K_m for arachidonic is 8 μM. Our radiochromatographic studies (Darska, 1976) reveal that under these experimental conditions 68% of arachidonic acid is converted to radioactive products comprising 44% of PGE_2, in 13% of PGD_2, in 2% of $PGF_{2\alpha}$, and in 9% of unidentified products. On the other hand, 97.7% of biological activity that can be extracted from chromatographic plate is located at the narrow region of PGE_2 standard. No trace of malonyldialdehyde can be detected by thiobarbituric method in the incubation mixture (Robak *et al.*, 1975). We have found that the potency of indomethacin to inhibit prostaglandin synthetase in BSVM is practically the same whether calculated by direct bioassay of prostaglandin E_2-like activity in the crude incubation mixture or by bioassay of PGE_2 separated chromatographically or by radiochemical assay of PGE_2 formed from [^{14}C]-1-arachidonic acid or by measuring oxygen uptake by Clark electrode. Similar concordance of the results for these four assay techniques has been found in the case of aspirin and mefenamic acid (Table I). Therefore we felt free to use *larga manu*, our simple and fast technique for bioassay of antiprostaglandin synthetase activity of anti-inflammatory drugs and newly synthesized compounds. Figure 2 shows the method for calculation of antiprostaglandin synthetase potencies.

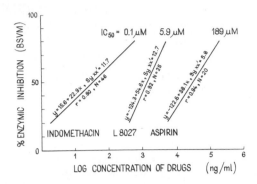

FIG. 2. Regression lines and equations of regression lines for inhibition of prostaglandin synthetase in bovine seminal vesicle microsomes by indomethacin, L 8027, and aspirin. $S_{y\ xx}$, standard deviation of regression line; r, regression coefficient; N, number of pairs; IC_{50}, the concentration of a drug needed for 50% inhibition of enzymic activity (μM).

Nonsteroidal anti-inflammatory drugs inhibit prostaglandin biosynthesis at a very early stage of the cyclooxygenase activity (Smith and Lands, 1971; Lands *et al.*, 1975). Because of that, aspirin-like drugs also suppress the formation of cyclic endoperoxides (PGG_2 and PGH_2) and thromboxanes (Hamberg *et al.*, 1975; Samuelsson *et al.*, 1976). This last effect was observed in biological experiments as the suppression of generation of a "rabbit aorta contracting substance" (RCS) by aspirin-like drugs (Piper and Vane, 1969; Vargaftig and Dao Hai, 1971; Gryglewski and Vane, 1972a,b; Willis, 1974) before the identity of RCS with prostaglandin endoperoxides and/or thromboxane A_2 was established (Samuelsson *et al.*, 1976; Hamberg *et al.*, 1975; Svensson *et al.*, 1975; Needleman *et al.*, 1976a). Most of the acidic anti-inflammatory drugs are equipotent inhibitors of the generation of prostaglandins and thromboxane A_2 in the chopped guinea pig lungs (Fjalland, 1974). Since RCS from lung seems to be composed mainly of thromboxane A_2 (Hamberg *et al.*, 1975; Svensson *et al.*, 1975; Gryglewski *et al.*, 1976b), the results obtained by Fjalland (1974) are in agreement with the observation made by the Vane group (Bunting *et al.*, 1976a) that indomethacin and other acidic antiinflammatory drugs do not inhibit thromboxane A_2 isomerase. The same group has reported that a basic anti-inflammatory drug, benzydamine, is a weak *($IC_{50} = 320$ μM)* but selective inhibitor of thromboxane A_2 isomerase in horse platelet microsomes. This finding has stimulated us to look for potential thromboxane A_2 isomerase inhibitors within a group of basic anti-inflammatory drugs. Indeed a potent inhibitor of thromboxane A_2 biosynthesis has been found and its properties will be discussed later.

Mechanism of inhibition of prostaglandin synthetase by anti-inflammatory drugs is complex and might differ for various drugs (Flower *et al.*, 1973; Flower, 1974; Horodniak *et al.*, 1974; Ku and Wasvary, 1975). Obvious differences exist between aspirin and the rest of acidic polycyclic aspirin-like drugs, as well as between acidic and nonacidic anti-inflammatory drugs. The antienzymic effect of indomethacin is time dependent and substrate dependent (competitive), but amazingly enough it is also irreversible. In other words indomethacin is a competitive inhibitor of prostaglandin synthetase in BSVM provided that the substrate and the inhibitor are added to the enzymic preparation at the same time. However, when indomethacin is preincubated for 5 min with microsomes, inhibition of the enzymic activity is no longer dependent on the amount of arachidonic acid used (Robak *et al.*, 1975). Most acidic anti-inflammatory drugs behave like indomethacin (Ku and Wasvary, 1975). It might well be that this type of inhibition is similar to the "active-site-directed irreversible inhibition" which has been described for inhibition of adenosine desaminase by adenine derivatives (Schaeffer, 1971).

Inhibitory action on prostaglandin synthetase is a common feature for all acidic nonsteroidal anti-inflammatory drugs. Certain acidic drugs have an asymmetric carbon atom in their molecules; in each case the *in vivo* active enantiomer has been found to be a more potent prostaglandin synthetase inhibitor than its partner (Ham *et al.*, 1972; Takeguchi and Sih, 1972; Tomlinson *et al.*, 1972; Shen *et al.*, 1974; Gaut *et al.*, 1975). This stereo-specific effect could not be detected in other *in vitro* tests (Mizushima *et al.*, 1975).

Nonacidic anti-inflammatory drugs may or may not inhibit the enzyme (Table I). The best known nonacidic inhibitors of prostaglandin synthetase are 1' (isopropyl-2-indolyl)-3-pyridyl-3-ketone (L 8027) (Deby *et al.*, 1971), indoxole (Ham *et al.*, 1972), benzydamine (Flower *et al.*, 1973), and flumizole (Wiseman *et al.*, 1975). The most potent is flumizole. It is at least as potent (Table I) or even more potent (Wiseman *et al.*, 1975) than indomethacin. A comparative kinetic study of antienzymic activities of these two potent prostaglandin synthetase inhibitors should reveal the differences between the mechanism of action of acidic and nonacidic nonsteroidal anti-inflammatory drugs.

Steroidal anti-inflammatory drugs are not inhibitors of prostaglandin synthetase (Flower *et al.*, 1972; Table I) though they are capable of inhibiting prostaglandin release from tissues (Gryglewski, 1976). This type of activity implies the possibility of a direct interaction of cortcosteroids with biomembranes, which may either impair the supply of endogenous substrates for prostaglandin biosynthesis or inhibit transmembrane transport of prostaglandins (Lewis and Piper, 1975).

III. Binding to Albumin

Several reviews have been published on the character of drug-protein interaction (Brodie and Hogben, 1957; Meyer and Guttman, 1968; Settle *et al.,* 1971) and on the methods for studying this interaction (Chignell, 1971). The binding of nonsteroidal anti-inflammatory drugs to protein is usually assessed by methods of equilibrium dialysis (Zaroslinski *et al.,* 1974), circular dichroism (Chignell, 1969), or displacement of a probe from the probe-protein complex (Whitehouse *et al.,* 1971). We have chosen the last procedure. 1-Anilino-8-naphthalene sulfonate (ANS) was used as a probe and bovine serum albumin (Cohn fraction V) (BSA) as an acceptor protein. Displacement of ANS from BSA by prostaglandin synthetase inhibitors was determined by measuring the intensity of fluorescence due to the albumin-bound ANS (Daniel and Weber, 1966). The excitation wavelength was 380 nm and the fluorescence maximum 485 nm. BSA (mol. wt. 66,000) at a concentration of 10 μM in 0.1 M phosphate buffer of pH 7.0 was incubated at 22°C for 30 min with a prostaglandin synthetase inhibitor at three to six concentrations (0.01–4.0 mM). Then ANS was added to yield the final concentration of 40 μM. Quenching of ANS-BSA fluorescence by prostaglandin synthetase inhibitors was measured against fluorescence of a solution containing only BSA and ANS. A concentration of prostaglandin synthetase inhibitor that quenched the fluorescence by 50% (IC_{50}) was calculated graphically. Each compound in the highest concentration used was tested for intrinsic fluorescence excited at 380 nmoles and for quenching ANS fluorescence in methanol.

For special purposes the experiments could be carried out at various concentrations of BSA (1–50 μM) in the presence of ANS at a concentration of 40 μM, as well as at various concentrations of ANS (4–30 μM) in the presence of BSA at a concentration of 10 μM. These experiments allowed us to calculate a number of binding sites for ANS in BSA (n) and an apparent association constant (K_{app}) using the method of Scatchard (Scatchard, 1949; Flanagan and Ainworth, 1968; Wiethold *et al.,* 1973). Table II shows the influence of six anti-inflammatory drugs on the number of binding sites in BSA for ANS and on the affinity of ANS to BSA. Indomethacin, phenylbutazone and mefenamic acid decrease the number of binding sites and the affinity of ANS to BSA. Aspirin decreases only the affinity, whereas nonacidic chloroquine and amidopyrine are ineffective in both respects. This finding is in the favor of the concept that polycyclic acidic prostaglandin synthetase inhibitors are stronger ligands to enzymic and nonenzymic proteins than aspirin. Their anionic radicals interact with the surface polar groups of proteins (Skidmore and Whitehouse,

Table II

APPARENT ASSOCIATION CONSTANTS (K_{app}) AND
NUMBER OF BINDING SITES (n) OF 1-ANILINO-8-
NAPHTHALENE SULFONATE TO BOVINE SERUM
ALBUMIN IN THE ABSENCE AND IN THE PRESENCE
OF ANTI-INFLAMMATORY DRUGS AT A
CONCENTRATION OF 1 mM

Drugs	$K_{app} \times 10^5\ M^{-1}$	n
None	0.82	1.71
Indomethacin	0.52	0.32
Mcfenamic acid	0.12	0.70
Phenylbutazone	0.51	0.93
Aspirin	0.45	1.51
Amidopyrine	0.90	1.66
Chloroquine	1.03	1.50

1966), whereas their lipophylic moieties are anchored into hydrophobic clefts of protein molecules (Chignell, 1971). Both sites of binding are essential for a profound distortion of the tertiary structure of proteins, and this effect may be helpful in inactivating cyclooxygenase (Gryglewski, 1974). However, an excessive potency to bind to proteins is not a desired property for prostaglandin synthetase inhibitors. Then the avidity to interact with any protein has to be compensated by a highly stereospecific and electronic arrangement of the molecule of an inhibitor which would fit to the code of an active site or to an allosteric area of the cyclooxygenase molecule. That is the case for indomethacin. On the other hand, aspirin (a weak ligand to protein) has a unique property to act as a selective active-site acetylating agent for cyclooxygenase (Roth *et al.,* 1975). This finding can explain a relatively strong (Table III) and persistent anti-aggregatory action of aspirin.

For screening purposes it is sufficient to find IC_{50} for binding to albumin of a prostaglandin synthetase inhibitor (Table I). The ratio of antienzymic and albumin-binding potencies roughly correlates with anti-inflammatory potencies in a series of compounds.

IV. Antiaggregatory Activity and Inhibition of Thromboxane A$_2$ Generation in Aggregating Platelets

Screening for antiaggregatory activity of prostaglandin synthetase inhibitors is recommended not only to confirm their anticyclooxygenase potency but also there might be a chance to find a selective thromboxane

Table III
THRESHOLD ANTIAGGREGATORY CONCENTRATIONS OF
ACIDIC NONSTEROIDAL ANTI-INFLAMMATORY DRUGS [a]

Drugs	Range of the threshold anti-aggregatory concentrations (μM)
Indomethacin	0.3–1
Dipyrone	3–30
Mefenamic acid	4–12
Aspirin	5–55
Niflumic acid	10–106
Phenylbutazone	32–81
Fenoprofen	38–227
Ibuprofen	73–121
Naproxen	130–260

[a] Aggregation of rabbit platelet-rich plasma was induced by arachidonic acid at a concentration of 150 μM. The listed concentrations of anti-inflammatory drugs also inhibited formation of thromboxane A_2 by platelet-rich plasma, as measured by contractions of mesenteric artery (Figs. 3 and 4). Each drug was tested at 4–6 concentrations in 3–10 separate experiments.

A_2 isomerase inhibitor in platelets. Benzydamine is an example for this possibility (Bunting et al., 1976a). Another possibility is that a selective inhibitor of platelet cyclooxygenase will be found. In either case one can stop thinking about anti-inflammatory drugs and try to develop an antiplatelet drug with potential activity in thromboembolic diseases.

Aspirin (Weiss et al., 1968), phenylbutazone (O'Brien, 1968), indomethacin (Glenn et al., 1972), sudoxicam (Constantine and Purcell, 1973), suprofen (De Clerck et al., 1975), and a number of other prostaglandin synthetase inhibitors (Mustard and Packham, 1975) release ADP, serotonin, and acid hydrolases from aggregating platelets. Anti-inflammatory drugs also suppress the generation of prostaglandins (Smith and Willis, 1971; Glenn et al., 1972; Patrono et al., 1976), prostaglandin endoperoxides, and thromboxanes (Hamberg et al., 1974, 1975; Samuelsson et al., 1976). These last two (or one of them) are triggers of the release reaction in platelets, which is followed by platelet aggregation (Malmsten et al., 1975). Therefore a great number of nonsteroidal anti-inflammatory drugs inhibit platelet aggregation in vitro and in vivo in various species including human beings (Mustard and Packham, 1975). In these experiments aggregation has usually been induced by collagen which probably activates phospholipase A_2 in platelets, thus liberating endogenous arachidonic acid that is transformed to prostaglandin endoperoxides and thromboxane A_2 (Flower *et al.,* 1976). For aggregation, we prefer to use exogenous arachidonic acid (Silver *et al.,* 1973; Vargaftig and Zirinis, 1973; Willis and Kuhn, 1973) and to measure in parallel platelet aggregation and thromboxane A_2 formation.

Our procedure is as follows: Blood from healthy donors, who have not taken any drugs for at least 10 days, is collected from the anticubital vein (50–100 ml) with 0.12 vol of 0.1 M trisodium citrate. Alternatively rabbit blood can be used. Platelet rich plasma (PRP) is prepared by centrifugation at 400 g for 10 min at room temperature. Aggregation of platelets in 1 ml of PRP is monitored in a Chrono-log aggregameter at 37°C. Drugs and the corresponding solvents (20–50 μl) are added to PRP at zero time, and 6 min later kalium arachidonate at concentrations of 150–1500 μM for human PRP and 30–300 μM for rabbit PRP is instilled. Thirty to sixty seconds later a 100-μl aliquot of PRP is withdrawn and immediately bioassayed for thromboxane A_2, prostaglandin endoperoxides, and prostaglandins.

Differential bioassay of the substances previously cited has been based on the recent discovery by the Vane group (Bunting *et al.,* 1976b) that strips of rabbit coeliac and mesenteric arteries are relaxed by prostaglandin endoperoxides (PGG_2 and PGH_2) and contracted by thromboxane A_2 (Fig. 3). A bank of assay organs consisting of rabbit mesenteric artery, rabbit aorta or vena cava, rat stomach, and rat colon is superfused in cascade (Vane, 1964) with Krebs bicarbonate (37°C, 3 ml/min) which contains a mixture of antagonists (Gilmore *et al.,* 1968) and indomethacin (1 μg/ml). The contractile potency of thromboxane A_2 on rabbit aorta (and vena cava) is about 50 times higher than that of prostaglandin endoperoxides (Needleman *et al.,* 1976a), whereas mesenteric artery is contracted by thromboxane A_2 and relaxed by PGG_2 and PGH_2 (Bunting *et al.,* 1976a). All three vascular strips are insensitive to $PGF_{2\alpha}$ while PGE_2 relaxes only a strip of mesenteric artery. On the other hand rat colon is insensitive to thromboxane A_2 and prostaglandin endoperoxides, being contracted by $PGF_{2\alpha}$ and PGE_2. Rat stomach is contracted by PGE_2, $PGF_{2\alpha}$, prostaglandin endoperoxides and thromboxane A_2 in decreasing order of potency (Bunting *et al.,* 1976a). This natural and excellent differentiation between thromboxane A_2 and other biologically active products of arachidonic acid metabolism (Fig. 3) may be reinforced by checking the instability of a substance that behaves like thromboxane A_2. A half-life time of thromboxane A_2 is about 30 sec at 37°C (Hamberg *et al.,* 1975). The aggregated PRP is sucked into a syringe through a millipore filter (0.8 μm) and the filtrate is kept for 2 min at 37°C. Then its contractile activity on vascular strips disappears or is greatly suppressed.

Thromboxane A_2 is generated by aggregating human and rabbit PRP

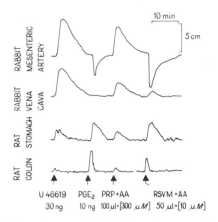

FIG. 3. Bioassay of thromboxane A_2 which was generated by human platelet-rich plasma from arachidonic acid (PRP + AA) after 60 sec of incubation. The assay organs were rabbit mesenteric artery, rabbit vena cava, rat stomach, and rat colon superfused in cascade. The organs were calibrated with 30 ng of a prostaglandin endoperoxide analog, (15S)-hydroxy-11α,9α-(epoxymethano)prosta-5Z,13E-dienoic acid (U 46619), with 10 ng of PGE_2 and with the crude extract of prostaglandin endoperoxides that were formed during a 3-min incubation of ram seminal vesicle microsomes with arachidonic acid (RSVM + AA). Note that the profile of biological action of thromboxane A_2 is similar to that of U 46619 but not to those of PGE_2 and prostaglandin endoperoxides.

and the amount of formed thromboxane A_2 is dependent on the concentration of arachidonic acid which is used for aggregation (Fig. 4). Minute amounts of thromboxane A_2 are also generated by low concentrations of arachidonic acid which are unable to induce platelet aggregation (e.g., 200 μM in Fig. 4). Acidic anti-inflammatory drugs that inhibit platelet aggregation also inhibit formation of thromboxane A_2 (Table III) at a very early stage of cyclooxygenation of arachidonic acid. Dipyrone and aspirin are much more active and naproxen is less active as antiaggregatory agents compared to their anticyclooxygenase activity in BSVM (Tables I and III). However, all acidic anti-inflammatory drugs have in common that their antiaggregatory potencies hardly depend on the pro-aggregatory concentrations of arachidonic acid used (Fig. 5). At a wide range of pro-aggregatory concentrations of arachidonic acid, the antiaggregatory concentrations of these drugs may not vary more than 10-fold. The same is true for potencies of acidic anti-inflammatory drugs to inhibit formation of thromboxane A_2 in PRP.

There is a nonacidic anti-inflammatory agent, L 8027 (Deby et al., 1971, Fig. 5) that deserves special attention. L 8027 is an inhibitor of cyclooxygenase in BSVM with $IC_{50} = 5.9$ μM (Fig. 1, Table I). This

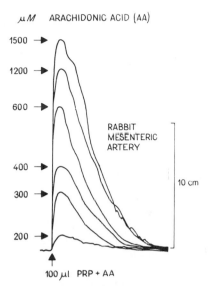

μM   ARACHIDONIC ACID (AA)

FIG. 4. Dependence of the amount of thromboxane A_2 generated by human platelet-rich plasma (PRP) on the concentration of arachidonic acid (AA) which was used for aggregation. Thromboxane A_2 was bioassayed by contractions of rabbit mesenteric artery.

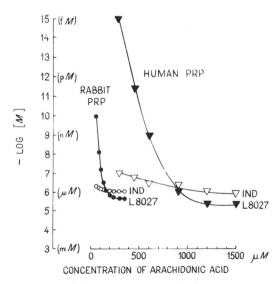

FIG. 5. Threshold antiaggregatory potencies of 1'-(isopropyl-2-indolyl)-3-pyridyl-3-ketone (L 8027) and indomethacin (IND) in human and rabbit platelet-rich plasmas (PRP). Ordinate: −log of the threshold antiaggregatory concentration. Abscissa: micromolar concentrations of arachidonic acid which were used to induce platelet aggregation.

anticyclooxygenase potency is too low to explain its potent antiaggregatory action that is observed at a concentration of 1 nM in rabbit PRP and at a concentration of 1 fM (!) in human PRP (Fig. 5). This powerful anti-platelet action of L 8027 occurs at the threshold pro-aggregatory concentrations of arachidonic acid. When concentrations of arachidonic acid rise the antiaggregatory potency of L 8027 declines to reach its plateau at a region of 0.4–4 μM (Fig. 5). A completely different picture is seen for indomethacin. Its antiaggregatory potency depends on the concentration of arachidonic acid used to a very slight extent (Fig. 5). Indomethacin is an irreversible inhibitor of cyclooxygenase (Ku and Wasvary, 1975; Robak *et al.*, 1975). This fact can explain the independence of anti-aggregatory potency of indomethacin from the amount of arachidonic acid used for aggregation. One cannot explain the mode of antiaggregatory action of L 8027 in terms of its anticyclooxygenase activity. Indeed, L 8027 has been found to inhibit thromboxane A$_2$ synthetase in platelet microsomes when crude extract of prostaglandin endoperoxides is used as the substrate (Gryglewski, 1977). Thus a simple technique for platelet aggregation can help to differentiate between cyclooxygenase and thromboxane A$_2$ synthetase inhibitors. Figure 5 shows that the inhibition of arachidonate-induced platelet aggregation parallels the inhibition of thromboxane A$_2$ formation by platelets. These results strongly indicate that thromboxane A$_2$ is an essential link in the process of platelet aggregation induced by arachidonic acid in contrast to the suggestion of Needleman *et al.* (1976b).

Summing up, additional tests for antiplatelet and antithromboxane A$_2$ synthetase activities of prostaglandin synthetase inhibitors are valuable complementary procedures that should be incorporated into the scheme of the *in vitro* screening (Fig. 6).

V. Conclusions

Oxidative metabolism of arachidonic acid in microsomes gives rise to many biologically active products. Pharmacological interference in the enzymic conversion of arachidonic acid is or might be useful in the treatment of inflammation, pain, pyresis, and arterial thrombosis. All acidic nonsteroidal anti-inflammatory drugs inhibit prostaglandin biosynthesis by inactivation of arachidonic acid cyclooxygenase. A single *in vitro* test for inactivation of microsomal cyclooxygenase is not sufficient to predict anti-inflammatory potency of an inhibitor. This enzymic test should be supplemented by measuring the potency of an inhibitor to bind to albumin. The ratio of antienzymic and albumin-binding potencies gives a rough approximation of an index for anti-inflammatory potency

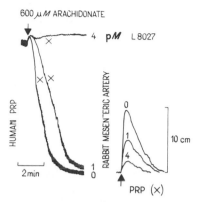

FIG. 6. Simultaneous assay of antiaggregating and antithromboxane A$_2$ synthetase activities of L 8027 at concentrations of 1 and 4 pM. Human platelet-rich plasma (PRP) was aggregated with arachidonic acid at a concentration of 600 μM in the absence (0) or in the presence (1 and 4 pM) of L 8027. Crosses denote the withdrawal of 100-μl aliquots of PRP for bioassay of thromboxane A$_2$ using a strip of rabbit mesenteric artery (Figs. 3 and 4). Note that depression of thromboxane A$_2$ formation by a half with L 8027 at a concentration of 1 pM was not sufficient to inhibit platelet aggregation. Inhibition of platelet aggregation occurred with L 8027 at concentration of 4 pM, and then only minute amounts of thromboxane A$_2$ were formed.

in vivo within a series of chemical analogs. Some nonacidic anti-inflammatory drugs also inhibit cyclooxygenase. One of them, 1'-(isoproyl-2-indolyl)-3-pyridyl-3-ketone (L 8027) with a moderate anticyclooxygenase activity has been found to be a powerful inhibitor of thromboxane A$_2$ synthetase in platelets. This biochemical activity of L 8027 can explain its antiplatelet action. Therefore it is strongly recommended to test any prostaglandin synthetase inhibitor for its antiaggregating and antithromboxane A$_2$ activities. Hydrocortisone and synthetic anti-inflammatory steroids inhibit the release of prostaglandin and thromboxane A$_2$ from stimulated intact cells, tissues, and organs but do not inhibit microsomal cyclooxygenase.

ACKNOWLEDGMENT

I gratefully acknowledge the generous grant of equipment from the Trustees of the Wellcome Trust, London, Great Britain.

References

Brodie, B. B., and Hogben, C. A. M. (1957). *J. Pharm. Pharmacol.* **9**, 345–380.
Brown, J. H., Mackey, H. K., and Rigillo, D. A. (1967). *Proc. Soc. Exp. Biol. Med.* **125**, 837–843.

Bunting, S., Moncada, S., Needleman, P., and Vane, J. R. (1976a). *Br. J. Pharmacol.* **58**, 334P–345P.

Bunting, S., Moncada, S., and Vane, J. R. (1976b). *Proc. Br. Pharmacol. Soc.* **1**, 48.

Caprino, L., Borelli, F., and Falchetti, R. (1973). *Arzeim.-Forsch.* **23**, 1277–1283.

Chignell, C. F. (1969). *Mol. Pharmacol.* **5**, 455–462.

Chignell, C. F. (1971). *Handb. Exp. Pharmakol.* **28**, Part 1, 187–212.

Constantine, J. W., and Purcell, I. M. (1973). *J. Pharmacol. Exp. Ther.* **187**, 653–665.

Daniel, E., and Weber, C. (1966). *Biochemistry* **5**, 1893–1907.

Darska, J. (1976). Ph.D. Thesis, Copernicus Academy of Medicine in Cracow.

Deby, C., Descamps, M., Binon, F., and Bacq, Z. M. (1971). *C. R. Seances Soc. Biol. Ses Fil.* **165**, 2465–2468.

De Clerck, F., Vermylen, J., and Reneman, R. (1975). *Arch. Int. Pharmacodyn. Ther.* **216**, 263–279.

Dembinska-Kiec, A., Zmuda, A., and Krupinska, J. (1976). *Adv. Prostaglandin Thromboxane Res.* **1**, 99.

Ferreira, S. H., Moncada, S., and Vane, J. R. (1971). *Nature (London), New Biol.* **231**, 237–239.

Fjalland, B. (1974). *J. Pharm. Pharmacol.* **26**, 448–451.

Flanagan, M. T., and Ainworth, S. (1968). *Biochim. Biophys. Acta* **168**, 16–26.

Flower, R. J. (1974). *Pharmacol. Rev.* **26**, 33–67.

Flower, R. J., and Vane, J. R. (1972). *Nature (London)* **240**, 410–411.

Flower, R. J., Gryglewski, R., Herbaczynska-Cedro, K., and Vane, J. R. (1972). *Nature (London), New Biol.* **238**, 104–106.

Flower, R. J., Cheung, H. S., and Cushman, D. W. (1973). *Prostaglandins* **4**, 325–341.

Flower, R. J., Blackwell, G. J., and Parsons, M. F. (1976). *Proc. Int. Congr. Pharmacol., 6th, 1975* Abstract, p. 292.

Gaut, Z. N., Baruth, H., Randall, L. O., Ashley, C., and Paulsrud, J. R. (1975). *Prostaglandins* **10**, 59–66.

Gerber, D. A., Cohen, N. M., and Giustra, R. (1967). *Biochem. Pharmacol.* **16**, 115–120.

Gilmore, N., Vane, J. R., and Wyllie, J. H. (1968). *Nature (London)* **218**, 1135–1137.

Glenn, E. M., Wilks, J., and Bowman, B. J. (1972). *Proc. Soc. Exp. Biol. Med.* **141**, 879–886.

Glenn, E. M., Rohloff, N., Bowman, B. J., and Lyster, S. C. (1973). *Agents Actions* **3/4**, 210–216.

Gryglewski, R. (1966). *J. Pharm. Pharmacol.* **18**, 474.

Gryglewski, R. (1974). *In* "Prostaglandin Synthetase Inhibitors" (H. J. Robinson and J. R. Vane, eds.), pp. 33–52. Raven, New York.

Gryglewski, R. J. (1976). *Pharmacol. Res. Commun.* **8**, 337–348.

Gryglewski, R. J., Zmuda, A., Korbut, R., Krecioch, C., and Bieroń, K. (1977). *Nature (London)*, **267**, 627–630.

Gryglewski, R., and Vane, J. R. (1972a). *Br. J. Pharmacol.* **45**, 37–47.

Gryglewski, R., and Vane, J. R. (1972b). *Br. J. Pharmacol.* **46**, 449–457.

Gryglewski, R. J., Ryznerski, A., Gorczyca, M., and Krupinska, J. (1976a). *Adv. Prostaglandin Thromboxane Res.* **1**, 117–120.

Gryglewski, R. J., Dembinska-Kiec, A., Grodzinska, L., and Panczenko, B. (1976b). *In* "Lung Cells in Disease" (A. Bouhuys, ed.) pp. 289–307. Elsevier, Amsterdam.

Ham, E. A., Cirillo, K. J., Zanetti, M., Shen, T. Y., and Kuehl, F. A. (1972). *In* "Prostaglandins in Cellular Biology" (P. W. Ramwell and B. B. Pharriss, eds.), pp. 345–352. Plenum, New York.

Hamberg, M. (1972). *Biochem. Biophys. Res. Commun.* **49**, 720–726.

Hamberg, M., Svensson, J., Wakabayashi, T., and Samuelsson, B. (1974). *Proc. Natl. Acad. Sci. U.S.A.* **71**, 345–349.

Hamberg, M., Svensson, J., and Samuelsson, B. (1975). *Proc. Natl. Acad. Sci. U.S.A.* **72**, 2994–2998.

Ho, P. P., and Esterman, M. A. (1974). *Prostaglandins* **6**, 107–113.

Horodniak, J. W., Julius, M., Zarembo, J. E., and Bender, D. (1974). *Biochem. Biophys. Res. Commun.* **57**, 539–545.

Ku, E. C., and Wasvary, J. M. (1975). *Biochim. Biophys. Acta* **384**, 360–368.

Lands, W. E. M., Lee, R., and Smith, W. (1971). *Ann. N.Y. Acad. Sci.* **180**, 107–122.

Lands, W. E. M., Cook, H. W., and Rome, L. H. (1975). *Abstr. Int. Conf. Prostaglandins, 19??* p. 3.

Levine, L. (1972). *Biochem. Biophys. Res. Commun.* **47**, 888–896.

Lewis, G. P., and Piper, P. J. (1975). *Nature (London)* **254**, 308–311.

Malmsten, C., Hamberg, M., Svensson, J., and Samuelsson, B. (1975). *Proc. Natl. Acad. Sci. U.S.A.* **72**, 1446–1450.

Meyer, M. C., and Guttman, D. E. (1968). *J. Pharm. Sci.* **57**, 895–917.

Miller, W. S., and Smith, J. G. (1966). *Proc. Soc. Exp. Biol. Med.* **122**, 634–636.

Mizushima, Y. (1964). *Arch. Int. Pharmacodyn. Ther.* **149**, 1–7.

Mizushima, Y., Ishi, Y., and Masumoto, S. (1975). *Biochem. Pharmacol.* **24**, 1589–1592.

Moffat, A. C., Patterson, D. A., Curry, A. S., and Gwen, P. (1972). *Eur. J. Toxicol.* **5**, 160–162.

Mustard, J. F., and Packham, M. A. (1975). *Drugs* **9**, 19–76.

Needleman, P., Moncada, S., Bunting, S., Vane, J. R., Hamberg, M., and Samuelsson, B. (1976a). *Nature (London)* **261**, 558–560.

Needleman, P., Minkes, M., and Raz, A. (1976b). *Science* **193**, 163–165.

O'Brien, J. R. (1968). *Lancet* **1**, 894–895.

Patrono, C., Ciabattoni, G., Greco, F., and Grossi-Belloni, D. (1976). *Adv. Prostaglandin Thromboxane Res.* **1**, 125–131.

Piper, P. J., and Vane, J. R. (1969). *Nature (London)* **233**, 29–35.

Robak, J., Dembinska-Kiec, A., and Gryglewski, R. (1975). *Biochem. Pharmacol.* **24**, 2057–2060.

Roth, G. J., Stanford, N., and Majerus, P. W. (1975). *Proc. Natl. Acad. Sci. U.S.A.* **72**, 3073–3076.

Samuelsson, B., Granström, E., and Hamberg, M. (1967). *Prostaglandins, Proc. Nobel Symp., 2nd, 1966* pp. 31–44.

Samuelsson, B., Hamberg, M., Svensson, J., and Malmsten, C. (1976). *Abstr., Int. Congr. Pharmacol. 6th, 1975* p. 40.

Scatchard, G. (1949). *Ann. N.Y. Acad. Sci.* **51**, 660–672.

Schaeffer, H. J. (1971). *Drug Des.* **2**, 129–160.

Settle, W., Hegeman, S., and Featherstone, R. M. (1971). *Handb. Exp. Pharmakol.* **28**, Part 1, 175–186.

Shen, T. Y., Ham, E. A., Cirillo, V. J., and Zanetti, M. (1974). *In* "Prostaglandin Synthetase Inhibitors" (H. J. Robinson and J. R. Vane, eds.), pp. 19–31. Raven, New York.

Sih, C. J., and Takeguchi, C. A. (1973). *In* "Prostaglandins" (P. W. Ramwell, ed.), Vol. 1, pp. 83–100. Plenum, New York.

Silver, M. J., Smith, J. B., Ingerman, C., and Kocsis, J. J. (1973). *Prostaglandins* **4**, 863–875.

Skidmore, I. F., and Whitehouse, M. W. (1965). *J. Pharm. Pharmacol.* **17**, 671–673.

Skidmore, I. F., and Whitehouse, M. W. (1966). *J. Pharm. Pharmacol.* **18**, 558–560.

Smith, J. B., and Willis, A. L. (1971). *Nature (London) New Biol.* **231**, 235–237.

Smith, W. L., and Lands, W. E. M. (1971). *J. Biol. Chem.* **246**, 6700–6702.

Svensson, J., Hamberg, M., and Samuelsson, B. (1975). *Acta Physiol. Scand.* **94**, 222–228.

Takeguchi, G., and Sih, C. J. (1972). *Prostaglandins* **2**, 169–184.

Takeguchi, G., Kohono, E., and Sih, C. J. (1971). *Biochemistry* **10**, 2372–2376.

Tomlinson, R. V., Ringold, H. J., Quershi, M. C., and Forchielli, E. (1972). *Biochem. Biophys. Res. Commun.* **46**, 552–559.

Vane, J. R. (1957). *Br. J. Pharmacol. Chemother.* **12**, 344–349.

Vane, J. R. (1964). *Br. J. Pharmacol. Chemother.* **23**, 360–373.

Vane, J. R. (1971). *Nature (London), New Biol.* **231**, 232–235.

Vane, J. R. (1972a). *In* "Inflammation: Mechanisms and Control" (I. H. Lepow and P. A. Ward, eds.), pp. 261–279. Academic Press, New York.

Vane, J. R. (1972b). *Hosp. Pract.* **7**, 61–71.

Vargaftig, B. B., and Dao Hai, N. (1971). *Pharmacology* **6**, 99–108.

Vargaftig, B. B., and Zirinis, P. (1973). *Nature (London), New Biol.* **244**, 114–116.

Weinryb, I., Chasin, M., Free, C. A., Harris, D. M., Goldenberg, H., Michel, I. M., Raik, V. S. Phillips, M., Samamiego, S., and Hess, S. (1972). *J. Pharm. Sci.* **61**, 1556–1567.

Weiss, H. J., Aledort, L. M., and Kochwa, S. (1968). *J. Clin. Invest.* **47**, 2169–2180.

Whitehouse, M. W., and Haslam, J. M. (1962). *Nature (London)* **196**, 1323–1324.

Whitehouse, M. W., Kippen, I., and Klinenberg, J. R. (1971). *Biochem. Pharmacol.* **20**, 3309–3320.

Wiethold, G., Hellenbrecht, D., Lemmer, B., and Palm, D. (1973). *Biochem. Pharmacol.* **22**, 1437–1449.

Willis, A. L. (1974). *Science* **183**, 325–327.

Willis, A. L., and Kuhn, D. C. (1973). *Prostaglandins* **4**, 127–129.

Wiseman, E. H., McIlhenny, H. M., and Bettis, J. W. (1975). *J. Pharm. Sci.* **64**, 1469–1475.

Zaroslinski, J. F., Keresztes-Nagy, S., Mass, R. F., and Oester, Y. T. (1974). *Biochem. Pharmacol.* **23**, 1767–1776.

Atherosclerosis, Hypothyroidism, and
Thyroid Hormone Therapy

PAUL STARR

*R.I.A. Laboratories, Inc.,
South Pasadena, California*

I. Introduction

The disorders of cholesterol and triglycerides, which may be studied by analyzing the lipoproteins which transport them, have been shown in many clinics and laboratories to be associated with coronary artery disease, and it has been quite logical to seek protection from coronary heart disease (CHD) by correcting these disorders. This also led to the question of the etiological role that hypothyroidism might exert, and it appears to be true that years of myxoedema are followed by more severe coronary atherosclerosis. On the other hand, very few men suffering from advanced CHD are myxoedematous. In fact, in Wren's series (1968),

345

only 6% had the usual laboratory evidence of any degree of hypothyroidism. Thus, efforts at prevention were directed at the atherosclerosis itself rather than the thyroid state.

But subclinical hypothyroidism is very frequent and affects many physiological and biochemical systems with a wide variety of clinical syndromes. Thyroxine acts on a large number of enzymes, such as succinoxidase, creatine phosphokinase, and 6-glucose phosphate hydrogenase and many others, particularly in organs probably involved in atherosclerotic myocardial disease, i.e., liver, kidney, heart, and skeletal muscles.

The administration of thyroxine and triiodothyronine together, as they occur in USP desiccated thyroid tablets, has a significant effect on several parameters. Three grains of this medication contain 300 μg of thyroxine and 90 to 120 μg of triiodothyronine. Several authors, discussed below, have found that sustained daily oral ingestion of this dose in apparently euthyroid patients, lowers cholesterol levels, changes the lipoprotein pattern, and protects against heart attacks. What other biochemical or physiological changes are brought about which reduce heart attacks should be the subject of intensive clinical investigation.

II. Argument

1. Atherosclerosis and hypothyroidism exist together in subclinical pathogenic states, in a large fraction of the population of the United States.

2. The diagnostic difficulty: The hormone serum concentrations, indicated by the PBI, the Murphy-Pattee, and TSH are associated with, but do not constitute, hypothyroidism.

3. The therapeutic dilemma: The thyroid hormone has a beneficial long-term biochemical effect but a dangerous acute inotropic effect.

4. Studies relating hypothyroidism to atherosclerosis: Myxoedema alone does not aggravate CHD.

5. Dextrothyroxine studies, 1958–1964.

6. Therapeutic experience: Desiccated thyroid medication sufficient to lower serum cholesterol without raising physiological processes above normal reduces the incidence of CHD by 75%.

III. Atherosclerosis, Hypothyroidism, and Thyroid Hormone Therapy

Atherosclerosis is a vascular abnormality that has reached high endemic frequency, especially in America, and now constitutes one of the major public health problems. As Frederickson (1971) has said: "There is the undeniable demonstration of a steep increase in incidence of coronary artery disease in patients with plasma cholesterol levels ranging from 220 mg/100 ml to 270 mg/100 ml. . . . A note of urgency is added by the magnitude of the problem, for the present number of deaths in the U.S. from myocardial infarction in persons under the age of 65 exceeds 160,000 per year."

Twenty-five percent of American men, 45 to 54 years of age, and 28% of American women of that age, have serum cholesterol levels greater than 250 mg% (U.S. National Center for Health Statistics, 1967). Articles by Keys (1970, 1972), Kannel *et al.* (1964), and Paul (1971) emphasize the frequency of atherosclerosis and the associated CHD.

The problem of the possible relationship of hypothyroidism to CHD is made significant by the fact that nonmyxoedematous (called *subclinical*) hypothyroidism is also an endemic disease occurring in the same individuals who have hypercholesterolemia.

The classical Framingham study (Kannel *et al.*, 1964) of 5127 persons free of coronary artery disease demonstrated that the later occurrence of coronary heart disease was a direct function of the level of serum cholesterol. Unfortunately, no measurement of thyroid hormone magnitude was included in the study.

Full-blown clinical myxoedema associated with extreme hypercholesterolemia, neurologic, myopathic, dermatological, and severely slowed metabolism is not common. This lack of frequency of total athyreosis, which one may guess constitutes only 5% of all cases of hypothyroidism in a population, is responsible for the lack of diagnostic investigation of all patients with hypercholesterolemia, in regard to hypothyroidism.

IV. Indications of the Common Occurrence of Subclinical Hypothyroidism

This subject was reviewed by Lowrey *et al.* in 1957. The PBI was determined in 2807 men: 610 of these were "white collar" executive or supervisory men in industry in Southern California; 340 or 12% of the total, including the blood bank men, had PBI levels below 4.0 μg/100 ml. If three-quarters of the men with serum PBI values of 4.0 μg% or less have clinical hypothyroidism, as this study indicated, the total of American men in the middle age group with this important deficiency may exceed 1 million.

In a similar study (Lowrey and Starr, 1959), including this population, plus 735 male physicians (tested at the annual meeting of the American Medical Association) and 1015 women employees of the Los Angeles County General Hospital (a total of 5755 persons) the serum PBI levels were as follows: the mean for the men was 5.3 μg% with a standard deviation of $\pm$ 1.19%, and the mean for the women was 5.6 μg% with a standard deviation of $\pm$ 1.22.

On the basis of interviews, physical examinations, and laboratory studies, it was concluded that the PBI values below 4.0 μg% in men and 4.5 μg% in women are diagnostic of hypothyroidism. In these four populations, such evidence of hypothyroidism was found in 4.9% of working men, 9.2% in blood bank patients, 4.2% in the physicians, and 7.3% among the women hospital employees.

The effects of correcting the subclinical hypothyroidism were reviewed in 1962. "As the PBI is raised to normal, physical signs change; previously unfelt symptoms are demonstrated by their disappearance! Well being is restored, abnormal chemical conditions are corrected, and vital functions become healthful: children grow, women ovulate, pregnancy carries through, hypercholesterolemia is reduced, anemia is corrected, fatigue alleviated, fibrositis resolves, and mental activity and good spirits increase" (Starr, 1962). With all this, it seems possible that atherosclerosis may be prevented or even reversed.

Lisser (1955) emphasized the frequency and the multiplicity of clinical symptoms due to subclinical hypothyroidism: "The patient may not look myxoedematous at all, and the dominating or motivating reason for which relief is sought may lead the consultant astray." He listed nine categories of symptoms or disorders that warrant study for possible hypothyroidism: (1) Circulatory; (2) gastrointestinal; (3) anemia-hematologic; (4) arthritis; (5) gynecologic or urologic; (6) ear, nose, and throat; (7) skin; (8) psychic or central nervous system; and (9) metabolic.

An excellent and exhaustive analysis of the problem of this diagnosis of hypothyroidism was given by Wayne (1960) in the second Lumblein lecture. He gave a list of 12 symptoms and 9 signs which may be helpful and concluded, "When the clinician fails to recognize the possibility of an obvious case of hypothyroidism, it is often because the possibility of this condition has not entered his mind."

Billewicz et al. (1969) add a long list of symptoms and signs of hypothyroidism and analyze them statistically to arrive at a diagnosis.

Jeffries (1961) also emphasized the occurrence of "occult hypothyroidism." These clinical observations and chemical determinations of the level of circulating thyroxine in the individuals of a large and varied human population indicated that subclinical hypothyroidism is common.

V. Preliminary Summary

We then have two subclinical pathogenic states: atherosclerosis, in a large fraction of the population which does not have overt symptomatic CHD, and hypothyroidism, present in this same cohort without the symptoms and signs of myxoedema. Are they causally related?

VI. The Diagnostic Difficulty

An excellent analysis of the relationship of subclinical hypothyroidism to coronary vascular disease is given by DeGroot in the Keating Symposium (1972). He pointed out that "the most troubling problem in accepting the suggested relationship is how one diagnoses subclinical hypothyroidism." One might add that the establishment of the presence of non-symptomatic coronary artery insufficiency— coronary occlusive disease— is rarely made. It would require elaborate, expensive, and risky cardiac work, electrocardiographic and radiocinematic cardiac arteriography which the uncomplaining patient and conservative family doctor are not usually prone to carry out.

DeGroot goes on to say that a high level of RIA-TSH values are suggestive but not absolute proof of hypothyroidism; however, low free T_4 or free T_4 plus low T_3 levels are certainly indicative. But as we have said, the fundamental principle cannot be forgotten; *the serum concentration of any hormone does not establish the metabolic state of the processes in the body dependent on that hormone.*

VII. Definition of Hypothyroidism

Hypothyroidism is the subnormal condition of biochemical processes dependent on thyroxine and/or triiodothyronine (Starr, 1971). The state of hypothyroidism cannot be proved by the measurement of the concentration of thyroid hormone (PBI) in the circulating blood. Only an increasing probability is indicated by progressively lower values. It is worthwhile to study individuals with PBI values below 4 μg/100 ml, but it is certain that many such people do not have hypothyroidism and equally certain that some with PBI values above this level do have hypothyroidism. The method for determining which do and which do not is at present not established.

We suggest a change of emphasis from the thyroid hormone concentration in the sera to the measurement of biochemical parameters dependent for normality on optimal amounts of freely functioning intracellular thy-roxine, such as the erythrocytic glucose-6-phosphate dehydrogenase, serum creatine phosphokinase, fibrinolytic activity, urinary and serum hydroxy-proline, tyrosine, cholesterol, and lipoproteins. Doubtless measurable changes due to hypothyroidism occur in other systems, such as the central nervous, genitourinary, gastrointestinal, and skeletal. When such indicators of optimal thyroid hormone intracellular availability are evaluated as to the quantitative specificity, the diagnosis of subclinical hypothyroidism may be put on a firm basis. The use of the serum PBI concentration as a screen-ing procedure may still be valid (Starr, 1971).

It seems probable that the pituitary TSH secretion, which is dependent on homeostatic feedback physiology, may indicate the state of hypothyroid-ism as previously defined. In the light of studies of TSH (Odell et al., 1967; Greenberg et al., 1970; Lemarchand et al., 1969; Hall et al., 1971; Hersh-man and Pittman, 1971; Mayberry et al., 1971; Gordin et al., 1972), the correct procedure for the demonstration of cases of subclinical as well as clinical hypothyroidism in any population may be the measurements of serum TSH by radioimmunoassay technique.

The mean value of serum TSH found in 119 euthyroid patients at the R.I.A. Laboratories was 3.0 μunits/ml, $SD \pm 0.9$ giving a range of 0.3 to 6.5 μunits/ml. Of 602 serum tests for TSH in untreated patients from office practice 6.3% were above 6.5 μunits/ml. Of 1375 serum tests of a popula-tion of outpatients, including clinic and ^{131}I-treated patients, 11.3% were abnormally elevated. Of 2779 citizens of Whickham, England, 5% had serum TSH values above normal. When such subjects, even without overt hypothyroidism, are given small maintenance doses of sodium L-thyroxine (such as 0.15 mg) the TSH level is reduced to normal.

If possible, determination of serum TSH should be accompanied by RIA measurements of T_3, T_4, TBG, and TG.

But still the demonstration of hypothyroidism in any person should be the measurement of the somatic processes depending on thyroxine, such as succinoxidase (Barker, 1964).

Because of this diagnostic difficulty, we do not have the facts to prove which men in the community are hypothyroid, and if they were found, we would not, in many cases, have the data to demonstrate, before death, that they have atherosclerosis. For example, diminished available intracellular thyroxine causes significant changes in (1) the cholesterol-lipoprotein sys-tems; (2) the somatic and cardiac muscle system (CPK); (3) cardiac contraction (lengthening of isovolumetric contraction time and ECG potential); and (4) the hematopoetic system (reduction of red cell mass). Clinical observations (Lisser, 1955; Wayne, 1960; Billewicz et al., 1969) are valuable but not equivalent to quantitative biochemical measurements.

These observations are essential to provide indication for the biochemical tests.

VIII. The Therapeutic Dilemma

In addition to the diagnostic difficulty, there is a therapeutic dilemma. Both L- and D-thyroxine stimulate beta adrenergic reception of catecholamines (cardiac inotropism) with consequent relative coronary artery insufficiency, angina pectoris, and risk of myocardial infraction even while reducing cholesterolemia and possibly reducing the atherosclerosis which favors CHD.

Hence the use of thyroid hormones to reduce atherosclerosis (via reduction of serum cholesterol) is constantly complicated by increased cardiac inotropism, which may lead to heart attack.

The titration of the permissible dose in each case makes wholesale prescription completely incorrect, since the increase of thyroxine metabolism, presumably antiatherosclerotic, may be great in one patient as compared with the thyroxine effect in another patient; the susceptibility of lipoproteins to reduction may be quite variable, and especially the amount of sensitivity of the anginagenic mechanisms (cathecholamine or adrenergic reception) may be extremely variable. The coronary narrowing may be slight in one patient, and permit successful use of significant amounts of thyroxine which at this larger dosage may reduce serum cholesterol and actually reduce vascular pathology, whereas in another patient the coronary narrowing may be so severe that an effective dose of thyroxine is not possible to reach.

IX. The Coronary Drug Project

The requirements for determining the "definitive role of thyroid preparations (Choloxin) in cardiologic therapy," so eloquently stated in the review of hormonal therapy by Stamler, Best, and Turner in 1963, were met in the Coronary Drug Project reported in 1972 (Stamler *et al.*, 1972).

The therapeutic dilemma was disclosed and the insoluble paradox became evident.

The therapeutic agent being studied, dextrothyroxine, has a long-term beneficial biochemical or metabolic effect (reduction of cholesterol and modification of atherogenic lipoproteins), while at the same time it has a dangerous immediate or acute myocardial effect, i.e., aggravation of ischemia dependent on increased inotropism. The balance between these effects—one good and one bad—is a matter of dosage on the basis of individual inotropic susceptibility.

One criticism of the Steering Committee (of the CDP) may be that they did not realize the physiological thyronine potency of D-thyroxine itself; they refer to "the inability to render DT_4 totally free of the naturally active levothyroxine medium" as though the dextrothyroxine sodium did not have naturally active potency of its own.

From the studies cited in the following discussion, it can be proven that D-thyroxine, as itself, has thyroid hormone potency in its own right for the production of oxygen consumption, growth, and cardiac inotropism.

One rationalization of the results of the Coronary Drug Project in the population of 1083 postmyocardial infarction patients (all treated with 6 mg of D-thyroxine a day) of whom 14.8% died, is that they died from increased myocardial inotropism (Ausman *et al.*, 1973), while others expected to die of progressive coronary disease did not, and that the 12.5% of the 2715 placebo patients who died did so from the progressive atherosclerotic coronary disease. What the result would have been if D-thyroxine had been used giving 4 mg daily for all patients, or best of all, if the daily dose had been adjusted to each individual, cannot be assumed now (Schoch, 1969).

Stamler, Best, and Turner summarized their report in 1972 as follows:

It is a reasonable assumption that timely correction of hypercholesterolemia should favorably influence prognosis. It should reduce premature mortality and morbidity from atherosclerotic heart disease, particularly when serum cholesterol levels are lowered relatively early, prior to the onset of clinically manifest disease.

Nevertheless, responsible clinicians and investigators must always recognize that such assumptions require validation. And the fact is that at this juncture, no long-term studies have been done evaluating either the primary or secondary preventive potential of thyroid or D-thyroxine. The decisive endpoint is, of course, not effects of serum lipid levels per se, but rather influences on occurrence and recurrence rates of myocardial infarction, sudden death, congestive heart failure, and particularly effects on survival. Elucidation of these critical questions requires long-term studies, 4 to 5 years in duration, with hundreds of patients properly assigned on a double blind basis to control the treatment groups. Such work remains to be done for thyroid preparations. Pending its accomplishment, the definitive role of thyroid preparations in cardiologic therapy remains sub judice.

In recent years, two research groups have carefully explored the effects of desiccated thyroid on hypercholesterolemia in man. In the first of these studies (Strisower *et al.,* 1957), a dosage of 195 mg/day (3 grains) of ordinary powder was given to euthyroid patients.

The subjects were 30 males and 30 females, ages 20–59, with schizophrenia, who were otherwise clinically healthy. A marked depression of serum cholesterol levels resulted after 3 weeks of administration, from a control mean for the group of 216–157 mg/100 ml. However, when therapy was continued, "escape" occurred, so that by weeks 20–30, serum cholesterol levels had risen to 210 mg/100 ml. Subsequently, it was reported that no escape occurred when the hormone was given in doses of 260–325 mg/day (4–5 grains). With this higher dosage of desiccated thyroid powder, a sustained fall occurred in total serum cholesterol, and in the lipoprotein S_f classes 0–12, 12–20, 20–100, and 100–400. With this higher dosage, serum cholesterol levels were kept in the range of 184–200 mg/100 ml for as long as 2 years. After discontinuance of the 5-grain dose of desiccated thydroid, the serum cholesterol rose rapidly to 269 and gradually fell to 235 mg for the remaining 15 weeks of follow-up (Strisower *et al.,* 1957).

Moses and Danowski (1963) observed significant reduction of serum cholesterol, phospholipids, and triglycerides in 38 male subjects during a period of 5 months with the oral administration of 3 grains daily of desiccated thyroid. There was no evidence of hypothyroidism in these men before treatment, i.e., body weight, pulse rate, blood pressure, and serum protein bound iodine levels were not altered from pretreatment values.

With the high dosage level, however (actually unnecessary), a distressingly large number of cardiac patients develop tachycardia, angina pectoris, diarrhea, weight loss, and/or insomnia. These results drive home the need for caution in the use of large doses of thyroid hormone. This is particularly true for patients with frank clinical atherosclerotic coronary heart disease, for older persons, and for patients with overt hypothyroidism.

On the other hand, D-thyroxine in daily dosage of 4–8 mg is well tolerated by the majority of patients, especially those without coronary artery heart disease. The reduction of serum cholesterol is of the order of 15–25%.

Several years before the Coronary Drug Project, the Veterans Administration Drug Lipid Cooperative Study results were reported by Schoch (1969). From February 1963 to August 1966, 570 male patients were entered into the study. Changes in the dosage of D-thyroxine or its placebo were frequent in the early stages of the study, but increasing sophistication on the part of the investigators led to a resumption of full dosage of this drug in at least 95% of patients. At the end of the study the mortality in the placebo group was 28.7%, whereas the only group showing a lower overall mortality was in that group treated with D-thyroxine alone, 23.0%.

In summary, D-thyroxine (in a minimum dose of 4 mg daily) had a slightly beneficial effect on mortality rates for total deaths as well as for cardiovascular deaths. Sudden deaths were fewer, and major cardiovascular morbid events were also less frequent. Side effects were not discernible and adherence was good. The cholesterol-lowering effect was moderate (Schoch, 1969).

But the physician must remember that D-thyroxine DT_4 is a true calorigenic thyroid hormone of about one-tenth (to as little as one-fortieth) the strength of its L-isomer, but since the daily dosage is 10 times that of L-thyroxine, i.e., whole milligram versus tenths of milligrams, clinical symptoms are to be expected.

The very nature of the Coronary Drug Project stipulated that all subjects would have previously recognized heart disease. In this array of patients were a group with heart pathology, undergoing treatment with a digitalis glycoside. DT_4 was introduced into the treatment regimen in specific fashion at a rate greater than the prescribed course for the drug, a 2-mg/day increase each month versus the prescribed 1-mg/day increase, and to a level higher than that suggested for a patient with heart disease, 6 mg versus 4 mg/day. The data presented suggest that DT_4 and digitalis glycosides may have a synergistic and unfavorable effect on cardiac rhythmicity.

The report of the Coronary Drug Project (1972) suggested the presence of an important LT_4 contaminant in DT_4. Our studies have shown consistently (and we had reported previously to CDP investigators) that the LT_4 component is quite small, less than 0.1%. Therefore, we believe that LT_4 contamination had no part in the problems encountered in the Coronary Drug Project.

In conclusion, Ausman et al. (1973) reached the following judgments:

1. Chronic administration of D-thyroxine (DT_4), like thyroxine, has been demonstrated to augment the force of contraction of the heart.

2. D-Thyroxine and digitalis glycosides have an addictive, possibly synergistic unfavorable effect on cardiac rhythmicity when used in combination.

3. Excess deaths reported for the DT_4 group of the Coronary Drug Project may have resulted from lack of appreciation of the synergistic effect of digitalis glycosides and DT_4.

4. It appears that the study design, a double-blind randomization with absolute drug dosage, resulted in a dosage of DT_4 and digitalis that was, in some cases, too much.

5. Because of its inflexibility, we feel the double-blind randomized protocol is not a good choice when patients with adverse clinical elements

are to be admitted and particularly when combinations of treatment are permitted.

X. Studies Relating Hypothyroidism to Atherosclerosis

In regard to myxoedema as a cause of atherosclerosis, Steinberg (1968) studied the degree of coronary artery narrowing in 38 autopsies of myxoedema patients with atherosclerosis. Twenty-seven of these patients had been hypertensive and 11 were normotensive. The degree of myxoedema and the age distribution were similar and all are females, but the duration of the myxoedema and the associated obesity, and possible nicotine addiction was not given. It was found that the patients with normal blood pressure, even with the same degree of athyreosis, had less than half as much coronary artery narrowing (1.1 degrees) as those that had hypertension (3.2 degrees). It would seem then, that in the absence of the hypertensive vascular mechanism, the myxoedema did not produce more atherosclerosis (Table I).

In a similar autopsy study by Vanhaelst *et al.* (1967) on 25 patients whose myxoedema status was established by standard and special laboratory studies, 84% were found to have severe coronary atherosclerosis as

Table I

CORONARY DISEASE IN FEMALE PATIENTS WITH MYXOEDEMA, AGE-MATCHED CONTROLS AND WOMEN WITH BENIGN GENITAL LESIONS [a]

Patients	No.	Degree of coronary disease [b]	Statistical comparison with myxoedema group
Myxoedema	38	2.6	—
Matched controls	38	1.5	$p < .001$
Gynecologic controls [c]	77	1.8	$p < .01$
Hypertensive			
Myxoedema	27	3.2	—
Matched controls	23	1.6	$p < .001$
Gynecologic controls	44	1.8	$p < .001$
Normotensive			
Myxoedema	11	1.1	—
Matched controls	15	1.2	Not significant
Gynecologic controls	33	1.7	Not significant

[a] After Steinberg (1968).

[b] Scale, 0–4.

[c] Gynecologic controls: women with benign genital lesions.

compared to autopsy findings in 50 matched controls without hypothyroidism who had severe coronary atherosclerosis in only 46% of the cases. It would appear from the studies of Bastenie and Steinberg who measured the degree of atherosclerosis in 25 (Bastenie) and 38 (Steinberg) autopsies of patients with myxoedema that they had twice as much coronary artery narrowing as their "matched controls."

Another study by Bastenie in 1971 is summarized as follows:

In a systematic study, 406 female and 400 male patients admitted to clinical wards for miscellaneous non-thyroid diseases were screened for thyroid antibodies and serum-cholesterol levels. The clinical and laboratory data were analyzed by computer. In the female population, asymptomatic thyroiditis (i.e., preclinical hypothyroidism) represents an important risk factor for coronary heart disease (CHD). It abolishes the well-established sex ratio for CHD. Increased levels of serum cholesterol may play a part in this pathogenic mechanism. However, an alternative explanation is that a genetic factor may be responsible for both the tendency to develop atherosclerosis and for the lymphocytic thyroiditis.

XI. Dextrothyroxine Studies

Certainly the correction of hypothyroidism, subclinical or overt, is required. If atherosclerosis with cardiac dysfunction is present, or anticipated because of associated hypercholesteremic lipoprotein disease, sodium D-thyroxine would seem to be the drug of choice. With this in mind, a thorough familiarity with its pharmacology, physiology, and biochemistry is required. As has been suggested, lack of such knowledge was a handicap to the physicians conducting the Coronary Drug Project. The following studies demonstrate some of the peculiar characteristics of the dextrorotary thyroxine.

In 1958, clinical and biochemical effects of the isomers of thyroxine were compared using small doses of sodium L-thyroxine and sodium D-thyroxine given orally (Starr, 1958).

In four athyreotic patients, dosage of the l-isomer from 0.1 to 0.8 mg was effective in initiating the rise of BMR and the lowering of serum cholesterol, but the D-isomer at this dose level had negligible effects.

In another series, with doses of this order of magnitude, it was found that it required five times as much D-thyroxine as L-thyroxine to produce the same serum PBI level. This is curious since Tanaka (Tanaka and Starr, 1959) showed the binding capacity of TBG for DT_4 was the same as for LT_4.

The small doses of L-thyroxine were not able to control hypothyroid hypercholesterolemia. Later it was shown that milligram doses of D-thyroxine lowered the high serum cholesterol of hypothyroidism without raising the BMR or the T waves of the myxoedema ECG (Starr, 1960).

Depression of [131]I 24-hour uptake was studied in euthyroid medical students before and after being given 0.5 mg of either L- or, for comparison, D-thyroxine, daily for 8 days. The reduction was 82% during L-thyroxine medication and 9% during D-thyroxine (Starr, 1958).

In a myxoedematous patient with ECG showing no T wave potential, a very small dose of L-thyroxine (25 μg orally daily) for 20 days produced low normal T waves, whereas in a similar case (not the same patient) 10,000 μg (10 mg) a day of sodium D-thyroxine for 18 days produced no T-wave potential in the ECG (Starr, 1958).

The BMR in eight successive myxoedematous patients rose from − 40%, the recognized athyroxic level, to within normal range (average − 10%) on D-thyroxine oral dosage from 4 to 12 mg a day. In other words, D-thyroxine is calorigenic (Starr, 1961a). Furthermore, in a deliberate overdosage, thyrotoxicosis medicamentosa was produced with D-thyroxine. Sixteen milligrams a day given one patient increased the BMR to +17 and the serum cholesterol to 155 mg/100 ml and at the same time, this hypermetabolism was accompanied by a pulse rate of only 75, again indicating the lower effect on the myocardium. Other patients, however, withstood such a dose without thyrotoxicosis (Starr *et al.*, 1960).

The restoration of basal metabolism to normal by D-thyroxine was similar to the restoration of growth to normal in weanling thyroidectomized rats (Lew *et al.*, 1963).

In the previous studies, it was found that in some patients high dosage (10 mg daily) of sodium D-thyroxine raised the metabolic rate and lowered the serum cholesterol level without an initial effect on the electrocardiogram. This was taken as pharmacologic evidence that the D-thyroxine was actually free of contamination by the L-isomer. One to two milligrams a day in three successive cases of untreated myxoedema lowered the serum cholesterol level in 32–42 days from 500 to 300, 330 to 215, and 375 to 280 mg/100 ml without raising the basal metabolic rates, which at the end of the study were − 36%, − 40%, and −40%, respectively. The electrocardiograms also remained unchanged. These results suggest that the metabolic pathway by which D-thyroxine or its products produces the reduction in serum cholesterol concentration is independent of that by which it raises the BMR or potentiates the ECG (Starr, 1960).

A striking difference in increase of cardiac output, stroke volume, left ventricular work, and left ventricular stroke work after administration of epinephrine was found in the same athyreotic patients when euthyroid on L-thyroxine as compared to those cardiac measurements when they were euthyroid on D-thyroxine. The cardiac output increased 47% when these patients were on L-thyroxine, and only 35% when they were on D-thyroxine (Starr, 1964).

Our clinical and pharmacologic experience during the last decade with a pure preparation of sodium D-thyroxine leads us to believe that the D-isomer of thyroxine molecule has (1) minimal activity in calorigenesis which may be made up for, if desired, by massive dosage; (2) equal or greater activity in lipid metabolism; (3) partial but effective function in the hypothalamic-pituitary thyroid homeostatic feedback mechanism; i.e., it can suppress pituitary thyrotropic hormone secretion; and (4) little activity in catecholamine physiology, perhaps because of the levorotary requirements of the levorotary epinephrine.

There are many data which suggest that the D-thyroxine used in our experiments was essentially free of the L-isomer.

Electrophoresis of a large amount of D-thyroxine labeled with ^{131}I shows only one large peak indicating that this sample was not mixed with other analogues, but this also does not exclude the presence of L-thyroxine which would travel in the same peak.

Much better evidence with some quantitative, rather than merely qualitative, characterization is given by the studies of Dr. Adeline Mather of Baxter Laboratories, Inc., Morton Grove, Illinois. In these studies, ^{131}I radioactive D-thyroxine was exposed to the action of L-amino acid oxidase with failure to produce any tetraiodothyroacetic acid, which would have indicated the presence of as little as 3% of L-thyroxine.

Clinical studies, which may be regarded as biological tests, are even better evidence of purity.

The intercomplex isoelectric base line of the electrocardiogram in the patients with complete athyreosis is very sensitive to the administration of sodium L-thyroxine; in one patient, as little as 25 μg daily by mouth produced normal T waves after 2 weeks. In another patient the administration of 2 mg (nearly 100 times as much daily) of sodium D-thyroxine did not produce any T waves at all in 30 days. This suggests an absence of as little as 1% of L-thyroxine which might be contained in the D-isomer preparation.

A further clinical experience, making it seem likely that the D-thyroxine preparation is free of the L-isomer, is provided by the basal metabolic rates of euthyroid patients receiving very large amounts of sodium D-thyroxine. For example, one patient, age 38, taking 10 mg a day for many months, had a basal metabolic rate of -20% which did not rise during this period of time when the serum PBI was over 20 mg %. The latter, of course, indicates a circulating D-thyroxine concentration of more than 30 μg %.

In contradiction to this apparent lack of a calorigenic effect, it is now possible to demonstrate that with this D-isomer preparation of thyroxine, apparently free of L-thyroxine, athyreotic myxoedema patients can be maintained indefinitely in a euthyroid condition. Nine athyreotic patients with initial basal metabolic values of about —40%, serum PBI values of about 1.0 μg %, and negligible ^{131}I uptake values have been treated from 3 to 12 months with sodium D-thyroxine alone, in dosage from 2 to 12 mg a day by mouth, with resulting normal BMRs, normal serum cholesterol concentrations, normal ECG tracings, and normal subjective and objective personal findings.

The dose of D-thyroxine which restores normal thyroid hormone biochemistry in myxoedema patients is about 10-fold that of the L-isomer. It has already been shown that it requires 5 times as much D-thyroxine daily by mouth to produce the same level of serum thyroxine as that produced by a dose of L-thyroxine.

The calorigenic effect of D-thyroxine in athyreotic myxoedematous patients does not at all invalidate the findings that (1) in such patients an initial minimal dose can be found which lowers serum cholesterol without raising the basal metabolic rate at all or (2) in euthyroid hypercholesterolemic patients, a large dose of sodium D-thyroxine will lower the serum cholesterol without raising the metabolic rate above normal.

Clinical experience of this effect may be summarized as follows: Sodium D thyroxine in daily oral dosage, varying from 2 to 16 mg, was given from 1 to 18 months to 11 patients having corrected, partial or complete hypothyroidism; 13 euthyroid patients having diabetes mellitus, and 17 euthyroid patients with idiopathic hypercholesterolemia. In any of these with original serum cholesterol values above 400 mg (12 patients), the average concentration of cholesterol on sodium D-thyroxine became 251 mg %; in those whose original value was between 300 and 400 mg % (20 patients), it was reduced to 242 mg %; in those whose initial value was between 200 and 300 mg % (11 patients), the average value on sodium D-thyroxine medication was 194 mg %. Obviously, the higher the initial abnormality, the greater was the effect of the D-thyroxine.

No instance of "escape" or failure to control the serum-cholesterol level occurred after several months of treatment in this series.

It is not suggested or claimed that this dissociation of biochemical from total calorigenic effect is not also produced by other thyronines or thyroxine analogues. But it does seem that this is accomplished with this preparation without thyrotoxicosis medicamentosa, and without any cardiotoxic effect as indicated either by angina, congestive failure, or ECG changes.

But perhaps the most striking difference between D- and L-isomers of thyroxine is in relation to epinephrine synergism. The synergistic or potentiating effect of L-thyroxine upon epinephrine is well known. Studies in our laboratory of electrocardiograms of rabbits given daily injections of L-thyroxine show violent increase in heart rate and action when given L-epineph-rine, whereas rabbits given daily injections of 10 times as much sodium D-thyroxine do not show such changes when given L-epinephrine. The after surviving auricle of such rabbits given L-thyroxine likewise shows exaggerated responsiveness to epinephrine, whereas the after surviving auricle of the animals maintained on D-thyroxine does not.

Further study of the use of D-thyroxine in patients with angina, arrhythmia, and congestive failure is being explored with the purpose of replacing entirely the endogenous L-thyroxine and triiodo-L-thyronine. Whether this will occur as a result of direct TSH suppression by the sodium D-thyroxine or will require the reduction of endogenous thyroid hormone secretion by antithyroid drugs, it is hoped that the replacement of the L-isomer by the D-isomer will reduce the catecholamine stimulus to the heart and ameliorate the cardiac insufficiency.

For this result to be compatible with general health, it has been necessary to demonstrate that sodium D-thyroxine alone will sustain normal biochemistry. The current euthyroid status of the athyreotic myxoedema patients reported in this communication established this therapeutic prerequisite (Starr, 1961b).

XII. Therapeutic Experience

Though a relationship between hypercholesterolemia and hypothyroidism has long been recognized, it has been generally assumed that thyroid deficits do not exist if the usual indices such as serum protein-bound iodine, ^{131}I trapping, and protein-bound ^{131}I conversion ratios are normal. However, the possibility exists that some degree of unrecognized hypothyroidism may exist even when these indices are normal and this may contribute to the increase in cholesterol and alteration in lipoprotein partition that occurs in aging but otherwise healthy adults.

To test this possibility, full replacement dosages of desiccated thyroid, 2–3 g/day, have been administered up to 10 months to aging diabetics, and nondiabetics institutionalized for custodial care. Measurement of body weight, pulse rate, and blood pressure and analyses of the protein-bound iodine, total and free cholesterol, phospholipids, and α- and β-lipoprotein cholesterol were made before and at regular intervals, after beginning the experimental regime.

While maintaining a normal bound iodine level, statistically significant decreases in total cholesterol and lipoprotein cholesterol were found in a great majority of subjects. While there was considerable variation in the persistence of the hypocholesteremic effect, the data indicated that even in subjects euthyroid by the usual indices, a thyroid deficit exerting considerable effect on the cholesterol-lipoprotein partition may be present. This study confirms the later report of Moses and Danowski (1963).

Eaton (1954) made a brief report of a very large clinical experience with this therapy. Several hundred diabetics given thyroid with no effect on diabetic control experienced improved circulation, increased redness, reduced infection and arterial thrombosis, and reduced incidence of gangrene.

The reduction of serum cholesterol and the lipoprotein of Gofman's atherogenic index by desiccated thyroid in daily oral dosage increased individually from 3 to 5 grains for 102 weeks with negligible weight loss, was interpreted as reducing the risk of coronary heart disease, possibly by reduction of atherosclerosis (Strisower *et al.,* 1957).

Alloxanized, cholesterol-fed rabbits transported massive concentrations of cholesterol in lipoproteins of S_f values greater than 80, almost none in S_f 12–40 lipoproteins. The normal rabbit, fed cholesterol, carries the excess cholesterol in the S_f 12–40 lipoproteins and develops atherosclerosis. Alloxan-diabetic rabbits carry the cholesterol in the lipoproteins above S_f 100 and do not show atherosclerosis. Strisower *et al.* reported in 1957 the treatment of euthyroid schizophrenic patients with at first 3 grains, and later 5 grains of USP desiccated thyroid with reduction of serum cholesterol concentration and S_f lipoprotein classes for as long as 2 years Stamler *et al.* (1972) assert as established that atherosclerosis tends to be frequent, premature and severe in hypothyroid persons (Vanhaelst *et al.,* 1967; Bastenie, 1971), and others deny this (Steinberg, 1968). How they were so sure of this is not evident.

Since USP desiccated thyroid (whether bovine or porcine) contains from 20% to 40%, i.e., 20 to 40 μg of triiodothyronine for each 100 mg of thyroxine, thyrotoxic clinical effects must be expected in some individuals (Devlin and Steefinin, 1962). In other words, the "therapeutic dilemma" is especially handicapping when this form of thyroid hormone is used. Nevertheless, by individualizing dosage, it is possible to maintain a euthyroid patient at an elevated thyrogenous metabolic state with reduced lipoproteins and cholesterol, particularly for several years.

A series of studies (Starr, 1970) reported from 1958 to 1964 concluded that sodium D-thyroxine (1) has therapeutic usefulness in all forms of hypothyroidism, particularly cases complicated by heart disease; (2) is an effective cholesterol-reducing agent in hypothyroid and idiopathic hypercholesterolemia and especially in diabetes mellitus; and (3) has an important field of clinical usefulness in heart disease, suggested by its ability to maintain normal oxygen consumption in a dose which reduces serum cholesterol without stimulating the heart through catecholamine synergism.

This conclusion is directly opposed to the advice of the Food and Drug

Administration, which states as contraindications known organic heart disease, including angina pectoris, history of myocardial infarction, cardiac arrhythmia, tachycardia, etc.

All of the cardiac patients constituting the clinical material of this paper (Starr, 1970) with the exception of one patient, who died of a cerebral vascular accident, are still alive, taking D-thyroxine, having experienced a reduction of serum cholesterol without aggravation of heart disease. It seems to us that this warning of the FDA against the use of D-thyroxine in heart disease may deprive such patients of a beneficial drug.

XIII. Cardiac Tolerance for Cholesteropenic Doses of Dextrothyroxine

Table II demonstrates the cholesterol-lowering effect of sodium D-thyroxine at a dose which does not significantly alter the pulse rate.

The clinical and laboratory data of the eight patients who have received sodium D-thyroxine from 5 to 10 years are presented in Table III. The clinical history and remarks in Table III are more significant than even the negative ECG findings; no case experienced heart failure or myocardial infarction.

In these eight patients, average PBI rose from 4.5 to 24.8; cholesterol fell from 342 to 262 (−23%); blood pressure changed 143/83 to 134/83; the average pulse rate did not change.

XIV. Discussion

These long-term patients with clinical evidence of heart disease are selected from a large number of clinic and private patients who have been given D-thyroxine, when indicated, for long periods of time. In our experience, no aggravation of cardiac pathology has occurred; individualization of dosage governed by cardiac response is essential. The use of D-thyroxine for such patients is routine in our practice. Signs of overdosage are the same as those produced by L-thyroxine, nervousness, tachycardia, cardiac consciousness, stenocardia, or angina pectoris. They subside promptly when dosage is reduced. It is important to remember that the high protein-bound iodine (PBI) produced by the usual dosage of D-thyroxine is not indicative of thyrotoxicosis. It is due to the 10-fold increase in organic iodine administered in the D-thyroxine which has less than one-tenth the thyrotoxic effect of the L-isomer.

Moyer (1967) reviewing 2340 patients without heart disease and approximately 2000 patients with heart disease, both treated with D-thy-

Table II

HEART RATE DETERMINED BY ECG BEFORE AND DURING SODIUM DEXTROTHYROXINE THERAPY

Patient	Diagnosis[a]	Age (years)	Cholesterol (mg/100 ml)		Resting ECG rate		Daily dose (mg)	Duration of treatment (months)
			Pre RX	End RX	Pre RX	End RX		
A. S.	Athy.	73	455	225	64	56	4	12
S. E.	Athy.	79	380	270	72	74	6	9
W. C.	Athy.	47	475	235	60	64	12	7
W. P.	Idio.	60	320	240	52	52	6	4
M. J.	Idio.	24	305	195	75	81	12	3
M. B.	Idio.	67	337	305	100	90	2–8	9.5
R. B.	Xan.	49	444	270	74	78	16	13
B. N.	Xan.	37	325	200	68	64	12	12
C. C.	Diab.	58	490	175	81	80	6	6
J. H.	Diab.	69	230	290	84	90	6	4
M. M.	Diab.	61	578	—	56	64	2	2.25

[a] Athy. = athyrotic; idio. = idiopathic hypercholesterolemia; xan. = xanthomatosis; diab. = diabetes mellitus.

Table III
CLINICAL AND LABORATORY DATA OF CARDIAC PATIENTS TREATED WITH
DEXTROTHYROXINE FOR MORE THAN 5 YEARS

Patient	Sex	Age (years)	Duration (months)		Laboratory findings	
					Initial	Final
W. C.	M	55	118	PBI	6.6	25.0
				Chol. *a*	500	304
				B.P.	190/120	150/100
				Pulse	60	100
I. T.	M	80	70	BPI	1.8	8.5
				Chol.	390	224
				B.P.	120/64	120/60
				Pulse	60	60
O. H.	F	65	120	PBI	1.6	10.5
				Chol.	464	178
				B.P.	130/70	130/80
				Pulse	76	80
G. H.	M	67	100	PBI	5.5	22.0
				Chol.	337	230
				B.P.	150/90	140/84
				Pulse	72	40–60
H. S.	F	60	91	PBI	5.9	17.0
				Chol.	352	224
				B.P.	156/100	150/100
				Pulse	72	72
R. B.	F	50	128	PBI	5.1	55.0
				Chol.	528	338
				B.P.	136/70	140/80
				Pulse	80	72
M. B.	M	25	108	PBI	4.6	13.3
				Chol.	375	330
				B.P.	140/80	140/90
				Pulse	64	72
B. N.	F	46	108	PBI	5.2	47.0
				Chol.	320	268
				B.P.	120/70	100/70
				Pulse	80	64

a Chol. = cholesterol, mg/100 ml

roxine, concluded that long-term administration of D-thyroxine does not appear to be specifically associated with serious cardiovascular effect.

His discussion of dosage is quite exact and agrees entirely with our experience and recommendations. He states that "dextrothyroxine is effective in lowering the blood cholesterol. Selection of the proper dosage for the individual patient is critically important and euthyroid patients without cardiac disease should receive 4–8 mg/day on a long-term basis. However, patients with severe coronary artery disease should be given a small dose initially—not more than 1 or 2 mg/day. This dosage should be increased at intervals of 2 weeks or more to a maximum of 4 mg/day. If the hypocholesterolemic effect is clearly inadequate, the dosage may be gradually increased to 6 mg/day. When this program is followed, the side effects will be minimal and reduction of blood cholesterol can be expected in approximately 85% of the patients treated."

A recent review of this subject was published by Cohen (1969). He reports that among a group of 53 patients, treated with D-thyroxine, there were 20 with angina pectoris. Of these, 15 reported amelioration while on D-thyroxine, four had no symptomatic change, and one considered himself worse. Of seven patients, with intermittent claudication, all experienced increased exercise tolerance. He concludes that the observations are consistent with his earlier impression of sustained benefit in subjects with and without cardiovascular disease on an individualized treatment program.

One of the most extensive studies of the relationship of endemic goiter and thyroid gland auto-antibodies to coronary heart disease was made by Bastenie (1971).

XV. Bastenie's Summary

The prevalence of coronary heart disease (CHD), serum cholesterol, protein-bound iodine (PBI), butanol-extractable iodine (BEI), nonbutanol-extractable iodine (non-BEI), thyroglobulin antibodies, and cytoplasmic antibodies were determined in four cohorts of men, 50 to 69 years, in Finland and Yugoslavia. Twelve hundred men were examined. Two of the areas, East Finland and Slavonia, have endemic goiter. The two Yugoslavian populations differed from each other only in regard to thyroid antibodies. These were more prevalent in Slavonia (4.0%) than in Dalmatia (1.2%). The Finns had more CHD than the Yugoslavs, higher mean levels of cholesterol, PBI, BEI, and non-BEI, and a higher prevalence of thyroid antibodies (6.0%). Within Finland, the eastern cohort had more CHD than the western one, higher cholesterol, PBI, BEI, and non-BEI. Thyroid antibodies occurred with equal frequency in East and West Finland. There was a tendency to higher PBI, BEI, and non-BEI among the East Finnish men with CHD than among those without it, but these tendencies did not reach statistical significance. There was a tendency to a higher prevalence of thyroid antibodies in CHD patients, but only in West Finland did this reach statistical significance.[1]

As shown in Table IV, goiter is endemic in East Finland, the mean serum

---

[1] This unpublished material was generously offered to us by Professors Keys and Bastenie.

Table IV
DATA FROM WEST AND EAST FINLAND

	West	East
Endemic goiter	—	+
No. of men [a]	279	213
Mean cholesterol	257 mg/100 ml	271 mg/100 ml
CHD no./1000 [b]	103	230
Mean PBI mg/100 ml	6.61 mg/100 ml	9.15 mg/100 ml
Mean BEI mg/100 ml	5.18	7.04
Mean BEI mg/100 ml (non-ex)	1.42	2.10
No. of cases T-ANTI-B	17(6%)	16(5.9%)
CHD cases [c]	5	5

[a] Number of men who had been followed for 10 years before taking blood samples when they were 50–69 years of age.

[b] Coronary Heart Disease rate per 1000.

[c] Number of cases of CHD in patients who had strongly positive thyroid antibodies.

cholesterol is higher than in West Finland which would suggest the presence of hypothyroidism or genetic lipoprotein disease or both; the rate of CHD in the East is twice as great as in the West.

The striking laboratory finding is a mean PBI in East Finland of 9.15 mg/100 ml as compared to 6.61 mg/100 ml in West Finland. This is very unusual, and appears to indicate very abnormal thyroid chemistry, certainly suggesting some nonfunctional serum organic iodine such as thyroglobulin or other iodinated protein. The butanol-extractable and non-butanol extractable iodine values are also abnormally high.

Unfortunately, the study does not indicate the presence of endemic hypothyroidism or even euthyroidism. This emphasizes the need for a truer demonstration of euthyroidism which might be provided by the RIA-TSH measurement, or other biochemical parameters characterizing euthyroidism.

Perhaps the most striking therapeutic experience is that reported by Barnes and Barnes (1972). For many years he has been treating patients in his practice on the basis of basal body temperature below 97.8°F obtained in the axilla, in bed, before the body surface is exposed, or muscular activity has occurred. Barnes concludes: "Thyroid dosage should be low initially, and increased at monthly intervals." The usual dose is 2 grains of desiccated thyroid, occasionally 3 grains, and rarely 4 grains. The basal temperature should never become elevated over 98.2°F. His results are tabulated in Table V.

The number of cases expected using the Framingham Study rate would

Table V

RARITY OF NEW CASES OF CORONARY DISEASE IN THYROID-TREATED PATIENTS

Sex	Condition	Number of patients treated	Patient years	Number of cases of coronary disease expected [a]	Number of cases of coronary disease observed
F	Age group, 30–59	490	2705	7.6	0
F	High risk [b]	172	1086	7.3	0
F	Age over 60	182	955	7.8	0
M	Age group, 30–59	382	2192	12.8	1
M	High risk [b]	186	1070	18.5	2
M	Age over 60	157	816	18.0	1
Total		1569	8824	72.0	4

[a] Compared with the Framingham study.
[b] Hypertension and/or hypercholesterolemia.

be 72; Barnes observed 4. This result was only due to change in diet, stoppage of smoking, exercise, or any change in living habits.

Twenty years before this monograph by Barnes, Kountz published "Thyroid Function and Its Possible Role in Vascular Degeneration" (1951). He reported on the results of treating 288 patients divided into three age groups, 55, 61, and 67 years old, in which some were treated with thyroid and the remainder as controls.

In the youngest age group, none of the thyroid-treated patients died while 15 of the controls had fatal vascular accidents; in the second group, 3% of the treated patients died, and 19% of the controls; while in the older patients, fatalities were one-half as great in the thyroid-treated patients as in the controls.

The observations were made over a period of 5 years. Recently, Wren (1968) reported the 5-year observation of the effect of 2 grains of desiccated thyroid daily dosage in 104 patients, and three grains daily in an additional 190 patients, all of whom had CHD. The final dosage level was obtained after starting with 1/4- and later 1/2-grain daily dosage. The biochemical effectiveness of the 2- and 3-grain dosages is established by the reduction of the average serum cholesterol from 280 mg/100 ml to 240 at the end of 1 year, 230 at 2 years, and 210 at the end of 5 years. There was symptomatic and ECG improvement, and statistical analysis indicated that the mortality rate for these thyroid-treated atherosclerotic patients was lower than that for the population at large; 4 male deaths in the treated cohorts versus 13.8 in U.S. Life Tables; 7 female deaths versus 11.1 in U.S. Life Tables.

XVI. Resolution

The results of Strisower *et al.* (1957), Wren (1968), Barnes and Barnes (1972), Kountz (1951), Moses and Danowski (1963), and Schoch (1969) all prove that it is possible to treat patients who do not have measurable hypothyroidism with desiccated thyroid dosage that is cholesteropenic without undesirable cardiac symptoms, and without escape. The treatment must begin with small dosage and increase with small increments at intervals of a month. This obviously requires patience, patient cooperation, individualization of dosage, and conviction on the part of the physician. If this is done, the incidence of CHD mortality is significantly reduced. It would be most interesting to know the biochemical and physiological changes this sustained treatment produces. Decrease in serum cholesterol and S_f 0–12 and S_f 0–20 lipoproteins occurs. Basal axillary body temperature increases. Hypertension is frequently reduced. Other probable changes are (1) basal metabolism, i.e., O_2 consumption increases; (2) total heat production and homeostatic heat radiation increases; (3) acceleration of thyroxine dependent enzymatic processes; (4) increase of prostaglandin and cyclic AMP (possibly); (5) increase of heart rate and cardiac output (possibly); (6) reduction of total isovolumetric contraction time; (7) more rapid circulation rate; (8) decreased coagulability; (9) increased red cell mass; (10) A-VO_2 difference, either $+$ or $-$ (possibly).

The thyroxine effects are produced by enzymatic mechanisms. In the specific instances of liver, kidney, heart, and skeletal muscle, the tissue in which energy production is related to thyroxine concentration, the activities of the succinoxidase system, as well as their content of cytochrome c parallel the changes in O_2 consumption produced by lack of excess T_4 (Barker, 1964).

All this without thyrotoxic symptoms, but with enjoyment of better health, as described under the treatment of subclinical hypothyroidism.

The significant clinical effects achieved by Danowski, Wren, Barnes, etc., on administering desiccated thyroid to patients who have "normal" serum concentrations of thyroid hormone iodine (PBI) is an example of the dictum: "The serum concentration of any hormone does not establish the metabolic state of the processes in the body dependent on that hormone." Obviously, the addition of 2 or 3 grains of desiccated thyroid is improving the metabolic state of the myocardium!

Thus, it seems probable that in our population, there are large cohorts whose thyroxine and triiodothyronine (desiccated thyroid) dependent parameters are below the mean, to be called *lower euthyroids,* who can be treated until these parameters are above the mean to be called *upper euthyroids,* and that this condition prevents CHD.

XVII. Discussion

The most interesting clinical subject emerging from this meandering study of the relationship of thyroid hormone effects to atherosclerotic heart disease might be called "the effect of euthyroid replacement therapy on some clinical states." The most significant fact is that the patients of Strisower and others were not hypothyroid; Barnes and Wren deliberately state that they could not demonstrate laboratory evidence of hypothyroidism in their patients so dramatically protected from CHD, and Moses and Danowski reported normal laboratory thyroid tests in their patients and state that the results were obtained without finding hypothyroidism or producing hyperthyroidism.

Hence, these reports are based on a pharmacologic action of thyroxine and triiodothyronine in euthyroid subjects that may be called "euthyroid replacement therapy," which must be controlled so as not to become thyrotoxic and be strong enough not to allow escape. This obviously makes the problem of the etiological relationship of hypothyroidism to atherosclerosis unimportant, but raises the analysis of the mechanism of effect of euthyroid replacement therapy to the level of greatest clinical importance.

CHD can be prevented, not by concentrating on cholesterol metabolism and hypothyroidism, but by superimposing thyroid hormone therapy on euthyroid subjects.

ACKNOWLEDGMENTS

Supported in part by NIH Grants, 1948–1958; Baxter Laboratories, Inc. (Dr. Thomas A Garrett, Dr. Leonard G. Ginger, and Dr. Robert K. Ausman), 1958–1968; White Memorial Medical Center, 1968–1972; R.I.A. Laboratories, Inc. (Mr. Benjamin Clayton, Mr. William Clayton, Sr., The Lloyd Foundation, The Pasadena Community Foundation, and The Santa Anita Foundation), 1972–1974.

References

Ausman, R. H., Schmitz, T. H., and Caereti, V. T. (1973). *Cardiovasc. Dis. Epidemiol. Conf., 1973* (unpublished).

Barker, S. B. (1964). *In* "The Thyroid Gland" (R. Pitt-Rivers, ed.), p. 199. Butterworth, London.

Barnes, B. O., and Barnes, C. W. (1972). "Heart Attack Rareness in Thyroid 2nd.

Bastenie, P. A. (1971). *Lancet* 1, 203.

Billewicz, W. Z., Chapman, R. S., Crooks, J., Dag, M. E., Gossage, J., Wayne, E., and Young, J. A. (1969). *Q. J. Med.* 38, 255.

Cohen, B. M. (1969). *J. Clin. Pharmacol.* 9, 45.

DeGroot, L. J. (1972). *F. Raymond Keating, Jr. Mem. Symp., Mayo Clin. Proc.,* 2nd.

Devlin, W. F., and Steefinin, N. R. (1962). *J. Pharm. Pharmacol.* 14, 597.

Eaton, C. D. (1954). *J. Mich. State Med. Soc.* 53, 1101.

Frederickson, D. S. (1971). "Medical World News: Cardiovascular Review." McGraw-Hill, New York.

Gordin, A., Heinomen, O. P., Saarinen, F., and Lamberg, B. A. (1972). *Lancet* 1, 551.

Greenberg, A. H., Czernicho, W. P., Hung, W., Shelley, W., Blizzard, R. M., and Winship, T. (1970). *J. Clin. Endocrinol. Metab.* 30, 293.

Hall, R., Amos, J., and Ormston, B. J. (1971). *Br. Med. J.* 1, 582.

Hershman, J. M., and Pittman, J. A. (1971). *Ann. Intern. Med.* 74, 481.

Jeffries, W. M. (1961). *J. Chronic Dis.* 14, 582.

Kannel, W. B., Dauber, T. R., Friedman, G. D., Glennon, W. E., and McNamara, P. M. (1964). *Ann. Intern. Med.* 61, 888.

Keys, A. (1970). *Am. Heart Assoc., Monogr.* No. 29, Circ. 41, Suppl. 1.

Keys, A. (1972). *Ann. Intern. Med.* 77, 15.

Kountz, W. B. (1951). "Thyroid Function and Its Possible Role in Vascular Degeneration." Thomas, Springfield, Illinois.

Lemarchand, B., Scazziga, B. R., and Vanottin, A. (1969). *Acta Endocrinol. (Copenhagen)* 62, 593.

Lew, M., Lepp, A., and Starr, P. (1963). *Endocrinology* 72, 160.

Lisser, H. (1955). *Trans. Am. Goiter Assoc.* p. 457.

Lowrey, R., and Starr, P. (1959). *J. Am. Med. Assoc.* 171, 2045.

Lowrey, R., Ware, A. G., and Starr, P. (1957). *Calif. Med.* 87, 285.

Mayberry, W. E., Charis, H., Bilstoad, J. A., and Sizemoro, G. W. (1971). *Ann. Intern. Med.* 74, 471.

Moses, C., and Danowski, T. A. (1963). *Metab., Clin. Exp.* 12, 126.

Moyer, J. H. (1967). *Arch. Environ. Health* 14, 337.

Odell, W. D., Wilbur, J. F., and Utiger, R. D. (1967). *Recent Prog. Horm. Res.* 23, 47.

Paul, O. (1971). *Br. Heart J.* 33, Suppl. 116.

Schoch, H. K. (1969). *Adv. Exp. Med. Biol.* 4, 405.

Stamler, J., Best, M. M., and Turner, J. D. (1972). *J. Am. Med. Assoc.* 220, 996.

Starr, P. (1958). *Arch. Intern. Med.* 101, 722.

Starr, P. (1960). *J. Clin. Endocrinol. Metab.* 20, 116.

Starr, P. (1961a). *Acta Endocrinol. (Copenhagen)* 37, 110.

Starr, P. (1961b). *Adv. Thyroid Res., Trans. Int. Goitre Conf., 4th, 1960* p. 398.

Starr, P. (1962). *Calif. Med.* 97, 263.

Starr, P. (1964). *Am. J. Med. Sci.* 248, 683.

Starr, P. (1970). *J. Clin. Pharmacol. J. New Drugs* 10, 400.

Starr, P. (1971). *Am. J. Clin. Pathol.* 55, 342.

Starr, P., Roen, P., Freiburn, T. L., and Schleishoner, L. A. (1960). *Arch. Intern. Med.* 105, 830.

Steinberg, A. D. (1968). *Ann. Intern. Med.* **68,** 338.

Strisower, B., Gofman, J. W., Galioni, E. F., Rubinger, J. H., Pouteau, J., and Guzvick, P. (1957). *Lancet* **1,** 120.

Tanaka, S., and Starr, P. (1959). *Acta Endocrinol. (Copenhagen)* **31,** 161.

U.S. National Center for Health Statistics. (1967). *U.S. Public Health Serv. Publ.* **1000,** Ser. 11, No. 22.

Vanhaelst, L., Neve, P., Chailly, P., and Bastenie, P. A. (1967). *Lancet* **2,** 800.

Wayne, E. J. (1960). *Br. Med. J.* **1,** 78.

Wren, J. E. (1968), *J. Am Geriatr. Soc.* **16,** 696.

Author Index

Numbers in italics refer to the pages on which the complete references are listed.

A

Abad, C., 104, *111*
Abdulla, Y. H., 229, 230, 232, 236, *262*
Abdumalikov, A. Kh., 277, 281, 297, 299, 301, 303, 304, 316, 317, 319, 320, *325*
Abe, M., 70, 82, *111*
Abernethy, M., 155, *161*
Abood, L. G., 3, *121*
Abraham, S., 156, *163*
Abrahamson, S., 21, *111*
Acker, L., 269, 283, 286, 297, 303, 322, *325*
Adams, C. W. M., 157, *160*, 222, 223, 224, 229, 230, 232, 236, *262, 263*
Addison, I. E., 144, *160*
Admirand, W. H., 44, *111*, 196, *215*
Aftergood, L., 140, 149, *160*
Agranoff, B. W., 58, 61, 90, 106, *111, 112, 115, 120, 121*
Ahmed, S., 33, *111*
Aiba, T., 251, *264*
Ainworth, S., 334, *342*
Akesson, B., 3, 4, 9, 10, 16, 58, 60, 61, 62, 67, 68, 69, 70, 73, 74, 75, 78, 79, 80, 83, 84, 87, 98, *111, 117, 123*, 311, *326*
Akino, T., 3, 70, 82, 91, *111*
Akiyama, M., 140, *162*
Aladjem, E., 271, 274, 276, 284, 287, 288, 291, 299, 301, 303, 305, 316, *324*
Aledort, L. M., 336, *344*
Alexander, A. E., 21, *111*
Alexander, M., 222, 229, 242, *265*
Alfano, M. C., 199, *215*
Alfin-Slater, R. B., 140, 149, *160, 229*, 232, 235, 236, 240, 241, 243, 256, *263*
Allen, R. H., 47, *123*
Almaden, P., 210, *220*
Alter, B. J., 137, *160*
Altschul, R., 173, *215*
Amako, T., 66, 85, *116*
Amos, B., 138, *160*
Amos, J., 350, *370*
Anderson, C. B., 143, *160*
Anderson, J., *215*
Anderson, P. J., 27, *111*
Anderson, T. W., 208, *215*
Anhalt, B., 81, 86, *125*
Anitschkow, N. N., 173, *215*
Ansell, G. B., 48, 71, *111*
Antia, N. J., 271, 276, 285, 288, 297, 299, 301, *322*
Antunes-Madeira, M. C., 36, *119*
Arad, R., 273, 274, 275, 281, 291, 301, 303, 304, 305, 320, *324*
Arai, T., 70, 82, *111*
Arienti, G., 88, *120*, 311, *325*
Arner, A., 80, 84, *111*
Arvidson, G. A. E., 3, 10, 16, 41, 46, 58, 60, 61, 66, 67, 68, 69, 72, 73, 77, 78, 79, 83, 85, 86, 87, 103, 104, 105, *111, 133, 311, 326*
Ascher, Y., 271, *322*
Ashley, C., 333, *342*
Astrachan, L., 295, 296, *322*
Atherton, R. W., 99, *111*
Audet, A., 288, 304, *322*
Auerbach, R., 140, *164*
Augenstein, L. G., *324*
Ausman, R. H., 352, 354, *369*
Austen, K. F., 278, 279, 282, 298, 300, 302, 304, *324*
Austin, J. P., 32, 33, *112*
Austin, W., 102, *115*

B

Babala, J., 168, 175, 177, 179, 203, *215, 217*
Bach, F. H., 137, *160*
Backer, J., 156, *164*
Bacq, Z. M., 329, 330, 333, 338, *342*
Baer, E., 3, 8, *111, 114*
Baer, P. R., 33, *117*

Subject Index

CONTENTS OF PREVIOUS VOLUMES